The Study of Kinetics and Mechanism of Reactions of Transition Metal Complexes

The Study of Kinetics and Mechanism of Reactions of Transition Metal Complexes

RALPH G. WILKINS

New Mexico State University

Allyn and Bacon, Inc.   Boston

Library of Congress Cataloging in Publication Data

Wilkins, R   G
    *The study of kinetics and mechanism of reactions of
transition metal complexes.*

Includes bibliographies.
    *1. Complex compounds.   2. Transition metal
compounds.   3. Chemical reaction, Conditions and laws
of.   I. Title.*

QD474.W54   546'.6   74-10756

Contents

PART II   RESULTS

Preface

At a small, informal gathering—that was to become the First International Conference on Coordination Chemistry—held at Welwyn, England in 1950, not one paper on kinetics was read. Today, kinetics and mechanism is a major topic and one of the main sources of lectures delivered at such conferences. Its development in the past quarter of a century is due largely to various theoretical approaches, particularly ligand-field theory, the availability of fast reaction measurement techniques, and the growth of interest in the impact and ramifications of kinetics and mechanism on organometallic and biological catalytic systems.

This book is concerned with reactions of the Werner-type transition metal complexes. I particularly emphasize the methodology of the subject—how to obtain the rate law, what to do with it, and what results have been obtained. I concentrate on the aspects that I find most interesting, but all major areas are covered. Considerations of space and my own competence made me omit the important related topics of organometallic and nonthermal reaction kinetics. Many of the ideas expressed in the book are others' ideas. I have tried to acknowledge them, and I apologize for any omissions. References to recent articles, up to about the end of 1973, were preferred because these articles give acknowledgements to earlier workers in the area.

The approach used in the book has been employed on a number of occasions for courses at the State University of New York at Buffalo, where most of the book was written. The units, kcal mole^{-1} and kcal mole^{-1} deg^{-1} are used exclusively (often without so designating) for $\Delta H^{\ddagger}$ and $\Delta S^{\ddagger}$ in the book.

Many people helped make the book possible. Don Darensbourg and Bob Kurland made very useful suggestions about some parts. Gordon Harris read the whole book in manuscript stage and offered many criticisms and suggestions. Errors that remain are, of course, my responsibility alone. A number of people helped with the typing of the manuscript, including Marj Perkins, Susan Sims, my wife Shirley, who typed the whole book in draft form, and my daughter Sue, who typed all the references. Pamela Starr, of the Allyn and Bacon staff, was extremely helpful in the production of the book. Many authors and copyright holders gave permission to reproduce figures and tables. All those persons have my sincere thanks.

The preface of a book affords the author an opportunity to acknowledge help given him over the years. Joe Chatt, Arthur Adamson, and Manfred Eigen are scientists who have had profound influences in stimulating and guiding my interests, and I shall always be grateful to them. Finally, I dedicate this book to my wife for her patience, understanding, and encouragement during the long, and sometimes grueling, period occupied in writing a book.

R. G. Wilkins

Ligand Abbreviations

A great deal has been accomplished with a surprisingly small number of types of ligands. These, with their common abbreviations, are listed below:

Ligand	Abbreviation
$NH_2(CH_2)_xNH_2$	en $(x = 2)$ tn $(x = 3)$
$NR_2(CH_2)_2NH(CH_2)_2NR_2$	dien $(R=H)$ Et_4dien $(R=Et)$
$NH_2(CH_2)_xNH(CH_2)_yNH(CH_2)_zNH_2$	x, y, z-tet $(x = y = z = 2$ is commonly termed trien)
$N[(CH_2)_2NH_2]_3$	tren
$N(CH_2COO^-)_3$	NTA
$[^-OCOCH_2]_2N{-}X{-}N[CH_2COO^-]_2$	EDTA $(X=(CH_2)_2)$ PDTA $(X=CH(CH_3)CH_2)$ CyDTA $(X = 1,2$-cyclohexyl$)$
$[^-OCOCH_2]_2N(CH_2)_2N{\overset{\displaystyle CH_2COO^-}{\underset{\displaystyle CH_3}{\Big\langle}}}$	MEDTA

phen

py ($n = 1$)
bipy ($n = 2$)
terpy ($n = 3$)

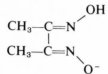

DH

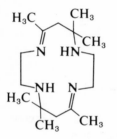

cyclam (R=H)
tet *a* or *meso* (R=CH$_3$)
tet *b* or *rac* (R=CH$_3$)

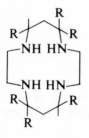

trans[14]diene

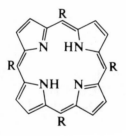

porphine (basic structure, R=H) gives metalloporphyrins on replacement of two H's by M, e.g., *meso*-tetraphenyl porphine (R= C$_6$H$_5$

PART I

Methods

In Part I, we are concerned with the mechanics of the reactions of transition metal complexes. The construction of the rate law governing rate of a reaction is considered first. The methods for deducing the mechanism from the rate law are then examined, and other means for assessing mechanism are dealt with. The final chapter in Part I details the experimental methods that the kineticist has available for measuring the rates of reactions.

Chapter 1

The Determination of the
Rate Law

The single most important factor that determines rate of a reaction is concentration—the concentrations of the reactants, and of other species that may not even appear in the reaction equation. The relation between the rate of a reaction and the concentration of chemical species is termed the rate law; it is the cornerstone of reaction mechanisms. The rate law alone allows much insight into the mechanism. The effect of other factors on the rate can also be revealing. (For these, see Chap. 2.)

1.1 THE RATE OF A REACTION AND THE RATE LAW

The *rate*, or *velocity*, of a reaction is usually defined as the change with time t of the concentration (denoted by square brackets) of one of the reactants or of one of the products of the reaction; that is,

$$\text{rate} = V = \frac{-d[\text{reactant}]}{dt} = \frac{n \times d[\text{product}]}{dt} \tag{1.1}$$

The negative sign arises because there is a loss of reactant. The value of n is often 1, but a value other than unity arises when one molecule of the reactant produces other than one molecule of the product. Rates are usually expressed in moles per liter per second, or $M \text{ sec}^{-1}$. The rate law expresses the rate of a reaction in terms of the concentrations of the reactants and of any other species in solution, including the products that may affect the rate.

3

Suppose that the rate of a reaction depends only on the concentrations of A and B. The proportionality factor k relating rate to the concentrations of [A] and [B] in the rate law, or rate expression,

$$V = k[A]^a[B]^b \tag{1.2}$$

is usually termed the *rate constant*, although it is sometimes referred to as the *specific rate*, or *rate coefficient*. Although the latter terms are in some respects preferable, since the proportionality factor is rarely invariant, the term *rate constant* is used in most of the literature and it is unlikely that it will be replaced. The values of a and b in (1.2) determine the *order of the reaction*. If $a = 1$, the reaction is termed *first-order* in A, and if $a = 2$, the reaction is *second-order* in A. These are the most frequently encountered orders of reaction. The overall order of the reaction is $(a + b)$. If the rate is independent of the concentration of A, $a = 0$, and the reaction is *zero-order* in A. The concentration of A does not then feature in the rate law.

The formation of a number of chromium(III) complexes $Cr(H_2O)_5X^{2+}$ from their constituent ions $Cr(H_2O)_6^{3+}$ and X^-,

$$Cr(H_2O)_6^{3+} + X^- \rightarrow Cr(H_2O)_5X^{2+} + H_2O \tag{1.3}$$

where X^- represents a unidentate ligand, obeys the two-term rate law (the coordinated water being usually omitted from the formulas)

$$V = \frac{d[CrX^{2+}]}{dt} = k_1[Cr^{3+}][X^-] + k_2[Cr^{3+}][X^-][H^+]^{-1} \tag{1.4}$$

over a wide range of concentration of reactants and acid.[1] Symbols such as a and b instead of k_1 and k_2 may be used in (1.4), since these quantities are often composite values, made up of rate and equilibrium constants. To maintain both sides of (1.4) dimensionally equivalent,

$$V = M \sec^{-1} = k_1 \times M^2 = k_2 \times M \tag{1.5}$$

k_1 and k_2 must obviously be expressed in units of $M^{-1} \sec^{-1}$ and $\sec^{-1}$ respectively. This simple application of dimension theory is often useful in checking the correctness of a complex rate law (see (1.95) and Prob. 1, Chap. 2).

If we consider specifically the formation of $CrBr^{2+}$, the rate law

$$V = (3.0 \times 10^{-8} + 3.6 \times 10^{-9}\,[H^+]^{-1})[Cr^{3+}][Br^-] \tag{1.6}$$

holds at $25.0°$ $(I = 1.0\,M)$.[1] At high acid concentrations $(\geqslant 1\,M)$, the first term in (1.6) is larger than the second, and the reaction rate is virtually acid-independent. At lower acid concentrations $(\sim 10^{-2}\,M)$, the second term dominates and the rate of reaction is now inversely proportional to H^+]. This emphasizes the importance of studying the rate of a reaction over as wide a range of concentrations of species as possible so as to obtain an extensive rate law.

1.2   THE RATE LAW DIRECTLY FROM RATE MEASUREMENTS

If the rate of a reaction can be measured at a time for which the concentrations of the reactants are known, and if this determination can be repeated using different concentrations of reactants, it is clear that the rate law (1.2) can be deduced directly. It is not often obtained in this manner, however, despite some distinct advantages inherent in the method.

1.2.1   Initial-Rate Method

The rate of reaction is measured at the commencement of the reaction, when the concentrations of the reactants are accurately known, indeed predetermined.

The reaction of pyridoxal phosphate (PLP) with glutamate (Glu) has been studied in the presence of copper ions.[2] The spectra of the mixture of reactants changes to one of a copper–Schiff base complex, with sharp isosbestic points, indicating no buildup of intermediates in the process (Sec. 3.6.2). The initial reaction rates are estimated from initial tangents to the absorbance/time traces. These initial gradients (absorbance units/ sec) are easily converted into M/sec by using the known molar absorptivities of product and reactants. Some results are shown in Table 1.1. It is

TABLE 1.1.   Initial Rate Data for the Reaction of Pyridoxal Phosphate (PLP), Sodium Glutamate (Glu), and Cu^{2+} at 25° and pH = 4.0[2]

[PLP] mM	[Glu] mM	[Cu^{2+}] mM	$10^7 \times$ Initial rate M sec^{-1}	k M^{-1} sec^{-1}
0.1	8.0	0.2	1.2	0.15
0.1	8.0	1.0	1.1	0.14
0.2	8.0	0.2	2.4	0.15
0.3	8.0	1.0	3.3	0.14
0.5	8.0	1.0	5.6	0.14
0.5	8.0	0.2	5.9	0.15
0.2	0.7	0.4	0.23	0.17
0.2	1.9	0.4	0.54	0.14
0.2	3.2	0.4	0.94	0.15
0.2	8.0	0.4	2.3	0.14
0.2	11.0	0.4	3.1	0.14

apparent from these results that the initial rate is proportional to the initial concentrations of PLP and Glu but independent of the copper concentration. A rate law,

$$V = k[\text{PLP}][\text{Glu}] \tag{1.7}$$

applies therefore, and values of k calculated on this basis are reasonably constant; they are shown in the last column of Table 1.1. In more complicated examples of the use of initial rates, the raw data are included in the papers describing the study of the Cr(VI)–I$^-$ reaction,[3] and the catalysis of decomposition of H_2O_2 by copper-imidazole complexes.[4] The merits and difficulties in the use of the method are summarized as follows.

1.2.2   Advantages of the Initial-Rate Method

(a) The initial-rate method avoids problems in tackling reversible equilibria (Sec. 1.5). The reverse reaction in

$$Cr(H_2O)_6^{3+} + NCS^- \rightleftharpoons Cr(H_2O)_5NCS^{2+} + H_2O \tag{1.8}$$

is unimportant during the early stages of the forward reaction, when the products have not accumulated. The reaction can be studied in either direction by starting with $Cr(H_2O)_6^{3+}$ or $Cr(H_2O)_5NCS^{2+}$ ions. A small initial loss (forward reaction) or gain (reverse direction) of free thiocyanate ion can be accurately monitored by using the sensitive Fe(III) colorimetric method.[5] The rate laws for the forward and reverse directions can therefore be separately determined.

(b) This method is useful in the study of reactions complicated by side reactions or subsequent steps. The hydrolysis

$$Co(NH_3)_5F^{2+} + H_2O \rightarrow Co(NH_3)_5H_2O^{3+} + F^- \tag{1.9}$$

is best studied by initial rates, since the slow production of fluoride is attended by loss of ammonia, which is autocatalytic and which complicates kinetics as the reaction proceeds.[6] Since the catalytic influence of enzymes often changes during their reaction with a substrate, the initial-rate method is used in the study of enzyme kinetics. In addition, complicated integrated expressions are avoided.[7]

1.2.3   Disadvantages of the Initial-Rate Method

(a) A sensitive method of monitoring is required to obtain accurate concentration/time data for the first 1% or so of the reaction.[2] Large spectral absorbance changes (1.8) or microtitration techniques are helpful.[8]

(b) A complex rate law can be disguised.[9,10] The method of initial rates, used in study of the reaction between $Fephen_3^{2+}$ and MnO_4^- ions, indicates a second-order reaction. It can be shown that this is not the whole story since the accumulation of products lowers the computed second-order rate constant. A complex rate law thus applies, and in the integrated form is used to collect the data.[9] (See also Ref. 10.)

1.2.4   Steady-State Approach

In the steady-state approach to determining the rate law, solutions containing reactants are pumped separately at a constant flow rate into a vessel ("reactor"), the contents of which are vigorously stirred. After a while, products and some reactants will flow from the reactor at the same total rate of inflow and a steady state will be attained, in which the reaction will take place in the reactor with a *constant concentration of reactants*, and therefore a *constant rate*. This is the basis of the stirred-flow reactor, or capacity-flow method.[11] As an illustration of the method, consider a second-order reaction between A and B with rate constant k:

Now, in the reactor, $V = k(a - x)(b - x) = \dfrac{x}{t}$ **(1.10)**

where a, b = concentrations of reactants A and B (after mixing) flowing into the reactor.

            x = amounts of A and B that have reacted after the steady state has been reached.

            u = combined rate of inflow of reactant solutions, which equals rate of outflow.

            v = volume of reactor.

            t = average time spent by A and B in reactor, which equals v/u.

Since a, b, x, and t can be determined experimentally, the rate expression can be used directly to determine k. A series of experiments with different flow rates will indicate whether a second-order designation is correct from the constancy of k. Although the method has been little used, it has the advantages of a simplified kinetic treatment even for complex systems.[12]

1.2.5   Rates of Relaxation and Exchange

Relaxation of chemical equilibria (Sec. 1.8) and group or atom exchange within systems at equilibrium (Sec. 1.9) are always first-order processes, and so the concomitant rates and rate laws are more easily derived. These approaches will be discussed at length later.

1.3   INTEGRATED FORMS OF THE RATE EXPRESSION

Consider a reaction that proceeds to completion in which the concentration of only one reactant, A, changes appreciably during the reaction. This may arise because (1) there is only one reactant A involved—for example, in a stereochemical change; (2) all the other possible reactants are in much larger ($\geqslant$ tenfold) concentration than A; or (3) the concentration of one of the other reactants may be held constant by buffering, or be constantly replenished, as it would be if it were acting in a catalytic role. Attention needs to be focused therefore only on the change of concentration of A as the reaction proceeds, and we can, for the present, forget about the other reactants. Now,

$$\frac{-d[A]}{dt} = k[A]^a \tag{1.11}$$

The manner in which [A] varies with time determines the order of the reaction with respect to A. Since it is usually much easier to measure a concentration than a rate, the form (1.11) is integrated.[13] We need only consider three situations, $a = 0$ to 2, with $a = 1$ the most common.

$a = 0$, zero-order in A:

$$V = \frac{-d[A]}{dt} = k \tag{1.12}$$

$$[A]_t = [A]_0 - kt \tag{1.13}$$

FIGURE 1.1   The characteristics of (a) zero- (b) first- and (c) ▶ second-order reactions. In (a) the concentration of A decreases linearly with time until it is all consumed (at time t_0). The value of the zero-order rate constant is given by A_0/t_0. In (b) the loss of A is exponential with time. It does not matter, therefore, at which point on the curve the first reading is taken. The plot of log [A] vs time is linear, from the slope of which k, the first-order rate constant is obtained ($-2.3 \times$ slope). In (c) the loss of A is hyperbolic with time. The plot of $[A]^{-1}$ vs time is linear, with a slope equal to k, the second-order rate constant.

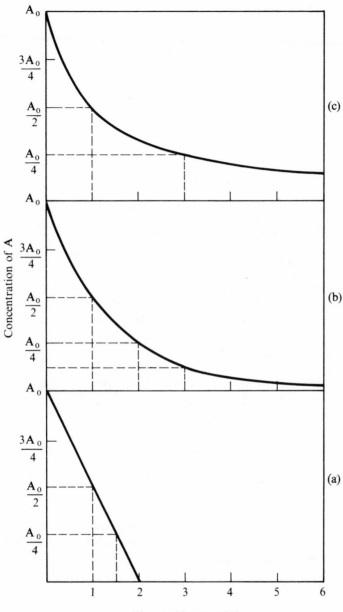

FIGURE 1.1

$a = 1$, first-order in A:

$$V = \frac{-d[A]}{dt} = k[A] \tag{1.14}$$

$$\log [A]_t = \log [A]_0 - \frac{kt}{2.3} \tag{1.15}$$

$a = 2$, second-order in A:

$$V = \frac{-d[A]}{dt} = k[A]^2 \tag{1.16}$$

$$\frac{1}{[A]_t} = \frac{1}{[A]_0} + kt \tag{1.17}$$

The differential (rate) forms are (1.12), (1.14), and (1.16), and the corresponding integrated forms are (1.13), (1.15), and (1.17). The designations $[A]_0$ and $[A]_t$ represent the concentrations of A at zero time and time t. Linear plots of $[A]$, $\log [A]$, or $[A]^{-1}$ vs time therefore indicate zero-, first-, or second-order dependence on the concentration of A. The important characteristics of these order reactions are shown in Fig. 1.1, page 9.

It should be emphasized that k is a *pseudo* zero-, first-, or second-order rate constant however, since it does not take into account the effect of the other reactants B, and so on. Having settled the value of a, we may now separately vary the concentrations of the other reactants, say B and C, still keeping them, however, in excess of the concentration of A. The variation of k with $[B]$ and $[C]$ will give the orders of reaction b and c with respect to these species, leading to the expression

$$k = k_1[B]^b[C]^c \cdots \tag{1.18}$$

and therefore the full rate law

$$V = \frac{-d[A]}{dt} = k_1[A]^a[B]^b[C]^c \tag{1.19}$$

We can use this approach also to examine the effects on the rate of reactants that may not be directly involved in the stoichiometry (for example, H^+) or even of products. It is the most popular method for determining the rate law, and only rarely cannot be used.

1.4 MONOPHASIC UNIDIRECTIONAL REACTIONS

We shall first consider some straightforward kinetics, in which the loss of A, in the treatment referred to above, is monophasic and the reaction is unidirectional, that is, it leads to $\geqslant 95\%$ loss of A.

1.4.1 Zero-Order Dependence

It is impossible to conceive of a reaction rate as being independent of the concentration of *all* the species involved in the reaction. The rate might, however, very easily be independent of the concentration of one of the reactants; that is, a, b, or c might be zero in (1.19). If this species, say A, is used in deficiency, then a pseudo zero-order reaction results. The rate $-d[A]/dt$ will not vary as [A] decreases, and will *not* depend on the initial concentration of A.

In the substitution reaction

$$NiP_4 + C_6H_{11}NC \xrightarrow{k_1} NiP_3(C_6H_{11}NC) + P \qquad (1.20)$$

the loss of $C_6H_{11}NC$ has been followed in the presence of excess Ni complex NiP_4, where $P = POEt_3$.[15] The linear plots of absorbance, which is proportional to isonitrile concentration, vs time indicate a reaction zero-order in isonitrile (Fig. 1.2). The slope of the zero-order plot (when absorbance is converted into concentration) is k. The value of k is found to be proportional to the concentration of NiP_4, which is used in excess (Fig. 1.2),[16]

$$\frac{-d[NiP_4]}{dt} = \frac{-\frac{1}{2}d[C_6H_{11}NC]}{dt} = k = k_1[NiP_4] \qquad (1.21)$$

The reaction is therefore overall first-order, with a first-order rate constant k_1 (sec^{-1}). The situation of a zero order is not often encountered; some other examples in the literature are contained in Refs. 17 to 19. Particularly interesting is the iron(III)-catalyzed oxidation of cysteine by molecular oxygen.[17] This reaction is zero-order in both cysteine and oxygen and two-thirds–order in iron(III). The absorption of oxygen thus occurs at a constant rate until it is all consumed by the excess cysteine.

1.4.2 First-Order Dependence

First-order reactions are extremely common and form the bulk of reported kinetic studies. The rate of loss of the reactant A decreases as the concentration of A decreases. The differential form (1.14) leads to a number of equivalent integrated expressions, in addition to (1.15):

$$[A]_t = [A]_0 \exp(-kt) \qquad (1.22)$$

$$\log\frac{[A]_0}{[A]_t} = \frac{kt}{2.3} \qquad (1.23)$$

$$\frac{-d\ln[A]_t}{dt} = k \qquad (1.24)$$

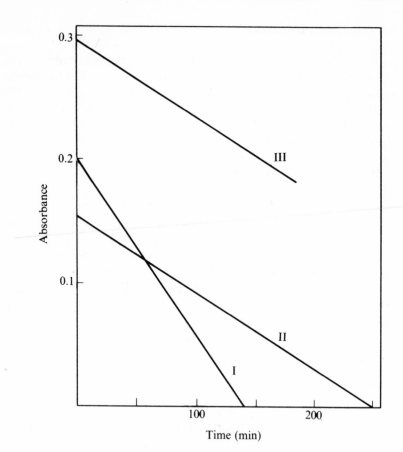

FIGURE 1.2   Zero-order kinetic plots for reaction (1.20). $[NiP_4] =$ $9.5 \times 10^{-2} \, M(I), 4.8 \times 10^{-2} \, M(II), 4.7 \times 10^{-2} \, M(III); [C_6H_{11}NC] =$ $6.5 \times 10^{-3} \, M(I), 5.0 \times 10^{-3} \, M(II), 9.7 \times 10^{-3} \, M(III).$[15]

Important quantities characteristic of a first-order reaction are $t_{1/2}$, the half-life of the reaction, which is the value of t when $[A]_t = [A]_0/2$, and τ, the relaxation time, defined as k^{-1}.

$$k = \frac{0.693}{t_{1/2}} = \frac{1}{\tau} \qquad\qquad (1.25)$$

The latter is invariably used in the relaxation approach to rate measurement (Sec. 1.8). Half-lives or relaxation times are constants over the complete reaction for first-order or pseudo first-order reactions.

    Since such kinetics feature so prominently in transition metal chemistry, there have been many attempts to improve the usual treatments of

(1.15), (1.23), and (1.24). Guggenheim's method does not require a knowledge of the final equilibrium parameters and also avoids dependence on a single equilibrium value.[20] It is useful in spectral monitoring of first-order reactions in which complications may set in towards the end of the primary reaction.[21] It is easily shown that a plot of log $(D_{t+\Delta t} - D_t)$ vs time should be linear with slope $-k/2.3$. The D's represent absorbances at times $t + \Delta t$ and t, respectively, with Δt chosen arbitrarily to be at least equal to two or more half-lives.[22]

The Guggenheim approach has been further modified by Mangelsdorf.[23] Both methods have been described at length and their relative merits discussed.[24] (See Prob. 3, Chap. 3.) They are useful when the reaction under study is followed by a slower one so that the final value for the first stage is difficult to assess. Otherwise they have little advantage over the conventional approach.

Computer programs have been described for the treatment of first-order kinetic data.[25] One program accepts any data that are linear in concentrations, uses the "best" infinity value, discards "poor" points, and even does Guggenheim-type calculations at the same time that it does a least-square fit!

An apparently simple first-order reaction may hide two or more concurrent reactions and yet remain first-order. The change in the visible spectrum of $1,2,6\text{-Cr(trienH)}(H_2O)_3{}^{4+}$ with time is only compatible with concomitant hydrolysis and isomerization, both first-order processes.[26]

$$\text{Cr(trienH}_2)(H_2O)_4{}^{5+} \qquad \textbf{(1.26)}$$
$$\text{(C)}$$

$$\overset{H_3O^+}{\underset{k_1}{\nearrow}}$$

$$1,2,6\text{-Cr(trienH)}(H_2O)_3{}^{4+}$$
$$\text{(A)}$$

$$\underset{k_2}{\searrow}$$

$$1,2,3\text{-Cr(trienH)}(H_2O)_3{}^{4+} \qquad \textbf{(1.27)}$$
$$\text{(B)}$$

For this system,

$$\frac{-d[A]}{dt} = k[A] = (k_1 + k_2)[A] \qquad \textbf{(1.28)}$$

Estimation of the amounts of B and C produced allows separate determination of k_1 and k_2 from (1.28) in conjunction with

$$\frac{k_1}{k_2} = \frac{[C]}{[B]} \qquad \textbf{(1.29)}$$

The reaction of a mixture of species A and A', which interconvert rapidly compared with the reaction under study, leads also to a single first-order (or pseudo first-order) process. It is not possible to split up the composite rate constant without information on the $A \rightleftharpoons A'$ equilibrium, for example the relative amounts of the two species, and these data may not be available. Indeed the presence of more than one species (which could be conformational isomers or tautomeric forms) may not even be suspected. When the relative amounts of A and A' are pH-controlled however (Sec. 1.10.1), or when the products of reaction of A and A' differ and do not interconvert readily,[27] the problem is in principle resolvable.

In a few cases only, the dependence of the rate on the concentration of the species in deficiency, A, may be second-order. The relationship between the concentration of A and time for this pseudo second-order reaction is given by (1.17).

1.4.3 Conversion of Pseudo to Real Rate Constants

Having established the reaction order with respect to A (it will be termed m below and will often be first-order), we determine the variation of the pseudo rate constant k with the concentrations of the other reactants. Considering just one other reactant B, we find a limited number of observed variations of k $(= V/[A]^m)$ with $[B]^n$. These are shown as (a) to (c) in Fig. 1.3. Nonlinear plots of k vs $[B]^n$ signify complex multistep behavior (Sec. 1.6.3).

(a) The rate and value of k may be independent of the concentration of other reactants. This situation may occur in the study of a rearrangement or conformational change involving A or in hydrolysis reactions, when the reaction order with respect to solvent, the concentration of which cannot be changed, is indeterminable. It may also represent a limiting behavior and be a less simple function at much lower [B] (Sec. 1.6.3).

(b) The value of k may be linear with respect to $[B]^n$, where n will often be 1. At zero concentration of B however, there may be a residual reaction. This behavior is compatible with a concurrent first- and multi-order reaction of A. The rate law for the oxidation of $Fephen_3^{2+}$ by Tl(III) is given by

$$V = \frac{-d[Fephen_3^{2+}]}{dt} = k_1[Fephen_3^{2+}] + k_2[Fephen_3^{2+}][Tl^{III}] \quad (1.30)$$

The second-order redox reaction, giving rise to the rate constant k_2, is accompanied by hydrolysis of the iron(II) complex, which leads to the k_1 term. The latter can be more accurately measured in the absence of

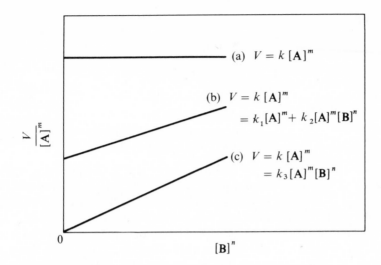

FIGURE 1.3   Common variations of $V/[A]^m$ with $[B]^n$.

Tl(III).[28]   The kinetics of substitution of many square-planar complexes conform to behavior (b), (4.107).

(c) The dependence of k on $[B]^n$ with a zero intercept for the appropriate plot (Fig. 1.3(c)) is consistent with a single-term rate law:

$$\frac{-d[A]}{dt} = k[A]^m = k_3[A]^m[B]^n \tag{1.31}$$

1.4.4   Second-Order Reactions

When $m = n = 1$, the overall reaction is second-order, and this type plays an important role in the reactions of complex ions.   Usually second-order reactions are studied under pseudo first-order conditions.   In a very limited number of cases, it may not be possible to use the simplified approach represented by (c) to study a second-order reaction.   This may happen, for example, if both reactants absorb heavily in the spectral region used for monitoring, or if large rate constants are involved; in these cases, large excess of either reactant, the basis of the pseudo first-order conditions, is to be avoided.   In these cases the full treatment for a second-order reaction is used, which is a straightforward procedure for unidirectional second-order reactions but which can be quite tedious for reversible reactions (Sec. 1.5).

For the reaction

$$A + B \xrightarrow{k_1} C \tag{1.32}$$

$$\frac{-d[A]}{dt} = k_1[A][B] \tag{1.33}$$

Integration results in

$$\frac{1}{[B]_0 - [A]_0} \log \frac{[A]_0[B]_t}{[B]_0[A]_t} = \frac{k_1 t}{2.3} \tag{1.34}$$

with subscripts t and 0 representing times t and 0, respectively. Applications of this equation are given in Refs. 29 to 31 and include the treatment of oscilloscope traces obtained from the flow method for studying the rapid second-order reaction between Eu(II) and Fe(III).[31] An unusual treatment of (1.32) is described by Hammett.[32a] A simplified form of (1.34) equivalent to (1.17) arises when the starting concentrations of A and B are equal, although this condition $[A]_0 = [B]_0$ must be set up experimentally with care.[33]

A popular alternative approach to the study of (1.32) casts the differential and integrated forms in terms of a variable x, which represents the amount of one of the reactants (starting concentrations A_0 and B_0) *consumed* at time t. The equations obtained are

$$\frac{-d(A_0 - x)}{dt} = \frac{dx}{dt} = k_1(A_0 - x)(B_0 - x) \tag{1.35}$$

and

$$\frac{1}{B_0 - A_0} \log \frac{A_0(B_0 - x)}{B_0(A_0 - x)} = \frac{k_1 t}{2.3} \tag{1.36}$$

In the case of (1.32), the value of x is the same for A and B. When the stoichiometry of the reaction is not 1:1 however, this is no longer the case, and this situation must be considered in deriving the rate equation (see Prob. 2).

1.5 MONOPHASIC REVERSIBLE REACTIONS

The only reactions considered so far have been those that proceed to all intents and purposes ($\geqslant 95\%$) to completion. The treatment of *reversible* reactions is analogous to the treatment given above, although now it is even more important to establish the stoichiometry and the thermodynamic characteristics of the reaction. A number of reversible reactions are reduced to pseudo first-order opposing reactions:

$$A \rightleftharpoons X \qquad k_1, k_{-1}, K \tag{1.37}$$

when reactants or products or both are used in excess of A and X. The order with respect to these can then be separately determined. The approach to equilibrium for (1.37) is still first-order, but the derived first-order rate constant k is the sum of k_1 and k_{-1}:

$$2.3 \times \log \frac{[A]_0 - [A]_e}{[A]_t - [A]_e} = kt = (k_1 + k_{-1})t \tag{1.38}$$

This equation resembles (1.23) but includes $[A]_e$, the concentration of A at equilibrium, which is not now equal to zero. The ratio of rate constants, $k_1/k_{-1} = K$, the so-called *equilibrium constant*, can be determined independently from equilibrium constant measurements. The value of k, or the half-life for (1.37), will be independent of the direction from which the equilibrium is approached, that is, of whether one starts with pure A or X or even a nonequilibrium mixture of the two. A first-order reaction that hides concurrent first-order reactions (Sec. 1.4.2) can apply to reversible reactions also.

The scheme

$$A + B \rightleftharpoons X \qquad k_1, k_{-1} \tag{1.39}$$

can be reduced to (1.37) by using B in excess, and creating thereby a pseudo first-order reversible reaction. The rate law that arises is

$$V = k[A] = (k_1[B] + k_{-1})[A] \tag{1.40}$$

where $k_1[B]$ and k_{-1} are the forward and reverse first-order rate constants.

Such a situation arises in the interaction of $V(H_2O)_6{}^{3+}$ with SCN^- ions,

$$V(H_2O)_6{}^{3+} + NCS^- \rightleftharpoons V(H_2O)_5NCS^{2+} + H_2O \qquad k_1, k_{-1}, K \tag{1.41}$$

which is studied using a large excess of V^{3+} ions, although an equilibrium position is still attained. A plot of the pseudo first-order rate constant k for the approach to equilibrium vs $[V^{3+}]$ is linear (Fig. 1.4).[34] The slope is k_1 and the intercept is k_{-1}:

$$k = k_1[V^{3+}] + k_{-1} \tag{1.42}$$

It is not always easy to obtain an accurate value for k_{-1} from such a plot. However, combination of k_1 with $K(= k_1/k_{-1})$ obtained from spectral measurements yields a good value for k_{-1}. The plots in Fig. 1.4 show the independence of the values of k_1 and k_{-1} on the acid concentrations in the range 0.15 to 1.0 M. There are slight variations to this approach, which have been delineated in a number of papers.[35] Since the k vs [B] plot in Fig. 1.4 is identical to the plot obtained for unidirec-

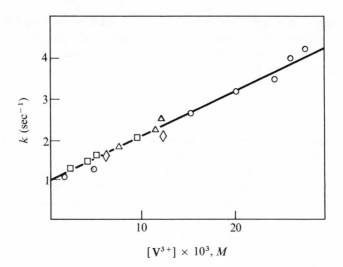

FIGURE 1.4   Plot of $k(\sec^{-1})$ vs $[V^{3+}]$ for reaction (1.41) at 25 °C. $[H^+] = 1.0\ M$ (circles); $[H^+] = 0.50\ M$ (triangles); $[H^+] = 0.25\ M$ (diamonds); $[H^+] = 0.15\ M$ (squares).[34]

tional concurrent first- and second-order reactions of A (Fig. 1.3(b)), confusion might result if the equilibria characteristics are not carefully assessed.[36]   It is clear that the case of a second-order reaction between A and B,

$$A + B \rightleftharpoons \text{products} \tag{1.43}$$

or a first-order decomposition of A to more than one product that reaches equilibrium,

$$A \rightleftharpoons \text{products} \tag{1.44}$$

can be reduced to reversible first-order kinetics by using all but one of the reactants or products in excess, and then separately determining the orders with respect to them.   The full treatment for $A + B \rightleftharpoons X + Y$,[37] $A \rightleftharpoons X + Y$,[38] and $A + B \rightleftharpoons X$,[39] which rarely needs to be used, is quite complex.[13]   It is best handled by computer methods.[40]

1.5.1   Conversion of Reversible to Unidirectional Reactions

An often useful approach is to eliminate the elements of reversibility from a reaction and force it to completion, either by the use of a large excess of reactant or by rapid removal of one of the products. A good illustration is afforded by the study of

$$PtCl(PPh_3)_2CO^+ + ROH \rightleftharpoons PtCl(PPh_3)_2COOR + H^+ \qquad k_1, k_{-1}, K_1$$

(1.45)

Since the equilibrium quotient K_1 is small, a nonnucleophilic base is added to the reaction mixture to react with liberated protons and drive the reaction to completion (left to right). Using an excess of ROH ensures simple unidirectional pseudo first-order (rate constant k_f) kinetics:

$$\frac{-d[\ln [PtCl(PPh_3)_2CO^+]]}{dt} = k_f = k_1[ROH] \qquad (1.46)$$

The reverse reaction also gives simple first-order (rate constant k_r) kinetics when studied with excess $HClO_4$:

$$\frac{-d\ln [PtCl(PPh_3)_2COOR]}{dt} = k_r = k_{-1}[H^+] \qquad (1.47)$$

It was verified that k_1/k_{-1} equaled K_1, determined in a separate experiment.[41]

The equilibrium

$$Ru^{2+} + X^- \rightleftharpoons RuX^+ \qquad k_1, k_{-1} \qquad (1.48)$$

where $X = Cl, Br, I$, lies so far over to the reactant side that it might be quite difficult to study kinetically. Rapid and complete oxidation of RuX^+ by Ru^{3+}

$$RuX^+ + Ru^{3+} \rightarrow RuX^{2+} + Ru^{2+} \qquad fast \qquad (1.49)$$

enables k_1 to be easily measured. It is interesting to note that in this case the net chemical reaction being studied is the anation of Ru^{3+} by X^- ions (Ru^{2+} catalyzed). The rate law indicates, however, that it is the rate of Ru^{2+} anation (1.48) that is controlling the process.[42]

1.6   MULTIPHASIC UNIDIRECTIONAL REACTIONS

Attention is now directed to reactions that show a nonlinear plot of the appropriate function or that have rate laws that are altered with changes in the concentration of the species involved in the reaction. Such deviations are usually associated with concurrent and consecutive reactions.

1.6.1 Concurrent Reactions

If a mixture of A and B undergoes parallel first-order or pseudo first-order reactions to give a common product C, and A and B do not interconvert readily compared with the reaction under study,

$$[C]_e - [C]_t = [A]_0 \exp(-k_1 t) + [B]_0 \exp(-k_2 t) \qquad (1.49a)$$

where k_1 and k_2 are the first-order rate constants for conversion of A and B, respectively.[13] The resultant semilog plot of [C] vs time will in general be curved.

The hydrolysis of the anions in the complexes Na[Co(MEDTA)Br] and K[Co(MEDTA)Br] has been examined. The semilog plots are decidedly different (Fig. 1.5). The Na salt gives marked curvature, whereas the plot of the K salt is linear over four half-lives. Both complexes have almost identical spectra over the 400–600-nm range. It is considered that the sodium salt is a mixture of isomers, in which the bromine is either in an equatorial or in an axial position of the cobalt(III) octahedron. The biphasic plot can be separated into a fast component and a slow one (Fig. 1.5). Significantly, the fast portion matches exactly the semilog plot for the K salt, which is considered isomerically pure.[43]

A similar concurrent hydrolysis pattern has been observed with other complex ions.[44] It is not always easy to distinguish concurrent from consecutive reactions, as we shall see in the next section.

1.6.2 Consecutive Reactions

Consecutive reactions figure prominently in Part II.[45,46] Since complex ions have a number of reactive centers, the product of one reaction may very well take part in a subsequent one. Nearly all the situations likely to be met in this area arise from the scheme

$$A \underset{k_{-1}}{\overset{k_1}{\rightleftharpoons}} B \underset{k_{-2}}{\overset{k_2}{\rightleftharpoons}} C \qquad (1.50)$$

where the first-order rate constants k_1, k_{-1}, k_2, and k_{-2} may be functions of the concentrations of other reagents but can be maintained as pseudo first-order if these reagents are maintained in excess of A, B, or C. The complexity associated with (1.50) can usually be avoided, although we shall return to its treatment in Sec. 1.7. Meanwhile, we shall consider some simpler forms of (1.50) that lead to biphasic first-order plots. The sequence of two irreversible first-order reactions

$$A \xrightarrow{k_1} B \xrightarrow{k_2} C \qquad (1.51)$$

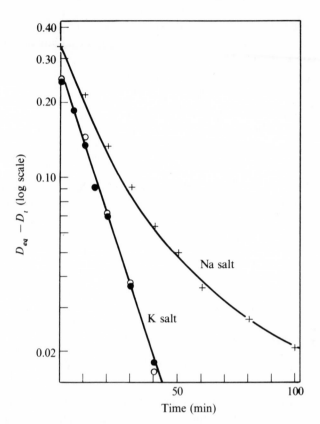

FIGURE 1.5   Semilog plot of optical absorbance vs time for aquation of Co(MEDTA)Br$^-$, λ = 540 nm, pH = 2.6, temp. = 78.8°.[43]

+ = mixture of isomers.

○ = "fast" component derived from mixture by subtraction of "slow" component.

● = experimental points for "fast" isomer.

is quite common.   The rate equations are

$$\frac{-d[A]}{dt} = k_1[A] \tag{1.52}$$

$$\frac{d[B]}{dt} = k_1[A] - k_2[B] \tag{1.53}$$

$$\frac{d[C]}{dt} = k_2[B] \tag{1.54}$$

Integrating these equations, and assuming $[A] = [A]_0$, $[B] = [C] = 0$ at $t = 0$, we obtain the concentrations of A, B, and C at any time t in terms of the concentration, $[A]_0$:

$$[A] = [A]_0 \exp(-k_1 t) \tag{1.55}$$

$$[B] = \frac{[A]_0 k_1}{k_2 - k_1} [\exp(-k_1 t) - \exp(-k_2 t)] \tag{1.56}$$

$$[C] = [A]_0 \left[1 - \frac{k_2}{k_2 - k_1} \exp(-k_1 t) + \frac{k_1}{k_2 - k_1} \exp(-k_2 t) \right] \tag{1.57}$$

If $k_1 \gg k_2$, then both steps A → B and B → C can be analyzed separately as described previously. If $k_2 \gg k_1$, then only the first step is observed and

$$\frac{-d[A]}{dt} = \frac{d[C]}{dt} = k_1[A] \tag{1.58}$$

and the only method for determining k_2 will be through isolation and separate examination of the behavior of B. If this is feasible experimentally, then even the otherwise difficult situation $k_1 \sim k_2$ can be easily resolved. This isolation technique was particularly helpful in the study of the hydrolysis reactions

$$Cren(H_2O)_4{}^{3+} \xrightarrow{\text{H}^+} Cr(enH)(H_2O)_5{}^{4+} \xrightarrow{\text{H}^+} Cr(H_2O)_6{}^{3+} + enH_2{}^{2+} \tag{1.59}$$

since the successive first-order rate constants are within a factor of 2 to 4 of each other.[47] If B is not isolatable however, and its properties are unknown, and $k_1 \lesssim k_2$, real difficulties might arise.[48]

Such systems as (1.51) appear to have been examined exclusively by spectral methods, and discussion will center around this monitoring method. Successive reactions are indicated by the lack of isosbestic points (Sec. 3.6.2) over some portion of the reaction. In addition, the appropriate kinetic plots are curved, although perhaps only at certain wavelengths—for example, a wavelength that monitors only the concentration of A will give a perfect first-order plot, rate constant k_1 (1.55). Sometimes the curvature will be barely noticeable, showing as an induction period of short duration.[49] Considering the optical absorbance D of the reacting solution at time t, in a cell of path length 1 cm, yields

$$D = \epsilon_a[A] + \epsilon_b[B] + \epsilon_c[C] \tag{1.60}$$

where ϵ_a is the molar absorptivity of A, and so on (Sec. 3.6). By substituting (1.55) through (1.57) into (1.60) and rearranging terms, it is not difficult to derive

$$D - D_e = a_1 \exp(-k_1 t) + a_2 \exp(-k_2 t) \tag{1.61}$$

where $D_e = \epsilon_c[A]_0$ and a_1 and a_2 are composed of rate constants and molar absorptivities:

$$a_1 = \epsilon_a[A]_0 + \frac{\epsilon_b[A]_0 k_1}{k_2 - k_1} + \frac{\epsilon_c[A]_0 k_2}{k_1 - k_2} \tag{1.62}$$

$$a_2 = \frac{k_1[A]_0(\epsilon_b - \epsilon_c)}{k_1 - k_2} \tag{1.63}$$

In Fig. 1.6 is shown the semilog plot of $(D - D_e)$ vs time for the hydrolysis of cis-$Cr(C_2O_4)_2(DMSO)_2^-$ in water, in which both dimethylsulfoxide (DMSO) molecules have been replaced at equilibrium:[50]

$$cis\text{-}Cr(C_2O_4)_2(DMSO)_2^- \xrightarrow[\text{H}_2\text{O}]{k_1} cis\text{-}Cr(C_2O_4)_2(DMSO)H_2O^-$$
$$\text{(A)} \hspace{4cm} \text{(B)}$$
$$\xrightarrow[\text{H}_2\text{O}]{k_2} cis\text{-}Cr(C_2O_4)_2(H_2O)_2^- \tag{1.64}$$
$$\text{(C)}$$

The straight-line portion of the $\log(D - D_e)$ vs t plot at longer times yields k_s, the first-order rate constant for the slow reaction ($2.3 \times$ slope).

The logarithm of the difference between the extrapolated straight-line portion and the experimental curve (right ordinate) is then plotted vs time and the resultant straight line yields k_f, the rate constant for the fast reaction. The basis for this procedure is seen from the additivity of the exponential terms in (1.61). However, we cannot at this stage assign k_1 and k_2 to k_f and k_s or to k_s and k_f respectively without additional information, since (1.61) is derived without specifying either of these conditions. The most popular method for resolving this ambiguity is by resort to spectral considerations. The spectrum of the intermediate B (ϵ_b at various wavelengths) can be calculated from (1.61), (1.62), and (1.63) on the basis that (a) $k_1 = k_f$; $k_2 = k_s$, or (b) $k_1 = k_s$; $k_2 = k_f$. The fast, slow sequence in (a) gives a plausible spectrum for the anticipated intermediate B. The sequence (b), however, leads to very large and sometimes negative molar absorptivities for B and for this reason is discarded. An approach of this type was first made[51] in a study of

$$Cren_3^{3+} \xrightarrow{H^+} cis\text{-}Cren_2(enH)(H_2O)^{4+} \xrightarrow{H^+} cis\text{-}Cren_2(H_2O)_2^{3+} + enH_2^{2+} \tag{1.65}$$

and has since been adopted on a number of occasions.[52,53] Indeed, opposite conclusions were reached as to which step in the biphasic reaction of $Pd(NH_3)_4^{2+}$ with HCl to produce $Pd(NH_3)_2Cl_2$ was the faster. The problem was resolved by considering the specta of the three species involved and the significance of a "delayed" isosbestic point.[53]

The separation of biphasic plots into their components,[54] including computer analysis,[47,55] has been fully discussed. If the spectrum of the

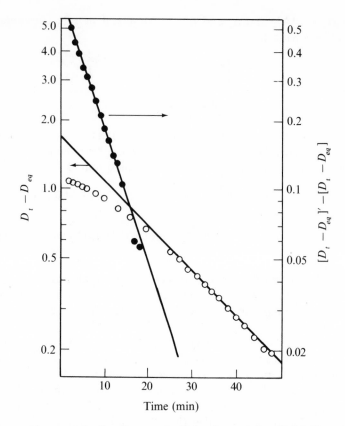

FIGURE 1.6   Semilog spectral plot for reaction (1.64).[50]

intermediate is known, a choice of observation wavelength may allow isolation of each stage. In the reaction of $Reen_2(OH)_2^{3+}$ with concentrated HCl,[56]

$$Reen_2(OH)_2^{3+} \xrightarrow[HCl]{k_1} ReenCl_2(OH)_2^+ \xrightarrow[HCl]{k_2} ReCl_4(OH)_2^- \quad (1.66)$$
$$(A) \qquad\qquad\qquad (B) \qquad\qquad\qquad (C)$$

examination at 395 or 535 nm (where $\epsilon_B = \epsilon_C$) gives $-d[A]/dt$ and hence a value for k_1. Observation at 465 nm (where $\epsilon_A = \epsilon_B$) allows a value for k_2 to be obtained after a short induction period. Absorbance changes at 685 nm ($\epsilon_A = \epsilon_C$) give an indication of $d[B]/dt$, and specifically an estimation of t_{max}, the time for the concentration of B to reach a maximum. This value can be shown to be related to k_1 and k_2 by

$$t_{max} = \frac{\ln(k_1/k_2)}{k_1 - k_2} \quad (1.67)$$

The maximum time and the time-ratio methods have been used to determine rate constants for successive reactions.[57,58,59]

The successive reactions so far encountered are first-order hydrolyses. An analogous approach can obviously be made to consecutive multi-order reactions by reducing them to pseudo first-order reactions. The successive pseudo first-order rate constants have been estimated for the acid and base hydrolysis of a Cr(III) dihydroxo bridged complex. By changing the (excess) concentrations of H^+, the rate law can be constructed.[60]

Finally, an intriguing example of the difficulty in distinguishing concurrent and consecutive first-order reactions is illustrated in a study of the reaction of methemoglobin (MHb) with azide ion.[61] By using a large excess of azide, the investigators obtained pseudo first-order plots. These were nonlinear, however, and attempted purification of the methemoglobin did not remove the biphasic character, which is ascribed to an inherent feature of the methemoglobin. The observed kinetic behavior,

$$s = a \exp(-k_1 t) + b \exp(-k_2 t) \tag{1.68}$$

where s = fractional saturation with N_3^-, can, however, correspond to two situations. Either (1) there are two kinetically different types of heme group in MHb that react independently with N_3^-, or (2) all hemes in unbound MHb react similarly with N_3^-, but after ligand binding to one heme center, the remaining sites have a modified reactivity, a familiar situation in hemoglobin kinetics. In (1), which corresponds to a concurrent process, the coefficients a and b in (1.68) are arbitrary (1.49a), whereas in (2), which is a consecutive process, the coefficients are functions of the rate constants ((1.62) and 1.63)).

Further experiments showed that the behavior of the azide adduct towards dissociation (by adding CN^-) conformed to the behavior expected for case (1), that is, methemoglobin-azide interaction is a biphasic independent process.

1.6.3   Change of Reaction Order with Reagent Concentration

Suppose that a reaction between A and B is examined in the usual way, with one of the reactants, B, held in excess. A loss of A will usually be a first-order process (rate constant k). At low concentrations of B (but still $\gg$ [A]), the value of k may be proportional to the concentration of B. At higher concentrations of B however, this direct proportionality may disappear and eventually k will become independent of [B]. Obviously, a second-order reaction at low reactant concentrations has lost its simplicity at higher reactant concentrations and eventually turned over to first-order in A alone. Such a situation is accommodated by a rate law of the form

$$V = \frac{-d[A]}{dt} = k[A] = \frac{a[A][B]}{1 + b[B]} \qquad (1.69)$$

The observed second-order (rate constant a), mixed-order, and first-order (rate constant a/b) behavior with increasing [B] will arise as $b[B] < 1$, $b[B] \sim 1$, and $b[B] > 1$ respectively. The $k/[B]$ plot is described by a hyperbola, and can be converted into a more attractive linear form for extracting kinetic data:

$$\frac{1}{k} = \frac{1}{a[B]} + \frac{b}{a} \qquad (1.70)$$

A comparable plot in terms of V is easily obtained. An example of this behavior is shown in the redox reaction

$$cis\text{-}Ru(NH_3)_4Cl_2{}^+ + Cr^{2+} \rightarrow Ru(NH_3)_4(H_2O)Cl^+ + CrCl^{2+} \qquad (1.71)$$

The effect of $[Cr^{2+}]$ on k is depicted in Fig. 1.7, representing Eqs. (1.69) and (1.70).[62]

1.6.4 Associated Reaction Schemes

There are a number of circumstances in which this rate behavior may arise.

(a) Consider the scheme[63]

$$A + B \underset{k_{-1}}{\overset{k_1}{\rightleftharpoons}} C \overset{k_2}{\longrightarrow} D \qquad (1.72)$$

It is likely that the first, reversible step is much more rapid than the second, irreversible step ($k_1, k_{-1} \gg k_2$) or we should most probably have seen deviations from a single first-order process (see below). This approximation considerably eases the derivation of the rate law. It means that C will be in equilibrium with A and B throughout the reaction and that

$$\frac{[C]}{[A][B]} = \frac{k_1}{k_{-1}} = K_1 \qquad (1.73)$$

will be continually maintained. We shall be monitoring the loss of [A] + [C] or the equivalent gain in [D].

$$V = \frac{d[D]}{dt} = k([A] + [C]) = k_2[C] = k_2K_1[A][B] \qquad (1.74)$$

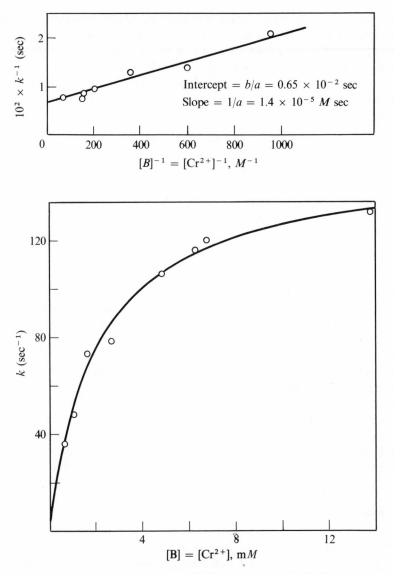

FIGURE 1.7   Rate data for (1.71) illustrating Eq. (1.69) in lower figure and Eq. (1.70) in upper figure.[62]

From (1.73) and (1.74),

$$k = \frac{k_2 K_1 [\mathrm{B}]}{1 + K_1 [\mathrm{B}]} \tag{1.75}$$

which is the form (1.69) with $k_2 K_1 = a$ and $K_1 = b$.

In reaction (1.71), C would represent an adduct between Cr^{2+} and cis-$Ru(NH_3)_4Cl_2^+$ (formation constant K_1), which would break down to products with a rate constant k_2. From Fig. 1.7, K_1 = intercept/slope = $4.65 \times 10^2 \, M^{-1}$ and k_2 = intercept^{-1} = $1.54 \times 10^2 \, sec^{-1}$.

(b) A related scheme to that of (a) is one in which A and B react directly to form D, but are also in a rapid "dead-end" equilibrium to give C:

$$A + B \rightleftharpoons C \qquad K_1 \tag{1.76}$$

$$A + B \rightarrow D \qquad k_3 \tag{1.77}$$

$$V = \frac{d[D]}{dt} = k([A] + [C]) = k_3[A][B] \tag{1.78}$$

whence
$$k = \frac{k_3[B]}{1 + K_1[B]} \tag{1.79}$$

The kinetic form is thus that of (1.69), but with $k_3 = a$.

In reaction (1.71), the reactants would still form an adduct with K_1 of the same value $4.65 \times 10^2 \, M^{-1}$, but the reactants would interact separately to give products with a rate constant k_3 = slope^{-1} = $7.2 \times 10^4 \, M^{-1} \, sec^{-1}$. Of the two possibilities, scheme (1.72) is preferred.[62] By examining the reaction progress *at very early times* while (1.76) is being set up, it may be possible to distinguish the two processes.[32b,64] Once the rapid equilibrium has been established however, the steady-state kinetics are identical for (a) and (b); arguments over which of the two schemes is preferred must then be based on chemical or rate considerations, and these are usually equivocal. Since the propensity to form adducts in transition metal chemistry is high and these might undergo a variety of reactions, the rate law (1.69) is quite common (see also (4.11), (4.57), and 4.84)), although the problem of differentiating (a) and (b) is difficult.

In reality, these reaction schemes and the rate law give biphasic first-order plots but because the first step is rapid, for example between A + B in (1.72), we do not normally examine this step unless we use special means (Secs. 3.3 and 3.4). However, the equilibrium can lead to a substantial amount of C (comparable to the amount of A) when the kinetics deviate from second-order and this can be detected experimentally (for example, the "starting" optical absorbances are not obtained from the sum of A and B alone, but include a contribution from C). The value of K_1 obtained kinetically can sometimes be checked with the value determined from the A + B $\rightleftharpoons$ C system before reaction to produce D occurs.

(c) It may not be easy to envisage adduct formation between A and B as a basis for the previous schemes. Even now the sequence

$$A \underset{k_{-1}}{\overset{k_1}{\rightleftharpoons}} C + D \tag{1.80}$$

$$C + B \xrightarrow{k_2} \text{products} \tag{1.81}$$

can in certain circumstances lead to the observed rate behavior depicted in (1.69). As in schemes (a) and (b), we make a simplifying assumption, that C does not accumulate during the reaction. Its concentration is always low and therefore changing only slightly and the steady-state or Bodenstein approximation is applicable, that is, that $d[C]/dt \sim 0$. But

$$\frac{d[C]}{dt} = k_1[A] - k_{-1}[C][D] - k_2[C][B] = 0 \tag{1.82}$$

Therefore $\quad\quad V = k[A] = k_2[C][B] = \dfrac{k_1 k_2[A][B]}{k_{-1}[D] + k_2[B]} \tag{1.83}$

This will be of the form (1.69) if the concentration of D, one of the products, is constant during the reaction. This will occur if an amount of D much greater than that produced during the reaction is added deliberately to the reaction mixture, or if the method of initial rates (before D can accumulate) is employed. The circumstance arises in the study of the rate of dissociation of metal complexes (A) from scavenging experiments (using B).

The reaction of $\text{Nidien}_2{}^{2+}$ with EDTA^{4-} leads eventually to NiEDTA^{2-} and dien but via intermediate formation of Ni(dien)EDTA^{2-}. The reaction has been studied in the presence of dien, and in a certain range of reactant concentration the rate of reaction (initial) in terms of the concentrations of reactants (initial) obeys the rate law:

$$V_i = \frac{k_1 k_2 [\text{Nidien}_2{}^{2+}]_i [\text{EDTA}]_i}{k_{-1}[\text{dien}]_i + k_2[\text{EDTA}]_i} \tag{1.84}$$

This is analogous to (1.83) and therefore in conformity with the reaction scheme

$$\text{Nidien}_2{}^{2+} \underset{k_{-1}}{\overset{k_1}{\rightleftharpoons}} \text{Nidien}^{2+} + \text{dien} \tag{1.85}$$

$$\text{Nidien}^{2+} + \text{EDTA}^{4-} \xrightarrow{k_2} \text{Ni(dien)EDTA}^{2-} \tag{1.86}$$

in which Nidien^{2+} is in (small) stationary-state concentrations. Inverting (1.84) leads to

$$\frac{[\text{Nidien}_2{}^{2+}]_i}{V_i} = \frac{k_{-1}[\text{dien}]_i}{k_1 k_2[\text{EDTA}]_i} + \frac{1}{k_1} \tag{1.87}$$

Plots of $[\text{Nidien}_2{}^{2+}]_i/V_i$ vs $[\text{EDTA}]_i{}^{-1}$ at constant $[\text{dien}]_i$, and vs $[\text{dien}]_i$ at constant EDTA are linear. From these k_1, k_{-1} (from k_1 and the formation constant k_{-1}/k_1 of $\text{Nidien}_2{}^{2+}$) and k_2 can be derived. At low [EDTA] and high [dien] the reaction is second-order, whereas at low [dien] and higher [EDTA] the reaction becomes first-order in $\text{Nidien}_2{}^{2+}$, as (1.84) would indicate.[65]

A decreasing value for k (in 1.69) as the reaction proceeds indicates above that a product is retarding the rate of the reaction. This is only possible if the product features in a reversible step that occurs prior to or at the rate-determining stage. Deliberate addition of the suspected retardant and observation of the effect will show whether this explanation is probable.

A multi-order or mixed-order rate law of the type we have been considering can be ascribed generally to the scheme[66]

$$A + B \rightleftharpoons C + F \qquad k_1, k_{-1} \tag{1.88}$$

$$C + B \rightleftharpoons D + F \qquad k_2, k_{-2} \tag{1.89}$$

$$D + B \rightarrow E + F \qquad k_3 \tag{1.90}$$

for which $\quad V = \dfrac{k_1 k_2 k_3 [\text{A}][\text{B}]^3}{k_2 k_3 [\text{B}]^2 + k_{-1} k_3 [\text{B}][\text{F}] + k_{-1} k_{-2} [\text{F}]^2} \tag{1.91}$

if we assume the steady-state treatment, or apply the Christiansen formulation.[67] The scheme, in varied and simplified forms, appears in a number of reactions of complexes.

$$V = k_1[\text{A}][\text{B}] \qquad\qquad \text{if } k_2 k_3 \text{ is large} \tag{1.92}$$

$$V = \frac{k_1 k_2}{k_{-1}}\,[\text{A}][\text{B}]^2[\text{F}]^{-1} \qquad \text{if } k_{-1} k_3 \text{ is large} \tag{1.93}$$

and $\quad V = \dfrac{k_1 k_2 k_3}{k_{-1} k_{-2}}\,[\text{A}][\text{B}]^3[\text{F}]^{-2} \quad \text{if } k_{-1} k_{-2} \text{ is large} \tag{1.94}$

A general rate law, wherein H^+ terms are ignored, for the oxidation of inorganic reductants by chromium(VI) is

$$\frac{-d[\text{Cr}^{\text{VI}}]}{dt} = \frac{k_1 k_2 [\text{Cr}^{\text{VI}}][\text{Red}]^2}{k_2[\text{Red}] + k_{-1}[\text{Ox}]} \tag{1.95}$$

which can be derived from steady-state treatment of the scheme

$$\text{Cr}^{\text{VI}} + \text{Red} \rightleftharpoons \text{Cr}^{\text{V}} + \text{Ox} \qquad k_1, k_{-1} \tag{1.96}$$

$$\text{Cr}^{\text{V}} + \text{Red} \rightarrow \text{Cr}^{\text{IV}} + \text{Ox} \qquad k_2 \tag{1.97}$$

$$\text{Cr}^{\text{IV}} + \text{Red} \rightarrow \text{Cr}^{\text{III}} + \text{Ox} \qquad \text{fast} \tag{1.98}$$

and also from (1.91) if the k_{-2}-containing term is neglected.

If the reaction is carried out in the presence of a large excess of oxidized product, this has the twofold effect of slowing down and therefore easing the measurement of an otherwise rapid reaction and of also producing good pseudo first-order kinetics that show second-order dependence on the reducing agent.[68]

1.6.5 Recapitulation

At this stage we ought to restate briefly the sequences necessary in the construction of the rate law.

1. Decide the reactant (A) whose concentration is most conveniently monitored. Use A in deficiency and determine whether it is totally ($\geqslant 95\%$) consumed in all the experimental conditions envisaged. If it is not, the reaction is reversible, and should be allowed for in the kinetic treatment.

2. Determine the order of the reaction with respect to A. The value of [A], (often) log [A], or $[A]^{-1}$ will be linearly related to time, indicating zero-, first-, or second-order, respectively. All other reactants are maintained in constant concentration.

3. Repeat the experiments with different concentrations of the other reactants B, and so on, varied one at a time. Thus determine the order with respect to these also. Plots of log k_{obsd} vs log [B], and so on, are useful in giving the reaction orders as slopes.

4. If a complexity is suspected from the kinetic behavior, the effect of products and of possible impurities and the occurrence of side reactions should be considered. Later we shall see that medium composition (Sec. 2.8) and temperature (Sec. 2.3.1) are other important parameters that affect rate. The rate law including these effects is obtained by further experiments of the type indicated in 3.

1.7 COMPLEX KINETIC BEHAVIOR

Several complicated kinetic situations have arisen and are mentioned for the sake of completeness. In the consecutive reaction (1.51), direct conversion of A to C may occur as well as conversion that proceeds via B.

$$A \xrightarrow{k_1} B \xrightarrow{k_2} C \qquad (1.99)$$
$$\underset{k_3}{\underline{\hspace{4cm}}\uparrow}$$

It can be shown[26,69] that

$$\frac{[C]}{[A]_0} = \left[1 - \frac{k_1}{k}\right][1 - \exp(-k_1 + k_3)t] + \frac{k_1}{k}[1 - \exp(-k_2t)] \quad (1.100)$$

where
$$k = k_1 + k_3 - k_2 \quad (1.101)$$

and
$$[B]_0 = [C]_0 = 0 \quad (1.102)$$

The situation has been met experimentally in the hydrolysis of *trans*-$Cren_2(H_2O)Cl^{2+}$ ion.[70] A computer was used to find a set of values of k_1, k_2, and k_3 that resulted in calculated values of $[C]/[A]_0$ most similar to the experimental values. The B → C transformation needs to be taken into account in the full description of (1.26) and (1.27) but its relative slowness does not interfere with the earlier analysis.[26]

If the interconversion of two species (say isomers A, A') occurs at rates comparable with the rate of their reactions, the kinetics are complex (so far we have only considered the interconversion as very fast or very slow). We have a demonstration in the reaction scheme

$$trans\text{-}Coen_2(CH_3OH)Cl^{2+} \rightleftharpoons cis\text{-}Coen_2(CH_3OH)Cl^{2+}$$

$$\downarrow + Cl^- \qquad \qquad + Cl^- \qquad \downarrow + Cl^- \qquad (1.103)$$

$$trans\text{-}Coen_2Cl_2^+ + CH_3OH \qquad cis\text{-}Coen_2Cl_2^+ + CH_3OH$$

the kinetic solution of which is quite tedious.[71]

Scheme (1.50) forms an important basis for many kinetic schemes. The addition of the reverse terms k_{-1} or k_{-2} or both to (1.51) complicates the matter considerably when steady-state simplifications cannot be made. Even though integration is possible when all the steps have a first-order or pseudo first-order dependence, extracting the first-order rate constants even from a large amount of experimental data is very tedious and difficult.[72] Fortunately the situation can nearly always be simplified. The approach to (1.50) is exemplified by the study of the reaction of Cu^{2+} with the keto, enol tautomeric mixture of acetylacetone (acacH) in acidic aqueous solution:[74]

$$keto \underset{k_{-1}[H^+]}{\overset{k_1[Cu^{2+}]}{\rightleftharpoons}} Cu(acac)^+ \underset{k_{-2}[Cu^{2+}]}{\overset{k_2[H^+]}{\rightleftharpoons}} enol \quad (1.104)$$

Since the metal and H^+ ions are in large excess, all the rate constants are pseudo first-order, and k_1, k_{-1}, k_2, and k_{-2} are the desired second-order rate constants.

It can be shown that[75,76]

$$[keto] - [keto]_e = \alpha \exp(-\lambda_1 t) + \beta \exp(-\lambda_2 t) \quad (1.105)$$

where α and β are constants, depending on initial concentrations and rate constants. Of more interest to us are the observed rate constants λ_1 and λ_2. These are related to the intrinsic rate constants as follows:

$$\lambda_{1,2} = \tfrac{1}{2}(p \pm q) \tag{1.106}$$

where

$$p = k_{-1}[H^+] + k_2[H^+] + k_1[Cu^{2+}] + k_{-2}[Cu^{2+}] \tag{1.107}$$

$$q = \{p^2 - 4(k_1 k_2[Cu^{2+}][H^+] + k_{-1}k_{-2}[Cu^{2+}][H^+] + k_1 k_{-2}[Cu^{2+}]^2)\}^{1/2}$$

$$= (p^2 - 4b)^{1/2} \approx p\left(1 - \frac{2b}{p^2}\right) \tag{1.108}$$

It would be extemely difficult to extract values for the second-order rate constants from the observed values for λ_1 and λ_2 without further simplification. These involve $k_{-2} \gg k_1$ and $k_2 \gg k_{-1}$, assumptions that can be justified. Now

$$k_{-2} = \frac{\lambda_1}{[Cu^{2+}] + [H^+]/K_2} \tag{1.109}$$

$$k_1 = \frac{\lambda_2([H^+] + K_2[Cu^{2+}])}{(1 + (K_2/K_1))[H^+][Cu^{2+}] + K_2[Cu^{2+}]^2} \tag{1.110}$$

with $K_2 = k_{-2}/k_2$ and $K_1 = k_{-1}/k_1$, both known equilibrium constants. It turns out that λ_1 and λ_2 are well separated, and the data give the appearance of two reactions from which λ_1 and λ_2 are easily extracted.[77]

There are a variety of combinations of consecutive first-order and second-order reactions, including reversible and irreversible steps.[69] Exact integrated rate expressions for systems of linked equilibria may be derived by the use of the Laplace-Carson transform, in combination with a computer program.[78] Examples of their application are rarely encountered except in enzyme chemistry, and such complexity is to be avoided if at all possible.

1.8　RELAXATION KINETICS

With the availability of perturbation techniques for measuring the rates of rapid reactions (Sec. 3.4), the subject of relaxation kinetics—rates of reaction near to chemical equilibrium—has become important in the study of complex ion reactions.[79] Briefly, a chemical system at equilibrium is perturbed, for example, by a change in the temperature of the solution. The rate at which the new equilibrium position is attained is a measure of the values of the rate constants linking the equilibrium (or equilibria in a multistep process), and is controlled by these values.

1.8.1 Single-Step Reactions

Consider a simple equilibrium, second-order in the forward direction and first-order in the reverse:

$$A + B \rightleftharpoons C \qquad k_1, k_{-1} \tag{1.111}$$

After the effect of the perturbation, let the final equilibrium concentrations be represented by A, B, and C. At any time t after the perturbation is imposed, and before the final equilibrium is reached, let the concentrations of A, B, and C be $(A - a)$, $(B - b)$, and $(C - c)$. Thus a, b, and c represent deviations from the final equilibrium concentrations. It is apparent from the stoichiometry of the system that

$$a = b = -c \tag{1.112}$$

At time t,

$$\frac{d(C - c)}{dt} = k_1(A - a)(B - b) - k_{-1}(C - c) \tag{1.113}$$

At final equilibrium,

$$\frac{dC}{dt} = 0 = k_1 AB - k_{-1} C \tag{1.114}$$

Since the perturbations are small, the term ab can be neglected for (1.113); then combination of (1.112), (1.113), and (1.114) gives

$$\frac{-dc}{dt} = [k_1(A + B) + k_{-1}]c \tag{1.115}$$

Similarly,

$$\frac{-da}{dt} = [k_1(A + B) + k_{-1}]a \tag{1.116}$$

The shift to the new equilibrium as a result of the perturbation, the *relaxation* of the system, is therefore a first-order process with a first-order rate constant $k = \tau^{-1}$ (1.25) made up of $k_1(A + B) + k_{-1}$.

A treatment similar to that above can be applied to other single equilibria. If the stoichiometry condition akin to (1.112), the zero net rate condition at final equilibrium (1.114), and the neglect of squared terms in the deviation concentrations are applied to the rate equation (1.113), it is found that there is always a linear relation of the form

$$\frac{-da}{dt} = ka \tag{1.117}$$

with a value for k characteristic of the system (Table 1.2). Thus the determination of the relaxation times for a number of different reactant concentrations (estimated in situ or from a knowledge of the equilibrium constant) will give both the reaction order and the associated rate constants.

If in the relaxation systems listed in Table 1.2 one of the reactants A or B and one of the products C or D is in large excess, that is, if pseudo

TABLE 1.2.   Values of Relaxation Rate Constants (k) for
Various Single Equilibria

System	k
$A \rightleftharpoons B$	$k_1 + k_{-1}$[a]
$2A \rightleftharpoons B$	$4k_1[A] + k_{-1}$
$A + B \rightleftharpoons C$	$k_1([A] + [B]) + k_{-1}$
$A + C \rightleftharpoons B + C$	$(k_1 + k_{-1})[C]$
$A + B \rightleftharpoons C + D$	$k_1([A] + [B]) + k_{-1}([C] + [D])$

[a] The symbols k_1, k_{-1} represent the forward and reverse rate
constants for all systems; [A], [B], etc., represent the final
equilibrium concentration of these species.

first-order conditions obtain, the relaxation expression is identical with
the rate law obtained starting from pure reactants (1.38). For conditions
other than these however, the simplified treatment with relaxation conditions is very evident, as can be seen, for example, in the simple expression
for the first-order relaxation rate constant for the $A + B \rightleftharpoons C + D$
scheme compared with the treatment starting from only A and B.

1.8.2   Multistep Reactions

Consider the common two-step mechanism

$$A + B \underset{k_{-1}}{\overset{k_1}{\rightleftharpoons}} C \underset{k_{-2}}{\overset{k_2}{\rightleftharpoons}} D \tag{1.118}$$

The most difficult situation arises when the rates associated with the two
steps are similar. This case will be treated first. The objective is to express da/dt and dc/dt each in terms of a and c, which are the deviations from
equilibrium concentrations symbolized A, B, C, and D. These provide
the basis for the two relaxation times observable with the system. Now

$$a = b = -(c + d) \tag{1.119}$$

$$\frac{d(A - a)}{dt} = -k_1(A - a)(B - b) + k_{-1}(C - c) \tag{1.120}$$

$$\frac{-da}{dt} = k_1(A + B)a - k_{-1}c \tag{1.121}$$

$$\frac{d(C - c)}{dt} = k_1(A - a)(B - b) - k_{-1}(C - c) - k_2(C - c) + k_{-2}(D - d) \tag{1.122}$$

$$k_{-2}D = k_2C \tag{1.123}$$

$$\frac{-dc}{dt} = -k_1(A + B)a + k_{-1}c + k_2c + k_{-2}(a + c) \tag{1.124}$$

$$\frac{-dc}{dt} = -(k_1(A + B) - k_{-2})a + (k_{-1} + k_2 + k_{-2})c \tag{1.125}$$

Equations (1.121) and (1.125) are of the forms

$$\frac{-da}{dt} = \alpha_{11}a + \alpha_{12}c \qquad (1.126)$$

$$\frac{-dc}{dt} = \alpha_{21}a + \alpha_{22}c \qquad (1.127)$$

Making the substitution $a = Xe^{-kt}$ and $c = Ye^{-kt}$ gives

$$kXe^{-kt} = \alpha_{11}Xe^{-kt} + \alpha_{12}Ye^{-kt} \qquad (1.128)$$

$$kYe^{-kt} = \alpha_{21}Xe^{-kt} + \alpha_{22}Ye^{-kt} \qquad (1.129)$$

whence $\qquad k^2 - (\alpha_{11} + \alpha_{22})k + \alpha_{11}\alpha_{22} - \alpha_{12}\alpha_{21} = 0 \qquad (1.130)$

The two first-order rate constants k_I and k_{II} associated with this scheme are given by

$$2k_{I,II} = (\alpha_{11} + \alpha_{22}) \pm \sqrt{(\alpha_{11} + \alpha_{22})^2 - 4(\alpha_{11}\alpha_{22} - \alpha_{12}\alpha_{21})} \qquad (1.131)$$

One of the rate constants is associated with the plus sign of the square root, and the other with the negative sign.

This treatment yields the *time* course of the relaxation, which is of most concern to us, but ignores the relative magnitude of the relaxations (contained in the α terms), which is of less interest. A treatment of (1.131) in order to obtain the individual rate constants from the experimental values, k_I and k_{II}, is given in Ref. 80 (see also Prob. 5d).

A common simplification arises when the bimolecular step equilibrates rapidly compared with the unimolecular step (it may, for example, be a proton-base reaction). This means that the change in concentrations of A, B, and C due to the first process in (1.118) will have occurred before D even starts to change. The relaxation time τ_I associated with it will therefore be the same as if it were a separated equilibrium:

$$\tau_I^{-1} = k_I = k_1(A + B) + k_{-1} \qquad (1.132)$$

The changes of concentration of C and D resulting from the second equilibrium are however coupled to the first, and the associated relaxation time τ_{II} might be expected to be a more complex function. It is fairly easily derived, however.

$$\frac{d(D - d)}{dt} = k_2(C - c) - k_{-2}(D - d) \qquad (1.133)$$

from which $\qquad \dfrac{dd}{dt} = k_2 c - k_{-2}d \qquad (1.134)$

Now we must express c in terms of d, so that an equation relating dd/dt and d only may be obtained. Since the first equilibrium is always maintained, compared with the second,

$$k_1(A - a)(B - b) = k_{-1}(C - c) \qquad (1.135)$$

$$k_1(Ab + Ba) = k_{-1}c \qquad (1.136)$$

Since $\qquad\qquad -a = -b = c + d \qquad (1.137)$

$$-k_1(A + B)(c + d) = k_{-1}c \qquad (1.138)$$

$$c = \frac{-k_1(A + B)d}{k_1(A + B) + k_{-1}} \qquad (1.139)$$

$$\frac{dd}{dt} = \frac{-k_1 k_2(A + B)d}{k_1(A + B) + k_{-1}} - k_{-2}d \qquad (1.140)$$

$$\tau_{\text{II}}{}^{-1} = k_{\text{II}} = k_{-2} + \frac{k_1 k_2(A + B)}{k_1(A + B) + k_{-1}} \qquad (1.141)$$

Equations (1.132) and (1.141) can be derived from the general expression (1.131) by using the relationship $k_1(A + B) + k_{-1} \gg k_{-2} + k_2$ and making the approximation $(1 - x)^{1/2} \sim 1 - x/2$.

In the interchange mechanism for complex formation (Sec. 4.3.1), an outer-sphere complex $(M \cdots L)$ is formed rapidly and this breaks down to the inner-sphere complex (ML) more slowly:

$$M + L \rightleftharpoons M \cdots L \qquad k_1, k_{-1}, K_1 \qquad (1.142)$$

$$M \cdots L \rightleftharpoons ML \qquad k_2, k_{-2}, K_2 \qquad (1.143)$$

Usually the outer-sphere complex is in very low concentration relative to the other species in the equilibria, and therefore $k_1([M] + [L]) \ll k_{-1}$, and there will be a very rapid relaxation and a slower one τ_{II} from (1.141):

$$\tau_{\text{II}}{}^{-1} = k_{-2} + \frac{k_1 k_2([M] + [L])}{k_{-1}} \qquad (1.144)$$

However, if the concentration of $M \cdots L$ is not negligible, which is a rare situation, the full equation must be used and values for k_2, K_2, and K_1 can then be obtained experimentally.[81]

Undoubtedly, the area in which relaxation kinetics have been most utilized is in the study of complex formation in solution. It is difficult to curtail such equilibria to one step, but fairly easy, by adjustment of concentrations, to avoid three successive equilibria, which can be treated only approximately.[82] The general scheme

$$M + L \rightleftharpoons ML \qquad (1.145)$$

$$ML + L \rightleftharpoons ML_2 \qquad (1.146)$$

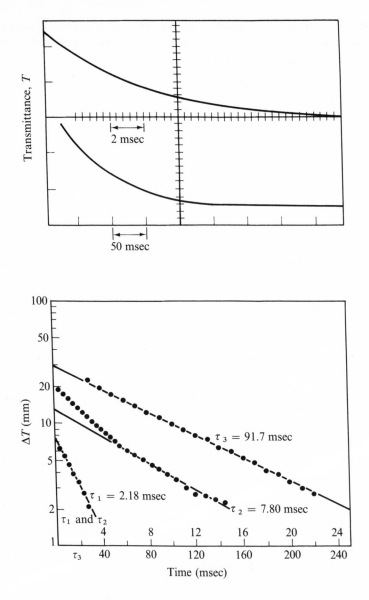

FIGURE 1.8 Temperature-jump relaxation spectra for reaction
(1.149) and associated first-order plots. The transmittance (which
is a function of concentration)/time curve (upper figure) can be
broken down into three first-order relaxations (lower figure). In
addition, there is a very fast relaxation seen, but not resolvable,
in the upper figure. This is resolved however by electric field relaxation methods (see Fig. 3.5).[87]

is therefore most encountered. The approach of Hammes and Steinfeld to the treatment of this scheme has been generally followed.[82] The ligand L or the metal M, or complexes ML and ML_2, usually have weak spectral absorption, and spectral changes accompanying perturbation of the equilibria (1.145) and (1.146) are too weak to detect. The ligand L, however, is often linked with a protonated form LH, and a small pH change accompanying the perturbation can be monitored by incorporating a suitable indicator, In. Now two additional equilibria

$$H + L \rightleftharpoons HL \tag{1.147}$$

$$H + In \rightleftharpoons HIn \tag{1.148}$$

must be considered. These are very labile and their associated relaxation times are usually too short to be resolved. Their presence does modify, however, the expression for the relaxation times associated with the schemes (1.145) and (1.146).[83] Involved equilibria in which metal-hydroxy and mono- and diprotonated ligand species take part have been analyzed.[84,85]

It is often difficult to distinguish two or more relaxation times when $\log y$ is plotted against time (y being some function of the concentration of one of the reactants). This situation has been analyzed mathematically[86] and discussed at length in the treatment of the hemoglobin-O_2 interaction,

$$Hb_4 + 4O_2 \rightleftharpoons Hb_4(O_2)_4 \tag{1.149}$$

a most complicated system, which has still not been resolved. At least four relaxation times can be associated with the process, Fig. 1.8.[87]

1.9 EXCHANGE KINETICS

Somewhat in the same vein as relaxation kinetics, there is a simplicity about the manipulation of isotopic exchange results that makes the method an important and useful tool for studying mechanism. When AX and BX, both containing a common atom or group of atoms X, are mixed, there will be a continual interchange of X between the two environments that may range from extremely rapid to negligibly slow. This exchange will go undetected unless we tag AX or BX with some labeled X, which we denote by *X:

$$AX + B{*}X \rightleftharpoons A{*}X + BX \tag{1.150}$$

Consider a mixture of AX and BX at chemical equilibrium. Let the rate of exchange of X between the two species AX and BX be V_{exch} (M sec^{-1}). The rate will be identical in both directions and will be a constant for a given set of conditions, concentrations of AX and BX and other species not directly involved in the exchange, pH, and so forth. Tracer X in the form of a very small amount of B*X is now injected into the equilibrium mixture. If the concentration of AX is a and the concentration of (BX + B*X) is b, and the fraction of exchange at time t is F, it is not difficult to show[88] that

$$V_{exch} = \frac{-2.303}{t} \frac{ab}{a+b} \log(1-F) = k_{exch} \frac{ab}{a+b} = \frac{0.693}{t_{1/2\,exch}} \frac{ab}{a+b}$$

(1.151)

The rate of exchange will therefore be always first-order, comparable to the situation with relaxation kinetics, and the semilog plot of $(1-F)$ vs time will be linear (Fig. 1.9).

If there is more than one exchanging atom of X in the interacting molecules, for example, AX_n exchanging with BX_m, the rate expression (1.151) is modified accordingly, with a and b replaced by na and mb

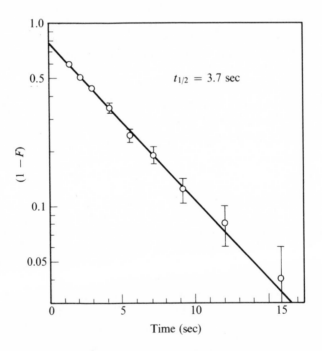

FIGURE 1.9   Exchange curve for the MnO_4^-, MnO_4^{2-} isotopic exchange, demonstrating (1.151). $[MnO_4^-] = 9.6 \times 10^{-5}\ M$, $[MnO_4^{2-}] = 4.0 \times 10^{-5}\ M$ at $0.1°$ in $0.16\ M$ NaOH.   Errors shown correspond to ± 0.02 in F values.[89]

respectively. This applies only when the nX or mX atoms are equivalent. The rate of exchange will also depend on the concentrations a, b, $[H^+]$, and so on, in a manner that determines the rate expression. The exchange rate is measured with different concentrations of AX and BX, and the rate law constructed exactly as in the initial-rate or stationary-state methods.

The exchange of Mn between MnO_4^- and MnO_4^{2-} has been followed using ^{54}Mn and quenched-flow methods (Sec. 3.3.1).[89] The results are shown in Table 1.3, from which it is apparent that

$$V_{exch} = k[MnO_4^-][MnO_4^{2-}] \qquad (1.152)$$

Even complex rate laws may be easily constructed by examining the dependence of V_{exch} on the concentration of the various species in solution. The rate of exchange of Ni between Ni^{2+} and $NiEDTA^{2-}$ obeys the rate law

$$V_{exch} = k_1[Ni^{2+}][NiEDTA^{2-}] + k_2[Ni^{2+}][NiEDTA^{2-}][H^+]$$
$$+ k_3[NiEDTA^{2-}][H^+] + k_4[NiEDTA^{2-}][H^+]^2$$
$$+ k_5[NiEDTA^{2-}][H^+]^3 \qquad (1.153)$$

The five terms simply represent paths through which exchange can occur (Sec. 4.5.8).[90]

TABLE 1.3. Dependence of ^{54}Mn Exchange Rate on Concentrations of MnO_4^{2-} and MnO_4^- at 0.1° in 0.16 M NaOH[89]

$10^5 \times [MnO_4^{2-}]$ M	$10^5 \times [MnO_4^-]$ M	$t_{1/2\ exch}$ sec	$10^6 \times V_{exch}$ $M\ sec^{-1}$	$10^{-2} \times k$ $M^{-1}\ sec^{-1}$
4.3	4.8	10.6	1.5	7.2
4.1	4.8	11.2	1.4	7.0
4.6	9.7	6.6	3.3	7.3
4.5	14.6	5.3	4.5	6.8
4.3	19.4	4.3	5.7	7.6
4.2	24.3	3.2	7.8	7.3
4.1	34.0	2.5	10.2	6.5
1.0	9.7	9.2	0.69	7.3
2.3	9.5	9.0	1.4	6.5
4.6	9.7	6.6	3.3	7.3
10.1	9.7	4.9	6.9	7.1
19.7	9.7	3.1	15	7.9
33.0	337	0.25	830	7.5
195	188	0.26	2550	7.0
29	381	0.25	750	6.8
			Average	7.1 ± 0.3

A special and important type of exchange arises when one of the exchanging species is the solvent. The rate of exchange of the N—H of sarcosine in $Co(NH_3)_4(NH(CH_3)CH_2COO)^{2+}$ with D_2O has been studied by nuclear magnetic resonance (see Fig. 3.10).[91] At a specific pH, since $[D_2O] \gg [Co(III)]$,

$$V_{exch} = k_{exch} \times \frac{2[D_2O][Co^{III}]}{2[D_2O] + [Co^{III}]} = k_{exch}[Co^{III}] \quad (1.154)$$

and therefore k_{exch} equals the first-order rate constant for deuteration.

It is clear from the previous example that a molecule can contain more than one type of exchanging atom; but since the exchange of the ammonia hydrogen is much slower than the exchange of the sarcosine with D_2O, it does not cause problems in the interpretation of the data. However, the position is not always so clear-cut, and nowhere has this been more evident than in the study of the exchange of oxygen between coordinated oxalate and solvent H_2O. It is now established that at 25 °C six of the twelve oxygens of $Co(C_2O_4)_3^{3-}$ exchange at a rate very much different from the rate of the other six.[92] This conclusion is based on the fact that a linear exchange plot results if there are assumed to be only six exchanging oxygen atoms (Fig. 1.10) and on the extent of distribution of ^{18}O between the exchanging species when equilibrium is apparently reached. At 55 °C, however, the two exchange rates become kinetically indistinguishable.[93] This dichotomy has lead to much confusion.

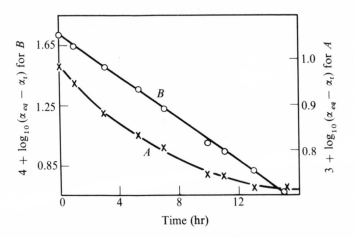

FIGURE 1.10 The exchange plot for the $Co(C_2O_4)_3^{3-}-H_2^{18}O$ system at 25 °C. [Complex] = 0.063 M, [HCl] = 1 M. Plot A calculated for exchange of all 12 oxygens. Plot B calculated for exchange of only 6 oxygens. The symbols α_t and α_{eq} are the atom fractions of oxygen-18 in the complex at times t and infinity respectively.[92]

1.10   THE INCLUSION OF H^+ TERMS IN THE RATE LAW

The effect of the concentration of "inert" ions on the rates of reactions can usually be accommodated by the general theories of the effect of ionic strength on the reaction rate (Sec. 2.8.1). These concentrations will appear in any fully descriptive rate law, which can be constructed in precisely the same way that has been described above for reactants more directly involved.

Most reaction rates are affected by the pH of the solution. It is therefore essential that as wide a range of pH as possible be studied so as to detail a full reaction scheme, and thus delineate the reactive forms of the reactants. Determining $[H^+]$ terms in the rate law presents little problem, the rate constant for the reaction being simply measured at a number of hydrogen ion concentrations. The $[H^+]$ may be in excess over that of other reagents, or alternatively the solutions may be buffered. In both cases, no change of pH occurs during the reaction. Since this is such an important parameter in effect on rates, we shall discuss in some detail the most common types of behavior (rate/pH profiles) encountered. The determination of rate constants at even a few pH values can often indicate the extent and type of H^+ (or OH^-) involvement. It may in certain cases be necessary to separate a "medium" from a "mechanistic" effect of $[H^+]$ on the rate (Sec. 2.8.2).

1.10.1   One Monoprotic Reactant, One Acid-Base Equilibrium

If the profile of the observed or the intrinsic rate constant plotted against pH resembles the profile for an acid-base titration curve, this strongly suggests that one of the reactants is involved in an acid-base equilibrium in that pH range. Such behavior is fairly common and is illustrated by the second-order reaction between the Co(II)-trien complex and O_2 (Fig. 1.11).[94] The limiting rate constants at the higher and low acidities correspond to the acidic and basic forms of the Co(II) reactant, probably,

$$\text{Cotrien}(H_2O)_2{}^{2+} \rightleftharpoons \text{Cotrien}(H_2O)OH^+ + H^+$$

$$\downarrow O_2 \qquad\qquad\qquad \downarrow O_2 \qquad\qquad\qquad \textbf{(1.155)}$$

$$\text{products} \qquad\qquad\qquad \text{products}$$

The rate law and the general reaction scheme associated with this system are easily derived. Consider the reaction of an acid AH and its conjugate base A with a substrate B (any charges are omitted from these for convenience):

$$AH \rightleftharpoons A + H^+ \qquad K_{AH} \qquad\qquad \textbf{(1.156)}$$

$$A + B \rightarrow \text{products} \qquad k_A \qquad\qquad \textbf{(1.157)}$$

$$AH + B \rightarrow \text{products} \qquad k_{AH} \qquad\qquad \textbf{(1.158)}$$

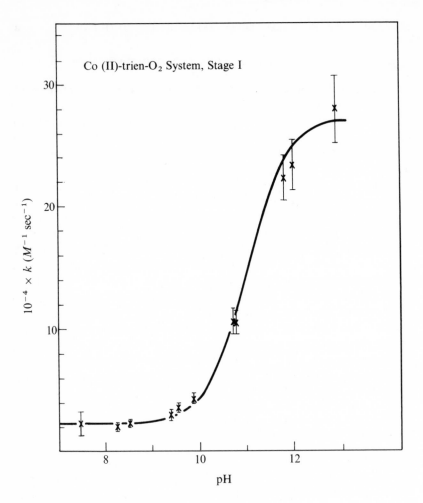

FIGURE 1.11   The pH dependence of the reaction between Co(II)-trien complex and O_2. The solid line represents Eq. (1.163), $K_{AH} = 6 \times 10^{-12}$, a spectrally determined value.[94]

Invariably, the total concentration of A and AH is monitored, and so the rate expression is formulated in terms of ([A] + [AH])

$$\frac{-d([AH] + [A])}{dt} = k([AH] + [A])[B]^n \qquad (1.159)$$

where k is the experimental rate constant, first-order if $n = 0$, second-order if $n = 1$, and so on. The rate is also the sum of the contributions of AH and A.

$$\frac{-d([AH] + [A])}{dt} = k_{AH}[AH][B]^n + k_A[A][B]^n \qquad (1.160)$$

Combining (1.159) and (1.160), we obtain

$$k = \frac{k_{AH}[AH] + k_A[A]}{([AH] + [A])} \tag{1.161}$$

Using

$$K_{AH} = \frac{[A][H^+]}{[AH]} \tag{1.162}$$

yields

$$k = \frac{k_{AH}[H^+] + k_A K_{AH}}{[H^+] + K_{AH}} \tag{1.163}$$

The full curve in Fig. 1.11 is drawn in accordance with (1.163).   Considering limits, we find $k = k_{AH}$ when $[H^+] \gg K_{AH}$ and $k = k_A$ with $[H^+] \ll K_{AH}$. Equation (1.163) can be converted into more attractive linear forms

$$k = \frac{k_{AH} - k_A}{1 + K_{AH}[H^+]^{-1}} + k_A \tag{1.164}$$

or

$$\frac{1}{k - k_A} = \frac{1}{k_{AH} - k_A} + \frac{K_{AH}}{[H^+](k_{AH} - k_A)} \tag{1.165}$$

which are easier to manipulate.[94,95]

A number of simplified behaviors have been observed.   If one of the forms in the acid-base equilibrium (say A) is unreactive,

$$k = k_{AH}(1 + K_{AH}[H^+]^{-1})^{-1} \tag{1.166}$$

This is seen in the reaction of thiocyanate with aquocobalamin; the hydroxocobalamin is unreactive.[96]   When one of the forms predominates over the whole pH range of investigation, yet the other form is much more reactive, only one limiting rate constant is obtained:

$$[A] \gg [AH], \quad [H^+] \ll K_{AH} \qquad k = k_A + \frac{k_{AH}[H^+]}{K_{AH}} \tag{1.167}$$

$$[AH] \gg [A], \quad [H^+] \gg K_{AH} \qquad k = k_{AH} + \frac{k_A K_{AH}}{[H^+]} \tag{1.168}$$

Such behavior is more common than the full rate/pH profile of (1.163). Equation (1.167) is observed in acid catalysis, and (1.168) in base catalysis. The rate constant for the reaction of only one of the two forms can be obtained directly, that is, k_A in (1.167) and k_{AH} in (1.168).   Ancillary information on K_{AH} is required to assess the rate constant of the acid-base partner.

A serious ambiguity in the interpretation of the rate law,

$$V = k[A][B][H^+]^n \tag{1.169}$$

exists when A and B are both basic and $n = 1$ (acid hydrolysis) and when A and B are both acidic and $n = -1$ (base hydrolysis).   The actual acidic species involved in the rate-determining step, AH with B or BH with A, cannot be assessed on the basis of kinetics but may sometimes be differentiated by resort to plausibility (Sec. 2.1.5).

1.10.2   Two Acid-Base Equilibria

When the sigmoidal shape of the rate constant/pH profile associated with (1.163) or the simpler derivatives (1.166) through (1.168) give way to a bell-shape or inverted bell-shape plot, the reactions of at least three acid-base-related species (two equilibria) have to be considered. This may involve acid-base forms of (a) one reactant or (b) two different reactants.

(a) Diprotic reactant A.   Consider the scheme

$$AH_2 \rightleftharpoons AH + H^+ \qquad K_{AH_2} \qquad \text{(1.170)}$$

$$AH \rightleftharpoons A + H^+ \qquad K_{AH} \qquad \text{(1.171)}$$

$$A \rightarrow \text{products} \qquad k_A \qquad \text{(1.172)}$$

$$AH \rightarrow \text{products} \qquad k_{AH} \qquad \text{(1.173)}$$

$$AH_2 \rightarrow \text{products} \qquad k_{AH_2} \qquad \text{(1.174)}$$

in which the rate constant may be first-order or pseudo first-order. Usually the products from the three steps are identical or pH-related. The observed rate constant k at any $[H^+]$ can be shown by reasoning similar to that used in developing (1.163):

$$k = \frac{k_{AH_2}[H^+]^2 + k_{AH}K_{AH_2}[H^+] + k_A K_{AH}K_{AH_2}}{[H^+]^2 + K_{AH_2}[H^+] + K_{AH}K_{AH_2}} \qquad \text{(1.175)}$$

If the species AH reacts more rapidly or more slowly than either A or AH_2, a bell shape or inverted bell shape respectively results for the k/pH profile.

The cobalt(III) complex of EDTA, in which the ligand acts only as a five-coordinate species and in which an acetate arm remains free, exists in three pH-related forms:

$$\text{(1.176)}$$

In all forms the free-CH_2COOH arm (in AH_2) or the free-CH_2COO^- arm (in AH and A) replaces the unidentate group, to give a common cobalt(III) product in which the EDTA is completely coordinated. The first-order rate constants at 15 °C for ring closure vs pH are shown in Fig. 1.12. They conform to the full line that represents (1.175) by the values shown in scheme (1.176).[97]

If the predominant form of the reactant is AH, this means that $K_{AH_2} \gg H^+ \gg K_{AH}$, and only the middle term of the denominator in (1.175) is important. Thus

$$k = \frac{k_{AH_2}[H^+]}{K_{AH_2}} + k_{AH} + \frac{k_A K_{AH}}{[H^+]} \tag{1.177}$$

which describes the behavior of a number of complexes toward hydrolysis, for example, $Co(NH_3)_5OReO_3{}^{2+}$ and CrX^{2+} (Sec. 4.5.1).[98]   Other simplified forms of (1.175) are possible.   For example, if only A is the reactive form and $[H^+] > K_{AH}, K_{AH_2}$, then

$$k\left\{\frac{1}{K_{AH}} + \frac{[H^+]}{K_{AH}K_{AH_2}}\right\} = \frac{k_A}{[H^+]} \tag{1.178}$$

The linear plot appropriate to (1.178) indicates that $SO_3{}^{2-}$ and not $HSO_3{}^-$ nor H_2SO_3 (nor SO_2) is the reactive species in the reduction of $(NH_3)_5CoO_2Co(NH_3)_5{}^{5+}$ ions.[99]

(b) Two protic reactants.   If in the first scheme described in this section ((1.156)–(1.158)) the reactant B can also be the partner in an acid-base equilibrium with BH, and if only BH is reactive:

$$AH \rightleftharpoons A + H^+ \qquad K_{AH} \tag{1.179}$$

$$BH \rightleftharpoons B + H^+ \qquad K_{BH} \tag{1.180}$$

$$AH + BH \rightarrow products \qquad k_{AH} \tag{1.181}$$

$$A + BH \rightarrow products \qquad k_A \tag{1.182}$$

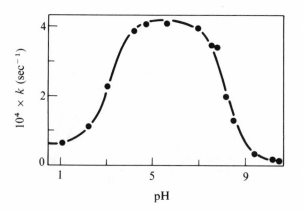

FIGURE 1.12   The pH dependence of reaction (1.176).   The full line represents Eq. (1.175), rate and equilibrium constants as indicated in (1.176).[97]

then the apparent association rate constant k is given by

$$k = \frac{k_{AH}}{(1 + K_{BH}/[H^+])(1 + K_{AH}/[H^+])} + \frac{k_A}{(1 + K_{BH}/[H^+])(1 + [H^+]/K_{AH})}$$

(1.183)

This relationship reduces to (1.163) when K_{BH} is small, that is, when BH is aprotic. Equation (1.183) predicts that k should approach a limiting value of k_{AH} at high $[H^+]$ and approach zero at low $[H^+]$. Equation (1.183) is obeyed in the reaction of $HN_3(AH)$ and $N_3^-(A)$ with aquocobalamin (BH), the basic form of which, hydroxocobalamin, B, is unreactive (Fig. 1.13).[100] When the protonated form AH does not react either, as in the reaction of cyanate (A) with aquocobalamin (BH) (Fig. 1.13),[100] the expression is

$$k = \frac{k_A^{BH}}{(1 + K_{BH}/[H^+])(1 + [H^+]/K_{AH})}$$

(1.184)

in which k_A^{BH} is the rate constant for the reaction of A with BH. We cannot in principle differentiate this reaction couple from the reaction couple AH with $B(k_{AH}^B)$ since the derived expression is similar:

$$k = \frac{k_{AH}^B K_{BH}/K_{AH}}{(1 + K_{BH}/[H^+])(1 + [H^+]/K_{AH})}$$

(1.185)

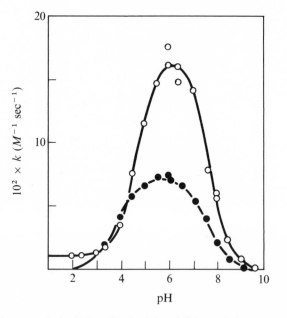

FIGURE 1.13   The pH dependence of the reaction between aquocobalamin and azide, $\bigcirc$; cyanate $\bullet$. The solid lines represent Eqs. (1.183) and (1.184) respectively.[100]

With (1.184) and (1.185), at high and low pH, $k \to 0$. At the maximum, $k \sim k_A{}^{BH}$ or $k_{AH}{}^B K_{BH}/K_{AH}$ and $[H^+] = (K_{AH}K_{BH})^{1/2}$. We can guess that in the reaction system under discussion the A, BH combination is correct since we know that hydroxocobalamin is unreactive.[96] In the reaction of carbonic anhydrase with sulfonamides, the second-order association rate constant varies with pH according to (1.184) or (1.185). This can arise either through reaction of the acid form of the enzyme with the basic (deprotonated) sulfonamide or vice versa (Sec. 2.1.5(b)).[101]

1.10.3   The Effect of High Acid Concentrations

In higher acidity, the rate constant may correlate better with h_0 (the Hammet-Deyrup acidity scale) than with the stoichiometric concentration of H^+. Deviations from a linear k/h_0 plot may reside in appreciable protonation of the substrate, and pK_a values in terms of H_0 may be obtained kinetically and compared with the value obtained spectrally.[102,103] Since nearly all the studies involve hydrolysis reactions, the depletion of the reagent water may be an important consideration also.

These points are illustrated nicely in the study of the aquation of $CrN_3{}^{2+}$ in 1–11 M $HClO_4$.[103] The loss of $CrN_3{}^{2+}$ monitored at 270 nm is first-order (rate constant $= k$). The $\log k$ vs $-H_0$ profile is reproduced in Fig. 1.14. It is marked by a linear dependence at lower acidities, a short plateau, and a decrease in k with increasing acidity at $[HClO_4] > 8.0\ M$, at which point there is decreasing value for a_w, the activity of water. This behavior conforms to a rate law of the form

$$\frac{-d \ln [CrN_3]_T}{dt} = k = \left(\frac{h_0}{K_1 + h_0}\right)(k_1 a_w + k_2) \qquad (1.186)$$

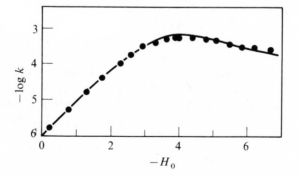

FIGURE 1.14   The variation of $-\log k$ with $-H_0$ for the aquation of $CrN_3{}^{2+}$ in 1–11 M $[HClO_4]$. The line is calculated from Eq. (1.186).[103]

where $[CrN_3]_T = [CrN_3{}^{2+}] + [CrN_3H^{3+}]$, and the $h_0[K_1 + h_0]^{-1}$ term allows for substantial protonation of $CrN_3{}^{2+}$:

$$K_1 = \frac{[CrN_3{}^{2+}]h_0}{[CrN_3H^{3+}]} \tag{1.187}$$

The k_2 term must be included since a plot of $k(K_1 + h_0)h_0{}^{-1}$ vs a_w, although linear (slope k_1), has a positive intercept (k_2) at $a_w = 0$.

A simple mechanism consistent with this rate law is

$$Cr(H_2O)_5N_3H^{3+} + H_2O \xrightarrow{k_1} Cr(H_2O)_6{}^{3+} + HN_3 \tag{1.188}$$

$$Cr(H_2O)_5N_3H^{3+} \xrightarrow{k_2} Cr(H_2O)_5{}^{3+} + HN_3 \tag{1.189}$$

$$Cr(H_2O)_5{}^{3+} + H_2O \longrightarrow Cr(H_2O)_6{}^{3+} \tag{1.190}$$

with $k_1 = k_1{}^0 f_{3+}/f_{\ddagger}$ and $k_2 = k_2{}^0 f_{3+}/f_{\ddagger}$ (2.172). The ratios of activity coefficients may remain constant even when the reaction medium changes.

1.11   CONCLUDING REMARKS

It is important in building up the rate law that a wide range of concentrations of species involved in the reaction be examined so that a complete picture can be obtained. This will involve a thorough study of the effect on the rate of reactants, added electrolytes, products, and so forth.

In the study of the Fe(II)–Cr(VI) reaction at low (μM) concentrations of Fe(II), a term first-order in Fe(II) appears in addition to a well-characterized term containing $[Fe(II)]^2$ (1.95).[104]

$$\frac{-d[Fe^{II}]}{dt} = k_1[Fe^{II}][HCrO_4{}^-][H^+] + \frac{k_2[Fe^{II}]^2[HCrO_4{}^-][H^+]^3}{[Fe^{III}]} \tag{1.191}$$

The latter dominates when the experiments are carried out at only slightly higher than μM concentrations of Fe(II).

Some confusion regarding the rate law governing the reaction of $Co(CN)_5{}^{3-}$ with H_2 has been resolved by extending, through the use of high pressures, the range of H_2 concentrations that could be studied.[105] This approach speeded up the main reaction over some troublesome side reactions. The loss of $Co(CN)_5{}^{3-}$, used in deficiency, is second-order. The pseudo second-order rate constant is proportional to $[H_2]$:

$$\frac{-d[H_2]}{dt} = k[Co(CN)_5{}^{3-}]^2[H_2] \tag{1.192}$$

Finally, it would be blatantly untrue to suggest that the rate behavior of all complex-ion reactions could be fitted into categories contained in this chapter. There are many complicated reaction schemes that require solution by computer, and these must be treated as they arise, with only general rules for guidance. However, it is true that many complicated reactions can be reduced in complexity by judicious choice of reaction conditions, through the use of which they become amenable to the type of treatment outlined above.

REFERENCES

1. J. H. Espenson, *Inorg. Chem.*, **8**, 1554 (1969) for Table and References.
2. M. E. Farago and T. Matthews, *J. Chem. Soc.*, *A*, 609 (1969).
3. K. E. Howlett and S. Sarsfield, *J. Chem. Soc.*, *A*, 683 (1968); D. C. Gaswick and J. H. Krueger, *J. Amer. Chem. Soc.*, **91**, 2240 (1969).
4. V. S. Sharma and J. Schubert, *J. Amer. Chem. Soc.*, **91**, 6291 (1969).
5. C. Postmus and E. L. King, *J. Phys. Chem.*, **59**, 1216 (1955).
6. T. W. Swaddle and W. E. Jones, *Can. J. Chem.*, **48**, 1054 (1970).
7. W. W. Cleland, "Steady State Kinetics," in *The Enzymes, Kinetics and Mechanism*, ed. P. D. Boyer (Academic, New York, 1970), Chap. 1.
8. Y. Abdul Majid and K. E. Howlett, *J. Chem. Soc.*, *A*, 679 (1968).
9. K. W. Hicks and J. R. Sutter, *J. Phys. Chem.*, **75**, 1107 (1971).
10. R. C. Thompson, *Inorg. Chem.*, **10**, 1892 (1971).
11. K. G. Denbigh, *Trans. Faraday Soc.*, **40**, 352 (1944).
12. J. E. Taylor, *J. Chem. Educ.*, **46**, 742 (1969).
13. No attempt will be made to derive the integrated form for these and subsequent differential equations. This has been done in a number of places, including Frost and Pearson, and Harris, and particularly in Capellos and Bielski. A discussion of the merits of integration of rate equations by inspection has been recently given. (See Ref. 14.)
14. D. D. Shillady, *J. Chem. Educ.*, **49**, 347 (1972).
15. M. Meier, F. Basolo, and R. G. Pearson, *Inorg. Chem.*, **8**, 795 (1969).
16. The factor $\frac{1}{2}$ enters into (1.21) because a second stage $NiP_3(C_6H_{11}NC)$ + $C_6H_{11}NC \rightarrow NiP_2(C_6H_{11}NC)_2$ + P, which consumes another molecule of isonitrile, follows rapidly each first stage. The rate of loss of $C_6H_{11}NC$ is therefore twice that of NiP_4.
17. J. E. Taylor, J. F. Yan, and Jin-liang Wang, *J. Amer. Chem. Soc.*, **88**, 1663 (1966).
18. J. V. Rund and F. A. Palocsay, *Inorg. Chem.*, **8**, 2242 (1969).
19. J. S. Littler, *J. Chem. Soc.*, 827 (1962).
20. E. A. Guggenheim, *Phil. Mag.*, **2**, 538 (1926).
21. E. L. King, *J. Amer. Chem. Soc.*, **74**, 563 (1952).
22. J. H. Espenson and S. R. Helzer, *Inorg. Chem.*, **8**, 1051 (1969).
23. P. C. Mangelsdorf, *J. Appl. Phys.*, **30**, 443 (1959); E. S. Swinbourne, *J. Chem. Soc.*, 2371 (1960).
24. D. Margerison, in Bamford and Tipper, p. 388.

25. R. C. Williams and J. W. Taylor, *J. Chem. Educ.*, **47**, 129 (1970); P. Moore, *Trans. Faraday Soc.*, **68**, 1891 (1972).
26. D. A. Kamp, R. L. Wilder, S. C. Tang, and C. S. Garner, *Inorg. Chem.*, **10**, 1396 (1971).
27. R. G. Wilkins and R. E. Yelin, *J. Amer. Chem. Soc.*, **92**, 1191 (1970).
28. J. Burgess, *J. Chem. Soc.*, *A*, 3123 (1968).
29. S. C. Chan and S. F. Chan, *J. Chem. Soc.*, *A*, 202 (1969).
30. J. Barrett and J. H. Baxendale, *Trans. Faraday Soc.*, **52**, 210 (1956).
31. D. W. Carlyle and J. H. Espenson, *J. Amer. Chem. Soc.*, **90**, 2272 (1968).
32. Hammett, (a) p. 59, (b) p. 88.
33. Harris, p. 44.
34. B. R. Baker, N. Sutin, and T. J. Welch, *Inorg. Chem.*, **6**, 1948 (1967).
35. F. Below, Jr., R. E. Connick, and C. P. Coppel, *J. Amer. Chem. Soc.*, **80**, 2961 (1958); J. H. Espenson and D. F. Dustin, *Inorg. Chem.*, **8**, 1760 (1969); W. F. Pickering and A. McAuley, *J. Chem. Soc.*, *A*, 1173 (1968).
36. C. D. Falk and J. Halpern, *J. Amer. Chem. Soc.*, **87**, 3003 (1965).
37. B. Bosnich, F. P. Dwyer, and A. M. Sargeson, *Aust. J. Chem.*, **19**, 2051, 2213 (1966).
38. C. K. Poon and M. L. Tobe, *J. Chem. Soc.*, *A*, 2069 (1967).
39. D. B. Rorabacher, T. S. Turan, J. A. Defever, and W. G. Nickels, *Inorg. Chem.*, **8**, 1498 (1969).
40. T. R. Crossley and M. A. Slifkin, *Progr. Reac. Kinet.*, **5**, 409 (1970).
41. J. E. Byrd and J. Halpern, *J. Amer. Chem. Soc.*, **93**, 1634 (1971).
42. T. W. Kallen and J. E. Earley, *Inorg. Chem.*, **10**, 1149 (1971).
43. M. Evans and R. G. Wilkins, unpublished work.
44. D. H. Busch, *J. Phys. Chem.*, **63**, 340 (1959); P. Krumholz, *Inorg. Chem.*, **4**, 609 (1965); J. Burgess, *J. Chem. Soc.*, *A*, 497 (1968); W. C. E. Higginson, *J. Chem. Soc.*, 340 (1960).
45. R. M. Noyes, *Progr. Reac. Kinet.*, **2**, 339 (1964).
46. Rodiguin and Rodiguina.
47. R. F. Childers, Jr., K. G. Vander Zyl, Jr., D. A. House, R. G. Hughes, and C. S. Garner, *Inorg. Chem.*, **7**, 749 (1968).
48. These problems may be circumvented if one of the steps is multi-order, since the associated pseudo first-order rate constant is modified by changes in reagent concentrations. (See 8.42.)
49. H. G. Kruszyna and R. M. Milburn, *Inorg. Chem.*, **10**, 1578 (1971).
50. K. R. Ashley and R. E. Hamm, *Inorg. Chem.*, **5**, 1645 (1966).
51. E. Jørgensen and J. Bjerrum, *Acta Chem. Scand.*, **13**, 2075 (1959).
52. J. A. Weyh and R. E. Hamm, *Inorg. Chem.*, **8**, 2298 (1969).
53. R. A. Reinhardt and J. S. Coe, *Inorg. Chem. Acta*, **3**, 438 (1969).
54. D. J. Francis and R. B. Jordan, *J. Amer. Chem. Soc.*, **91**, 6626 (1969); A. Giacomelli, A. Indalli, and U. Belluco, *Inorg. Chem.*, **8**, 519 (1969).
55. N. W. Alcock, D. J. Benton, and P. Moore, *Trans. Faraday Soc.*, **66**, 2210 (1970).
56. J. H. Beard, J. Casey, and R. K. Murmann, *Inorg. Chem.*, **4**, 797 (1965).
57. Frost and Pearson, pp. 165, 170.

58. A. Haim and N. Sutin, *J. Amer. Chem. Soc.*, **88**, 5343 (1966).
59. R. W. Hay and L. J. Porter, *J. Chem. Soc., A*, 127 (1969); R. G. Pearson, R. E. Meeker, and F. Basolo, *J. Amer. Chem. Soc.*, **78**, 709 (1956).
60. A. A. El-Awady and Z. Z. Hugus, Jr., *Inorg. Chem.*, **10**, 1415 (1971).
61. Q. H. Gibson, L. J. Parkhurst, and G. Geraci, *J. Biol. Chem.*, **244**, 4668 (1969).
62. W. G. Movius and R. G. Linck, *J. Amer. Chem. Soc.*, **92**, 2677 (1970).
63. F. M. Beringer and E. M. Findler, *J. Amer. Chem. Soc.*, **77**, 3200 (1955), where this scheme is fully analyzed.
64. J. Halpern, *J. Chem. Educ.*, **45**, 372 (1968).
65. D. W. Margerum and H. M. Rosen, *Inorg. Chem.*, **7**, 299 (1968).
66. E. L. King, in *Catalysis*, ed. P. H. Emmett, vol. 2 (Reinhold, New York, 1954).
67. J. A. Christiansen, *Z. Phys. Chem.*, **339**, 145 (1936); **378**, 374 (1937).
68. J. H. Espenson, *Accounts Chem. Research*, **3**, 347 (1970).
69. R. A. Alberty and W. G. Miller, *J. Chem. Phys.*, **26**, 1231 (1967).
70. D. J. MacDonald and C. S. Garner, *Inorg. Chem.*, **1**, 20 (1962).
71. B. Bosnich, J. Ferguson, and M. L. Tobe, *J. Chem. Soc., A*, 1636 (1966).
72. The kinetic analysis of (1.50) has been fully discussed in a number of texts. A full analysis of $A \rightleftharpoons B \rightarrow C$ and the conditions under which simplification may be made is also available. (See Ref. 73.)
73. C. W. Pyun, *J. Chem. Educ.*, **48**, 194 (1971).
74. R. G. Pearson and O. P. Anderson, *Inorg. Chem.*, **9**, 39 (1970).
75. First demonstrated by T. M. Lowry and W. T. John, *J. Chem. Soc.*, 2634 (1910). (See also Ref. 76.)
76. F. A. Matsen and J. J. Franklin, *J. Amer. Chem. Soc.*, **72**, 3337 (1950); E. S. Lewis and M. D. Johnson, *J. Amer. Chem. Soc.*, **82**, 5399 (1960).
77. M. R. Jaffe, D. P. Fay, and N. Sutin, *J. Amer. Chem. Soc.*, **93**, 2878 (1971).
78. E. McLaughlin and R. W. Rozett, *Chem. Tech.*, **1**, 120 (1971).
79. For a general treatment of relaxation kinetics, see the selected bibliography and also R. A. Alberty, G. Yagil, W. F. Diven, and M. Takahashi, *Acta Chem. Scand.*, **17**, 534 (1963); G. W. Castellan, *Ber. Bunsenges. Phys. Chem.*, **67**, 898 (1963); E. M. Eyring, *Survey Prog. Chem.*, **2**, 57 (1964).
80. B. Havsteen, *J. Biol. Chem.*, **242**, 769 (1967); M. Eigen, *Quart. Rev. Biophysics*, **1**, 1 (1968).
81. H. Brintzinger and G. G. Hammes, *Inorg. Chem.*, **5**, 1286 (1966).
82. G. G. Hammes and J. I. Steinfeld, *J. Amer. Chem. Soc.*, **84**, 4639 (1962). Based on M. Eigen and L. De Maeyer in Friess, Lewis and Weissberger, Chap. 18.
83. K. Kustin, R. F. Pasternack, and E. M. Weinstock, *J. Amer. Chem. Soc.*, **88**, 4610 (1966); W. B. Makinen, A. F. Pearlmutter, and J. E. Stuehr, *J. Amer. Chem. Soc.*, **91**, 4083 (1969).
84. P. F. Knowles and H. Diebler, *Trans. Faraday Soc.*, **54**, 977 (1968).
85. K. Kustin and R. F. Pasternack, *J. Amer. Chem. Soc.*, **90**, 2805 (1968);

R. F. Pasternack, K. Kustin, L. A. Hughes, and E. Gibbs, *J. Amer. Chem. Soc.*, **91**, 4401 (1969); R. F. Pasternack, E. Gibbs, and J. C. Cassett, *J. Phys. Chem.*, **73**, 3814 (1969); R. F. Pasternack and H. Sigel, *J. Amer. Chem. Soc.*, **92**, 6146 (1970); G. Daires, K. Kustin, and R. F. Pasternack *Trans. Faraday Soc.*, **64**, 1006 (1968); A. F. Pearlmutter and J. Stuehr, *J. Amer. Chem. Soc.*, **90**, 858 (1968).

86. H. Strehlow, *Chem. Instrum.*, **3**, 47 (1971).

87. T. M. Schuster and G. Ilgenfritz, "Studies on the Mechanism of Oxygen Binding to Hemoglobin" in *Symmetry and Function of Biological Systems at the Macromolecular Level*, ed. A. Engström and B. Strandberg (Wiley-Interscience, New York, 1969).

88. H. A. C. McKay, *Nature (London)*, **142**, 497 (1938).

89. J. C. Sheppard and A. C. Wahl, *J. Amer. Chem. Soc.*, **79**, 1020 (1957).

90. C. M. Cook, Jr., and F. A. Long, *J. Amer. Chem. Soc.*, **80**, 33 (1958).

91. B. Halpern, A. M. Sargeson, and K. R. Turnbull, *J. Amer. Chem. Soc.*, **88**, 4630 (1966).

92. J. A. Broomhead, I. Lauder, and P. Nimmo, *J. Chem. Soc.*, *A*, 645 (1971).

93. A. L. Odell and D. B. Rands, *J. Chem. Soc.*, *A*, 749 (1972).

94. F. Miller and R. G. Wilkins, *J. Amer. Chem. Soc.*, **92**, 2687 (1970), and unpublished results.

95. Y. Ae Im and D. H. Busch, *J. Amer. Chem. Soc.*, **83**, 3357 (1961); R. Dyke and W. C. E. Higginson, *J. Chem. Soc.*, 2788 (1963); T. J. Meyer and H. Taube, *Inorg. Chem.*, **7**, 2369 (1968).

96. W. C. Randall and R. A. Alberty, *Biochem.*, **5**, 3189 (1966).

97. A. W. Shimi and W. C. E. Higginson, *J. Chem. Soc.*, 260 (1958).

98. E. Lenz and R. K. Murmann, *Inorg. Chem.*, **7**, 1880 (1968); J. P. Birk and J. H. Espenson, *Inorg. Chem.*, **7**, 991 (1968).

99. R. Davies, A. K. E. Magopian, and A. G. Sykes, *J. Chem. Soc.*, *A*, 623 (1969).

100. W. C. Randall and R. A. Alberty, *Biochem.*, **6**, 1520 (1967).

101. P. W. Taylor, R. W. King, and A. S. V. Bergen, *Biochem.*, **9**, 3894 (1970).

102. C. S. Davis and G. C. Lalor, *J. Chem. Soc.*, *A*, 445 (1970).

103. T. C. Templeton and E. L. King, *J. Amer. Chem. Soc.*, **93**, 7160 (1971).

104. D. R. Rosseinsky and M. J. Nicol, *J. Chem. Soc.*, *A*, 2887 (1969).

105. J. Halpern and M. Pribanic, *Inorg. Chem.*, **9**, 2616 (1970).

SELECTED BIBLIOGRAPHY

General Treatments of Kinetics

AMDUR, I., and HAMMES, G. G. *Chemical Kinetics—Principles and Selected Topics*. McGraw-Hill, New York, 1966. An account of new developments in selected areas, particularly fast reactions.

BAMFORD, C. H., and TIPPER, C. F. H., eds. *Comprehensive Chemical Kinetics*, Vol. 1, *The Practice of Kinetics*. Elsevier, New York, 1969. Mainly devoted to gaseous reactions, but includes chapters on fast reactions and treatment of chemical data.

BENSON, S. W. *The Foundations of Chemical Kinetics*. McGraw-Hill, New York, 1960. A comprehensive account.

CAPELLOS, C., and BIELSKI, B. H. J. *Kinetic Systems*. Wiley-Interscience, New York, 1972. Mathematical derivations of most of the kinetic schemes likely to be met in practice.

FRIESS, S. L., LEWIS, E. S., and WEISSBERGER, A., eds. *Investigation of Rates and Mechanisms of Reactions*. Part 1. Interscience, New York, 1961.

FROST, A. A., and PEARSON, R. G. *Kinetics and Mechanism*. Wiley, New York, 1961. Probably the best and most quoted account of the treatment of kinetic data.

GUTFREUND, H. *An Introduction to the Study of Enzymes*. Wiley, New York, 1965. Also: *Enzymes: Physical Principles*. Wiley-Interscience, New York, 1972. Much readable, practical kinetics.

HAMMETT, L. P. *Physical Organic Chemistry*. 2nd ed. McGraw-Hill, New York, 1970. Beautiful account of all aspects of kinetics and mechanism.

HARRIS, G. M. *Chemical Kinetics*. Heath, Boston, 1966. Short, excellent account of the subject. Recommended for students.

JENCKS, W. P. *Catalysis in Chemistry and Enzymology*. McGraw-Hill, New York, 1969. Chapter 11 is devoted to "practical kinetics."

KING, E. L. *How Chemical Reactions Occur*. Benjamin, New York, 1963. Excellent elementary account of subject from beginnings.

LAIDLER, K. J. *Chemical Kinetics*. McGraw-Hill, New York, 1965. A comprehensive account.

RODIGUIN, N. M., and RODIGUINA, E. N. *Consecutive Chemical Reactions*. Van Nostrand, Princeton, N.J., 1964. Comprehensive. Devoted entirely to consecutive reactions.

STRANKS, D. R. "The Reaction Rates of Transitional Metal Complexes." In *Modern Coordination Chemistry*, edited by J. Lewis and R. G. Wilkins. Interscience, New York, 1960. Short, meaty account of all aspects of subject.

SWINBOURNE, E. S. *Analysis of Kinetic Data*. Nelson, London, 1971. Detailed account of treatment of kinetic data, errors, and computer manipulation.

SYKES, A. G. *Kinetics of Inorganic Reactions*. Pergamon, Oxford, 1966. A concise account, mainly devoted to metal complexes.

Relaxation Kinetics

CZERLINSKY, G. H. *Chemical Relaxation*. Marcel Dekker, New York, 1966. Advanced text. Derivation of relaxation equations for *all* conceivable reaction schemes and some improbable ones.

FRIESS, S. L., LEWIS, E. S., and WEISSBERGER, A., eds. *Investigation of Rates and Mechanisms of Reactions*. Part 2. Interscience, New York, 1963.

The chapter by M. Eigen and L. De Maeyer (pp. 895–1054) is still the important definitive account of relaxation and rapid reaction techniques.

HAGUE, D. N. *Fast Reactions.* Wiley-Interscience, New York, 1971. A popular treatment concerned mainly with a broad survey of fast reactions.

PROBLEMS

1. Deduce the rate law and the value of the rate constant for the reaction

$$Cr_2O_7^{2-} + 14H^+ + 6I^- \rightarrow 2Cr^{3+} + 3I_2 + 7H_2O$$

from the initial-rate data given herewith for 25° and ionic strength 0.1 M.

Starting concentrations			Initial rate
$[H^+]$ mM	$[Cr^{VI}]$ mM	$[I^-]$ mM	$10^4 \times -d[I^-]/dt$ $M\,sec^{-1}$
20.0	4.0	10.0	5.0
20.0	4.0	20.0	20
20.0	4.0	30.0	46
20.0	4.0	40.0	77
4.0	4.0	30.0	1.9
16.0	4.0	30.0	26
40.0	4.0	30.0	179
50.0	4.0	30.0	256
12.0	4.0	30.0	16
12.0	8.0	30.0	29
12.0	12.0	30.0	37
12.0	16.0	30.0	43
12.0	28.0	30.0	59

For the equilibria

$$Cr_2O_7^{2-} + H_2O \rightleftharpoons 2HCrO_4^- \qquad K = 0.018\ M$$
$$HCrO_4^- + H_3O^+ \rightleftharpoons H_2CrO_4 + H_2O \qquad K = 5\ M^{-1}$$

[K. E. Howlett and S. Sarsfield, *J. Chem. Soc.*, A, 683 (1968).]

2. Consider a reaction that has the stoichiometry

$$2A + B \rightarrow products$$

but that is second-order, with a probable mechanism

$$A + B \xrightarrow{k} AB$$
$$AB + A \longrightarrow products \qquad fast$$

Show that a plot of $\log[(2b - x)/(a - x)]$ against t should be linear with the characteristics

$$\text{slope} = \frac{(2b - a)k}{2.3} \qquad \text{intercept} = \log\frac{2b}{a}$$

where a and b are the initial concentrations of A and B and x is the amount of A that has been consumed at time t. Use (1.35) and (1.36) to help with the integration.

The situation is encountered in the second-order reaction of $Mn(III) \equiv A$ with $p\text{-}C_6H_4(OH)_2 = B$. [G. Davies and K. Kustin, *Trans. Faraday Soc.*, **65**, 1630 (1969).]

3. The reaction

$$Fe^{3+} + HCrO_4^- \rightleftharpoons FeCrO_4^+ + H^+$$

is studied, using excess $[Fe^{3+}]$ and $[H^+]$ and following the gain of $[FeCrO_4^+]$. It is found that

$$\frac{d\ln[FeCrO_4^+]}{dt} = k$$

There is a linear relation between k and $[Fe^{3+}]/[H^+]$. Deduce the rate law. [J. H. Espenson and S. R. Helzer, *Inorg. Chem.*, **8**, 1051 (1969).]

4. Show that if in the interconversion of A and B an intermediate C is believed to occur,

$$A \rightleftharpoons C \rightleftharpoons B$$

but is in undetectably small concentration, the system will give simple first-order reversible kinetics as in (1.37) and (1.38).

5. **a.** Estimate the approximate relaxation time for the equilibrium

$$H^+ + OH^- \rightleftharpoons H_2O$$

at 25°. [M. Eigen and L. De Maeyer, *Z. Elektrochem.*, **59**, 986 (1955), E-field; G. Ertl and H. Gerischer, *Z. Elektrochem.*, **66**, 560 (1962), T-jump; D. M. Goodall and R. C. Greenlaw, *Chem. Phys. Lett.*, **9**, 583 (1971), ir-radiation-induced.]

b. Derive the expression for the relaxation times for the system $A \rightleftharpoons B \rightleftharpoons C$. Compare your answer with that given in (1.106)–(1.108), substituting $k_1[Cu^{2+}]$ for k^1, $k_{-1}[H^+]$ for k^2, and so on. Thus satisfy yourself that with such a scheme, identical results are obtained when any of pure A, pure C, or a mixture is allowed to react, or when the equilibrium is perturbed.

c. Derive the expression for the relaxation times for

$$A + B \rightleftharpoons C \rightleftharpoons D + E$$

This system is fully discussed and analyzed in the early pressure-jump work on

$$CO_2 + H_2O \rightleftharpoons H_2CO_3 \rightleftharpoons H^+ + HCO_3^-$$

[S. Ljunggren and O. Lamm, *Acta Chem. Scand.*, **12**, 1834 (1958).]

d. Consider Eq. (1.131). Show how plots of $k_I k_{II}$ vs ([A] + [B]), and $(k_I + k_{II})$ vs ([A] + [B]), will lead to values for the rate constants k_1, k_{-1}, k_2, and k_{-2} (Ref. 80).

6. Determine the rate law for the exchange of Ag between Ag(I) and Ag(II) in 5.9 M HClO$_4$ at 0°. Use the accompanying data, obtained by the quenched-flow method. Suggest a mechanism for the exchange.

[Ag^I], mM	[Ag^{II}], mM	$t_{1/2}$ exch, sec
2.23	0.64	0.77
3.72	1.36	0.35
3.57	1.53	0.34
3.90	1.24	0.42
6.77	2.24	0.26
7.58	1.89	0.34
10.0	1.30	0.49
9.7	2.00	0.29
10.6	1.81	0.32
15.5	1.41	0.45
17.7	1.16	0.51
24.1	1.34	0.54
30.25	1.21	0.60

[B. M. Gordon and A. C. Wahl, *J. Amer. Chem. Soc.*, **80**, 273 (1958).]

7. Fe(CN)$_6$$^{3-}$ catalyzes the isotopic exchange of Mn between MnO$_4$$^-$ and MnO$_4$$^{2-}$ ions, which remains second-order (k in M^{-1} sec $^{-1}$). From the two pieces of kinetic data for 0.16 M NaOH at 0°:

[MnO$_4$$^{2-}$], mM	[MnO$_4$$^-$], mM	[Fe(CN)$_6$$^{3-}$], mM	k
0.1	0.1	None	710
0.04	0.1	1.0	1,180

estimate the values of k_1 and k_{-1} for the reaction between Fe(CN)$_6$$^{3-}$ and MnO$_4$$^{2-}$ ions (which is the cause of the rate enhancement).

$$\text{Fe(CN)}_6{}^{3-} + \text{MnO}_4{}^{2-} \rightleftharpoons \text{Fe(CN)}_6{}^{4-} + \text{MnO}_4{}^- \qquad k_1, k_{-1}$$

[J. C. Sheppard and A. C. Wahl, *J. Amer. Chem. Soc.*, **79**, 1020 (1957).] The values of k_1 and k_{-1} have been determined directly by stopped-flow with good agreement with the indirectly measured values. [B. M. Gordon, L. L. Williams, and N. Sutin, *J. Amer. Chem. Soc.*, **83**, 2061 (1961); M. A. Rawoof and J. R. Sutter, *J. Phys. Chem.*, **71**, 2767 (1967).]

8. The second-order rate constant for oxidation of $Fe(CN)_6^{4-}$ by OH radicals, produced by low-intensity-pulse radiolysis of water, varies with pH as in the accompanying table. Determine the pK for acid dissociation

pH	$10^{-10} \times k$ $M^{-1} sec^{-1}$
neutral	1.2
11.94	0.49
12.10	0.36
12.57	0.19
13.07	0.06

of the OH radical in aqueous solution. (This is difficult to obtain by any other method.) [J. Rabani and M. S. Matheson, *J. Amer. Chem. Soc.*, **86**, 3175 (1964).]

Chapter 2

The Deduction of Mechanism

We are concerned in this chapter with the mechanism of a reaction, that is, the detailed manner in which it proceeds, with emphasis on the number and nature of the steps involved. There are several means available for elucidation of the mechanism, including using the rate law, determining the effect on the rate constant of varying the structure of reactants (linear free energy relations), and chemical experiments. These means will all be analyzed.

2.1 THE RATE LAW AND MECHANISM

The kineticist should always strive to get as complete (and accurate!) a rate law as conditions will allow. The mechanism that is suggested to account for the rate law is, however, a product of the imagination, and since it may be one of several plausible mechanisms, it might very well turn out to be incorrect. Indeed, it is impossible to prove any single mechanism; however, much favorable data may be amassed for a mechanism so that one can be fairly certain of validity.

Some general rules exist for deducing the mechanism from a rate law, and the subject is hardly a magical one.[1] Probably the most important single statement is that *the rate law gives the composition of the activated complex—nothing more nor less—but yields no clue about how it is assembled.* Once this is appreciated, many of the problems and ambiguities that have arisen on occasion are easily understood, though not necessarily resolved.

For the moment, we can consider the activated complex as a type of "intermediate" (although not isolatable) reached by the reactants as the

60

highest energy point of the most favorable reaction path. The activated complex is in equilibrium with the reactants and is commonly regarded as an ordinary molecule, except that movement along the reaction coordinate will lead to decomposition. The activated complex can be assumed to have the associated properties of molecules, such as heat content,[2] acid-base behavior,[3] entropy,[4] and so forth. Indeed, formal calculations of equilibrium constants involving reactions of the activated complex to form another activated complex can be carried out (Sec. 5.4(b)).[5]

Consider the formation of CrO_5 from $Cr(VI)$ and H_2O_2 in an acid medium:[6]

$$HCrO_4^- + 2H_2O_2 + H^+ \rightarrow CrO_5 + 3H_2O \qquad (2.1)$$

The reaction is third-order:

$$\frac{d[CrO_5]}{dt} = k[HCrO_4^-][H_2O_2][H^+] \qquad (2.2)$$

From the rate law, the composition of the activated complex must therefore be

$$[HCrO_4^-, H_2O_2, H^+, (H_2O)_n]^{\ddagger} \qquad (2.3)$$

although we do not know how the various groups are assembled. The activated complex might arise, for example, from a rate-determining step (rds) involving H_2CrO_4 reacting with H_2O_2, $HCrO_4^-$ reacting with $H_3O_2^+$, or even, in principle, CrO_4^{2-} reacting with $H_4O_2^{2+}$. Also involved in the step will be an unknown number of solvent molecules.

Any reagent that appears as part of the reaction stoichiometry but does not feature in the rate law must react in a step that follows the rate-determining one. It is clear from the stoichiometry of (2.1) that one H_2O_2 molecule must react after the rds. In light of these various points, two possible mechanisms would be:

$$HCrO_4^- + H^+ \rightleftharpoons H_2CrO_4 \qquad\qquad K_1 \qquad (2.4)$$

$$H_2CrO_4 + H_2O_2 \rightarrow H_2CrO_5 + H_2O \qquad k_1 \;\; (rds) \qquad (2.5)$$

$$H_2CrO_5 + H_2O_2 \rightarrow CrO_5 + 2H_2O \qquad\;\; fast \qquad (2.6)$$

and

$$H_2O_2 + H^+ \rightleftharpoons H_3O_2^+ \qquad\qquad\qquad K_2 \qquad (2.7)$$

$$H_3O_2^+ + HCrO_4^- \rightarrow H_2CrO_5 + H_2O \quad k_2 \;\; (rds) \qquad (2.8)$$

$$H_2CrO_5 + H_2O_2 \rightarrow CrO_5 + 2H_2O \qquad\;\; fast \qquad (2.9)$$

Activated complexes will be associated with all three steps of each mechanism since each step is in principle a separable reaction. The important activated complex is that produced in the rds. This is as far as we can advance, using the rate law, but we shall return to this problem later (Sec. 2.1.5(a)).

It is clear that many reactions, particularly those without simple stoichiometry, will have mechanisms containing several steps, one or more of which may include reversible equilibria (consider for example (1.96) to (1.98)). The number of separate terms in the rate law will indicate the number of paths by which the reaction may proceed, the relative importance of which will vary with the conditions. The complex multiterm rate laws, although tedious to characterize, give the most information on the detailed mechanism.

We shall discuss in the following sections the mechanisms that might be associated with the common rate laws. We have already referred to reaction schemes (mechanisms) in discussing rate laws in Chap. 1. Indeed, experienced kineticists often have some preconceived notions of the mechanism before they plan a kinetic study. Certainly in principle, however, the rate law can be obtained before any thoughts of mechanism arise.

2.1.1 First-Order Reactions

A number of reactions between A and B that might have been expected to be second-order, first-order in A and in B, turn out to be first-order only (say in A). Obviously some feature of A, not directly connected with the main reaction with B, must be determining the rate. The product of this rds, A′, must react more readily with B than A does. It is possible to check the correctness of this idea by independent study of the $A \rightarrow A'$ interconversion.

The reaction of Co(III) complexes with Cr^{2+} is almost universally a second-order process (Chap. 5). The reaction of $Co(NH_3)_5OCOCH(OH)_2{}^{3+}$ with Cr^{2+} is second-order at low concentrations of reductant, but becomes almost independent of $[Cr^{2+}]$ when the concentration is high.[7] The glyoxalate is hydrated in the complex ($> 98\%$ from nmr measurements) and the rate behavior can be understood on the basis of the scheme

$$Co(NH_3)_5OCCH(OH)_2{}^{2+} \rightleftharpoons Co(NH_3)_5OCCHO^{2+} + H_2O \qquad k_1, k_{-1}$$
$$\underset{O}{\overset{\|}{}} \qquad\qquad\qquad \underset{O}{\overset{\|}{}} \qquad\qquad\qquad\qquad\qquad \textbf{(2.10)}$$

$$Co(NH_3)_5OCCHO^{2+} + Cr^{2+} \rightarrow products \qquad k_2 \qquad\qquad \textbf{(2.11)}$$
$$\underset{O}{\overset{\|}{}}$$

for which a rate law of the form (1.83) applies:

$$V = \frac{-d[Co^{III}]}{dt} = \frac{k_1 k_2 [Co^{III}][Cr^{2+}]}{k_{-1} + k_2[Cr^{2+}]} \qquad\qquad \textbf{(2.12)}$$

At high $[Cr^{2+}]$,

$$V = k_1[Co^{III}] \qquad\qquad \textbf{(2.13)}$$

This explanation is supported by nmr rate data for the dehydration of hydrated pyruvic acid, which is similar to glyoxalate. For this, at 25°,

$$k_1 = 0.22 + 1.25 \, [\text{H}^+] \tag{2.14}$$

compared with

$$k_1 = 0.075 + 0.64 \, [\text{H}^+] \tag{2.15}$$

for the glyoxalate complex from the reduction data.[7]

An isomerization within a complex may limit the rate of its reaction with another reagent. The conversion of complex **1** to complex **2** is considered the rate-determining step in the oxidation of **1** to **3** by Ce(IV), a process that is independent of [Ce(IV)] at high concentrations of the latter.[8] The conversion of **2** to **1** is rate-determining (in a minor path) in

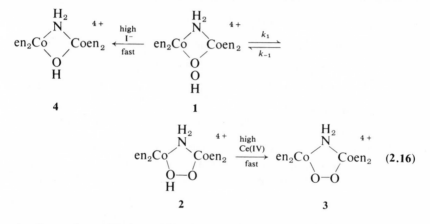

the first-order reduction of **2** by I^- ion to form **4**.[9] The isomerization rate constants k_1 and k_{-1} can be determined independently and are in good agreement with those obtained from the oxidation and reduction experiments.[8]

2.1.2   Multi-Order Reactions

Multi-order reactions almost invariably result from the combination of a preequilibrium, or preequilibria, with a unidirectional, often rate-determining step. They are fairly common in complex-ion chemistry, because of the stepwise nature of complex formation. Even second-order reactions may proceed in this stepwise manner:

$$\text{A} + \text{B} \rightleftharpoons \text{intermediate} \rightarrow \text{products} \tag{2.17}$$

and distinguishing this behavior from a single step,

$$\text{A} + \text{B} \rightarrow \text{products} \tag{2.18}$$

may prove very tedious (Sec. 5.5).

(*a*) *Third-Order Reactions.* An activated complex containing three definite species (other than solvent or electrolyte) is not likely to arise from a single termolecular reaction involving the three species. A third-order rate law,

$$V = k[\text{A}][\text{B}][\text{C}] \tag{2.19}$$

is usually best understood as arising from a rate-determining reaction of the binary product, say AB, of a rapid preequilibrium, with the third reactant C.

The Pt(II)-catalyzed substitution of Pt(IV) complexes was first established in 1958.[10] The rate of exchange of chloride between $\text{Pten}_2\text{Cl}_2^{2+}$ and Cl^- ions is *extremely* slow, but the rate is markedly enhanced in the presence of Pten_2^{2+} ions. The third-order exchange law

$$V_{\text{exch}} = k[\text{Pten}_2\text{Cl}_2^{2+}][\text{Pten}_2^{2+}][\text{Cl}^-] \tag{2.20}$$

can be beautifully rationalized by the mechanism

$$\text{Pten}_2^{2+} + \text{Cl}^- \rightleftharpoons \text{Pten}_2\text{Cl}^+ \qquad K_1 \tag{2.21}$$

$$\text{Pten}_2\text{Cl}_2^{2+} + \text{Pten}_2\text{Cl}^+ \rightleftharpoons \text{exchange} \qquad k_2, \text{slow} \tag{2.22}$$

for which (see (1.93))

$$k = K_1 k_2 \tag{2.23}$$

Exchange is visualized as occurring through a symmetrical intermediate or transition state **5**, which allows for interchange of Cl between Pt(II) and Pt(IV). Breakage of the Cl bridge at *a* produces the original

$$\begin{array}{ccc}
\overset{\text{en}}{\underset{\text{en}}{*\text{Cl Pt}}}{}^+ + \overset{\text{en}}{\underset{\text{en}}{\text{Cl Pt Cl}}}{}^{2+} & \rightleftharpoons & \overset{a \qquad b}{\overset{\text{en}}{\underset{\text{en}}{*\text{Cl Pt}}}\!-\!\text{Cl}\!-\!\overset{\text{en}}{\underset{\text{en}}{\text{Pt Cl}}}}{}^{3+} \\
& & \mathbf{5}
\end{array} \tag{2.24}$$

$$\Updownarrow$$

$$\overset{\text{en}}{\underset{\text{en}}{*\text{Cl Pt Cl}}}{}^{2+} + \overset{\text{en}}{\underset{\text{en}}{\text{Pt Cl}}}{}^+$$

isotopic distribution, while cleavage at *b* leads to exchange. It should be noted that this mechanism leads also to exchange of both Pt and en between Pt(II) and Pt(IV), catalyzed by Cl^- ion. All these exchanges have been studied and the existence of similar values for k from Cl^- exchange (12–15 M^{-2} sec^{-1}), Pt exchange (11 M^{-2} sec^{-1}), and en exchange (16 M^{-2} sec^{-1}, all data at 25°) is striking evidence for the correctness of the mechanism.[11] These original studies have led to substantial developments in the chemistry of substitution in Pt(IV).[12]

A third-order rate law of the form

$$V = k[\text{A}]^2[\text{B}] \tag{2.25}$$

immediately suggests that a dimer A_2 is rapidly formed, in small quantities, from the monomer A, and that it is this dimer that reacts with B in the rate-determining step. Such a situation may apply in the H_2 reduction of $Co(CN)_5{}^{3-}$:

$$2Co(CN)_5{}^{3-} + H_2 \rightleftharpoons 2Co(CN)_5H^{3-} \qquad k_1, k_{-1} \qquad (2.26)$$

for which the rate law

$$\frac{-d[Co(CN)_5{}^{3-}]}{dt} = 2k_1[Co(CN)_5{}^{3-}]^2[H_2] - 2k_{-1}[Co(CN)_5H^{3-}]^2 \quad (2.27)$$

suggests a mechanism

$$2Co(CN)_5{}^{3-} \rightleftharpoons Co_2(CN)_{10}{}^{6-} \qquad\qquad (2.28)$$

$$Co_2(CN)_{10}{}^{6-} + H_2 \rightleftharpoons 2Co(CN)_5H^{3-} \qquad\qquad (2.29)$$

There is evidence for a monomer, dimer equilibrium, although it has not been quantitatively characterized. It has been suggested that a termolecular reaction, as shown in (2.26), may also account for the rate law.[13] The detailed geometries of the transition states are likely to be different with the two mechanisms. If the dimer contains Co–Co bonding, as seems likely, then the activated complex should resemble **6**, whereas in a termolecular reaction the less sterically hindered and therefore preferred configuration **7** might be expected. The rate law gives information about the composition but not about the geometry or structure of the transition complex.

$$(NC)_5Co \cdots\cdots Co(CN)_5{}^{6-\ddagger}$$
$$\vdots \qquad\qquad \vdots$$
$$H \cdots\cdots\cdots H$$
6

$$Co(CN)_5{}^{6-\ddagger}$$
$$H \cdots H$$
$$(NC)_5Co$$
7

(b) Even Higher-Order Reactions.   In the formation of the highly colored $Febipy_3{}^{2+}$ ion from Fe^{2+} ion and excess bipyridine in acid solution, the following rate law has been demonstrated

$$\frac{d[Febipy_3{}^{2+}]}{dt} = k[Fe^{2+}][bipy]^3 \qquad\qquad (2.30)$$

with $k = 1.4 \times 10^{13}\ M^{-3}\ sec^{-1}$ and temperature-independent from $0°$ to $35\ °C$.[14]   This rate law follows from (1.88)–(1.90); B = bipy, since $[H_2O] \equiv [F]$ is invariant.

$$Fe(H_2O)_6{}^{2+} + bipy \rightleftharpoons Febipy(H_2O)_4{}^{2+} + 2H_2O \qquad K_1 \quad (2.31)$$

$$Febipy(H_2O)_4{}^{2+} + bipy \rightleftharpoons Febipy_2(H_2O)_2{}^{2+} + 2H_2O \qquad K_2 \quad (2.32)$$

$$Febipy_2(H_2O)_2{}^{2+} + bipy \rightarrow Febipy_3{}^{2+} + 2H_2O \qquad k_3 \quad (2.33)$$

On this basis, k is a composite rate constant (see (1.94)):

$$k = K_1 K_2 k_3 \tag{2.34}$$

Since $K_1 K_2$ is $10^8 \ M^{-2}$ at 25 °C, $k_3 = 1.4 \times 10^5 \ M^{-1} \ sec^{-1}$, a reasonable value from our knowledge of the substitution reactions of iron(II); see Table 4.13.[15]

2.1.3   Negative-Order Reactions

The inclusion in the rate law of a simple inverse dependence on the concentration of a species (negative-order reactions) usually indicates that this reagent features as the product of a rapid step preceding the rate-determining step. This is illustrated by the multiterm rate law that governs the reaction of Fe(III) with V(III) in acid,[16]

$$Fe^{III} + V^{III} \rightarrow Fe^{II} + V^{IV} \tag{2.35}$$

$$\frac{-d[Fe^{III}]}{dt} = \frac{-d[V^{III}]}{dt} = k_1[Fe^{III}][V^{III}] + k_2[Fe^{III}][V^{III}][V^{IV}][Fe^{II}]^{-1} \tag{2.36}$$

At high initial [Fe(II)], the term in k_2 is negligible and the k_1 term represents a straightforward second-order (acid-dependent) reaction,

$$k_1 = k + k'[H^+]^{-1} + k''[H^+]^{-2} \tag{2.37}$$

From experiments at high initial [V(IV)], the second term becomes important and is then easily measurable. For this term a possible mechanism is

$$Fe^{III} + V^{IV} \rightleftharpoons Fe^{II} + V^{V} \qquad k_3, k_{-3} \tag{2.38}$$

$$V^{V} + V^{III} \rightarrow 2V^{IV} \qquad k_4 \tag{2.39}$$

The stationary-state approximation, $d[V(V)]/dt = 0$, leads to

$$\frac{-d[V^{III}]}{dt} = \frac{k_3 k_4 [Fe^{III}][V^{III}][V^{IV}]}{k_{-3}[Fe^{II}] + k_4[V^{III}]} \tag{2.40}$$

and if $k_{-3}[Fe(II)] \gg k_4[V(III)]$, the observed rate term is obtained with $k_2 = k_3 k_4 / k_{-3}$. The value of k_3/k_{-3} equals the equilibrium constant for reaction (2.38) and can be independently determined. From this, and the k_2 value obtained experimentally, k_4 can be calculated. A later direct determination of the rate constant for the V(III), V(V) reaction gave a value (and pH dependence)[17] in good agreement with that obtained indirectly, thus affording strong support for the correctness of the mechanism. The reader is directed to the literature for other examples of this behavior.[18]

2.1.4 Fractional-Order Reactions

A fractional order may arise when a reaction with a multiterm rate law (containing no fractional orders) is examined over only a small range of concentrations (see (1.69)). Such an origin can be easily detected, since it disappears when the rate law is fully resolved.

Monomer, polymer equilibria can be the basis of a genuine fractional order. In the Cr(II)-catalyzed reduction of $Cr(NH_3)_5Cl^{2+}$ in an acetate medium, the Cr(II) is present predominantly as the dimeric form, but it is only the monomeric form that reacts.[19]

$$Cr_2(OAc)_6{}^{2-} \rightleftharpoons 2Cr(OAc)_3{}^- \qquad K_1 \qquad \textbf{(2.41)}$$

$$Cr(OAc)_3{}^- + Cr(NH_3)_5Cl^{2+} \rightarrow products \qquad k_2 \qquad \textbf{(2.42)}$$

$$V = \frac{-d[Cr^{III}]}{dt} = k_2[Cr(OAc)_3{}^-][Cr(NH_3)_5Cl^{2+}] \qquad \textbf{(2.43)}$$

$$= k_2 K_1{}^{1/2}[Cr_2(OAc)_6{}^{2-}]^{1/2}[Cr(NH_3)_5Cl^{2+}] \quad \textbf{(2.44)}$$

This leads to the observed rate law

$$V = k[Cr^{II}]^{1/2}[Cr^{III}] \qquad \textbf{(2.45)}$$

2.1.5 The Inclusion of [H$^+$] Terms in the Rate Law

There are problems in correctly ascribing $[H^+]$ terms in the rate law to a mechanism for the reaction. First, it must be decided whether a medium effect rather than a distinctive reaction pathway might be responsible for the variation of rate with $[H^+]$, particularly if this is a small contribution. This is an important point that we shall deal with later (Sec. 2.8.2). Secondly, even though it has been established that the pH term has a mechanistic basis, there may be an ambiguity in the interpretation of the rate law. On occasion, such ambiguity has been quite severe and has led to much discussion.

(a) *Positive Dependence on* [H$^+$]. Inclusion of an $[H^+]^n$, $n \geqslant 1$, term in the rate law can usually be explained by the operation of a rate-determining reaction of a protonated species. Usually there is a likely basic site on one of the reactants for protonation, and the greater reactivity of the protonated species compared with the unprotonated form can usually be rationalized (see Sec. 4.5.1). A two-term rate law for the acid hydrolysis of CrX^{n+} (see (1.177)),

$$\frac{-d\ln[CrX^{n+}]}{dt} = k + k'[H^+] \qquad \textbf{(2.46)}$$

has been noted with a number of basic ligands F^-, N_3^-, and so forth. The terms can be attributed to reaction of protonated and unprotonated forms of the complex

$$CrX^{n+} + H^+ \xrightleftharpoons{K_1} CrXH^{(n+1)+} \xrightarrow[H_2O]{k_1} \text{products} \qquad (2.47)$$

$$CrX^{n+} \xrightarrow[H_2O]{k_0} \text{products} \qquad (2.48)$$

with $k_0 = k$ and $K_1 k_1 = k'$. The depletion of the reagent water will be an important consideration in high acid concentrations if water features in the activated complex.

The rate of hydrolysis of $Co(NH_3)_5OPO_3H_3^{3+}$ (P) decreases with an increase of perchloric acid concentration, $> 5\ M$.[20] This may be rationalized in terms of

$$P + H_2O \xrightleftharpoons{K_1} P \cdot H_2O^{\ddagger} \xrightarrow{k'} Co(NH_3)_5H_2O^{3+} + H_3PO_4 \qquad (2.49)$$

for which (see (2.172))

$$V = \frac{k'[P \cdot H_2O^{\ddagger}]}{f_{P \cdot H_2O^{\ddagger}}} = \frac{K_1 k'[P]f_P a_w}{f_{P \cdot H_2O^{\ddagger}}} \qquad (2.50)$$

Since $f_P / f_{P \cdot H_2O^{\ddagger}}$, the ratio of the appropriate activity coefficients, is approximately one,

$$V \sim k[P]a_w \qquad (2.51)$$

Similar linear rate dependencies on the activity of water are observed in the hydrolysis of $CrOCOCH_3^{2+}$ in 6–8 M $HClO_4$[21] and of $CrClO_4^{2+}$ in 5–10 M $HClO_4$.[22]

Acid-catalyzed reaction between species A and B, both of which are basic, leads to interpretive difficulties since we are uncertain whether A or B takes the proton into the activated complex. From the reaction considered at the beginning of this chapter, the third-order rate constant k will equal $K_1 k_1$ on the basis of (2.4) and $K_2 k_2$ if mechanism (2.7) is correct. It is possible to make rough estimations of the values (at 4°) of k_1 ($2.5 \times 10^4\ M^{-1}\ \text{sec}^{-1}$) and k_2 ($\sim 5 \times 10^8\ M^{-1}\ \text{sec}^{-1}$) from the values of K_1 ($0.1\ M^{-1}$), K_2 ($\sim 2 \times 10^{-5}\ M^{-1}$), and k ($5 \times 10^3\ M^{-2}\ \text{sec}^{-1}$). The improbably high value for k_2 is the reason that the first mechanism is preferred.[6] Deviation from a first-order dependence on $[H^+]$ occurs at high acidity since a stage is being reached where H_2CrO_4 is in significant concentration (see (1.75)).[23] Even here and in the limiting region, where the rate is independent of $[H^+]$ because H_2CrO_4 is the major chromium species and its concentration is pH-independent, it is not difficult to see that the concentration products $[H_2CrO_4][H_2O_2]$ and $[HCrO_4^-][H_3O_2^+]$ are still kinetically indistinguishable.

(b) *Negative Dependence on* $[H^+]$. Inclusion of an $[H^+]^n$ term in the rate law, where n is a negative integer, can be attributed to a proton's being a product of a preequilibrium step (see Sec. 2.1.3), and therefore arising from the rate-determining reaction of a "deprotonated" species. It is often likely to occur when one of the reactants is acidic.

The formation of $FeCl^{2+}$ from Fe^{3+} and Cl^- ions in acid solution obeys the rate law (compare with (1.4))[24]

$$\frac{d[FeCl^{2+}]}{dt} = k_1[Fe^{III}][Cl^-] + k_2[Fe^{III}][Cl^-][H^+]^{-1} \qquad (2.52)$$

The first term simply represents the reaction between the fully hydrated iron(III) ion, $Fe(H_2O)_6^{3+}$, abbreviated Fe^{3+}, the predominant iron species, and chloride ion, with an associated activated complex $[FeCl(H_2O)_n]^{\ddagger}$.

$$Fe^{3+} + Cl^- \rightarrow FeCl^{2+} \qquad k_1 \qquad (2.53)$$

Inclusion of the $[H^+]^{-1}$ term is reasonably ascribed to the reaction of $Fe(H_2O)_5OH^{2+}$, abbreviated $FeOH^{2+}$, with Cl^- ions in the slow step:

$$Fe^{3+} + OH^- \rightleftharpoons FeOH^{2+} \qquad K \qquad (2.54)$$

$$H_2O \rightleftharpoons H^+ + OH^- \qquad K_w \qquad (2.55)$$

$$FeOH^{2+} + Cl^- \rightarrow Fe(OH)Cl^+ \qquad k \qquad (2.56)$$

$$Fe(OH)Cl + H^+ \rightarrow FeCl^{2+} \qquad \text{fast} \qquad (2.57)$$

for which $\qquad\qquad\qquad k_2 = kK_wK \qquad\qquad\qquad (2.58)$

The similar rate law for the reaction of Fe(III) with a number of aprotic ligands can be rationalized in the same manner. The rate constants for ligation of Fe^{3+} and $FeOH^{2+}$ are shown in Table 2.1. In the reaction of Fe(III) with ligands that can take part in acid-base equilibria, however, interpretive difficulties arise.[25] With $HCrO_4^-$, for example, the term $k_2[Fe(III)][HCrO_4^-][H^+]^{-1}$ can arise from reaction of Fe^{3+} with CrO_4^{2-},

$$HCrO_4^- \rightleftharpoons CrO_4^{2-} + H^+ \qquad K_{Cr} \qquad (2.59)$$

$$Fe(H_2O)_6^{3+} + CrO_4^{2-} \rightarrow Fe(H_2O)_5OCrO_3^+ + H_2O \qquad k_{Cr} \qquad (2.60)$$

or from $FeOH^{2+}$ interacting with $HCrO_4^-$,

$$Fe(H_2O)_6^{3+} \rightleftharpoons Fe(H_2O)_5OH^{2+} + H^+ \qquad K_{Fe} \qquad (2.61)$$

$$Fe(H_2O)_5OH^{2+} + HCrO_4^- \rightarrow Fe(H_2O)_5OCrO_3^+ + H_2O \qquad k_{Fe} \qquad (2.62)$$

In scheme (2.59, 2.60), $k_2 = K_{Cr}k_{Cr}$, and in scheme (2.61, 2.62), $k_2 = K_{Fe}k_{Fe}$. Since $K_{Cr} = 3 \times 10^{-7} M$ and $K_{Fe} = 1.7 \times 10^{-3} M$, the observed value of k_2, 15 sec^{-1}, leads to values for k_{Cr} of $5 \times 10^7 M^{-1} sec^{-1}$

TABLE 2.1. Rate Constants (k, M^{-1} sec^{-1}) for Reactions of Fe^{3+} and $FeOH^{2+}$ with Ligands at 25°

Ligand	Fe^{3+}, k	$FeOH^{2+}$, k	Ref.
Cl^-	9.4	1.1×10^4	From 25
Br^-	3.4	3×10^3	a
NCS^-	127	1.0×10^4	From 25
HF	11.4	...	From 25
HN_3	4.0	...	25
$Fe(CN)_6^{3+}$	8.0×10^2	3.6×10^4	b
Ambiguous			
$\{CrO_4^{2-}$	5×10^7		
$\{HCrO_4^-$		9.2×10^3	26
$\{F^-$	5×10^3		
$\{HF$		3.2×10^3	From 25
$\{N_3^-$	1.6×10^5		
$\{HN_3$		6.3×10^3	25
$\{CNO^-$	$1.6 \times 10^{3\,d}$		
$\{HCNO$		$2.1 \times 10^{3\,d}$	139
$\{H_2PO_2^-$	2.7×10^2		
$\{H_3PO_2$		2.1×10^4	c
$\{SO_4^{2-}$	4×10^3		
$\{HSO_4^-$		2.4×10^4	From 25

[a] D. W. Carlyle and J. H. Espenson, *Inorg. Chem.*, **8**, 575 (1969).
[b] R. G. Walker and K. O. Watkins, *Inorg. Chem.*, **7**, 885 (1968).
[c] J. H. Espenson and D. F. Dustin, *Inorg. Chem.*, **8**, 1760 (1969).
[d] 1.6°.

and for k_{Fe} of 9×10^3 M^{-1} sec^{-1}, all at 25°. Thus, the calculated value for $FeOH^{2+}$ reacting with $HCrO_4^-$ seems much more reasonable, fitting into the general range of rate constants, than the calculated value for Fe^{3+} with CrO_4^{2-}, which is inordinately high; the former is thus preferred.[26] Table 2.1 shows a number of other examples that may be resolved similarly.[25] Although $FeOH^{2+}$ is the minor iron(III) species present in the acid media used in such studies (1.6% at pH = 1), its reactivity compared with reactivity of Fe^{3+} ensures its participation, and results in the inclusion of the $[H^+]^{-1}$ term. The reactions of Cr(III) have been rationalized in a manner similar to that used for the reactions of Fe(III).[27] Enhanced reactivity of the hydroxo form of a metal ion or complex is quite common in substitution and electron transfer reactions.[28]

The ambiguity described above is a general problem in the interpretation of rate laws of the form

$$V = k[AH][BH][H^+]^{-1} \tag{2.63}$$

where AH and BH are acidic species. We encountered this in Chap. 1 (Sec. 1.10.2). The rate constant for reaction of the acid form of bovine carbonic anhydrase with deionized p-(salicyl-5-azo) benzenesulfonamide is calculated as 10^{10} M^{-1} sec^{-1}. This appears to be slightly too large a value for such a reaction. For this reason then, the alternative (kinetically equivalent) reaction of the deprotonated enzyme reacting with the uncharged sulfonamide (2.2×10^7 M^{-1} sec^{-1}) is preferred.[29]

A special problem arises when one of the acidic partners is water. Does the activated complex now arise from an rds between AH and OH^-, or between A^- and H_2O, or even from the reaction of A^- alone? This ambiguity has been particularly vexing in the study of the base hydrolysis of cobalt(III) complexes, and was a point of discussion for many years (see Sec. 4.5.3).

Finally, when the rate law indicates that there is more than one activated complex of importance, the composition but not the order of appearance of the activated complexes in the reaction scheme is defined by the rate law. Haim[30] has drawn attention to this in considering the reduction of V(III) by Cr(II) in acid solution.[31] The second-order rate constant k in the rate law

$$\frac{d[\mathrm{Cr^{III}}]}{dt} = k[\mathrm{Cr^{II}}][\mathrm{V^{III}}] \tag{2.64}$$

is dependent on $[H^+]$:

$$k = \frac{a}{b + [\mathrm{H^+}]} \tag{2.65}$$

The limiting forms of the rate law yield the compositions of the activated complexes. These will be, at low H^+, $[\mathrm{VCr^{5+}}]^{\ddagger}$, and at high H^+, $[\mathrm{VCr(OH)^{4+}}]^{\ddagger}$. Thus two mechanisms are possible. In one of these, $[\mathrm{VCr^{5+}}]^{\ddagger}$ precedes $[\mathrm{VCr(OH)^{4+}}]^{\ddagger}$:

$$\mathrm{Cr^{2+} + V^{3+} + H_2O \rightleftharpoons Cr(OH)V^{4+} + H^+} \qquad k_1, k_{-1} \tag{2.66}$$

$$\mathrm{Cr(OH)V^{4+} \rightleftharpoons CrOH^{2+} + V^{2+}} \qquad k_2, k_{-2} \tag{2.67}$$

$$\mathrm{CrOH^{2+} + H^+ \rightarrow Cr^{3+}} \qquad \text{rapid} \tag{2.68}$$

for which

$$\frac{d[\mathrm{Cr^{3+}}]}{dt} = \frac{k_1 k_2 [\mathrm{V^{3+}}][\mathrm{Cr^{2+}}]}{k_2 + k_{-1}[\mathrm{H^+}]} \tag{2.69}$$

which is of the required form with $a = k_1 k_2 / k_{-1}$ and $b = k_2 / k_{-1}$ (with k_{-2} ignored).

In the other scheme, $[VCr^{5+}]^{\ddagger}$ occurs after $[VCr(OH)^{4+}]^{\ddagger}$ in the reaction sequence

$$V^{3+} + H_2O \rightleftharpoons VOH^{2+} + H^+ \qquad\qquad \text{rapid, } K \qquad \textbf{(2.70)}$$

$$Cr^{2+} + VOH^{2+} \rightleftharpoons Cr(OH)V^{4+} \qquad\qquad k_1, k_{-1} \qquad \textbf{(2.71)}$$

$$Cr(OH)V^{4+} + H^+ \rightleftharpoons Cr^{3+} + V^{2+} + H_2O \qquad k_2, k_{-2} \qquad \textbf{(2.72)}$$

$$\frac{d[Cr^{3+}]}{dt} = \frac{k_1 k_2 K[V^{3+}][Cr^{2+}]}{k_{-1} + k_2[H^+]} \qquad\qquad \textbf{(2.73)}$$

Equation (2.73) is of the form (2.65) with $a = k_1 K$ and $b = k_{-1}/k_2$ (with k_{-2} ignored). Obviously the rate laws are identical in form for both mechanisms. Consideration of rate constants, it has been suggested, may help resolve this problem.[28] The values for k_{-2} can be estimated for both mechanisms from a knowledge of the overall equilibrium constants and the values for $k_1 k_2/k_{-1}$ or $k_1 k_2 K/k_{-1}$. Calculated values for k_{-2} are $3.0 \ M^{-1} \sec^{-1}$ (mechanism 1) and $10^{-3} \ M^{-1} \sec^{-1}$ (mechanism 2), both of which are plausible values. However, the first k_{-2} value is very reminiscent of rate constants for V^{2+} substitution (Table 5.2) and for this reason the first mechanism is favored. An opposite assignment has been put forward also.[32]

2.1.6   Comparison with Rate Data for Related Reactions

We have already seen (Sec. 2.1.1) that it may be possible to predict from a suggested mechanism either the rate constant, or lower or upper limits to the rate constant, for a related reaction. Confirmation of this lends support to the proposed mechanism.

A mechanism for the oxidation of thiols, RSH, by $Fe(CN)_6^{3-}$ is suggested in which ligand displacement on $Fe(CN)_6^{3-}$ occurs as part of a sequence:

$$RSH + OH^- \rightleftharpoons RS^- + H_2O \qquad\qquad \textbf{(2.74)}$$

$$RS^- + Fe(CN)_6^{3-} \rightleftharpoons Fe(CN)_5 SR^{3-} + CN^- \qquad\qquad \textbf{(2.75)}$$

$$Fe(CN)_5 SR^{3-} \rightarrow RS\cdot + Fe(CN)_5^{3-} \qquad\qquad \textbf{(2.76)}$$

$$2RS\cdot \rightarrow RSSR \qquad\qquad \textbf{(2.77)}$$

$$Fe(CN)_5^{3-} + CN^- \rightarrow Fe(CN)_6^{4-} \qquad\qquad \textbf{(2.78)}$$

If the reaction is carried out in the presence of $^{14}CN^-$, such a mechanism should lead to the introduction of $^{14}CN^-$ into $Fe(CN)_6^{4-}$ as it is formed in (2.78) during the reaction. This is not observed, and this mechanism and an analogous one for oxidation of SO_3^{2-} or I^- by $Fe(CN)_6^{3-}$ can be ruled out from the results of similar types of experiments.[33]

2.1.7 Rate Law and Stoichiometry

In a reaction where the overall stoichiometry differs from that of the rds, care should be taken in expressing the rate in terms of the change of the concentrations of reactants or products. Neglecting to consider a possible stoichiometric factor can lead to problems when two reactions with a common step are compared.

The oxidation of Ag(I) by Co(III) is second-order. This reaction is also considered to be the rds, under certain conditions, in the Ag(I)-catalyzed reaction between Co(III) and Cr(III),

$$Co^{III} + Ag^{I} \rightleftharpoons Co^{II} + Ag^{II} \qquad k_1 \qquad (2.79)$$

$$3Ag^{II} + Cr^{III} \rightarrow 3Ag^{I} + Cr^{VI} \qquad \text{fast} \qquad (2.80)$$

for which at low [Co(II)], when the reverse reaction in (2.79) is negligible,

$$\frac{-d[Co^{III}]}{dt} = 3 \times \frac{d[Cr^{VI}]}{dt} = k_1[Co^{III}][Ag^{I}] \qquad (2.81)$$

The experimental rate constant is consistent with that for Ag(I) reacting with Co(III) once the factor of 3 is allowed for.[34]

2.2 FURTHER CHECKS OF MECHANISM FROM CHEMICAL-TYPE EXPERIMENTS

The rate law, although important, can give only a somewhat crude picture of the mechanism, detailing at the most the number and nature of the steps involved. Finer detail can sometimes be obtained by subsidiary experiments, usually chemical in nature.

2.2.1 The Detection of Intermediates [35]

(*a*) *Direct.* It may happen that the form of the rate law can be accommodated only by a mechanism where intermediates are postulated. Therefore, strong evidence for such a mechanism is the detection of these intermediates. In some cases this may present little difficulty since the intermediate may accumulate in relatively large amounts and therefore be easily detected during the course of the reaction. V^{2+} mixed with

VO^{2+} produces a more rapid loss of V^{2+} than a gain of V^{3+}, the ultimate product. In concentrated solution, an intermediate brown color (ascribed to VOV^{4+}) can actually be discerned.[36] Much more difficult is the support for intermediates of fleeting existence. Then special means must often be used, involving sophisticated equipment and techniques. The mode and power of the approach is well illustrated by the work on detecting the HO_2 radical in aqueous solution.

The kinetics of the Ce(III)–Ce(IV) exchange reaction catalyzed by H_2O_2,[37] and a later study of the kinetics of the Ce(IV) reaction with H_2O_2 in H_2SO_4 by stopped-flow methods,[38] argues for a mechanism for the Ce(IV)–H_2O_2 reaction,

$$Ce^{IV} + H_2O_2 \rightleftharpoons Ce^{III} + HO_2 + H^+ \qquad k_1, k_{-1} \qquad (2.82)$$

$$Ce^{IV} + HO_2 \rightarrow Ce^{III} + O_2 + H^+ \qquad k_2 \qquad (2.83)$$

in which $k_1 = 1.0 \times 10^6\ M^{-1}\ sec^{-1}$ and $k_2/k_{-1} = 13$. It is apparent from these results that a sizable amount of HO_2 should be produced, at least for a short while, by mixing large amounts of H_2O_2 (0.1 M) with small amounts of Ce(IV) ($10^{-3}\ M$), which are used up in step 1 and thus cannot remove HO_2 in step 2. If this is carried out in an efficient mixer, and the mixed solutions examined within 10 msec by electron spin resonance (esr), then HO_2 is detected in the flow tube.[39] The HO_2 esr signal is weakened when Ce(III) is added to Ce(IV) before being mixed with H_2O_2. This might constitute evidence for the reversibility of step 1, but the effect could also arise from the formation of a diamagnetic Ce(III)·HO_2 complex.[40] Indeed, subsequent studies of the kinetics of the Ce(IV)–H_2O_2 reaction[41] suggest that additional steps must be postulated to account for the extended kinetic data, involving the production of such a complex:

$$Ce^{III} + HO_2 \rightleftharpoons Ce^{III} \cdot HO_2 \qquad (2.84)$$

$$Ce^{III} \cdot HO_2 + Ce^{IV} \rightarrow 2Ce^{III} + O_2 + H^+ \qquad (2.85)$$

However, direct proof for the k_{-1} step has been obtained by efficiently mixing Ce(IV) with excess H_2O_2, to generate HO_2, and then treating this in a second mixer with Ce(III) in H_2SO_4, when the spectra of Ce(IV) in H_2SO_4 (a maximum at 320 nm) is obtained.[41]

The trapping of reactive intermediates at low temperatures in a rigid medium prevents them from reacting, and allows a leisurely examination. This, with esr examination, has been important in studies of certain biological systems.[42]

(b) Indirect. The presence of an intermediate can be deduced from the behavior of the system in the presence of reagents that can effectively react with that intermediate. The scavenger may react rapidly with the

intermediate to give a product to the exclusion of the normal product, or in addition to it.

Neither Cr(VI) nor Fe(III) can oxidize iodide ions rapidly. However, a mixture of Cr(VI) and Fe(II) forms iodine rapidly from iodide ions. It is apparent that Cr(VI) and Fe(II) produce an intermediate with strong oxidizing ability. This is believed to be Cr(V), from the rate law (1.95). The oxidation of I^- is said to be induced by the Fe(II)–Cr(VI) reaction. At high $[I^-]/[Fe^{2+}]$ ratios, Cr(V) is scavenged completely by the I^-:

$$Cr^{VI} + Fe^{II} \rightarrow Cr^V + Fe^{III} \qquad \textbf{(2.86)}$$

$$Cr^V + 2I^- \rightarrow Cr^{III} + I_2 \qquad \textbf{(2.87)}$$

The induction factor (ratio of I^- oxidized per Fe^{2+} oxidized (on a mole basis)) is 2.0 and supports Cr(V) as the responsible intermediate.[43a] The subject of induced reactions, in which intermediates can accomplish more than reactants or products, has been thoroughly reviewed.[43b]

Competition experiments (in which the intermediate is scavenged by two reactants and the products examined) have played an important role in establishing the mechanism for base hydrolysis of cobalt(III) complexes.[44]

The intermediate produced in the base hydrolysis of $Co(NH_3)_5X^{2+}$ is $Co(NH_3)_4NH_2^{2+}$ if the S_N1CB mechanism is correct (Sec. 4.5.3(a)). Normally this will react with water to produce $Co(NH_3)_5OH^{2+}$ but if another nucleophile Y^- is also present, which can attack the intermediate, then $Co(NH_3)_5Y^{2+}$ will also result:

$$Co(NH_3)_4(NH_2)^{2+} \begin{array}{l} \xrightarrow{H_2O} Co(NH_3)_4NH_2(H_2O)^{2+} \xrightarrow{\text{fast}} Co(NH_3)_5OH^{2+} \quad \textbf{(2.88)} \\ \\ \xrightarrow{Y^-} Co(NH_3)_4NH_2Y^+ \xrightarrow[H_2O]{\text{fast}} Co(NH_3)_5Y^{2+} \quad \textbf{(2.89)} \end{array}$$

If a series of complexes (X = Cl, Br, I, and NO_3) are hydrolyzed in the presence of a constant concentration of Y^- (for example, NO_2^-), then a constant competition ratio $[Co(NH_3)_5Y^{2+}]/[Co(NH_3)_5OH^{2+}]$ should result because the common intermediate is independent of X. Such experiments are difficult to set up and carry out, but when they are successful (see Table 2.2) they constitute strong evidence for the S_N1CB mechanism.[44]

2.2.2   The Examination of Products

Sometimes the identification of the immediate product of a reaction can contribute significant insight into the detailed mechanism. The oxidation

TABLE 2.2. Percentage Formation of $Co(NH_3)_5Y^{2+}$ in the Base Hydrolysis of $Co(NH_3)_5X^{2+}$ ($OH^- = 0.125$ M) in the Presence of 1.0 M [Y^-] at 25°[44]

Y	X = Cl	X = Br	X = I	X = NO₃
NO₂	4.2	5.0	4.5	5.1
SCN	5.5	6.1	6.3	6.9
N₃	8.5	8.7	9.8	10.2

of formatopentaamminecobalt(III) by MnO_4^- ion is second-order, and could easily be dismissed as a straightforward reaction. However, examination of the products, namely Co^{2+}, $Co(NH_3)_5H_2O^{3+}$, CO_2, and MnO_2, shows that it cannot be simple, especially since the ratio [Co(III)]/[Co(II)] is dependent on [MnO_4^-].[45] The reaction mechanism must be of the form

$$Co(NH_3)_5OCHO^{2+} + MnO_4^- \rightarrow \text{intermediate} \qquad k_1 \qquad (2.90)$$

$$Co^{2+} \qquad (2.91)$$

Intermediate

$$\xrightarrow{MnO_4^-} Co(NH_3)_5H_2O^{3+} \qquad (2.92)$$

$$\frac{-d[Co(NH_3)_5OCHO^{2+}]}{dt} = k_1[Co(NH_3)_5OCHO^{2+}][MnO_4^-] \quad (2.93)$$

The intermediate may be $Co(NH_3)_5OCO \cdot ^{2+}$ or low-spin $Co(NH_3)_5^{2+}$. A direct reaction between $Co(NH_3)_5OCHO^{2+}$ and MnO_4^- without proceeding through the intermediate also appears to take place.[46]

Two mechanisms are favored for the Cr(VI) oxidation of secondary alcohols. In both, Cr(IV) is formed in two steps,

$$R_2CHOH + HCrO_4^- + H^+ \rightleftharpoons R_2CHOCrO_3H + H_2O \quad (2.94)$$

$$R_2CHOCrO_3H \rightarrow R_2C{=}O + Cr^{IV} \qquad (2.95)$$

Then either (I)

$$Cr^{IV} + Cr^{VI} \rightarrow 2Cr^V \qquad (2.96)$$

$$2Cr^V + 2R_2CHOH \rightarrow 2Cr^{III} + 2R_2C{=}O \qquad (2.97)$$

or (II)

$$R_2CHOH + Cr^{IV} \rightarrow R_2\dot{C}OH + Cr^{III} \qquad (2.98)$$

$$R_2\dot{C}OH + Cr^{VI} \rightarrow R_2C{=}O + Cr^V \qquad (2.99)$$

$$R_2CHOH + Cr^V \rightarrow R_2C{=}O + Cr^{III} \qquad (2.100)$$

takes place. The esters and Cr(V) have been characterized for R = CH_3, by spectral-flow and esr-flow methods.[47] Rate constants for the disappearance, k_1, of Cr(VI) (= appearance of Cr(V)) and the disappearance, k_2, of Cr(V) have been determined.

In (I), 2 equivalents of Cr(V) are formed for 1 equivalent of acetone, whereas in (II) the reverse occurs. Thus, a determination of the stoichiometry of the reaction during the buildup and loss of Cr(V) should differentiate between the two mechanisms.[48] Figure 2.1 shows the calculated rate of formation (with k_1 and k_2 known) of acetone on the basis of (I) and (II) and the amount found experimentally (after quenching the reaction with Cr(II)). It is apparent that mechanism (II) is supported. In both cases, of course, the yield of acetone/Cr(VI) is 1.50 at *complete* reaction.

Product identification using *isotope labeling* can be a powerful combination in aiding the elucidation of mechanism. As a simple example, the immediate products of the reaction of $Co(NH_3)_5OH^{2+}$ with Cr^{2+} in acid are identical—Cr^{3+}, Co^{2+}, $5NH_4^+$, whether the reaction proceeds via an inner- or an outer-sphere process (Sec. 5.2). However, complete transfer of ^{18}O from $Co(NH_3)_5{}^{18}OH^{2+}$ to $Cr(H_2O)_5(H_2{}^{18}O)^{3+}$ as a result of the reaction confirms an inner-sphere redox mechanism.[49]

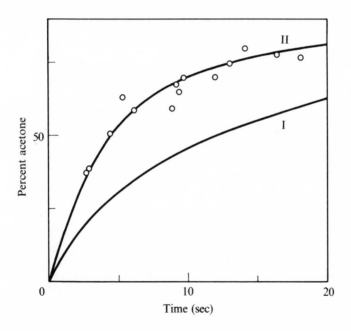

FIGURE 2.1 Calculated rates of formation of acetone on the basis of mechanisms I and II, and the experimental points. [ROH] = 0.126 M, [Cr(VI)] = 0.005 M, [H$^+$] = 0.0125 M in 97% acetic acid at 15 °C.[48]

The kinetic data often lead to a crude mechanism within which much must be hidden. We are concerned not only with the presence of five-coordinated intermediates in substitution reactions but also with their shape.

The identification of the product in the Hg^{2+}-catalyzed aquation of $Co(NH_3)_4(ND_3)X^{2+}$ as $Co(NH_3)_4(ND_3)H_2O^{3+}$, in both of which the ND_3 and the X or H_2O groups are *trans* to one another, strongly supports a square-pyramid intermediate in the reaction.[50] A trigonal-bipyramid intermediate would be expected to lead to some scrambling of the ND_3 and NH_3 groups (Fig. 2.2).

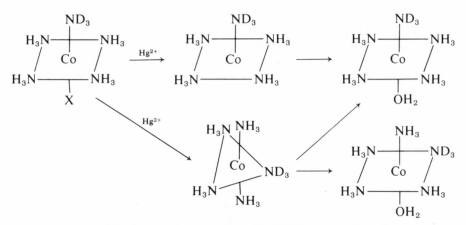

FIGURE 2.2   Expected products from the Hg(II)-catalyzed aquation of *trans*-$Co(NH_3)_4(ND_3)X^{2+}$ on the basis of a square-pyramid or trigonal-bipyramid intermediate.[50]

2.2.3   The Determination of Bond Cleavage

Definitive evidence regarding bond cleavage is possible by using isotopes. Thus $Co(NH_3)_5H_2{}^{18}O^{3+}$ reacts with $NO_2{}^-$ to give $Co(NH_3)_5{}^{18}ONO^{2+}$, confirming the absence of Co–O bond cleavage during the anation. This would be suspected from the speed of the reaction.[51] More surprising is the retention of ^{18}O in the product of the aquation of $Co(NH_3)_5NO_2{}^{2+}$ in concentrated H_2SO_4,[52] since we do not now have the Co–O linkage present to form the basis of the Co–OH_2 product. A plausible mechanism is

$$(NH_3)_5CoN\underset{*O}{\overset{O}{\diagdown}}{}^{2+} + H^+ \rightarrow \left[(NH_3)_5Co\overset{N=O}{\underset{*O\cdots H}{\cdots}}\right]^{3+} \rightarrow$$

$$(NH_3)_5Co\text{—}^*OH_2{}^{3+} \quad (2.101)$$

A large deuterium kinetic isotope effect ($k_H/k_D \gtrsim 5$) is strong support for an X–H (or X–D) bond cleavage in the rate-determining step. Compared with the rate constant for $Co(NH_3)_5OCDO^{2+}$, the 10.5-fold higher rate constant for the MnO_4^- oxidation of $Co(NH_3)_5OCHO^{2+}$ supports a mechanism in which the rate-controlling step is a one-electron oxidation via H atom abstraction: for example,[45]

$$(NH_3)_5CoOCHO^{2+} + MnO_4^- \rightarrow (NH_3)_5Co(OCO\cdot)^{2+} + HMnO_4^-$$
$$\hookrightarrow products \qquad (2.102)$$

In studying isomerization reactions, one must always be concerned with the question whether the process is an intramolecular or an intermolecular one. The relation between the isomerization rate constants and the dissociation rate constants will resolve whether bond cleavage accounts for isomeric change or not.

The rate of the isomerization

$$Ru(NH_3)_5{}^{15}NN^{2+} \rightleftharpoons Ru(NH_3)_5N^{15}N^{2+} \qquad (2.103)$$

which can be followed in solution by infrared, is much faster than the loss of N_2,

$$Ru(NH_3)_5N_2{}^{2+} + H_2O \rightarrow Ru(NH_3)_5H_2O^{2+} + N_2 \qquad (2.104)$$

indicating that the isomerization is intramolecular.[53] Other examples of the use of isotopes to detect bond breakage or bond stretching in the activated complex will occur in Part II. Determination of the fractionation factor by using isotopes can also lead to similar-type information (Sec. 3.14.1).

2.3 ACTIVATION PARAMETERS, THERMODYNAMIC FUNCTIONS, AND MECHANISM

So far we have considered rate laws and chemical behavior for one temperature only. Much information on the mechanism of a reaction may certainly be gleaned from this information alone. However, by carrying out measurements at a number of temperatures or pressures, or in different media, one may obtain additional useful information, even though the form of the rate law itself rarely changes.

2.3.1 The Effect of Temperature on the Rate of a Reaction

The rate of a chemical reaction may be affected by temperature in several ways, but the most common behavior by far is a type that was observed by Arrhenius some 80 years ago.[54] The empirical expression

$$k = A \exp \frac{-E_a}{RT} \qquad (2.105)$$

which relates the rate constant k to the absolute temperature $T\,^\circ K$, describes the behavior of a vast number of chemical reactions amazingly well, particularly over a fairly small temperature range but in some instances over as large a range as 100°.[55] The preexponential factor A, and the energy of activation E_a, are often constant over a moderate temperature range for a reaction. Thus a plot of $\log k$ vs T^{-1} is linear, with slope $-E_a/2.3\,R$ and intercept $\log A$.

This relationship is also derived by the absolute reaction rate theory, which is used almost exclusively in considering, and understanding, the kinetics of reaction in solution.[56]

The activated complex in the *transition state* is reached by reactants in the initial state as the highest point of the most favorable reaction path on the potential energy surface. The activated complex $X^{\ddagger}$ is in equilibrium with the reactants A and B, and the rate of the reaction V is the product of the equilibrium *concentration* of $X^{\ddagger}$ and the specific rate at which it decomposes. The latter can be shown to be equal to kT/h, where k is Boltzmann's constant and h is Planck's constant:

$$A + B \underset{}{\overset{K_c^{\ddagger}}{\rightleftharpoons}} X^{\ddagger} \rightarrow \text{ products} \qquad (2.106)$$

$$V = \frac{kT[X^{\ddagger}]}{h} = \frac{kTK_c^{\ddagger}[A][B]}{h} \qquad (2.107)$$

so that the experimental second-order rate constant k is given by

$$k = \frac{kTK_c^{\ddagger}}{h} \qquad (2.108)$$

The formation of the activated complex may be regarded as an equilibrium process involving an "almost"-normal molecule (almost, since it is short one mode of vibrational energy). The free energy of activation $\Delta F^{\ddagger}$ can therefore be defined as in normal thermodynamics,

$$\Delta F^{\ddagger} = -RT \ln K_c^{\ddagger} = \Delta H^{\ddagger} - T\Delta S^{\ddagger} \qquad (2.109)$$

leading to

$$k = \frac{kT}{h} \exp\left(\frac{-\Delta F^{\ddagger}}{RT}\right) = \frac{kT}{h} \exp\left(\frac{-\Delta H^{\ddagger}}{RT}\right) \exp\left(\frac{\Delta S^{\ddagger}}{R}\right) \qquad (2.110)$$

where $\Delta H^{\ddagger}$ and $\Delta S^{\ddagger}$ are the enthalpy and entropy of activation. This equation strictly applies to nonelectrolytes in dilute solution and must be modified for ionic reactions in electrolyte solutions (see (2.171)).

Since $E_a = \Delta H^{\ddagger} + RT$, it is not difficult to show that

$$A = \frac{ekT}{h} \exp\frac{(\Delta S^{\ddagger})}{R} \qquad (2.111)$$

For first- and second-order reactions in solution, with rate constants in $\sec^{-1}$ or $M^{-1}\,\sec^{-1}$ at 25°, $\Delta S^{\ddagger} = 4.6\,(\log A - 13.2)$ cal mole^{-1} deg^{-1}

(eu). There is some justification in quoting $\Delta S^{\ddagger}$ values only to the nearest eu.[57]

A plot of log (k/T) against $1/T$ is linear from (2.110), with a slope, $-\Delta H^{\ddagger}/2.3\ R$. This is sometimes referred to as the Eyring relationship. Both Arrhenius and Eyring plots are used and give very similar results.[58] The quantity $\Delta H^{\ddagger}$ is increasingly preferred for discussion and will be used hereafter.

The agreement in the values of $\Delta H^{\ddagger}$ and $\Delta S^{\ddagger}$ obtained by different workers investigating the same system is not always good. Consider the acid-catalyzed dissociation of $Fe_2(OH)_2^{4+}$. The first-order dissociation rate constant k is given by

$$k = k_1 + k_2[H^+] \qquad (2.112)$$

There is no disagreement on the rate law, and the values of k_1 and k_2 obtained from three different schools are in excellent agreement (Table 2.3).[59-61] There is, however, substantial disagreement between the reported activation enthalpies; possible reasons for this have been analyzed.[61] Since k_1 is obtained as a relatively small intercept and k_2 as a fairly reliable slope of a k vs $[H^+]$ plot (from (2.112)), it is easier to obtain a precise value for $\Delta H_2^{\ddagger}$ than for $\Delta H_1^{\ddagger}$; see Table 2.3. If as wide a temperature and acid range as is feasible is not employed however, this may account in part for a larger uncertainty in $\Delta H^{\ddagger}$ values than is quoted. There are also experimental difficulties associated with a rate study of this reaction. Other reactions, such as the base hydrolysis of $Co(NH_3)_5I^{2+}$, are more tractable, and the kinetic data for this particular reaction obtained by a number of workers and techniques lie on a common Arrhenius plot.[62]

2.3.2 Reaction Profiles

We can represent the progress of a reaction pictorially by a *reaction profile*, using the concept of the activated complex in the transition state.

TABLE 2.3. Kinetic Parameters for the Dissociation of $Fe_2(OH)_2^{4+}$ at 25° and I = 3.0 M in a $HClO_4$–$NaClO_4$ Medium [61]

Investigators	k_1, sec^{-1}	k_2, M^{-1} sec^{-1}	$\Delta H_1^{\ddagger}$	$\Delta H_2^{\ddagger}$
Lutz and Wendt [59]	0.4 ± 0.1	3.1 ± 0.2	17 ± 2	10.5 ± 0.5
Sommer and Margerum [60]	0.4 ± 0.2	3.1 ± 0.1	16 ± 2	6 ± 2
Po and Sutin [61]	0.42 ± 0.01	3.33 ± 0.02	12 ± 1	11.2 ± 0.1

The reaction profile shows in qualitative but useful fashion the free energy of a reaction system as a function of the extent of the reaction (termed the reaction coordinate). Since each step in a reaction will have an associated transition state, and thus a separate reaction profile, we may have a continuous series of such profiles joining the reactants to the ultimate product.

Consider the reaction scheme

$$A \underset{k_{-1}}{\overset{k_1}{\rightleftharpoons}} B \overset{k_2}{\longrightarrow} C \tag{2.113}$$

in which B is a reactive intermediate present in steady-state concentration

$$\frac{d[B]}{dt} = 0 = k_1[A] - (k_{-1} + k_2)[B] \tag{2.114}$$

$$\frac{d[C]}{dt} = k_2[B] = \frac{k_1 k_2 [A]}{k_{-1} + k_2} \tag{2.115}$$

The form of the reaction profile will depend on the relative values of the rate constants, Fig. 2.3.

Variations in the structures of the reactants may alter the energy level of A or $\ddagger_1$, and *both* will lead to changes in $\Delta F^\ddagger$. In the comparison of a reaction series, it is not always easy to diagnose which behavior is leading to the rate changes.

The principle of *microscopic reversibility* states that the mechanism of a reversible reaction is the same in microscopic detail in one direction as in the other, under the same conditions.[63] Applied to reaction profiles, it means that if the reaction A → C is represented as in Fig. 2.3, moving from left to right, then the reverse reaction C → A will be represented simply by the reverse process, traversed from right to left in the same diagram.

2.3.3   Variation of E_a or $\Delta H^\ddagger$ with Temperature

Most investigators are content to use the best linear plot of $\log k$ or $\log (k/T)$ vs $1/T$ in estimating E_a or $\Delta H^\ddagger$ values, and to consider that these

FIGURE 2.3   Reaction profiles for the reaction scheme (2.113), ▶ illustrating three types of behavior. (a) $k_2 \gg k_{-1}$, $d[C]/dt = k_1[A]$. The first step is rate-determining, and the first transition state $\ddagger_1$ is the barrier to be reached. (b) $k_{-1} \gg k_2$, $d[C]/dt = (k_1/k_{-1})k_2 = K_1 k_2$. There is a rapid preequilibrium between A and B and the rds is between B and C via $\ddagger_2$. (c) $k_{-1} \sim k_2$ and the full equation (2.115) must be used.

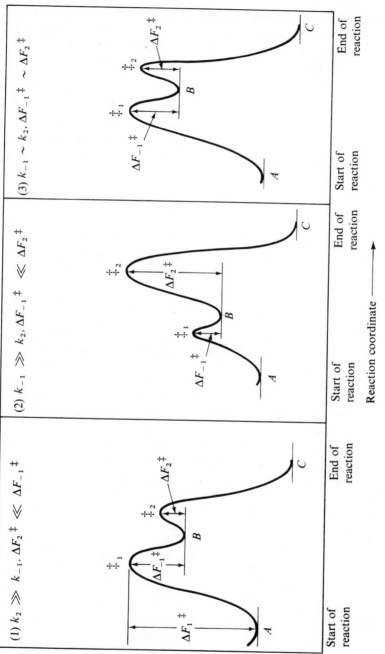

FIGURE 2.3

are constants over a narrow temperature range.[64] It is worth examining this aspect, however, since deviations from linearity of such plots might be ascribed to complexity in the reaction mechanism (see below).

Since the heat of a reaction ΔH is rarely temperature-independent and since for a single step

$$\Delta H = \Delta H_f^{\ddagger} - \Delta H_r^{\ddagger} \qquad (2.116)$$

then it would be expected that the enthalpy of activation in the forward direction, $\Delta H_f^{\ddagger}$, or in the reverse direction, $\Delta H_r^{\ddagger}$, or both, also would generally be temperature-variant even for a simple reaction. On a simple approach,

$$\frac{dE_a}{dT} = \Delta C_p^{\ddagger} \qquad (2.117)$$

where $\Delta C_p^{\ddagger}$ is the heat capacity of activation at constant pressure.

An elaborate attempt to accommodate the variation of $\Delta H^{\ddagger}$ with temperature T is contained in the relationship

$$\log k = \frac{A}{T} + B \log T + C \qquad (2.118)$$

where A, B, and C are constants containing $\Delta H^{\ddagger}$, $\Delta S^{\ddagger}$, and $\Delta C_p^{\ddagger}$ terms.[65]

Obviously, kinetic data must be accurate and cover a wide range of temperature in order to test (2.118). The data for the aquation of $Co(NH_3)_5ONO_2^{2+}$ in acid perchlorate from $0°$ to $59°$ has been carefully assessed.[66] A value for $\Delta C_p^{\ddagger}$ of -20 ± 7 cal deg^{-1} $mole^{-1}$ fits the data better using Eq. (2.118) than if $\Delta C_p^{\ddagger}$ is assumed zero. Values for $\Delta C_p^{\ddagger}$ within the range -10 to -30 have been found for the aquation of a number of $Co(NH_3)_5X^{2+}$ complexes.[66] It is concluded therefore that $\Delta H^{\ddagger}$ and $\Delta S^{\ddagger}$ values for a series of related reactions may be compared even if data are obtained from different temperature ranges. *Marked* variation of E_a or $\Delta H^{\ddagger}$ values with temperature (that is, nonlinear Arrhenius or Eyring plots) for reactions of complexes is unusual. This is perhaps surprising, since apart from the $\Delta C_p^{\ddagger}$ effect mentioned above, many observed rate constants, and therefore associated activation parameters, are composite values. It is easily seen that even if the rate constants for the individual steps vary exponentially with respect to temperature, the composite rate constants may well not. Therefore deviations should arise in reactions involving equilibria, parallel or consecutive processes.[65,67,68] However, there are few authentic examples of changing $\Delta H^{\ddagger}$ values that are understandable on this basis.

One such example may arise in the reaction of $Fe(NO)_2IP(C_6H_5)_3$ with $(C_6H_5)_3P$ to give $Fe(NO)_2(P(C_6H_5)_3)_2$.[68] The data in Table 2.4 show that the second-order rate constant k increases when the temperature

TABLE 2.4. Rate Constants $(k, M^{-1} \sec^{-1})$ for the Reaction between $Fe(NO)_2IP(C_6H_5)_3$ and $P(C_6H_5)_3$ in Toluene[68]

Temp., °C	$10^4 \times k$
−19	0.95
0	4.9
20	15.0
45	14.0
60	3.3

rises from $-19°$ to $+20°$ in a normal fashion but then begins to decrease up to a temperature of $60°$. A scheme that satisfactorily accounts for this behavior is

$$Fe(NO)_2IP(C_6H_5)_3 + P(C_6H_5)_3 \rightleftharpoons Fe(NO)_2I(P(C_6H_5)_3)_2 \qquad k_1, k_{-1}$$
(2.119)

$$Fe(NO)_2I(P(C_6H_5)_3)_2 \rightarrow Fe(NO)_2(P(C_6H_5)_3)_2 + I \qquad k_2$$
(2.120)

for which
$$k = \frac{k_1 k_2}{k_{-1} + k_2} \qquad (2.121)$$

If at low temperatures, $k_2 \gg k_{-1}$, then $k = k_1$ and $d \log(k/T)$ vs dT^{-1} will give $\Delta H_1^{\ddagger}$, the heat of activation for the forward associative step.

If k_{-1} increases much faster than k_2 with temperature, that is, if $\Delta H_{-1}^{\ddagger} > \Delta H_2^{\ddagger}$, then at higher temperatures k_{-1} could fairly easily exceed k_2 and then $k = k_1 k_2 / k_{-1}$. The observed heat of activation

$$\Delta H^{\ddagger} = \Delta H_1 + \Delta H_2^{\ddagger} \qquad (2.122)$$

is a sum that could easily be negative, leading to the observed decrease in k with increasing temperature above $20°$.

2.4 FREE ENERGY OF ACTIVATION AND MECHANISM

The actual value of a rate constant for a reaction only infrequently gives a clue to its mechanism. Assessment of values within a reaction series may be more revealing, while comparisons of free energies of activation $\Delta F^{\ddagger}$ with free energies for the reactions ΔF, leading to the linear free-energy relationships (LFER), can be very useful in diagnosing mechanism.

The existence of similar rate constants for a series of reactions in which only a change in the central metal or in the ligand is involved in one of the reactants suggests that a common mechanism is operative for the whole reaction series.

The rate constants for aquation of a series of complexes

$$M(NH_3)_5OCOCF_3{}^{2+} + H_2O \rightarrow M(NH_3)_5H_2O^{3+} + CF_3COO^- \quad (2.123)$$

are similar for M = Co, Rh, and Ir. This situation, being unusual, suggests that C–O rather than M–O bond cleavage is occurring, since the former process might be expected to be much less sensitive to the nature of M than M–O breakage would.[69] Some care must be exercised in using this type of argument. It has been pointed out that $\Delta F^\ddagger$ and $\Delta H^\ddagger$ values are similar also for some substitution reactions of Co(III) and Rh(III) in which the metal-ligand bond is definitely ruptured.[70]

Increasing steric hindrance in a reacting molecule will usually be relieved in the transition state if the mechanism is dissociative, but aggravated if the reaction proceeds by an associative one. Thus in a series of aquation reactions of octahedral complexes containing diamines, AA,

$$trans\text{-}Co(AA)_2Cl_2{}^+ + H_2O \rightarrow Co(AA)_2(H_2O)Cl^{2+} + Cl^- \quad (2.124)$$

marked steric acceleration is observed (Table 2.5), supporting their dissociative character.[71,72]

By contrast, the magnitude of k_2 for the associative reaction

$$Pt(Pr_3P)(Et_2NH)Cl_2 + amine \rightarrow Pt(Pr_3P)(amine)Cl_2 + Et_2NH \qquad k_2 \quad (2.125)$$

decreases as the effective size of the entering amine increases (see Fig. 4.8).[73]

Study of the relative rate constants for reaction of a series of similar complexes A with reagents B and C may reveal that deviations by a

TABLE 2.5. Rate Constants (k, sec^{-1}) for Reaction (2.124) at $25°$[71]

AA	$10^5 \times k$
$NH_2(CH_2)_2NH_2$	3.2
$CH_3NH(CH_2)_2NH_2$	1.7
$dl\text{-}NH_2CH(CH_3)CH(CH_3)NH_2$	15
$meso\text{-}NH_2CH(CH_3)CH(CH_3)NH_2$	410
$NH_2C(CH_3)_2CH_2NH_2$	210
$NH_2C(CH_3)_2C(CH_3)_2NH_2$	fast

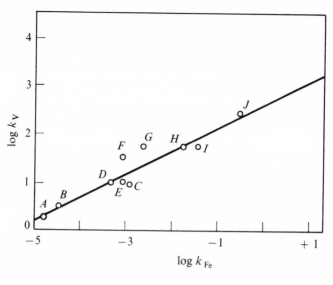

$A = cis$-Co en$_2$ (NH$_3$) Cl^{2+}

$B = cis$-Co en$_2$ (Bz NH$_2$) Cl^{2+}

$C = $ Co (NH$_3$)$_5$ Cl^{2+}

$D = cis$-Co en$_2$ (H$_2$O) Cl^{2+}

$E = cis$-Co en$_2$ Cl$_2{}^+$

$F = cis$-Co en$_2$ py Cl^{2+}

$G = cis$-Co en$_2$ (3-Clpy) Cl^{2+}

$H = trans$-Co en$_2$ Cl$_2{}^+$

$I = cis$-Co (NH$_3$)$_4$ (H$_2$O) Cl^{2+}

$J = trans$-Co en$_2$ (H$_2$O) Cl^{2+}

FIGURE 2.4   Plot of log k_V vs log k_{Fe} for reduction of a series of Co(III) complexes containing a chloride ligand.[75]

particular complex of the series A from a general pattern are attributable to a difference in mechanism from what is shown by the other members of the series.

The ratio of the rate constants for base and uncatalyzed hydrolysis of cobalt(III)–ammine complexes (k_{OH^-}/k_{H_2O}) is usually of the order 10^5 to 10^8. For the complex Coen$_2$CO$_3{}^+$, however, this ratio is 6.5, which suggests for this complex a drastic change in mechanism from that usually observed. A Co–O bond cleavage in base and a C–O cleavage in acid may be the explanation for this marked difference in behavior.[74]

There is a correlation of rate constants for reduction of Co(III) complexes by V(II) k_V and (inner-sphere) Fe(II) k_{Fe}, Fig. 2.4. The values for k_V extend from the region where the mechanism must be outer-sphere ($\gtrsim 10^2$) through the region where substitution control (inner-sphere) is considered likely from the values of the rate constants (see Table 5.2). *All* these reductions by V(II) may therefore be outer-sphere.[75]

2.5 LINEAR FREE-ENERGY RELATIONSHIPS—$\Delta F^{\ddagger}$ AND ΔF

So far we have considered a limited series of rate relationships and their potential value in substantiating mechanism. We now examine more detailed linear free-energy relationship (LFER), a subject that has had its full attention in organic chemistry but only recently has been exploited by the inorganic chemist.[67,76]

In spite of the justifiable warnings not to confuse the kinetics and thermodynamics of a reaction, there are circumstances, for example in a closely related series of reactions, in which it might be expected that the free energies of activation $\Delta F^{\ddagger}$ and of reaction ΔF would parallel one another. There is no problem in measuring or estimating the equilibrium constant, and hence ΔF, for many substitution and redox reactions, by using formation constants or standard oxidation potentials. This information, together with the rate data, might then be used to test LFER. In turn, such LFER might be used to diagnose mechanism by determining the extent of bond formation or breakage in the transition state or by assessing the importance of electronic, polar, or steric effects on the rate.

Since

$$-\Delta F^{\ddagger} = 2.3\,RT \log \frac{kh}{kT} \tag{2.126}$$

and

$$-\Delta F = 2.3\,RT \log K \tag{2.127}$$

this linearity between the free energies of activation and reaction might be most easily expressed in the form

$$\log k = A \log K + B \tag{2.128}$$

This idea can be tested by examining data for the aquation of a series of ions, $Co(NH_3)_5X^{2+}$, X being an unidentate ligand,

$$Co(NH_3)_5X^{2+} + H_2O \rightleftharpoons Co(NH_3)_5H_2O^{3+} + X^- \qquad k_1, k_{-1}, K_1 \tag{2.129}$$

The plot of $\log k_1$ vs $\log K_1$ is linear over a wide range of rate constants (Fig. 2.5).[77,78] Obviously, the faster the aquation, the more the reaction goes to completion! The slope A is 1.0 and this indicates that the activated complex and the products closely resemble one another, that is, that X^-

has substantially separated from the cobalt and that the mechanism of these reactions is dissociative in nature.[77] Since $K_1 = k_1/k_{-1}$,

$$\log k_1 = \log K_1 + \log k_{-1} \qquad (2.130)$$

and (2.130) is of the form (2.128) with $A = 1.0$ and $B = \log k_{-1}$. The value of B is approximately constant if a dissociative mechanism applies to anation, and the nature of X is relatively unimportant. The aquation of Cr(III) and other complexes has also been treated similarly (Sec. 4.3.7).

One of the most effective applications of LFER is to *outer-sphere redox reactions*. These are a rare class of reactions in chemistry since only very weak bonds are formed or broken in the formation of the activated complex. They lend themselves well therefore to theoretical treatment, and Marcus has developed a series of interesting LFER (Sec. 5.10).[79]

Often an equilibrium constant for a particular reaction may not be available. In that event, the rate constant may be correlated with the

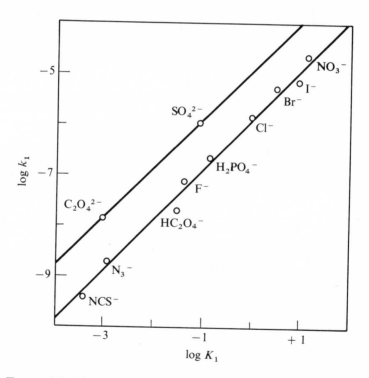

FIGURE 2.5   Plot of $\log k_1$ vs $\log K_1$ for reaction (2.129) at 25°. Ref. 78.

equilibrium constant for a related reaction, which can act as a good substitute.

A large amount of data is available for the metal cation catalysis of the elimination of chloride from $Co(EDTA)Cl^{2-}$.

$$Co(EDTA)Cl^{2-} \rightarrow CoEDTA^- + Cl^- \qquad k_1 \qquad (2.131)$$

Since the metal ion probably functions by interacting with both the unbound carboxylate ion, which is joining the cobalt, and the chloride group, which is leaving, a correlation between $\log k_1$ and $\log K_A + \log K_{Cl}$ might be attempted (Fig. 2.6).[80] The items K_A and K_{Cl} are formation constants for acetate and chloro complexes of M^{n+}

$$K_A = \frac{[M^{n+} \cdot OCOCH_3^-]}{[M^{n+}][OCOCH_3^-]} \qquad (2.132)$$

$$K_{Cl} = \frac{[M^{n+} \cdot Cl^-]}{[M^{n+}][Cl^-]} \qquad (2.133)$$

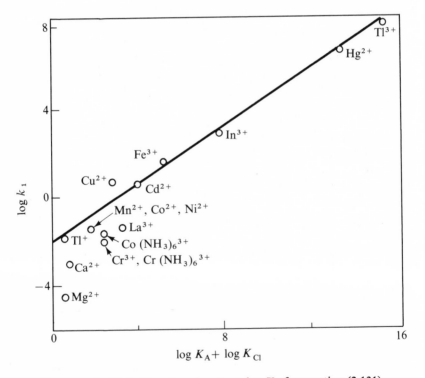

FIGURE 2.6   Plot of $\log k_1$ vs $\log K_A + \log K_{Cl}$ for reaction (2.131) at 25°.   Ref. 80.

The plot covers a very wide range of k_1 and $(K_A + K_{Cl})$ values. Those catalytic ions lying on or near the line are believed to enter into an inner-sphere association with the carboxylate and chloride sites, while those well below are believed to be in outer-sphere association with them. The latter include ions such as $Co(NH_3)_6{}^{3+}$, which obviously must be in this category, since it has no available sites for coordination with carboxylate or chloride groupings. Similarly, more limited correlations of rate constants for metal cation catalysis of isomerization and racemization reactions with complex formation constants have been noted.[81]

2.5.1   Hammett Relationship

The indirect approach just discussed is the basis for one of the oldest and most useful of LFER, the Hammett relationship.[82] This has been little exploited by the complex-ion kineticist, although the few examples reported show it to be applicable to inorganic reactions. The Hammett equation correlates the rates of reaction of a series of *meta*- and *para*-substituted aromatic compounds with a common substrate,

$$\log \frac{k}{k^0} = \rho \log \frac{K_a}{K_a{}^0} = \rho\sigma \qquad (2.134)$$

where k and k^0 are the reaction rate constants for the X-substituted and unsubstituted aromatic compounds respectively, and K_a and $K_a{}^0$ are the dissociation constants for the X-substituted and unsubstituted benzoic acids. This is of the general form (2.128) with $A = \rho$ and $B = \log k^0 - \rho \log K_a{}^0$, a constant for a reaction series.

The parameter σ depends on the substituent but is independent of the reaction series, whereas the value of ρ depends only on the actual reaction examined. Either $\log k$ or $\log (k/k^0)$ is plotted against σ. The slope of the line is ρ ($\Delta \log k/\Delta\sigma$) and is positive if k increases as the value of σ becomes more positive.

Second-order rate constants k for the replacement of a ring-substituted benzoate group by hydroxide ion in a number of complexes (base hydrolysis) have been carefully determined at 25° in 40% aqueous methanol:

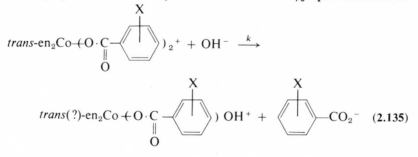

The log k vs σ plot is reasonably linear with no marked deviations for any X substituent (Fig. 2.7).[83] This suggests a common mechanism and mode of cleavage; thus all would entail, for example, either Co–O or C–O bond cleavage. Examination of the ρ value for the reaction helps determine which of these possibilities are likely. Its value (0.75) is much smaller than the value obtained for alkaline hydrolysis of esters (1.8–2.5) where acyl-oxygen fission has been established. Since ρ is a measure of the sensitivity of the reaction series to ring substitution, the smaller value of ρ with the cobalt complexes could be rationalized if the reaction site were further removed from the aromatic ring than it is in esters, that is, if Co–O cleavage rather than O–C bond breakage is involved. Substitution in the benzoate group that is not replaced apparently has little effect on the rate constant k. Strong deviations from linearity for the corresponding plot for *cis*-Co(III) complexes (Fig. 2.7) have been rationalized in terms of polar and steric interaction between the benzoato groups, which would be much more important than in the *trans* isomer. Other examples of

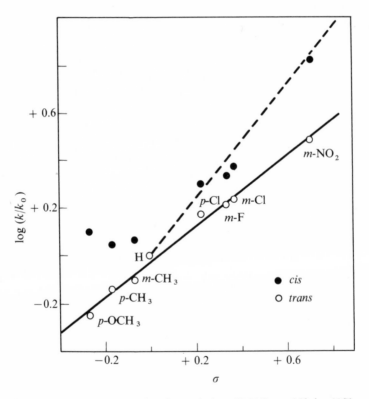

FIGURE 2.7 Hammett plot for reaction (2.135) at 25° in 40% aqueous methanol. Ref. 83.

the application of Hammett relationships to complex reactions are rare.[84]

2.5.2 Taft Relationship

The reactivity of aliphatic and o-substituted aromatic compounds, where proximity effects are important, is accommodated by the Taft modification of the Hammett equation,[85]

$$\log \frac{k}{k^0} = \sigma^*\rho^* \qquad (2.136)$$

where σ^* is the polar substituent constant and ρ^* is a reaction constant analogous to ρ in significance. By definition, $\sigma^* \equiv 0.0$ for CH_3 substitution.

The base hydrolysis of a number of carboxylatopentamminocobalt(III) complexes has been studied:[86]

$$Co(NH_3)_5O \cdot \underset{\underset{O}{\|}}{C} \cdot R^{2+} + OH^- \rightarrow Co(NH_3)_5OH^{2+} + RCOO^- \quad k_1 \quad (2.137)$$

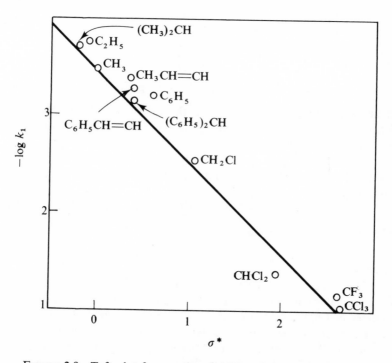

FIGURE 2.8   Taft plot for reaction (2.137) at 25° in water.   Ref. 86.

A plot of $\log k_1$ vs σ^* is reasonably linear (Fig. 2.8) but there are slight deviations with the three complexes containing carboxylato groups in which a π bond is conjugated with the carbonyl group. Such deviations indicate that mesomeric effects are important in the base hydrolysis. Since conjugation of an unsaturated center with the carbonyl group is destroyed in the $B_{Ac}2$ transition state in which acyl-oxygen fission is predicted, but retained in mechanisms involving a Co–O bond breakage, the latter is more likely (see discussion of (2.135)). The deviation of the trifluoracetato complex from the plot (also slight) *may* indicate acyl-oxygen fission in this case.

2.5.3 Brønsted Relationship

The earliest LFER, advanced by Brønsted, correlates the acid dissociation constant (K_A) and base strength ($1/K_A$) of a species with its effectiveness as a catalyst in general acid(k_A) and base(k_B)-catalyzed reactions respectively.[87] The relationships take the form

$$k_A = G_A K_A{}^\alpha \tag{2.138}$$

$$\log k_A = \log G_A + \alpha \log K_A \tag{2.139}$$

or
$$k_B = G_B\left(\frac{1}{K_A}\right)^\beta \tag{2.140}$$

$$\log k_B = \log G_B - \beta \log K_A \tag{2.141}$$

Equations (2.139) and (2.141) are both consistent with the generalized form (2.128). The values G_A and G_B and α and β are constants with $0 < \alpha$, $\beta < 1$.

Probably the most detailed study of the acid(HA)- and base(B)-catalyzed reactions of complex ions concerns the hydrolysis of the dichromate ion:

$$Cr_2O_7{}^{2-} + H_2O \rightleftharpoons 2HCrO_4{}^- \qquad k_1, k_{-1} \tag{2.142}$$

The hydrolysis rate constant k is given by

$$k = k_1[H_2O] + \sum k_B[B] + \sum k_A[HA] \tag{2.143}$$

The value of k_B has been determined for 27 different bases. There is a reasonable correlation of $\log k_B$ vs pK_a in agreement with (2.141) for a number of singly charged catalytic species (Fig. 2.9).[88] If allowance is made for the double charges on $HPO_4{}^{2-}$ and $CO_3{}^{2-}$ and for the zero charge on NH_3, because the substrate is negatively charged, these three bases fall much closer to the line.[88] The value of β is ~ 0.25, which indicates that general base catalysis holds. For specific base catalysis, β

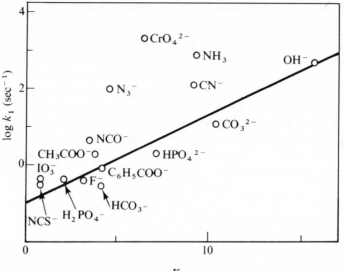

FIGURE 2.9 Brønsted plot for reaction (2.142) at 25°. Ref. 88.

would equal 1, while for reactions in which solvent catalysis predominates, β would be zero, since only the $k_1[H_2O]$ term is important.

There are a number of bases that do not come close to the line, even when charge effects are allowed for. These include H_2O, organic nitrogen bases, and 2,6-lutidine (which will be sterically hindered) and also a number of strong nucleophiles, such as CN^-, N_3^-, CrO_4^{2-}, and thiourea.

In an attempt to improve the correlation therefore, polarizability as well as the basicity of B are considered as factors governing the nucleophilic behavior. A modified version of (2.141) incorporating this addition is

$$\log \frac{k_B}{k_{H_2O}} = \alpha \log \frac{R_B}{R_{H_2O}} + \beta(pK_a - pK_{H_2O}) \qquad \textbf{(2.144)}$$

where α and β are substrate constants for a given reaction. The symbols R_B and R_{H_2O} represent the molar refractions of base and water.[89]

Plots of

$$\frac{\log k_B/k_{H_2O}}{pK_a - pK_{H_2O}} \quad \text{against} \quad \frac{\log R_B/R_{H_2O}}{pK_a - pK_{H_2O}}$$

give a semblance of a line, slope α, and intercept β.[88] In fact, two linear relationships with underlying base and nucleophilic catalysis may be contained in these large amounts of data.[90] Nucleophilic catalysis might take the form[88]

$$Cr_2O_7^{2-} + B \rightleftharpoons CrO_3B + CrO_4^{2-} \qquad \textbf{(2.145)}$$

$$CrO_3B + H_2O \rightleftharpoons CrO_4^{2-} + B + 2H^+ \qquad \textbf{(2.146)}$$

Such a mechanism is supported by the observation of $CrS_2O_6^{2-}$ in flow experiments on the $S_2O_3^{2-}$-catalyzed hydrolysis of $Cr_2O_7^{2-}$ ion.[90]

The Brønsted relationship can be strictly accurate only over a certain range of acid and base strengths. When k_A or k_B have diffusion-controlled values, which of course cannot be exceeded, the linear plot of $\log k_A$ vs $\log K_A$ must level off to a zero slope, that is, $\alpha = 0$.[91] This was first pointed out by Brønsted and Pedersen, and has since been proved experimentally with the use of fast-reaction measurement techniques.[91] We shall see an example of it later (Fig. 6.4).

2.5.4 Swain-Scott Relationship

A completely empirical LFER can also be constructed with recourse only to kinetic data. This has been the case in the setting up of a scale of nucleophilic power for ligands substituting in square-planar complexes, based on the Swain-Scott approach.[92] The second-order rate constants k_Y for reactions in MeOH of nucleophiles Y with *trans*-Ptpy$_2$Cl$_2$, chosen as the standard substrate

$$trans\text{-}Ptpy_2Cl_2 + Y^- \rightarrow trans\text{-}Ptpy_2ClY + Cl^- \qquad (2.147)$$

are compared with the rate constant for solvolysis $(Y = CH_3OH)$

$$k_s = \frac{k_{CH_3OH}}{[CH_3OH]} = \frac{k_{CH_3OH}}{26}$$

Then it is found that $(s = 1)$,

$$\log \frac{k_Y}{k_s} = sn_{Pt} \qquad (2.148)$$

On the basis of this equation, an index of nucleophilicity n_{Pt} can be assigned to each nucleophile Y (see Table 4.17).[93,94] It is found, moreover, that a plot of $\log k_Y$, for reaction of Y with another Pt(II) neutral substrate, vs n_{Pt} is also often linear. Thus, Eq. (2.148) applies, and s is termed the nucleophilic discrimination factor (Sec. 4.10.2).

2.6 ENTHALPY AND ENTROPY OF ACTIVATION AND MECHANISM

Negative or very small values of $\Delta H^{\ddagger}$ are rare. They obviously cannot be associated with a *single* step, and they give overwhelming evidence for a multistep process that includes a preequilibrium. Negative or near-zero values for $\Delta H^{\ddagger}$ for a few inner-sphere and outer-sphere redox reactions indicate the importance of complexes as intermediates, and rule out in these cases a single step, with a single activated complex (Sec. 5.5).

Values for $\Delta S^{\ddagger}$ can be positive or negative. The same types of arguments used in considering the magnitude and the sign of ΔS values for a reaction can be used in interpreting the values of $\Delta S^{\ddagger}$ in the formation of the activated complex from the reactants.[57] From general considerations, one might expect that $\Delta S^{\ddagger}$ would be more positive for reactions accompanied by topological change than for a similar series of reactions that proceed with retention of configuration. This was first pointed out for the aquation of several *cis* and *trans* cobalt(III) complexes (Table 2.6).[95] Subsequent studies have generally supported this behavior for octahedral Co(III) complexes, although there have been a couple of interesting exceptions (see Table 2.6).[96,97] The relationship means that the steric course is determined in the rate-determining step and this idea can be accommodated by a dissociative type of mechanism. When the five-coordinated intermediate is trigonal-bipyramidal, marked stereochemical change can be expected, leading to the positive $\Delta S^{\ddagger}$ values. With a square-pyramidal intermediate, which differs only slighly from the original octahedron, retention of configuration and more negative $\Delta S^{\ddagger}$ values can be expected.

TABLE 2.6. Entropies of Activation and Stereochemical Change for Aquation of Co^{III} Complexes at 25°

Complex	$\Delta S^{\ddagger}$	% Stereochemical change	Ref.
trans-$Coen_2Cl(OH)^+$	+20	75	
trans-$Coen_2Cl_2^+$	+14	35	
trans-$Co(NH_3)_4Cl_2^+$	+ 9	55	a
trans-$Co(RR,SS-2,3,2-tet)Cl_2^+$	+ 9	100	
cis- and *trans*-$Coen_2(NO_2)Cl^+$	− 2	0	
trans-$Co(cyclam)Cl_2^+$	− 3	0	
cis- and *trans*-$Coen_2(NH_3)PO_4H_3^{3+}$	− 3	0	
cis-$Coen_2Cl_2^+$	− 5	0	
cis-$CotrenF_2^+$ [c]	− 7	0	b
trans-$Co(tet\ a)Cl_2^+$	+17	0[d]	96
trans-$Co(3,2,3-tet)Cl_2^+$	+ 4	0	97

Source: Tables in Ref. 95, except where noted.
[a] R. G. Linck, *Inorg. Chem.*, **8**, 1016 (1969).
[b] K. W. Kuo and S. K. Madan, *Inorg. Chem.*, **10**, 229 (1971).
[c] A *cis* configuration is possible only with tren complexes.
[d] A *trans* product is very likely.

2.6.1 $\Delta S^{\ddagger}$ and ΔS Values

For the aquation of a large variety of CrX^{2+} ions, an LFER applies and the slope of the log k_1 vs log K plot (0.5) suggests substantial separation of the X from the Cr in the transition state (Sec. 2.5).[98] Examination of the $\Delta S^{\ddagger}$ values for these reactions allows us to make further reasonable deductions regarding their mechanism. In view of the LFER, a correlation of $\Delta S^{\ddagger}$ with the corrected[99] entropy of the free aqueous S^0_{corr} might be anticipated, and in fact is observed in a number of cases, namely when $X^- = Cl^-$, Br^-, I^-, NO_3^-, and NCS^- (Fig. 2.10).[100] For the hydrolysis of CrF^{2+}, CrN_3^{2+}, and $CrCN^{2+}$, however, the observed $\Delta S^{\ddagger}$ values are higher (-4, $+16$, and $+13$ eu) than the curve would indicate from the S^0_{corr} values (-16, -7, and -5).[101,102] This behavior can be explained by supposing that in these three cases the separation of the X group occurs as HX (and leaves $Cr(H_2O)_4OH^{2+}$) rather than as X^- (leaving $Cr(H_2O)_5^{3+}$). The latter apparently occurs with the X groups that lie on the $\Delta S^{\ddagger}/S^0_{corr}$ plot. The process

$$(H_2O)_5CrX^{2+} + H_2O \rightleftharpoons (H_2O)_5Cr(XH)OH^{2+} \rightleftharpoons (H_2O)_5CrOH^{2+} + HX$$

$$(2.149)$$

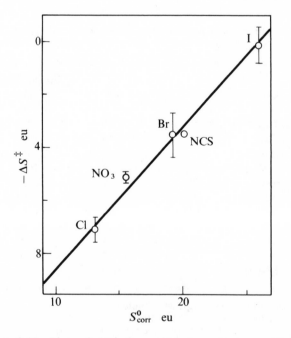

FIGURE 2.10 Plot of $\Delta S^{\ddagger}$ for acid-independent aquation of $Cr(H_2O)_5X^{2+}$ vs S^0_{corr}, entropy of the aqueous ion X^-, corrected for rotation of X^-. From Ref. 100.

generates no formal charges in the transition state, so that there is less electrostriction (more "freeing") of solvent, and a greater $\Delta S^\ddagger$ value would be expected than if X^- were generated in the activated complex.

In agreement with this concept, in the reverse direction the reactions of $CrOH^{2+}$ with HF, HN_3, and HCN are preferred over the reactions of Cr^{3+} with F^-, N_3^-, and CN^- respectively, which are kinetically indistinguishable (Sec. 2.1.5(b)).[27]

In a number of redox reactions involving a net chemical change for which the entropy of activation is $\Delta S^\ddagger$, and the entropy of reaction is ΔS, it has been shown that an approximate relationship,

$$\Delta S^\ddagger = \Delta S_0^\ddagger + \alpha\,\Delta S \tag{2.150}$$

holds. The term $\Delta S_0^\ddagger$ is the entropy of activation for a reaction of a similar charge type but one for which $\Delta S = 0$, that is, an isotopic exchange reaction. For a number of reactions,

$$\Delta S^\ddagger - \Delta S_0^\ddagger \sim \Delta S \tag{2.151}$$

that is, $\alpha = 1$, and this suggests that the configurations of the activated complex and final products are similar. An outer-sphere formulation for such reactions is favored.[18]

2.6.2 $\Delta S^\ddagger$ and the Charge of the Reactants

The relationship mentioned in the previous paragraph suggests that the entropies of activation and reaction are largely charge-controlled. This is an important concept in an area of chemistry that is dominated by ionic reactions. The relation between $\Delta S^\ddagger$ and the charge of the reacting species is a well-known rule of thumb. The reaction between unlike charged species is often attended by a positive $\Delta S^\ddagger$ because the solvent molecules are less restricted around a transition state of reduced charge and thus are released in forming it. The value of $\Delta S^\ddagger$ changes by about 10 eu per unit of $(z_A z_B)$, where z_A and z_B are the charges of reactants.[103]

However, for a number of reactions these rules do not even approximately hold. Newton and Rabideau have examined a large number of redox reactions of transition and actinide ions, involving both net chemical reactions and isotopic exchange.[4] They showed that the value for the *molar entropy of the transition state* $S^\ddagger$ is very much dictated by its charge:[4,104]

$$S^\ddagger = \Delta S^\ddagger + \sum S^0(\text{reactants}) - \sum S^0\,(\text{products in net activation process}) \tag{2.152}$$

Typical values in eu are indicated in the net activation process,[105]

$$Eu^{2+}(S^0 = -18) + VO^{2+}(S^0 = -26) \rightarrow [EuVO^{4+}] \qquad \Delta S^\ddagger = -33 \tag{2.153}$$

$$\therefore S^\ddagger = -33 - 26 - 18 = -77\ \text{eu}^{106} \tag{2.154}$$

It is found for $+3$, $+4$, $+5$, and $+6$ charged activated complexes that $-S^{\ddagger}$ values are 29–40, 60–80, 72–106, and 102–131, respectively.[107,108]

The relation may have a predictive value as well as represent a useful empirical correlation. Thus for the net activation process

$$V^{2+} + VO_2^{+} \rightarrow [(VO)_2^{3+}]^{\ddagger} \qquad (2.155)$$

the molar entropy of the activated complex is -65 eu, which is much more negative than expected and may result from all the coordinated water being retained in the process. This apparently is not the case in the net activation process

$$V^{2+} + VO_2^{+} + H^{+} \rightarrow [(VO)_2H^{4+}]^{\ddagger} \qquad (2.156)$$

since the $S^{\ddagger}$ value, -65 eu, is normal for a $4+$-charged activated complex.[109]

2.6.3 $\Delta H^{\ddagger}$ and $\Delta S^{\ddagger}$ Values—The Isokinetic Relationship

It is not rare in organic chemistry that only small changes in rate constants for a series of reactions involving common or common-type reactants may arise from parallel changes in $\Delta H^{\ddagger}$ and $\Delta S^{\ddagger}$ values. There is an excellent linear relationship between the activation energies and entropies, over a wide range of values, for a series of eleven Ru(II) phenanthroline

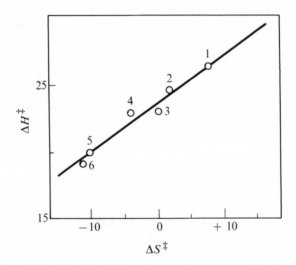

FIGURE 2.11 Isokinetic plot for the anation of $CrOH^{2+}$ by (1) Cl^-, (2) SCN^-, (3) NCS^-, (4) Br^-, (5) NO_3^-, and (6) HF. From Ref. 111.

and bipyridyl complexes being oxidized by Tl(III).[110] The parallel changes in $\Delta H^{\ddagger}$ and $\Delta S^{\ddagger}$ lead to only small changes in $\Delta F^{\ddagger}$, and for such a closely related series, a common mechanism is supported. Similar linear plots for $\Delta H^{\ddagger}$ vs $\Delta S^{\ddagger}$ hold for a large number of redox reactions involving actinide ions,[104] and for substitution at Pt(II) centers (Sec. 4.9.1), as well as for interaction of $CrOH^{2+}$ with a number of ligands (Fig. 2.11).[111] A common rate-determining step for each reaction series is proposed.

Since

$$\Delta H^{\ddagger} = T \Delta S^{\ddagger} + \Delta F^{\ddagger} \tag{2.157}$$

then the slope of the linear plot (Fig. 2.11) can be easily shown to be the value of the absolute temperature T at which all the reactions represented on the line occur at the same rate. This is termed the *isokinetic temperature* (58 °C in Fig. 2.11). Below this temperature the reactions are controlled by $\Delta H^{\ddagger}$ values (that is, the lower the $\Delta H^{\ddagger}$ value, the higher the rate constant) and above this temperature by $\Delta S^{\ddagger}$ values. The former usually occurs when electronic effects are paramount, and the latter when solvent effects are important. Although the concept has had little impact in the transition metal area, it is apparent that conclusions drawn on the basis of rate constants (especially if these are close to one another) should be supplemented by information on $\Delta H^{\ddagger}$ and $\Delta S^{\ddagger}$.

2.7   THE EFFECT OF PRESSURE ON THE RATE OF A REACTION

The effect of pressure P on the rate constant k for a reaction is summarized in the expression[112]

$$\left(\frac{d(\log k)}{dP}\right)_T = \frac{-\Delta V^{\ddagger}}{2.3RT} \tag{2.158}$$

The rate constants k_1 and k_2 at a constant temperature T °K and pressures P_1 and P_2 respectively are therefore given by

$$\log \frac{k_2}{k_1} = \frac{-\Delta V^{\ddagger}(P_2 - P_1)}{2.3RT} \tag{2.159}$$

P is expressed in dyne cm^{-2} ($= 10^{-6}$ bars) and $R = 83.1 \times 10^6$ cm dyne mole^{-1} deg^{-1}. The term $\Delta V^{\ddagger}$ represents the partial molar volume change when reactants are converted to the activated complex and is called the *volume of activation* (cm^3 mole^{-1}). Relations (2.158) and (2.159) show that the rate constant increases with increasing pressure if $\Delta V^{\ddagger}$ is negative (which is also predictable simply from Le Chatelier's principle). Usually $\Delta V^{\ddagger}$ *is* pressure-dependent because the compressibility of reactants and transition state is different. Values usually used are therefore based on low pressures, or extrapolated to low pressures by use of a relation of the form

$$\ln k = a + bP + cP^2 \qquad (2.160)$$

Pressures are usually expressed in bars or atmospheres (1.01 bars). Fairly high pressures (2,000–10,000 atmospheres) must be used to obtain a sufficiently marked effect on the rate to allow an accurate value of $\Delta V^{\ddagger}$ to be obtained. These values usually lie in the range $\pm 25\ cm^3\ mole^{-1}$. Pressures up to 50,000 atm are relatively easily attained and the complete setup is now commercially available. For a description of the technique see Refs. 112, 113. Normally the effect of pressure only on slow reactions can be assessed, because of the experimental difficulties. Recently a pressure-jump perturbation method for pressures up to 1–2 kbar with optical analysis has been described.

    Volumes of activation, like the other activation parameters, are often composite. Consider the simple reaction schemes

$$A + B \rightleftharpoons C \qquad\qquad \Delta V \qquad\qquad (2.161)$$

$$C \rightarrow products \qquad (\Delta V^{\ddagger})_1 \qquad\qquad (2.162)$$

$$\Delta V^{\ddagger} = \Delta V + (\Delta V^{\ddagger})_1 \qquad\qquad (2.163)$$

$$\Delta V^{\ddagger} = \frac{k_1}{k_1 + k_2}(\Delta V^{\ddagger})_1 + \frac{k_2}{k_1 + k_2}(\Delta V^{\ddagger})_2 \qquad (2.165)$$

for which the observed values $\Delta V^{\ddagger}$ are additive. A change of reaction path induced by a change of pressure is thus quite feasible. Expected values of $\Delta V^{\ddagger}$ on the basis of different types of processes have been listed.[112]

2.7.1 $\Delta V^{\ddagger}$ Values and Mechanism

Unlike the situation in organic chemistry, the effect of pressure on the rates of transition metal complex reactions has been little explored and patterns of behavior are still badly needed. Fortunately, there are indications that the situation is improving.

    The volume of activation $\Delta V^{\ddagger}$ can be considered as made up of two parts, (a) the direct volume change when reactants are transferred into the transition complex and (b) the attendant volume changes in the surrounding solvent when the transition state is formed (electrostriction of solvent).

Component (a) is less important in reactions in which the charge types of reactant and product are the same, as in exchange reactions. It is usually positive and small in dissociative mechanisms.

Consider the effect of pressure on the exchange rate constant k for the reaction

$$Cr(H_2O)_6{}^{3+} + H_2{}^{18}O \rightarrow Cr(H_2O)_5(H_2{}^{18}O)^{3+} + H_2O \qquad (2.166)$$

shown in Fig. 2.12.[113] The value of $\Delta V^{\ddagger}$ is -9.3 ± 0.3 cm^3 mole^{-1}, and since $\log k$ is a linear function of P, $[\partial \Delta V^{\ddagger}/\partial P]_T \sim 0$. The markedly smaller volume of the transition state compared with the volume of the reactants is interpreted in terms of an associative interchange (I_a) mechanism in which water in the second coordination sphere or solvation sheath is interchanged with water in the first coordination sphere via an activated process of the type

$$Cr(H_2O)_6 \cdot (H_2O)_x{}^{3+} \rightarrow [Cr(H_2O)_7 \cdot (H_2O)_{x-1}^{3+}]^{\ddagger} \qquad (2.167)$$

The species $Cr(H_2O)_6{}^{3+}$ and $Cr(H_2O)_7{}^{3+}$ are considered to have the same volume, so that the vacancy created in the solvation sheath leads to the negative $\Delta V^{\ddagger}$ value. A direct associative process appears to be ruled out because bulk and coordinated waters differ in their compressibility and therefore a pressure-dependent $\Delta V^{\ddagger}$ would be expected. Both first and second coordination sphere water would be expected to be relatively

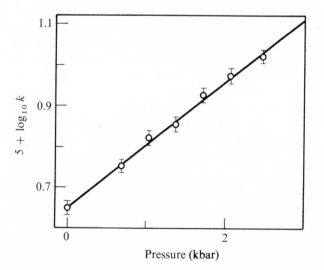

FIGURE 2.12   Pressure dependence of the exchange rate constant for reaction (2.166) at 25°. Ref. 113.

incompressible and therefore the $\Delta V^{\ddagger}$ for (2.167) would likely be pressure-independent, as is observed.

Hunt and Taube in an early study found $\Delta V^{\ddagger} = +1.2 \text{ cm}^3 \text{ mole}^{-1}$ for

$$Co(NH_3)_5H_2O^{3+} + H_2{}^{18}O \rightarrow Co(NH_3)_5H_2{}^{18}O^{3+} + H_2O \quad \textbf{(2.168)}$$

Since coordinated water occupies less volume than bulk water, this result can be interpreted in terms of a dissociative mechanism. This is now well established.[114]

Comparison of some parameter of the activated complex with the like parameter of reactants or products has been a continuous theme in this section. Thus, if $\Delta V^{\ddagger}$ can be compared with ΔV for the overall reaction, some estimate may be possible of the relative structures of product and activated complex. Such a comparison has been made with rewarding results.

The volume of activation at zero pressure $\Delta V_0^{\ddagger}$ is equal to ΔV, the molar volume of reaction, for the aquation of a series of Co(III) complexes (2.129), Table 2.7.[115] Such a result is entirely consistent with the dissociative (I_d) mechanism proposed for the reactions (Sec. 4.3.1). The final products have *almost* been formed in reaching the activated complex. Water from the solution sheath simply has to transfer to the first coordination sphere of the Co(III), and the volume change associated with this is quite small.[114] For the corresponding reaction of $Cr(NH_3)_5X^{n+}$, $X = Cl^-$, Br^-, I^-, and H_2O, the slope of the $\Delta V_0^{\ddagger}/\Delta V$ plot is only 0.59, indicating that separation of X^{n-} and provision of its solvation are only about half complete in the transition state.[116] The mechanisms of aquation of Co(III) and Cr(III) pentammine complexes are clearly different.

Since a neat method is available for the determination of ΔV,[116,117] this approach promises to be a useful one.

TABLE 2.7. Volumes of Activation and Volumes of Reaction for the Aquation of $Co(NH_3)_5X^{(3-n)+}$ at $25°$, $I = 0.1 \, M$[115]

X^{n-}	$\Delta V_0^{\ddagger}$ cm^3 mole^{-1}	ΔV cm^3 mole^{-1}
NO_3^-	-5.9	-7.2
Br^-	-8.7	-10.8
Cl^-	-9.9	-11.6
SO_4^{2-}	-17.0	-19.2
H_2O[a]	$+1.2$	0.0

[a] Ref. 114.

Although volumes and entropies of activation often parallel one another,[113,114] $\Delta V^{\ddagger}$ is the more easily understood and calculable parameter, and it is therefore likely to be the more sensitive criterion of mechanism.

2.8 MEDIUM EFFECTS ON THE RATE

The effect of the medium on the rate of a reaction has not yet played an important role in the deduction of mechanism, although its impact on rate must always be assessed.

2.8.1 The Effect of Electrolytes

The rate constant for a reaction is obtained by working at constant ionic strength or alternatively by extrapolating data obtained at different ionic strengths to a zero ionic strength.[118] This procedure is necessitated by the fact that ions (derived both from the reactants and from added electrolytes) often affect the rate of a reaction. This must be allowed for, or removed by "swamping" with electrolyte, in the derivation of a true rate law. The effect of ions on the rate constant for a reaction is easily derived from the absolute reaction rate theory. From (2.108),

$$k = \frac{kT}{h} K_{c}^{\ddagger} \tag{2.169}$$

and
$$K_{a}^{\ddagger} = K_{c}^{\ddagger} \frac{f_{X^{\ddagger}}}{f_{A} f_{B}} \tag{2.170}$$

The terms $K_{a}^{\ddagger}$ and $K_{c}^{\ddagger}$ are "activity" and "concentration" equilibrium constants and $f_{X^{\ddagger}}$, f_{A}, and f_{B} are activity coefficients of the activated complex and of the reactants. Thus,

$$k = \frac{kT}{h} K_{a}^{\ddagger} \frac{f_{A} f_{B}}{f_{X^{\ddagger}}} \tag{2.171}$$

This is equivalent to the earlier Brønsted-Bjerrum equation

$$k = k_{0} \frac{f_{A} f_{B}}{f_{X}} \tag{2.172}$$

where k_{0} is the rate constant at zero ionic strength, and X is a "critical" complex, the forerunner of the activated complex. Now,

$$-\log f_{i} = \alpha z_{i}^{2} F(I) \tag{2.173}$$

with $\alpha = 0.52$ at 25° and $F(I)$ some function of the ionic strength I. Thus since the charge on $AB^{\ddagger} = (z_A + z_B)$,

$$\log k = \log k_0 + (z_A{}^2 + z_B{}^2 - (z_A + z_B)^2)\alpha F(I) \qquad (2.174)$$

leading to

$$\log k = \log k_0 + 2\alpha z_A z_B I^{1/2} \qquad (2.175)$$

if the simple form $F(I) = I^{1/2}$ is used, and

$$\log k = \log k_0 + \frac{2\alpha z_A z_B I^{1/2}}{1 + I^{1/2}} \qquad (2.176)$$

if the extended form

$$F(I) = \frac{I^{1/2}}{1 + I^{1/2}} \qquad (2.177)$$

is substituted. The diameters of the reactant ions and the activated complexes are assumed equal.

These equations have been used quite successfully for correlating salt effects with the rate constants for reactions involving ions, and with the extended equation, even at relatively high ionic strength. They are the basis of the well-known Livingston and LaMer diagrams,[119] in which plots of $\log k$ vs $I^{1/2}$ or $I^{1/2}(1 + I^{1/2})^{-1}$ are linear, with slopes $\sim z_A z_B$ and intercept values $\log k_0$.[118b] The equations predict a positive salt effect (that is, an increasing rate constant with increasing salt concentration) when reactants have charges of the same sign and a negative salt effect when the charges are of opposite sign. Equation (2.176) has rarely been used to determine the charge on one of the reactants since this is invariably known. The characterization of $e_{aq}{}^{-}$[120] and $Cu(I)$[121] has been made, however, using the effects of ionic strength on the rates of their reactions.

The relationships are well illustrated by some data for the second-order reaction between $Co(NH_3)_5Br^{2+}$ and OH^{-}.[122] Excellent conformity with theory is observed when univalent anions only are used to make up the ionic strength. When divalent anions, such as $SO_4{}^{2-}$, are included in the medium, however, marked deviations from the expected behavior occur. This is usually ascribed to the formation of an outer-sphere complex between the Co(III) complex and the divalent anion (a phenomenon that will be much more important than for the univalent anion). Ion association will lead to a reduction in the computed ionic strength but, more important, might very easily produce species (outer-sphere complexes) that will react with rate constants different from those for the constituent ions (for, at the least, Coulombic reasons).[123] This effect can be accommodated by equating the observed rate constants to those for the constituent and complexed ions. There are two ways of going about this, and these can be shown to be related.[124]

(a) Considering the $Co(NH_3)_5Br^{2+}$–OH^- reaction in the presence of a bivalent anion L:

$$V = kC_1[OH^-] = k_0C_a[OH^-]\frac{f_af_{OH^-}}{f_{a\cdot OH^-}} + k_{ip}C_b[OH^-]\frac{f_bf_{OH^-}}{f_{b\cdot OH^-}} \qquad (2.178)$$

where C_1 = stoichiometric concentration of Co(III) complex = C_a + C_b

C_a = concentration of $Co(NH_3)_5Br^{2+}$, reaction rate constant k_0 at zero ionic strength

C_b = concentration of the ion pair, reaction rate constant k_{ip} at zero ionic strength

The value C_b is calculated from the dissociation constant of the sulfate ion pair. The term f represents activity coefficients, and reasonable assumptions are made as to their interrelationships.[125] The term on the left-hand side is obtained experimentally. The first term on the right-hand side of (2.178) can be calculated at any ionic strength using (2.176). The second term is obtained by difference. Consistent values for k_{ip} at different values of the ionic strength are obtained for the reaction of the ion pair $Co(NH_3)_5Br^{2+}\cdot X^{2-}$ with OH^-, for X = sulfate, malonate, succinate, and maleate.[126] These values are less than k_0 since the charged anion reduces the Coulombic attraction of the complex ion for OH^-.

(b) An alternative approach to (a) is to use an empirical expression for the observed rate constant k of the type

$$k = \frac{k_a + k_b[B] + k_c[B]^2}{1 + K'[B] + K''[B]^2} \qquad (2.179)$$

in which [B] is the formal concentration of the added ion, and k_a, k_b, k_c, K', and K'' are adjustable parameters.[127] The equation fits the extensive data obtained for the $Fe(CN)_6^{3-}$, $Fe(CN)_6^{4-}$ electron transfer.[128] The rate constant for this reaction is markedly increased by cations but little influenced by anions or by ionic strength per se—a type of behavior early observed and to which attention has been redrawn.[118,127] This rate behavior is particularly important for reactions between ions of like signs.

A simpler form of (2.179),

$$k = k_1 + k_2[A] \qquad (2.180)$$

is observed in the effect of anions (A) on the aquation of $Cr(NH_3)_5X^{2+}$ [129] and $Co(NH_3)_5X^{2+}$ [130] and the effect of cations (A) on the reactions between $Fe(CN)_6^{3-}$ and I^- [131] and $Mo(CN)_8^{3-}$ with I^-.[132]

For the reaction between an ion and a dipolar molecule, the rate is largely uninfluenced by ionic strength. A relation of the type

$$\log k = \log k_0 - cI \qquad (2.181)$$

or for small c values

$$k = k_0(1 + cI) \qquad (2.182)$$

sometimes holds. Thus the reversible aquation

$$Rh(NH_3)_5Cl^{2+} + H_2O \rightleftharpoons Rh(NH_3)_5H_2O^{3+} + Cl^- \qquad (2.183)$$

is attended by small and large ionic strength effects on the rate constants for the forward and reverse directions respectively.[133]

It is apparent from the above that one has to be cautioned that medium effects rather than definite reaction pathways might be responsible for the variation of rate with the concentration of ions in solution. For example, the reaction of Hg^{2+} with *trans*-$CrCl_2^+$ studied at a constant ionic strength made up of $HClO_4$ and $LiClO_4$ shows trends in the computed second-order rate constant with $[Hg^{2+}]$. These might reasonably be ascribed to the formation of appreciable amounts of an adduct such as $CrCl_2Hg^{3+}$ (see Secs. 1.6.3 and 1.6.4). Addition of Ba^{2+} rather than Li^+ to maintain the concentration of *dipositive ions constant* removes this trend however, indicating that it is a medium-based effect.[134] See also Ref. 135.

2.8.2 The Effect of [H⁺] on the Rate—Mechanistic or Medium Effects

Distinguishing a mechanistic from a medium effect may be difficult when there is a relatively small influence of H^+ on the rate. The following salient points can be made:[21,37,124,136-139]

(a) If in mixtures of H^+ with *different* added salts at constant ionic strength, the same rate law and constants do not persist, a medium effect is likely to be influencing the rate. For example, in the reduction of $(NH_3)_5CoNH_2Co(NH_3)_5^{5+}$ by V^{2+}, there is a 25% or so increase in the observed rate constant in going from 0.05 M to 2.0 M $HClO_4$ when the ionic strength of 2.0 M is made up with $NaClO_4$. This is a medium effect since it does not occur when $LiClO_4$ is used.[140] The problem arises because of the breakdown of the principle of constant ionic strength, particularly when such large and highly charged ions are reactants.[141] The examining media $LiClO_4$–$HClO_4$ and also $LiCl$–HCl are particularly useful ones since activity coefficients of ionic species are reasonably constant in such mixtures at constant ionic strength.[21] Any observed H^+ effects in this medium are more likely then to arise from mechanistic pathways.

(b) An allowance can be made for the effect of replacement by H^+

of another ion, say Na^+ or Li^+, in examining the effect of pH on the rate at a constant ionic strength.[142]

The reduction of $Co(NH_3)_5H_2O^{3+}$ ions by $Cr(II)$ has been examined in a ClO_4^- medium at $I = 1.0\ M$ over a $[H^+]$ range of 0.096–0.79 M, with the ionic medium held constant with $LiClO_4$.[143] The data (Table 2.8) could be interpreted as either (1) a two-term rate law of the form

$$k = a + b[H^+]^{-1} \qquad (2.184)$$

Least-squares analysis yields a *negative* value for $a = -0.72 \pm 0.14\ M^{-1}$ sec^{-1} and for $b = 3.12 \pm 0.05\ sec^{-1}$, or (2) a single-term rate law in which the Harned correction term takes care of changing activity coefficients[144]

$$k = c[H^+]^{-1} \exp(-\beta[H^+]) \qquad (2.185)$$

with $c = 3.13 \pm 0.05\ sec^{-1}$ and $\beta = 0.25 \pm 0.05\ M^{-1}$. The fit of Eq. (2.185) to the data is very good (Table 2.8). The values of b and c in (2.184) and (2.185) are almost identical, so that there is no ambiguity in the rate constant for the hydroxo form on either formulation. Reactivity ascribable to the aqua form, negative in (2.184) or zero in (2.185), must be very small. A computed value of $\beta = 0.96$ for the reaction between Fe^{3+} and Eu^{2+} on the basis of (2.185) is much higher than would be expected (≈ 0.1), and suggests that the k_0 term in

$$V = k_0[Fe^{3+}][Eu^{2+}] + k_1[Fe^{3+}][Eu^{2+}][H^+]^{-1} \qquad (2.186)$$

represents a genuine pathway.[145]

TABLE 2.8. Rate Constants for the Reduction of $Co(NH_3)_5H_2O^{3+}$ by Cr^{2+} at Various $[H^+]$ at 25.1°[143]

$[H^+]$, M	k, $M^{-1}\ sec^{-1}$	$k_{calcd.}$[a] $M^{-1}\ sec^{-1}$
0.794	3.39 ± 0.03	3.22
0.654	4.06 ± 0.04	4.12
0.560	4.83 ± 0.03	4.85
0.494	5.43 ± 0.02	5.59
0.438	6.53 ± 0.04	6.39
0.411	7.51 ± 0.16	6.86
0.386	6.72 ± 0.21	7.35
0.271	10.9 ± 0.1	10.8
0.202	14.9 ± 0.1	14.8
0.131	23.3 ± 0.2	23.0
0.114	27.1 ± 0.3	26.1
0.096	31.6 ± 2.5	31.7

[a] Calculated from $k = 3.13\ [H^+]^{-1} \exp(-0.25\ [H^+])$.

(c) One can usually be confident that H^+-containing terms in a rate law relate to a reaction pathway, in a number of circumstances: (1) All the terms in the rate expression for the aquation of $Cr(H_2O)_5N_3^{2+}$

$$\frac{-d \ln CrN_3^{2+}}{dt} = k_1[H^+] + k_0 + k_2[H^+]^{-1} + k_3[H^+]^{-2} \quad (2.187)$$

can be important, contributing $\geqslant 50\%$ towards the rate at different pH, and are therefore unlikely to be due to medium effects.[146] (2) A pK derived from a pH-dependent kinetic term (Sec. 1.10) agrees with a value determined spectrally.[21] (3) The reduction of cis-Coen$_2$(HCO$_2$)$_2^+$ by Cr^{2+} is inhibited by acid and the hydrolysis of the Co(III) complex is enhanced thereby. Similar pK values are derived in the two cases; these almost certainly cannot be due to medium effects.[147]

2.8.3 The Solvent Effect and Mechanism

We can arbitrarily divide solvents into three categories: protic, including both proton donors and acceptors; dipolar aprotic, solvent with dielectric constant > 15 but without hydrogen capable of forming hydrogen bonds; and aprotic, having neither acidic nor basic properties, for example, CCl_4. These may be expected to interact in widely different ways with complex ions containing large internal charges.

The effect of solvent on the rate of reactions of transition metal complexes as a means of interpreting mechanism has not been extensively explored. There are basically two ways in which the solvent may be regarded, although assessing their distinction and relative importance is very difficult.

(a) The solvent may be regarded as an "inert" medium. In this case, the dielectric constant of the solvent is the important parameter, and the effect can be semiquantitatively evaluated for ion-ion or ion-dipolar reactant mixtures, where electrostatic considerations dominate.

For a reaction between two ions, of charge z_A and z_B, the rate constant k (reduced to zero ionic strength) is given by

$$\ln k = \ln k_0 - \frac{e^2}{2DkT}\left[\frac{(z_A + z_B)^2}{r_\ddagger} - \frac{z_A^2}{r_A} - \frac{z_B^2}{r_B}\right] \quad (2.188)$$

where k_0 is the hypothetical rate constant in a medium of infinite dielectric constant, D is the dielectric constant, and r_A, r_B, and $r_\ddagger$ are the radii of the reactant ions A and B and the activated complex respectively.

If $r_A = r_B = r_\ddagger$, (2.188) becomes

$$\ln k = \ln k_0 - \frac{z_A z_B e^2}{DkTr_\ddagger} \quad (2.189)$$

and in a reaction between an ion z_A and a polar molecule (that is, $z_B = 0$), (2.188) becomes

$$\ln k = \ln k_0 + \frac{z_A^2 e^2}{2DkT}\left[\frac{1}{r_A} - \frac{1}{r_\ddagger}\right] \tag{2.190}$$

There should be a linear plot of $\log k$ vs $1/D$ with a negative slope if the charges of the ions are of the same sign and with a positive slope if the ions are oppositely charged. For the reaction of an ion and a polar molecule (common with solvolysis reactions), the linear plot of $\log k$ vs $1/D$ will have a positive slope irrespective of the charge of the ion since $(1/r_A - 1/r_\ddagger)$ is positive.

These expressions appear more applicable to *solvent mixtures* than to particular different solvents. The nature of the solvation process (and the radii and so forth of the solvated reactants) may stay approximately constant in the first situation but almost certainly will not in the second.

(b) The solvent may act as a nucleophile and an active participator in the reaction. It is extremely difficult to assess the function of the solvent in solvolysis reactions. Some attempts to define the mechanism for the replacement of ligand by solvent in octahedral complexes have been made using mixed solvents, and the solvating power concept.[148]

The rate of solvolysis (k_s) of *tert*-butyl chloride in a particular solvent S compared with the rate (k_0) in 80% v/v aqueous ethanol is used as a measure of that solvent's ionizing power, Y_s:

$$Y_s = \log \frac{k_s}{k_0} \tag{2.191}$$

For any other substrate acting by an S_N1 mechanism, it might be expected that

$$\log \frac{k_s}{k_0} = m Y_s \tag{2.192}$$

where m depends on the substrate, and equals 1.0 for t-BuCl. Such an expression holds for the aquation of a number of cobalt(III) complexes in a variety of mixed aqueous solvents.[149] The value of m is in the range 0.23–0.36; and although this much reduced value, compared with the value of t-BuCl, can be rationalized in terms of a dissociative mechanism, it is apparent that more data and patterns of behavior are required before the concept is likely to be diagnostic of mechanism. The Y_s parameter has been used in drawing conclusions about the mechanisms of isomerization of *trans*-$Co(C_2O_4)_2(H_2O)_2^-$ in aqueous mixtures with a number of solvents.[150]

REFERENCES

1. J. O. Edwards, E. F. Greene, and J. Ross, *J. Chem. Educ.*, **45**, 381 (1968); J. P. Birk, *J. Chem. Educ.*, **47**, 805 (1970).
2. D. A. House and H. K. J. Powell, *Inorg. Chem.*, **10**, 1583 (1971).
3. J. L. Kurz, *Accounts Chem. Research*, **5**, 1 (1972).
4. T. W. Newton and S. W. Rabideau, *J. Phys. Chem.*, **63**, 365 (1959).
5. A. Haim, *Inorg. Chem.*, **7**, 1475 (1968).
6. P. Moore, S. F. A. Kettle, and R. G. Wilkins, *Inorg. Chem.*, **5**, 466 (1966).
7. H. J. Price and H. Taube, *J. Amer. Chem. Soc.*, **89**, 269 (1967).
8. M. Mori and J. A. Weil, *Chem. Commun.*, 534 (1966); M. Mori and J. A. Weil, *J. Amer. Chem. Soc.*, **89**, 3732 (1967).
9. R. Davis, M. B. Stevenson, and A. G. Sykes, *J. Chem. Soc.*, A, 1261 (1970).
10. F. Basolo, P. H. Wilks, R. G. Pearson, and R. G. Wilkins, *J. Inorg. Nucl. Chem.*, **6**, 161 (1958).
11. F. Basolo, M. L. Morris, and R. G. Pearson, *Disc. Faraday Soc.*, **29**, 80 (1960).
12. W. R. Mason, *Coord. Chem. Rev.*, **7**, 241 (1972).
13. J. Halpern and M. Pribanic, *Inorg. Chem.*, **9**, 2616 (1970).
14. J. H. Baxendale and P. George, *Trans. Faraday Soc.*, **46**, 736 (1950).
15. T. S. Lee, I. M. Kolthoff, and D. L. Leussing, *J. Amer. Chem. Soc.*, **70**, 3596 (1948).
16. W. C. E. Higginson and A. G. Sykes, *J. Chem. Soc.*, 2841 (1962).
17. N. A. Dougherty and T. W. Newton, *J. Phys. Chem.*, **68**, 612 (1964).
18. W. C. E. Higginson, D. R. Rosseinsky, J. B. Stead, and A. G. Sykes, *Disc. Faraday Soc.*, **29**, 49 (1960).
19. R. D. Cannon, *J. Chem. Soc.*, A, 1098 (1968).
20. S. F. Lincoln and D. R. Stranks, *Aust. J. Chem.*, **21**, 67 (1968).
21. E. Deutsch and H. Taube, *Inorg. Chem.*, **7**, 1532 (1968).
22. K. M. Jones and J. Bjerrum, *Acta Chem. Scand.*, **19**, 974 (1965).
23. M. Orhanovic and R. G. Wilkins, *J. Amer. Chem. Soc.*, **89**, 278 (1967).
24. The second term could also be expressed as $(k_2/K_w)[Fe(III)][Cl^-][OH^-]$. In keeping with the tendency of expressing the rate law in terms of the predominant species, the form shown is preferred for data in acid medium.
25. D. Seewald and N. Sutin, *Inorg. Chem.*, **2**, 643 (1963).
26. J. H. Espenson and S. R. Helzer, *Inorg. Chem.*, **8**, 1051 (1969).
27. J. H. Espenson, *Inorg. Chem.*, **8**, 1554 (1969).
28. N. Sutin, *Accounts Chem. Research*, **1**, 225 (1968).
29. P. W. Taylor, R. W. King, and A. S. V. Bergen, *Biochem.*, **9**, 3894 (1970).
30. A. Haim, *Inorg. Chem.*, **5**, 2081 (1966).
31. J. H. Espenson, *Inorg. Chem.*, **4**, 1025 (1965); A. Adin and A. G. Sykes, *J. Chem. Soc.*, A, 351 (1968).
32. J. H. Espenson and O. J. Parker, *J. Amer. Chem. Soc.*, **90**, 3689 (1968).
33. K. B. Wiberg, H. Maltz, and M. Okano, *Inorg. Chem.*, **7**, 830 (1968).
34. D. H. Huchital, N. Sutin, and B. Earnquist, *Inorg. Chem.*, **6**, 838 (1967).
35. M. L. Bender, in Friess, Lewis, and Weissberger, Chap. 25.

36. T. W. Newton and F. B. Baker, *Inorg. Chem.*, **3**, 569 (1964).

37. P. B. Sigler and B. J. Masters, *J. Amer. Chem. Soc.*, **79**, 6353 (1957).

38. G. Czapski, B. J. H. Bielski, and N. Sutin, *J. Phys. Chem.*, **67**, 201 (1963).

39. E. Saito and B. H. J. Bielski, *J. Amer. Chem. Soc.*, **83**, 4467 (1961).

40. Y. S. Chiang, J. Craddock, D. Mickewich, and J. Turkevich, *J. Phys. Chem.*, **70**, 3509 (1966); M. S. Bains, J. C. Arthur, Jr., and O. Hinojosa, *J. Phys. Chem.*, **72**, 2250 (1968).

41. A. Samuni and G. Czapski, *Israel J. Chem.*, **8**, 551 (1970).

42. H. M. Swartz, J. R. Bolton, and D. C. Borg, eds., *Biological Applications of Electron Spin Resonance* (Wiley-Interscience, New York, 1972), chap. 2.

43. a. F. H. Westheimer, *Chem. Rev.*, **45**, 419 (1949); J. H. Espenson, *Accounts Chem. Research*, **3**, 347 (1970). b. L. J. Csanyi, in *Reactions of Metallic Salts and Complexes and Organometallic Compounds*, ed. C. H. Bamford and C. D. H. Tipper (Elsevier, Amsterdam, 1972), chap. 5.

44. D. A. Buckingham, I. I. Olson, and A. M. Sargeson, *J. Amer. Chem. Soc.*, **88**, 5443 (1966).

45. J. P. Candlin and J. Halpern, *J. Amer. Chem. Soc.*, **85**, 2518 (1963).

46. H. Taube, *Electron Transfer Reactions of Complex Ions in Solution* (Academic, New York, 1970), p. 92.

47. K. B. Wiberg and H. Schäfer, *J. Amer. Chem. Soc.*, **91**, 927, 933 (1969).

48. K. B. Wiberg and S. K. Mukherjee, *J. Amer. Chem. Soc.*, **93**, 2543 (1971).

49. R. K. Murmann, H. Taube, and F. A. Posey, *J. Amer. Chem. Soc.*, **79**, 262 (1957).

50. D. A. Buckingham, I. I. Olsen, and A. M. Sargenson, *Aust. J. Chem.*, **20**, 597 (1967).

51. R. K. Murmann and H. Taube, *J. Amer. Chem. Soc.*, **78**, 4886 (1956).

52. A. D. Harris, R. Stewart, D. Hendrickson, and W. L. Jolly, *Inorg. Chem.*, **6**, 1052 (1967).

53. J. N. Armor and H. Taube, *J. Amer. Chem. Soc.*, **92**, 2561 (1970).

54. S. Arrhenius, *Z. Phys. Chem.*, **4**, 226 (1889).

55. M. L. Yount and S. S. Zumda, *Inorg. Chem.*, **10**, 1212 (1971).

56. For a full account see Hammett, Chap. 5, and Leffler and Grunwald, pp. 62–73, 109; also S. Glasstone, K. J. Laidler, and H. Eyring, *The Theory of Rate Processes* (McGraw-Hill, New York, 1941).

57. L. L. Schaleger and F. A. Long, *Adv. Phys. Org. Chem.*, **1**, 1 (1963).

58. Harris, p. 50.

59. B. Lutz and H. Wendt, *Ber. Bunsenges. Phys. Chem.*, **74**, 372 (1970).

60. B. A. Sommer and D. W. Margerum, *Inorg. Chem.*, **9**, 2517 (1970).

61. H. N. Po and N. Sutin, *Inorg. Chem.*, **10**, 428 (1971).

62. A. J. Cunningham, D. A. House, and H. K. J. Powell, *J. Inorg. Nucl. Chem.*, **33**, 572 (1971).

63. R. M. Krupka, H. Kaplan, and K. J. Laidler, *Trans. Faraday Soc.*, **62**, 2754 (1966). R. L. Burwell, Jr., and R. G. Pearson, *J. Phys. Chem.*, **70**, 300 (1966).

64. G. Kohnstam, *Adv. Phys. Org. Chem.*, **5**, 121 (1967), for a discussion of heat capacities of activation and their uses in mechanistic studies.

65. J. R. Hulett, *Quart. Rev.*, **18**, 227 (1964).
66. W. E. Jones, R. B. Jordan, and T. W. Swaddle, *Inorg. Chem.*, **8**, 2504 (1969).
67. J. F. Bunnett, in Friess, Lewis, and Weissberger, Chap. 6.
68. S. Pignataro, G. Distefano, and A. Foffani, *J. Amer. Chem. Soc.*, **92**, 6425 (1970).
69. F. Monacelli, F. Basolo, and R. G. Pearson, *J. Inorg. Nucl. Chem.*, **24**, 1241 (1962).
70. R. Davies, G. B. Evans, and R. B. Jordan, *Inorg. Chem.*, **8**, 2025 (1969). C. Andrade, R. B. Jordan, and H. Taube, *Inorg. Chem.*, **9**, 711 (1970). E. Borghi and R. Monacelli, *Inorg. Chim. Acta*, **5**, 211 (1971).
71. R. G. Pearson, C. R. Boston, and F. Basolo, *J. Amer. Chem. Soc.*, **75**, 3089 (1953).
72. M. D. Alexander, *Inorg. Chem.*, **5**, 2084 (1966).
73. A. L. Odell and H. A. Raethel, *Chem. Commun.*, 1323 (1968).
74. D. J. Francis and R. B. Jordan, *J. Amer. Chem. Soc.*, **91**, 6626 (1969).
75. P. R. Guenther and R. G. Linck, *J. Amer. Chem. Soc.*, **91**, 3769 (1969).
76. See Selected Bibliography.
77. The relationship was first demonstrated in C. H. Langford, *Inorg. Chem.*, **4**, 265 (1965).
78. A. Haim, *Inorg. Chem.*, **9**, 426 (1970).
79. R. Marcus, *Ann. Rev. Phys. Chem.*, **15**, 155 (1964).
80. R. Dyke and W. C. E. Higginson, *J. Chem. Soc.*, 2788 (1963). S. P. Tanner and W. C. E. Higginson, *J. Chem. Soc.*, A, 1164 (1969).
81. K. R. Ashley and R. E. Hamm, *Inorg. Chem.*, **4**, 1120 (1965). N. W. D. Besse and C. H. Johnson, *Trans. Faraday Soc.*, **31**, 1632 (1935). J. A. Broomhead, N. Kane-Maguire, and I. Lauder, *Inorg. Chem.*, **9**, 1243 (1970).
82. L. P. Hammett, *J. Amer. Chem. Soc.*, **59**, 96 (1937).
83. F. Aprile, V. Cagliotti, and G. Illuminati, *J. Inorg. Nucl. Chem.*, **21**, 325 (1961).
84. P. Ellis, R. Hogg, and R. G. Wilkins, *J. Chem. Soc.*, 3308 (1959). R. K. Steinhaus and D. W. Margerum, *J. Amer. Chem. Soc.*, **88**, 441 (1966). J. Burgess and R. H. Prince, *J. Chem. Soc.*, 5752 (1963); A, 434 (1967). J. Halpern and P. F. Phelan, *J. Amer. Chem. Soc.*, **94**, 1881 (1972).
85. R. W. Taft, *J. Amer. Chem. Soc.*, **75**, 4231 (1953).
86. W. E. Jones and J. D. R. Thomas, *J. Chem. Soc.*, A, 1481 (1966). F. Basolo, J. G. Bergman, and R. G. Pearson, *J. Phys. Chem.*, **56**, 22 (1952).
87. J. N. Brønsted and K. J. Pederson, *Z. Phys. Chem.*, **108**, 185 (1924).
88. B. Perlmutter-Hayman and M. A. Wolff, *J. Phys. Chem.*, **71**, 1416 (1967). R. Bahwad, B. Perlmutter-Hayman, and M. A. Wolff, *J. Phys. Chem.*, **73**, 4391 (1969), and references therein.
89. J. O. Edwards, *J. Amer. Chem. Soc.*, **76**, 1541 (1954); **78**, 1819 (1956).
90. K. A. Muirhead, G. P. Haight, Jr., and J. K. Beattie, *J. Amer. Chem. Soc.*, **94**, 3006 (1972).

91. M. Eigen, *Angew. Chem.*, **3**, 1 (1964).
92. C. G. Swain and C. B. Scott, *J. Amer. Chem. Soc.*, **75**, 141 (1953).
93. U. Belluco, L. Cattalini, F. Basolo, R. G. Pearson, and A. Tures, *J. Amer. Chem. Soc.*, **87**, 241 (1965).
94. R. G. Pearson, H. Sobel, and J. Songstad, *J. Amer. Chem. Soc.*, **90**, 319 (1968).
95. M. L. Tobe, *Inorg. Chem.*, **7**, 1260 (1968).
96. M. D. Alexander and H. G. Hamilton, Jr., *Inorg. Chem.*, **8**, 2131 (1969).
97. J. A. Kernohan and J. F. Endicott, *Inorg. Chem.*, **9**, 1504 (1970).
98. T. W. Swaddle and G. Guastalla, *Inorg. Chem.*, **7**, 1915 (1968).
99. Correction is made for the rotational and vibrational (negligible) entropies that are lost when the free polyatomic anions become complexed in the transition state.
100. T. W. Swaddle and E. L. King, *Inorg. Chem.*, **4**, 532 (1965). T. W. Swaddle, *J. Amer. Chem. Soc.*, **89**, 4338 (1967).
101. J. P. Birk and J. H. Espenson, *Inorg. Chem.*, **7**, 991 (1968).
102. D. K. Wakefield and W. B. Schaap, *Inorg. Chem.*, **8**, 512 (1969).
103. Frost and Pearson, p. 142.
104. T. W. Newton and F. B. Baker, *Adv. Chem.*, **71**, 268 (1967).
105. A convenient representation of the formation of the activated complex from the predominant species in solution. (See Ref. 4.)
106. J. H. Espenson and R. J. Christiansen, *J. Amer. Chem. Soc.*, **91**, 7311 (1969).
107. B. Schiefelbein and N. A. Daugherty, *Inorg. Chem.*, **9**, 1716 (1970).
108. M. J. Burkhart and T. W. Newton, *J. Phys. Chem.*, **73**, 1741 (1969).
109. J. H. Espenson and L. A. Krug, *Inorg. Chem.*, **8**, 2633 (1969).
110. J. D. Miller and R. H. Prince, *J. Chem. Soc.*, *A*, 1048 (1966).
111. D. Thusius, *Inorg. Chem.*, **10**, 1106 (1971).
112. G. Kohnstam, *Progr. Reaction Kinetics*, **5**, 335 (1970). W. Le Noble, *Progr. Phys. Org. Chem.*, **5**, 207 (1965). E. Whalley, *Adv. Phys. Org.*, *Chem.* **2**, 93 (1964).
113. D. R. Stranks and T. W. Swaddle, *J. Amer. Chem. Soc.*, **93**, 2783 (1971).
114. H. R. Hunt and H. Taube, *J. Amer. Chem. Soc.*, **80**, 2642 (1958). See footnote 10 in Ref. 113.
115. W. E. Jones and T. W. Swaddle, *Chem. Commun.*, 998 (1969). W. E. Jones, L. R. Carey, and T. W. Swaddle, *Can. J. Chem.*, **50**, 2739 (1972).
116. G. Guastalla and T. W. Swaddle, *Can. J. Chem.*, **51**, 821 (1973).
117. T. G. Spiro, A. Revesz, and J. Lee, *J. Amer. Chem. Soc.*, **90**, 4000 (1968).
118. B. Perlmutter-Hayman, *Progr. Reaction Kinetics*, **6**, 239 (1971). A. D. Pethybridge and J. E. Prue, *Inorganic Reaction Mechanisms*, Part 2, p. 327, for comprehensive accounts.
119. R. Livingston, *J. Chem. Educ.*, **7**, 2887 (1930). V. K. La Mer, *Chem. Rev.*, **10**, 179 (1932).
120. G. Czapski and H. A. Schwarz, *J. Phys. Chem.*, **66**, 471 (1962).

121. O. J. Parker and J. H. Espenson, *J. Amer. Chem. Soc.*, **91**, 1968 (1969).

122. B. Perlmutter-Hayman and Y. Weissman, *J. Phys. Chem.*, **68**, 3307 (1964).

123. C. W. Davies, *Progr. Reaction Kinetics*, **1**, 163 (1961), for a good account of salt effects in solution kinetics.

124. S. H. Laurie and C. B. Monk, *J. Chem. Soc.*, 724 (1965).

125. If the activity coefficients of uni-, bi-, and tervalent ions are written f_1, f_2, and f_3, then the first term contains the quotient $f_2 f_1/f_{(2-1)} \sim f_2$, and the second term can be approximated $f_2\,{}^2f_1/f_1 \sim f_2{}^2$. Thus, $k_{1p} f_2{}^2$ plotted vs $f(I)$ is linear (theo) slope-4.

126. M. R. Wendt and C. B. Monk, *J. Chem. Soc.*, A, 1624 (1969).

127. A. R. Olson and T. R. Simonson, *J. Chem. Phys.*, **17**, 1167 (1949).

128. R. J. Campion, C. F. Deck, P. King, Jr., and A. C. Wahl, *Inorg. Chem.*, **6**, 672 (1967).

129. T. P. Jones, W. E. Harris, and W. J. Wallace, *Can. J. Chem.*, **39**, 2371 (1961). J. B. Walker and C. B. Monk, *J. Chem. Soc.*, 1372 (1966).

130. F. J. Garrick, *Trans. Faraday Soc.*, **33**, 486 (1937); **34**, 1088 (1938), early and perceptive papers.

131. Y. Abdul Majid and K. E. Howlett, *J. Chem. Soc.*, A, 679 (1968).

132. M. H. Ford-Smith and J. H. Rawsthorne, *J. Chem. Soc.*, A, 160 (1969).

133. G. C. Lalor and G. W. Bushnell, *J. Chem. Soc.*, A, 2520 (1968).

134. J. P. Birk, *Inorg. Chem.*, **9**, 735 (1970).

135. J. H. Espenson and J. P. Birk, *Inorg. Chem.*, **4**, 527 (1965).

136. A. Pidcock and W. C. E. Higginson, *J. Chem. Soc.*, 2798 (1963).

137. P. Krumholz, *J. Phys. Chem.*, **60**, 87 (1956).

138. A. J. Zielen and J. C. Sullivan, *J. Phys. Chem.*, **66**, 1065 (1962).

139. D. W. Carlyle and J. H. Espenson, *J. Amer. Chem. Soc.*, **91**, 599 (1969).

140. J. Doyle and A. G. Sykes, *J. Chem. Soc.*, A, 795 (1967). R. Davies and A. G. Sykes, *J. Chem. Soc.*, A, 2831 (1968).

141. In other words, there may be a relation of the form $\log f_H = \log f_0 + a[H^+]$, where f_H and f_0 are the activity coefficients of reactants and activated complex at $[H^+] = $ H and o respectively at constant I. From (2.171) this will lead to a rate law, $\log k \propto [H^+]$ from a purely medium effect.[136]

142. T. W. Newton and F. B. Baker, *Inorg. Chem.*, **4**, 1166 (1965).

143. D. L. Toppen and R. G. Linck, *Inorg. Chem.*, **10**, 2635 (1971).

144. R. A. Robinson and R. H. Stokes, *Electrolyte Solutions* (Butterworths, London, 1955), Chap. 15.

145. D. W. Carlyle and J. H. Espenson, *J. Amer. Chem. Soc.*, **90**, 2272 (1968).

146. T. W. Swaddle and E. L. King, *Inorg. Chem.*, **3**, 234 (1964).

147. J. R. Ward and A. Haim, *J. Amer. Chem. Soc.*, **92**, 475 (1970).

148. E. Grunwald and S. Winstein, *J. Amer. Chem. Soc.*, **70**, 846 (1948).

149. J. Burgess and M. G. Price, *J. Chem. Soc.*, A, 3108 (1971).

150. H. Kelm, H. Stieger, and G. M. Harris, *Chem. Ber.*, **104**, 2743 (1971).

SELECTED BIBLIOGRAPHY

Linear Free-Energy Relationships

BELL, R. P. *The Proton in Chemistry.* 2nd ed. Chapman and Hall, London, 1973. Contains full discussion of Brønsted relationships.

BENDER, M. L. *Mechanisms of Homogeneous Catalysis from Protons to Proteins.* Wiley-Interscience, New York, 1971.

EDWARDS, J. O. *Inorganic Reaction Mechanisms.* Benjamin, New York, 1964.

LEFFLER, J. E. and GRUNWALD, E. *Rates and Equilibria of Organic Reactions.* Wiley, New York, 1963. Definitive account of LFER.

WELLS, P. R. *Linear Free Energy Relationships.* Academic, London, 1968. Short but comprehensive account.

NOTE: See also works indicated in Chap. 1.

PROBLEMS

1. Suggest mechanisms (more than one in some cases) for the following reactions.

   a. $(NH_3)_5CoO_2Co(NH_3)_5^{4+} + 4V^{2+} + 14H^+$

$$\rightarrow 2Co^{2+} + 10NH_4^+ + 4V^{3+} + 2H_2O$$

$$\frac{-d[\text{Co complex}]}{dt} = k[\text{Co complex}]$$

   [A. B. Hoffman and H. Taube, *Inorg. Chem.*, 7, 1971 (1968).]

   b. $cis\text{-}Coen_2(H_2O)Cl^{2+} + Fe^{2+} + 4H^+$

$$\rightarrow Co^{2+} + 2enH_2^{2+} + Cl^- + Fe^{3+}$$

$$\frac{-d[Fe^{2+}]}{dt} = k_1[Co^{III}] + k_2[Co^{III}][Fe^{2+}]$$

   [P. Benson and A. Haim, *J. Amer. Chem. Soc.*, 87, 3826 (1965).]

   c. $7MoO_4^{2+} + 8H^+ \rightarrow Mo_7O_{24}^{6-} + 4H_2O$

$$\frac{d[Mo_7O_{24}^{6-}]}{dt} = k[MoO_4^{2-}]^7[H^+]^8$$

   [D. S. Honig and K. Kustin, *Inorg. Chem.*, 11, 65 (1972).]

   d. $2Cu^{2+} + 6CN^- \rightarrow 2Cu(CN)_2^- + (CN)_2$

$$\frac{d[Cu(CN)_2^-]}{dt} = k[Cu^{2+}]^2[CN^-]^6$$

[J. H. Baxendale and D. T. Westcott, *J. Chem. Soc.*, 2347 (1959). R. Patterson and J. Bjerrum, *Acta Chem. Scand.*, **19**, 729 (1965).]

e. $2Hg^{II} + 2V^{III} \rightarrow Hg^{I}_2 + 2V^{IV}$

$$\frac{-d[V^{III}]}{dt} = \frac{[Hg^{II}][V^{III}]^2}{a[V^{IV}] + b[V^{III}]} + \frac{[Hg^{II}][V^{III}]^2}{c[V^{IV}] + d[Hg^{II}]}$$

[W. C. E. Higginson, D. R. Rosseinsky, J. B. Stead, and A. G. Sykes, *Disc. Faraday Soc.*, **29**, 49 (1960).]

f. $*Cr^{III} + Cr^{VI} \rightleftharpoons Cr^{III} + *Cr^{VI}$

$V_{exch} = [k_1 + k_2[H^+]^{-2}][Cr^{III}]^{4/3}[H_2CrO_4]^{2/3}$

[C. Altman and E. L. King, *J. Amer. Chem. Soc.*, **83**, 2825 (1961).]

g. $Fe^{III} + Cu^I \rightarrow Fe^{II} + Cu^{II}$

$$\frac{-d[Fe^{III}]}{dt} = k[Fe^{III}][Cu^I][H^+]^{-1}$$

(This is a common type of rate law for reactions between two acidic metal ions.) [O. J. Parker and J. H. Espenson, *Inorg. Chem.*, **8**, 1523 (1969).]

h. $Pt(CO)(AsPh_3)ClC_2H_5 + AsPh_3 \xrightarrow{PhNO_2} Pt(AsPh_3)_2(COC_2H_5)Cl$

$$\frac{-d[Pt^{II}]}{dt} = k[Pt^{II}]$$

[R. W. Glyde and M. J. Mawby, *Inorg. Chem.*, **10**, 854 (1971).]

In each case specify the units for the rate constants (Sec. 1.1) and the composition of the activated complex(es) (Sec. 2.1).

2. **a.** The oxidation of Fe^{2+} by two-equivalent oxidants produces unstable oxidation states either of iron or of the oxidant. The immediate products of oxidation by (1) H_2O_2, (2) $HOCl$, and (3) O_3 in 0.1 *M* to 1.0 *M* $HClO_4$ are (1) > 99% Fe^{3+} (and $FeOH^{2+}$), (2) ~ 80% Fe^{3+} and ~ 15% $Fe_2(OH)_2^{4+}$, and (3) ~ 60% Fe^{3+} and 40% $Fe_2(OH)_2^{4+}$. Suggest reasons for this difference in behavior, and for the decreasing yield of $Fe_2(OH)_2^{4+}$ with increasing $[H^+]$ in reaction (2). [T. J. Conocchioli, E. J. Hamilton, and N. Sutin, *J. Amer. Chem. Soc.*, **87**, 926 (1965).]

b. The oxidation of Cr^{2+} by $HCrO_4^-$ is very rapid. About 50% of the Cr(III) product is $Cr(H_2O)_6^{3+}$ and the remainder the binuclear $Cr_2(OH)_2^{4+}$. A three-step mechanism is suggested, in conformity with other oxidations by Cr(VI):

$$Cr^{II} + Cr^{VI} \rightleftharpoons Cr^{III} + Cr^V$$

$$Cr^{II} + Cr^V \rightleftharpoons Cr^{III} + Cr^{IV}$$

$$Cr^{II} + Cr^{IV} \rightleftharpoons Cr(OH)_2Cr^{4+}$$

What would you expect as products of a reaction between Cr^{2+} and $H*CrO_4^-$ (containing ^{51}Cr)? How might you explain a small amount of $*Cr^{3+}$ in the product? [L. S. Hegedus and A. Haim, *Inorg. Chem.*,

6, 664 (1967). See also A. C. Adams, J. R. Crook, F. Bockhoff, and E. L. King, *J. Amer. Chem. Soc.*, **90**, 5761 (1968); and J. C. Kenny and D. W. Carlyle, *Inorg. Chem.*, **12**, 1952 (1973).]

3. The kinetic data shown below have been obtained for the reaction

$$Ni(H_2O)_5NH_3^{2+} + H_2O \rightleftharpoons Ni(H_2O)_6^{2+} + NH_3 \qquad k_f, k_r$$

in three independent studies. Are the results in agreement?

Temp. °C	k_f, sec^{-1}	Method	Ref.
4.8	1.1	Dissociation of complex in 0.2 M HNO$_3$,	a
15.2	2.8	measured by spectral stopped-flow	
25.0	6.0		
−25.0	0.01	pH-stat using 2.7-M Mg(NO$_3$)$_2$ to prevent freezing. Value is independent pH 3.1–5.8	b
11.0	1.1	Temperature-jump on equilibrium in 0.1-M NH$_4$NO$_3$	c
20.0	2.3		
30.0	5.0		

[a] G. A. Melson and R. G. Wilkins, *J. Chem. Soc.*, 4208 (1962).
[b] C. S. Garner and J. Bjerrum, *Acta Chem. Scand.*, **15**, 2055 (1961).
[c] D. B. Rorabacher, *Inorg. Chem.*, **5**, 1891 (1966).

4. Plot the data of Table 2.4 in the form of a k^{-1} (M sec) vs $1/T$ curve. Discuss, in terms of the rate constants of schemes (2.119) and (2.120), the significance of the two Arrhenius straight lines that asymptotically approach the curve. [S. Pignataro, G. Distefano, and A. Foffani, *J. Amer. Chem. Soc.*, **92**, 6425 (1970).]

5. Explore the relation between the rate constant k for base hydrolysis of of Co(NH$_3$)$_5$X$^{(3-n)+}$ and the formation constant K of the Co(III) complex from the data at 25° provided. What do the results suggest about the mechanism of base hydrolysis?

X^{n-}	K, M^{-1}	k, M^{-1} sec^{-1}
NO$_3^-$	0.08	5.7
I$^-$	0.12	3.7
Br$^-$	0.35	1.4
Cl$^-$	1.11	0.25
SO$_4^{2-}$	11.0	4.9×10^{-2}
F$^-$	~100	5.1×10^{-3}
N$_3^-$	8.3×10^2	1.6×10^{-4}
HCO$_2^-$	9.7×10^2	5.8×10^{-4}
NCS$^-$	2.7×10^3	1.0×10^{-4}
HC$_2$O$_4^-$	7.1×10^3	2.5×10^{-4}
CO$_3^{2-}$	6.6×10^4	3.3×10^{-6}

[W. E. Jones, R. B. Jordan, and T. W. Swaddle, *Inorg. Chem.*, **8**, 2504 (1969).]

6. A scheme proposed for the outer-sphere redox reaction between $Fe(4,7\text{-dimethylphenanthroline})_3^{2+}$, A^{2+}, and $IrCl_6^{2-}$, B^{2-}, is

$$A^{2+} + B^{2-} \rightleftharpoons A^{3+} + B^{3-} \qquad k_f, k_r$$

$$A^{2+} + B^{2-} \rightleftharpoons A^{2+} \cdots B^{2-} \qquad k_1, k_{-1}$$
$$\text{(i)}$$

$$A^{2+} \cdots B^{2-} \rightleftharpoons A^{3+} \cdots B^{3-} \qquad k_2, k_{-2}$$
$$\text{(ii)}$$

$$A^{3+} \cdots B^{3-} \rightleftharpoons A^{3+} + B^{3-} \qquad k_3, k_{-3}$$

Assuming steady-state concentrations for the two collision complexes (i) and (ii), derive the relation between the forward and reverse overall rate constants k_f and k_r and activation parameters $\Delta H_f^{\ddagger}$ and $\Delta H_r^{\ddagger}$ in terms of those of the individual steps. Consider limiting cases, and suggest which are likely to be operative in this reaction, for which $\Delta H_f^{\ddagger} = 0 \pm 0.5$ and $\Delta H_r^{\ddagger} = 5 \pm 1$ kcal mole^{-1}. [J. Halpern, R. J. Legare, and R. Lumry, *J. Amer. Chem. Soc.*, **85**, 680 (1963).]

7. Calculate, from the accompanying data (k's in M^{-1} sec^{-1}) at 25°, the values of $\Delta V^{\ddagger}$ for the successive second-order anation reactions

$$Cr(H_2O)_6^{3+} \xrightarrow[\text{HC}_2\text{O}_4^-]{k_1} Cr(H_2O)_4(C_2O_4)^+ \xrightarrow[\text{HC}_2\text{O}_4^-]{k_2}$$

$$Cr(H_2O)_2(C_2O_4)_2^- \xrightarrow[\text{HC}_2\text{O}_4^-]{k_3} Cr(C_2O_4)_3^{3-}$$

Discuss their probable significance after reading Chap. 4. [C. Schenk and H. Kelm, *J. Coord. Chem.*, **2**, 71 (1972).]

Pressure (atm)	$10^5 k_1$	$10^5 k_2$	$10^5 k_3$
1	4.17	50.7	24.7
100	4.20	57.5	26.2
250	4.20	59.8	28.8
500	4.32	65.0	29.2
750	4.40	65.2	35.0
1000	4.63	68.2	35.5
1500	4.78	68.0	36.5
2000	...	69.8	38.9

8. The reaction of $Co(NH_3)_5Br^{2+}$ with OH^- ion has been thoroughly studied with regard to the effect of added electrolyte on the second-order rate constant k (Sec. 2.8). Consider how the discussion is affected by the fact that the reaction is probably not simple second-order, but goes via an S_N1CB

mechanism (Sec. 4.5.3(a)), so that k is a composite value. [B. Perlmutter-Hayman and Y. Weissmann, *J. Phys. Chem.*, **68**, 3307 (1964).]

9. Determine the dependence of the first-order rate constant k for the reaction

$$Cr(H_2O)_5ONO^{2+} + H_3O^+ \rightarrow Cr(H_2O)_6^{3+} + HNO_2$$

on the proton concentration, $T = 10°$, $I = 1.0$. (See accompanying table.)

$[H^+]$, M	$10^2 k$, sec^{-1}	$[H^+]$, M	$10^2 k$, sec^{-1}
0.0114	0.345	0.150	7.9
0.0216	0.706	0.200	11
0.030	1.16	0.300	20
0.040	1.59	0.400	31
0.050	2.07	0.500	45
0.060	2.53	0.600	59
0.080	3.50	0.700	81
0.100	4.66	0.800	104
		0.900	129
		0.993	158

Suggest a mechanism, and analyze whether medium effects are likely to be a cause of the acidity dependence. [T. C. Matts and P. Moore, *J. Chem. Soc., A*, 1997 (1969).]

Chapter 3

The Experimental Determination
of the Rate of Reaction

3.1 PRELIMINARIES

In determining experimentally the rate of a reaction, it is imperative to define the reaction completely both as to the reactants—for example, whether they are hydrolyzed or polymerized—and to the stoichiometry. This is preferably carried out before any detailed rate measurements are made; otherwise difficulties in understanding the rate data are likely to arise. One of the problems, for example, in interpreting the rate law for oxidation by cerium(IV) or cobalt(III) ion arises from the difficulties in characterizing the species in aqueous solution, that is, the extent of formation of hydroxy or polymeric species.[1]

The successful study of the kinetics of the metal-ion-catalyzed base hydrolysis of cysteine methyl ester[2] or the dimerization of pyruvate[3] requires the complete characterization of the metal-ion substrate systems taking part in the reaction. Specific computer programs are available for obtaining these data from a knowledge of the formation constants of the various metal-ligand complexes.[4]

The importance of knowing the stoichiometry of a reaction can be simply illustrated by considering the aquation of cis-Cren$_2$(NCS)Cl$^+$ ion.[5] Is Cl$^-$ or NCS$^-$ replaced in the initial step and is the product cis or $trans$ or both? Does the product of this first step aquate further, and if so what groups are then replaced? Chemical analysis and spectrophotometric analysis have been used to answer these questions. The results reveal the surprising fact that the bidentate en is lost at one stage, a behavior that appears more common with Cr(III) than with Co(III), where its occurrence

$$\text{cis-Cren}_2(\text{NCS})\text{Cl}^+ + \text{H}_2\text{O} \xrightarrow{\substack{\leqslant 4\% \\ \leqslant 4\% \\ \geqslant 92\%}} \begin{array}{l} \textit{trans-}\text{Cren}_2(\text{H}_2\text{O})\text{NCS}^{2+} + \text{Cl}^- \\[4pt] \textit{cis-} \text{ and } \textit{trans-}\text{Cren}_2(\text{H}_2\text{O})\text{Cl}^{2+} + \text{SCN}^- \\[4pt] \textit{cis-}\text{Cren}_2(\text{H}_2\text{O})\text{NCS}^{2+} + \text{Cl}^- \end{array} \qquad (3.1)$$

$$\text{cis-Cren}_2(\text{H}_2\text{O})\text{NCS}^{2+} + \text{H}_2\text{O} \xrightarrow{\substack{33 \pm 10\% \\ 67 \pm 10\%}} \begin{array}{l} \text{Cren}(\text{H}_2\text{O})_3\text{NCS}^{2+} + \text{en} \\[8pt] \\[8pt] \textit{cis-} \text{ and } \textit{trans-}\text{Cren}_2(\text{H}_2\text{O})_2{}^{3+} + \text{SCN}^- \end{array} \qquad (3.2)$$

is usually ignored. (However, see Ref. 6.) If the rate constants for parallel reactions are to be resolved, then analysis of the products is essential (Sec. 1.4.2).

Inconsistencies in the values of equilibrium constants obtained from measurements on systems at equilibrium with those derived from rate measurements may also reveal unexpected reaction paths.[7,8]

3.1.1 The Control of Experimental Conditions

Some general considerations applicable to all rate studies can be outlined.[9] The materials used, including the solvent, should be as pure as possible. There are several instances recorded (and doubtless a number unrecognized) in which traces of impurities introduced inadvertently into a system catalyzed the reaction. A particularly frightening case involved chemically pure samples of the chlorides and bromides of sodium and potassium (added to adjust the ionic strength), which apparently contained sufficient Cu^{2+} to catalyze the reaction:

$$2\text{Fe(CN)}_6{}^{3-} + \text{SO}_3{}^{2-} + 2\text{OH}^- \rightarrow 2\text{Fe(CN)}_6{}^{4-} + \text{SO}_4{}^{2-} + \text{H}_2\text{O} \quad (3.3)$$

Copper(II) ion is a potent catalyst even in micromolar concentrations. This impurity, more than any specific effects of the inert electrolytes, could be shown to account for the rate enhancements.[10]

These catalytic effects are usually signaled by irreproducible behavior. If it is suspected that traces of metal ions may be causing peculiar rate effects, a strong ligand may be added to sequester the metal ion. The decomposition of Caro's acid is reproducible only when small amounts of EDTA are added to sequester traces of metal ion, which were introduced via the phosphate buffers used in the study.[11] The decomposition of permanganate in alkaline solution

$$4\text{MnO}_4{}^- + 4\text{OH}^- \rightarrow 4\text{MnO}_4{}^{2-} + \text{O}_2 + 2\text{H}_2\text{O} \qquad (3.4)$$

is markedly slowed when the reactants are extensively purified and metal ion concentrations are reduced below 10^{-9} M.[12]

Since the rate constant for many reactions is affected by the ionic strength of the medium (Sec. 2.8.1), it is necessary either to maintain a constant ionic strength with added electrolyte or to carry out a series of measurements at different ionic strengths and extrapolate to infinite dilution. The former practice is usually followed, employing $NaNO_3$ or $NaClO_4$ as added salts.

Many complex-ion reactions are accompanied by a pH change, and since the rate of these reactions is often pH-dependent, it is necessary to use buffers. It is easily ascertained whether the buffer has a marked effect on the rate of the reaction. The hydrolysis of certain cobalt(III) complexes for example, is accelerated by phthalate and phosphate but unaffected by borate buffers.[13]

A list of useful buffers for the pH region 5.5–11.0 is contained in Table 3.1.[14] Many of these are substantially nonnucleophilic and are unlikely to affect the course of the reaction. Occasionally one of the reactants being used in excess may possess buffer capacity, and this obviates the necessity for adding buffer. This situation will often arise in the study of complex-ion–ligand interaction when either reactant may be involved in an acid-base equilibrium.

The reaction of $Coen_2(H_2O)OH^{2+}$ with HPO_4^{2-},

$$Coen_2(H_2O)OH^{2+} + HPO_4^{2-} \rightarrow Coen_2PO_4 + 2H_2O \qquad (3.5)$$

has been studied at pH $\sim$ 7 using either reagent in excess, in which case both act as efficient internal buffers.[15] Concentrations of reactants cited usually refer to room temperature, and any change in concentration (from the volume change of the solvent) caused by carrying out the runs at other

TABLE 3.1.   Some Buffers Useful in Studying Complex-Ion Reactions[14]

Buffer	Approx. pK at 20°
2-Methylquinoline	5.7[a]
2-(N-Morpholino)ethane sulfonic acid	6.2[b]
2,6-Dimethylpyridine	6.7[a]
N,N-Bis(2-hydroxyethyl)-2-aminoethane sulfonic acid	7.2[b]
2,4,6-Trimethylpyridine	7.5[a]
Tris(hydroxymethyl)aminomethane	8.3[b]
cis-2,6-Dimethylpiperidine	10.9[a]

[a] pH of 50:50 mixture of amine and protonated amine.   See Ref. 14a.
[b] Ref. 14b.

temperatures can usually be ignored. It is often unnecessary to maintain the reaction temperature more constant than $\pm 0.05°$. Variations in rate constants due to such a temperature fluctuation are generally well within the experimental error.

It is obviously wise to exclude light or air if it is suspected that these might interfere with the reaction. Possible photocatalysis may be avoided by using blackened reaction vessels. Several effective pieces of apparatus have been described for studying reaction rates with the complete exclusion of oxygen.[16,17]

Special equipment must be used if the reaction is carried out at elevated pressure or temperature (say $> 100°$ in water) or if sparingly soluble gaseous reactants or products are involved.[18] A simple device for working at higher temperatures when continual opening of the apparatus is to be avoided has been described.[19] The reaction mixture is contained in a syringe immersed in a constant-temperature oil bath. A long needle attached to the syringe is bent up above the surface of the oil bath and from it samples are periodically withdrawn and analyzed.

3.2 THE METHODS OF INITIATING REACTION

Obviously the speed with which it is necessary to initiate a reaction will depend on its rate. If it is a slow process with half-lives longer than about 20 sec, then the reaction can be commenced simply by mixing the reactants together in prearranged concentrations and conditions. Alternatively, a system already at chemical equilibrium may be perturbed, for example by a change in concentration, pH or temperature, and the movement to the new equilibrium position then monitored. This is the basis of the *relaxation method* (Sec. 1.8), which has been little applied to the study of slow reactions,[20] but is extremely important for the measurement of rapid reactions (see below). An isotopic equilibrium may be disturbed by the addition of a tracer isotope. The distribution of the isotopes among the various chemical species containing it is then monitored. The *isotopic exchange* (Sec. 1.9) method has played an important role in our understanding of mechanisms of complex-ion reaction.

Even reactions with relatively short half-lives may be studied without recourse to sophisticated equipment. A simple mixer[20] in conjunction with a recording spectrophotometer, a pH-stat and a recorder, and a stirred-flow reactor[21] can all be used to measure reaction half-lives of a few seconds. A spring-loaded mixing device in conjunction with rapid-responding spectral monitoring can measure half-lives as short as 0.1 sec.[22]

3.3 FLOW METHODS

Comprehensive discussions of flow methods are available in the literature.[23] If specially designed mixers[24] are used as reaction initiators, half-lives as short as 0.001 sec may be measured. There are basically three ways in which the reaction solution may be treated after mixing (Fig. 3.1):

(a) It may be "quenched" after a predetermined time, governed by the distance between mixer and quencher and the flow rate. The quenched solution, in which reaction has ceased, may then be assayed at leisure by any convenient method.

(b) It may flow continuously along an observation tube, while conventional in situ monitoring is made, either at different points along the observation tube (with the flow maintained at a constant rate) or at a fixed point on the tube (with varied flow rates). In either case, a series of values for the extent of reaction is obtained at definite times after mixing. These values constitute the kinetic data required.

(c) It may be *abruptly* stopped after mixing, and observations made with a detector at a point quite near the mixer. In this case, unlike those of (a) and (b), the monitoring device must respond quickly to the rapid changes of concentration of species that occur in the stopped solution. These methods will now be discussed in detail.

3.3.1 Quenched Flow

A number of simple pieces of apparatus for using the quenched-flow method have been described.[25-30] One is shown in Fig. 3.2, with explana-

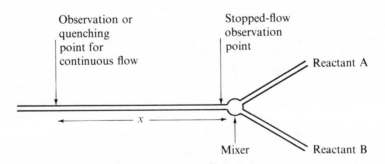

FIGURE 3.1 The operation of flow methods. The distance x and the combined flow rate govern the time that elapses between mixing and when the combined solutions reach the observation, or quenching, point. In the stopped-flow method, observation is made as near to the mixer as is feasible, and monitoring occurs after the solutions are stopped.

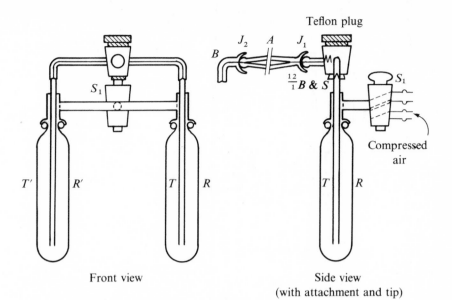

FIGURE 3.2 A simple quenched-flow apparatus.[30] The two reactant solutions in reservoirs R and R' are forced by air through stopcock S via tubes T and T'. They then pass through the mixing chamber M and pass along the reaction tube A and tip B and into the quenching mixture. The time of reaction (total volume traversed/flow rate) can be varied with different lengths of A. (For further details, see Ref. 30.)

tory legend.[30] By altering the volume of tubing between the mixer and the quencher or altering the flow rate, or both, or alternatively by adding quencher to the mixed solution with different delay times, a series of quenched solutions with different "ages" are obtained. These can be analyzed for the amount of reactant consumed.

Quenching can be effected by several means (Table 3.2), including rapid cooling,[25] precipitation of one reactant,[26-28] or chemical destruction such as by adding a complexing agent[29,30] or acid. The last-mentioned method is very effective for studying certain enzyme reactions.[31]

The quenched-flow method has been used particularly in studying several fairly rapid isotopic exchange reactions (Table 3.2). The use of radioisotopes necessitates a separation procedure (Sec. 3.13.3) so that the quenched flow is the only suitable flow technique that can be used when the exchange rate is too fast for a conventional (mixing) approach. Some of these reactions have also been studied, more conveniently, by nmr line-broadening methods (Sec. 3.6.8). The latter require fairly high reactant

TABLE 3.2. Some Rapid Isotopic Exchange Reactions Studied by Quenched Flow

Reactants pair	Second-order rate constant, M^{-1} sec^{-1}	Temp., °C	Quenching method	Ref.
$Fe(CN)_6^{4-}$, $Fe(CN)_6^{3-}$	2.3×10^{2a}	0.0	$(C_6H_5)_4As^+$ coprecipitates $Fe(CN)_6^{3-}$ in presence of $Co(CN)_6^{3-}$.	27
MnO_4^{2-}, MnO_4^{-}	7.1×10^{2b}	0.0	$(C_6H_5)_4As^+$ coprecipitates MnO_4^{-} in presence of ReO_4^{-}.	26
$IrCl_6^{3-}$, $IrCl_6^{2-}$	$\sim 2.3 \times 10^5$	25.0	2-Butanone extracts $IrCl_6^{2-}$.	28
Fe_{aq}^{2+}, Fe_{aq}^{3+}	8.4	25.0	Bipy complexes Fe^{II} rapidly and quenches exchange.	29
Fe_{aq}^{2+}, $FeOH_{aq}^{2+}$	3.0×10^3	25.0		29
Ag^I, Ag^{II}	1.0×10^3	0.0	Phen precipitates Ag^{II} rapidly.	30
$Al(H_2O)_6^{3+}$, H_2*O	$<70^c$	25.0	Add to chilled pentane ($-78°$).	25

a 0.01 M KOH.
b 0.16 M NaOH.
c sec^{-1}.

concentrations, so the subtleties of "inert ion effects" have been recognized only from the quenched-flow work, where lower concentrations may be used.

The base hydrolysis of complexes of the type $Coen_2Cl_2^+$ and $Coen_2ClBr^+$ proceeds rapidly (second-order rate constants 3.2×10^3 and $1.2 \times 10^4 \, M^{-1} \sec^{-1}$, respectively, at 25°). Nevertheless the rates are easily measured by mixing equivalent concentrations of Co(III) complex and OH$^-$ ions in a three-way tap and flowing the mixture for a short time before quenching the reaction by addition to acid. These Co(III) complexes hydrolyze quite slowly in acid solution so that estimation of halide ion in the quenched solution gives the extent of base hydrolysis in the time elapsing between mixing and quenching.[32]

The disadvantage of the quenched-flow technique is the tedium associated with the batch method of assay. Additionally, there is a relatively long reaction time limit, often $\geqslant 10$ msec, necessitated by the extended quenching times, although recent developments in this matter have been promising.[31] Offsetting these limitations are the simple equipment and the leisurely assay that are integral features of the method. For example, the study of xanthine oxidase by quenched flow and epr monitoring of the frozen solutions has proved very rewarding.[33]

3.3.2 Continuous Flow

The continuous-flow method suffers from the grave disadvantage of consuming relatively large, and in some cases prohibitively large, amounts of material. It has been virtually replaced by the stopped-flow method (Sec. 3.3.3) when spectral monitoring is used; but the continuous-flow method is still necessary when probe methods are used, which respond only relatively slowly to concentration changes.[31] These include pH[34] and metal-ion selective electrodes,[35] thermistors, and thermocouples, and also epr[36] and nmr detection. The continuous-flow method can be made the basis of a simple apparatus using conductivity monitoring.[37]

3.3.3 Stopped Flow

The stopped-flow technique is by far the most popular of the flow methods. Its greatest advantage is that it uses small volumes of material; also, it is easy to use and provides kinetic data that can be easily treated. Because of the mixing *and* stopping features, the stopped-flow method does give slightly longer resolving times (a few milliseconds) than the continuous-flow method does. Stopped-flow systems have employed nearly all the usual monitoring methods. Some that have been fully described are spectral,[38] fluorescent,[39] conductivity,[37] and thermal monotoring.[39] Some of these form the basis of commercial models (Fig. 3.3). The stopped-flow method has been used with polarographic detection, and it is superior in this use to continuous-flow, since flowing solutions can interfere with the diffusion layer around the electrode.[40] The linking of the flow method with nmr monitoring should represent an important monitoring combination.[41] Spectral monitoring is usually employed with the stopped-flow method. A popular "test" reaction is that between H^+ and HCO_3^- ions:[42]

$$H^+ + HCO_3^- \rightleftharpoons H_2CO_3 \rightarrow H_2O + CO_2 \tag{3.6}$$

The treatment of the raw data from spectral–stopped-flow experiments is deferred until later (Sec. 3.6.3). It is worth pointing out that some spurious traces that result from mixing effects can be obtained in stopped-flow experiments.[39,43]

3.3.4 The Application of Flow Methods to the Study of Complex-Ion Transients

The flow method is important for the measurement of certain properties of unstable species. The spectra of transients may be measured by rapid monochrometer scanning of a stopped-flow solution (which involves expensive and sophisticated[44] equipment), recording spectrophotometry of a continuously flowed solution (which uses large volumes of solution), or wavelength point-by-point measurement in a stopped-flow apparatus (cheap, but tedious). Such spectral data may be useful in defining certain thermodynamic characteristics, such as stability constant, of the transient.

The acid-base properties of a transient can be assessed by placing a glass electrode in a streaming fluid that is generating that transient a few msec (~ 10) after the mixer. The pH is measured when the electrode has come to equilibrium. A series of measurements will give the profile of the extent of protonation vs pH, from which a pK value may be determined in the usual manner. In this way the pK values of the various protonated forms of VO_4^{3-} could be measured before polymerization occurs, which takes place rapidly on protonation.[45] Similarly, the pK of $Co(NH_3)_5D_2O^{3+}$ may be measured in D_2O before exchange of the ammine H with D_2O takes place.[46]

The enthalpy of the reaction

$$HCrO_4^- + OH^- \rightleftharpoons CrO_4^{2-} + H_2O \tag{3.7}$$

may be determined in a thermal-flow apparatus from measurement of the very rapid heat change that occurs within the mixing chamber when

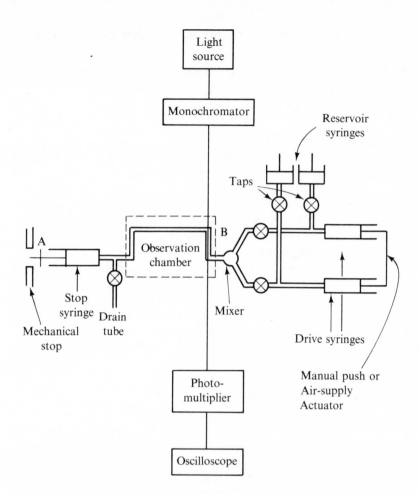

FIGURE 3.3 Block diagram of stopped-flow apparatus.[38b,86] Reagents from the reservoir syringes are transferred to the 2-ml drive syringes via taps. A small portion (about 0.25 ml) of the reactants in each syringe is pushed through the mixer and observation chamber into a syringe, where the flow is abruptly stopped when A hits a mechanical stop. The progress of the reaction in the portion of stopped solution in B is monitored spectrally. The spent solution in the stop syringe is ejected through a drain tube and the process repeated. Ultraviolet, or visible, light through a monochromator passes through the observation chamber to a photomultiplier and oscilloscope. Stopping the solution triggers the oscilloscope, which shows the current changes from the photomultiplier. These in turn reflect the changing light intensity arising from the absorption changes in B as the reaction proceeds. Usually, the oscilloscope trace is a direct measure of the concentration change of one of the reactants or products (see Prob. 2c, this chapter).

Cr(VI), which contains $HCrO_4^-$ and $Cr_2O_7^{2-}$, is treated with base. The parallel reaction

$$Cr_2O_7^{2-} + 2OH^- \rightarrow 2CrO_4^{2-} + H_2O \tag{3.8}$$

is slower and occurs after mixing.[47]

A combination of the continuous-flow method with epr detection has provided a powerful means for detecting organic or inorganic radicals in the early stages of oxidation or reduction reactions involving certain transition metal ions (see Sec. 2.2.1).[36,48] A flat cell about 10 msec from the mixer (at the maximum flow rates) is positioned in the microwave cavity of the epr apparatus. Care in interpretation of the results has been stressed in a searching analysis.[49]

Finally, by the use of multiple mixers, the chemical reactions of unstable intermediates can be studied. This approach, although little utilized yet, has great potential in complex-ion studies.[50] The reactions of the HO_2 radical, generated by mixing Ce(IV) with H_2O_2 (Sec. 2.2.1), can be studied after a second mixing with reagents.[50]

3.3.5   Accessible Rate Constants by Mixing Methods

It is the half-life of a reaction that will govern the choice of the initiation method, and it is the character of the reaction that will dictate the monitoring procedure. Reactions with relatively high rate constants at ordinary temperatures might still be measurable without recourse to the specialized techniques described in the previous sections.

Thus the half-life of a reaction with a kinetic order higher than one is lengthened as the concentration of the reactant in excesss is decreased (for example, Sec. 1.4.4). Provided that there is still a sufficient change of concentration during the reaction to be accurately monitored, quite large rate constants may be measured if low concentrations of reactants are used. The second-order redox reaction

$$Fe^{2+} + Co(C_2O_4)_3^{3-} \xrightarrow{H^+} Fe^{3+} + Co^{2+} + 3H_2C_2O_4 \tag{3.9}$$

can be followed at μM reactant concentrations because of the high molar absorptivity of $Co(C_2O_4)_3^{3-}$ (2.1×10^4 at 245 nm). The observed second-order rate constant, $1.2 \times 10^3 \, M^{-1} \sec^{-1}$ at 25°, $I \sim 0 \, M$, corresponds to *reaction times* of minutes.[51] It should be noted in this particular case, however, that additional features of the reaction show up when higher concentrations are used and the flow technique is applied (Sec. 3.6.2).

The concentration of a reactant (and the rate of a reaction) may be drastically reduced by adjustment of the pH. In the ring-closure reaction,

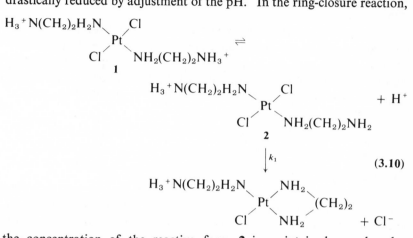

$$\tag{3.10}$$

the concentration of the reactive form **2** is maintained very low by working at pH ~ 3, far removed from the pK (8.0). It is in rapid equilibrium with the main species **1**, which can be easily monitored and whose rate of loss reflects the rate of loss for **2**. This permits k_1 (10.4 sec^{-1} at 25°) to be easily measured by a pH-stat method. (See Prob. 1a.) The value checks well with that determined spectrally by stopped flow at alkaline pH, where the predominant species is **2** and the k_1 step is measured directly.[52]

The rate of any reaction with a finite heat of activation will be reduced by lowering the temperature. Some reactions that are fast at normal temperatures were studied over twenty years ago by working in methanol at $-75°$, when quite long reaction times were observed.[53] Investigators have also used pH-stat methods at $-25°$ (2.7 M Mg(NO$_3$)$_2$).[54] A combination of flow method and low temperature ($-120°$) raises practical difficulties but permits the measurement of some diffusion-controlled reaction rates.[55]

Large second-order rate constants can be measured by flow methods, which must rank as the most important single aid to the kineticist in this area. Rate constants 10^7 to 10^8 M^{-1} sec^{-1} for certain redox reactions[38,56] and 10^6 to 10^7 M^{-1} sec^{-1} for substitution reactions[57] have been determined by spectral–stopped-flow methods. Recently, through improvements in cell design and by viewing down instead of across (Fig. 3.3) the observation tube, rate constants $>10^9$ M^{-1} sec^{-1} have been measured for a number of redox reactions; these being irreversible, are consequently not amenable to relaxation methods (see below).[58] If the spectral absorbance change accompanying a reaction is large, then there may still be sufficient absorption changes after the "loss" of reaction due to the deadtime (time for mixing and moving the solution from the mixer to the observation chamber). Thus, even with an instrument deadtime of 2 msec, reaction half-lives of 0.5 msec could be determined for the reaction of Cu(II) with glycine.[59]

Finally, it is worth mentioning that forward and reverse rate constants are related by an equilibrium constant for the process (for example, Sec. 1.5). Some care must be used, however, in the application of this approach.[60] Relatively high rate constants for the formation of nickel(II) complexes have been estimated from small and easily measured dissociation rate constants.

3.4 RELAXATION METHODS

If after adopting the various devices and ruses outlined in the previous sections the reaction is still too fast to measure, we must resort to methods in which a reaction change is initiated by means other than mixing, the so-called relaxation methods.

The amounts of species present in a chemical equilibrium may be changed by a number of methods. The rate of change of the system from the old to the new equilibrium, the *relaxation*, is dictated by (and is therefore a measure of) the rate constants linking the species at equilibrium (Sec. 1.8). Since such changes or perturbations can often be imposed in much shorter times than are involved in the mixing process, and since monitoring of very rapid processes rarely presents difficulties, reaction times may be extended to micro- and even nanoseconds. Obviously the rate constant for slow reactions, as well as those in the flow range, can also be determined by perturbation methods.[20,22,59,61] It is in the area of rapid reactions, however, that relaxation methods are most powerful and have been most applied.

Since the relaxation method demands only a small change in the concentrations of the reacting species (Sec. 1.8.1.), sensitive, as well as rapidly responding, methods of detecting these changes must be used, although these are invariably the same as with conventional and flow methods. The relaxation technique does not have the wide applicability associated with the flow method since one does not usually have, nor is it always easy to induce (say by pH or concentration adjustments), a reasonable degree of reversibility in a system. This is essential in order that measurable changes of concentration may be induced by the perturbation. However, relaxation methods cover time ranges not attainable by flow methods and have allowed the measurement of first-order processes with $k \geqslant 10^2 \sec^{-1}$, and certain second-order acid-base, complexation, and redox reactions. In addition, relatively small volumes of solution are required for most relaxation techniques and these can often be used repeatedly. The various types of relaxation techniques associated with specific perturbation modes will now be considered. These perturbations can be of two types: stepwise, meaning one abrupt change, and continuous, usually imposed as an oscillating perturbation.

3.4.1 Temperature Jump

The temperature jump is undoubtedly the most versatile and useful of the relaxation methods. Since the vast majority of reactions have nonzero values for the associated ΔH, a variation of equilibrium constant K with temperature is to be expected:

$$\frac{d \ln K}{dT} = \frac{\Delta H}{RT^2} \tag{3.11}$$

In the original and still most popular form of the apparatus,[62] electric heating is used, and temperature jumps of as much as 3° to 10° are obtained within μsec. The attendant concentration changes are usually monitored by absorption spectrometry. Fluorescence, polarimetry, and conductivity readouts have also been employed. There have been several full descriptions of temperature-jump equipment, some of which is now commercially available (Fig. 3.4).[63] Most experiments have been carried out on aqueous solutions, to which an electrolyte must be added for electrical conduction purposes. This is usually 0.1 M KNO_3 or KCl, neither of which presents any complicating features in the usual chemical systems. Some temperature-jump work in pyridine or pyridine-nitromethane mixtures uses tetraethylammonium perchlorate or chloride salts as inert electrolyte.[64] Temperature jump can be used for reactions involving dissolved gases, but then cavitational effects may last as long as 50 μsec and thus limit its application.[65]

Clever instrumental developments have improved the resolution time and sensitivity of the method. Laser heating has been used, and in principle any solvent may then be employed. Additives, for example inert dyes, must then be present to promote absorption at the laser wavelength, and these may interfere chemically. The stimulated Raman effect shifts the radiation emitted by Nd to longer wavelengths ($> 1 \mu$), where absorption by water is much greater. This approach has the promising features of dispensing with the dye additive, using small volumes of aqueous or nonaqueous solutions, a 25-nsec deadtime and a reasonable jump in temperature.[66] Microwave radiation heating of polar solvents requires no additives either, but the temperature rise is usually only small (~ 0.5)

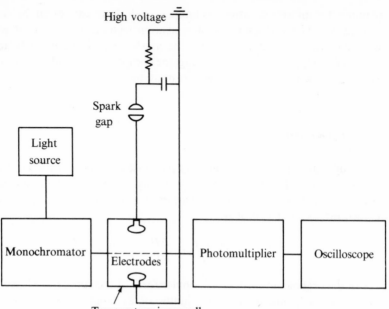

FIGURE 3.4   Block diagram of temperature-jump apparatus. The condenser is charged to 30–50 kilovolts and then discharged via a spark gap through the metal electrodes of the cell. This heats up a small portion of the solution some 3–10°. This portion is monitored spectrally in the same manner as with the flow apparatus.[63] An apparatus based on this arrangement was first manufactured by Messanlangen Studiengesellschaft, Göttingen, Germany.

and the more sensitive, and in certain respects less satisfactory, conductivity monitoring must be used.

Single-pulse perturbations have been replaced by repetitive excitation of the reaction, leading to an increased signal-to-noise ratio. The repetitive microwave pulses cause repetitive temperature jumps, and these are imposed on a flowing solution to prevent a continuous temperature rise. The jumps are about 0.5° and a time resolution of 10^{-5} sec can be achieved using only 0.1 ml of solution, with conductivity readout.[67]

Finally, a combination of the stopped-flow and temperature-jump methods has been successfully effected. This enables relaxation-type experiments on steady states, which are rapidly established but which may degrade further within seconds, thus precluding conventional temperature-jump experiments. The method has been applied so far only to certain enzyme systems.[68]

3.4.2 Pressure Jump

The expression

$$\frac{d \ln K}{dP} = \frac{-\Delta V}{RT} + \frac{V\alpha \Delta H}{C_p RT} + \beta \, \Delta\nu \qquad (3.12)$$

relates the variation of the equilibrium constant K with pressure,

where ΔV = molar change of volume in the overall reaction.

       ΔH = molar change of enthalpy.

       $\Delta\nu$ = change in the number of moles for the reaction.

       α = thermal coefficient of expansion.

       C_p = heat capacity at constant pressure for a volume of electrolyte solution V.

       β = isentropic compressibility.

Normally in aqueous solution, the first term is the major contributor ($>90\%$ of the total).[69] Usually the pressure change imposed is of the order of 50–150 atm; and since the sensitivity of the equilibrium constant is much lower to pressure change than to temperature change, conductivity monitoring is usually used.[70] This, together with the longer working times ($\geqslant 20 \, \mu$sec), renders the method much less useful and versatile than temperature jump. Attempts have been made to shorten the instrument times (to 1 μsec) by using shock waves to perturb the system.[71]

     The pressure change is usually brought about by rapidly rupturing, with a needle, a thin steel plate separating the system under pressure (compressed gas) from atmospheric pressure. No commercial setup is offered but the component parts are commercially available and there have been several good descriptions of the apparatus[69] and its application to the measurement of complexation rates in water[69] and in methanol.[72]

3.4.3 Electric-Field Jump

Any reaction occurring with a change in electric moment ΔM will show a dependence of the associated equilibrium constant K on the electric-field strength E:

$$\left(\frac{d \ln K}{dE}\right)_{P,T} = \frac{\Delta M}{RT} \qquad (3.13)$$

There is a modest increase in the electrical conductance with an increase in the electric-field gradient, an effect that operates with both strong and weak electrolytes (the first Wien effect). More important in the present context is the marked increase in electrical conductance of weak electrolytes when a high-intensity electric field is applied (second Wien effect). The shift in equilibrium in the field of high intensity arises from an increase in the concentration of ion pairs and hence in concentration of free ions relative to the concentration of the weak electrolyte. The magnitude of the effect is given by

$$\frac{\Lambda_x - \Lambda_0}{\Lambda_0} = \frac{(1 - \alpha)bE_x}{2 - \alpha} \tag{3.14}$$

where Λ_0 and Λ_x = conductances in the absence and the presence of the electric-field strength E_x.

   α = degree of dissociation of the weak electrolyte.

   b = a constant, being a function of the mobility and charge of the ions, the solvent dielectric constant, and the temperature.

Commonly, a 10^5 volt/cm field will produce a 1% change in conductance of weak electrolytes. The equilibria of the types

$$H^+ + OH^- \rightleftharpoons H_2O \tag{3.15}$$

$$HgCl^+ + Cl^- \rightleftharpoons HgCl_2 \tag{3.16}$$

can be perturbed by electric-field pulse methods, and the relaxation followed by conductivity methods, covering times as short as 0.05 μsec. A full description of the method has been given.[73]

   A single-pulse electric field with spectrophotometry detection has been recently exploited to characterize a very fast relaxation in the hemoglobin–O_2 reaction, seen but unresolved in the temperature-jump apparatus (see Fig. 1.8).[74] This is ascribed to a protein conformational change, with τ = 60–80 nsec (Fig. 3.5). The rapid interaction of alkali metals with murexide has also been measured by an electric-field perturbation technique.[75]

3.4.4 Ultrasonic Absorption

The methods so far discussed involve a single discrete perturbation of the chemical system with direct observation of the attendant relaxation. An oscillating perturbation of a chemical equilibrium can also lead to a hysteresis in the equilibrium shift of the system. This effect can lead to the determination of a relaxation time. The process will obviously be more complex than with discrete perturbations, and there will be problems in the monitoring.

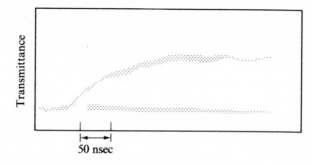

FIGURE 3.5   An example of an electric field jump relaxation. Spectral monitoring of a single pulse (60 kilovolts/cm) on a 43 mM sheep-oxyhemoglobin solution at pH 9 and 10 °C.   Monitoring is carried out at 580 nm.   The oscilloscope sweep rate is 50 nsec/cm, and the horizontal trace is the signal at zero field.   This relaxation corresponds to a very fast process that is seen but unresolved by the temperature-jump method (Fig. 1.8).[74]

Sound waves provide a periodic oscillation of pressure and temperature.[76]   In water, the pressure perturbation is most important; in non-aqueous solution, the temperature effect is paramount.   If ω ($=2\pi f$, where f is the sound frequency in cps) is very much larger than τ^{-1} (τ, relaxation time of the chemical system), then the chemical system will have no opportunity to respond to the very high frequency of the sound waves, and will remain sensibly unaffected.   If $\omega \ll \tau^{-1}$, then the changing concentrations of chemical species demanded by the oscillating perturbation can easily follow the low frequency of the sound waves.   In both cases there will be no absorption of sound.

Of greatest interest is the situation in which the relaxation time is of the same order of magnitude as the periodic time of the sound wave, that is, $\tau \approx \omega^{-1}$.   An amplitude and phase difference between the perturbation and the responding system develops and this leads to an absorption of power from the wave.   It can be shown that the sound absorption is proportional to $\omega\tau(1 + \omega^2\tau^2)^{-1}$ and that this value passes through a maximum at $\omega\tau = 1$.   Experimentally, one has then to measure the maximum attenuation of the wave as the ultrasonic frequency is changed. A variety of apparatus covers the frequency range 10^3 to 5×10^8 cps corresponding to relaxation times $\sim 10^{-4}$–10^{-9} sec.[77]   The disadvantage of the method at present is the number of complicated pieces of equipment required, as well as the relatively large concentrations of reactants used ($\geqslant 10^{-2}$ M) and the volumes of materials required for work at the lowest ultrasonic frequencies.   Figure 3.6 shows the excess sound absorption of $NiSO_4$ and $MnSO_4$ solution relative to water.[78]   Two maxima are clearly

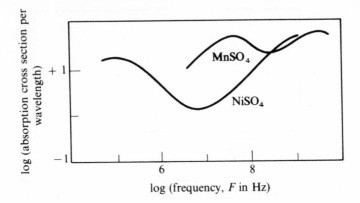

FIGURE 3.6   Excess (over water) absorption cross section per wavelength vs frequency for solutions of $NiSO_4$ and $MnSO_4$. Abscissa is in units of $Q\lambda (10^{-24}$ nep cm³$)$. The value of Q is $2\alpha/CN$, where α is the excess absorption coefficient, C the concentration of the electrolyte, and N Avogadros number.[78]

discernible for each salt. These maxima correspond to relaxation times $\tau_1 = (2\pi F_1)^{-1}$ and $\tau_2 = (2\pi F_2)^{-1}$.

3.5   THE METHODS OF MONITORING THE PROGRESS OF A REACTION

The rate of a reaction is usually measured in terms of the change of concentration, with time, of one of the reactants or products, $-d$[reactant]$/dt$ or $+d$[products]$/dt$, and is usually expressed as moles per liter per second, or M sec^{-1}. We have already seen how this information might be used to derive the rate law and mechanism of the reaction. Now we are concerned, as kineticists, with measuring experimentally the concentration change as a function of the time that has elapsed since the initiation of the reaction. In principle, any property of the reactants or products that is related to its concentration can be used.

It is obviously advantageous from a point of view of working up the data if the reactant property and concentration are linearly related. It is much easier and more likely to be accurate to monitor the reaction continuously in situ without disturbing the solution than to take samples periodically from the reaction mixture and analyze these separately, in the so-called batch method. The batch method cannot, however, be avoided when an assay involves a chemical method (which "destroys" the reaction). Separation of reactants or products or both also is necessary when an assay involving radioisotopes is employed. Separation prior to analysis is sometimes helpful when the system is complicated by a number of equilibria, or when a variety of species is involved.

Methods that have been used for monitoring slow and fast reactions are shown in Table 3.3. Several considerations will dictate the method chosen. If it is suspected that the reaction may be complex, then more than one method of analysis ought to be tried, so as to show up possible intermediates and characterize the reaction paths in more detail.

3.6 SPECTROPHOTOMETRY

Nearly all the spectral region has been used in one kinetic study or another to follow the progress of a chemical reaction.

TABLE 3.3.　Monitoring Methods for Slow and Fast Reactions

Method	Application
Spectral	
Ultraviolet and visible	Most popular method in slow, flow, and relaxation techniques, F, R.[a]
Fluorescence	In enzyme reactions, F, R.
Infrared	Some application to hydrogen exchange, F.
Polarimetry	Mainly limited to stereochemical change, R.
Nmr	Important in slow and fast exchange reactions, F.
Epr	Detection of free radical intermediates in flow experiments, F.
Probe Methods	
[H$^+$] change	Wide application. pH electrodes can be used in slow and flow methods; indicators and spectral for all techniques, F, R.
Ion electrodes	Ion-selective electrodes widely available, F.
Conductivity	Sensitive and rapidly responding monitor, F, R.
Polarography	Fairly specialized use, F.
Thermal	Using thermocouples or thermistors. Operational problems in flow, F.
Other Methods	
Volume or pressure changes	Useful when reactants or products are gaseous.
Isotopes	Basis of isotopic exchange method, F.

[a] F and R indicate method has value in flow and relaxation methods.

3.6.1   Ultraviolet and Visible Region

The optical absorbance D by a single chemical species A in solution is related to its concentration by the Beers-Lambert law:

$$D = \log \frac{I_0}{I_t} = \epsilon_\lambda \cdot l \cdot [\text{A}] \qquad (3.17)$$

where I_0 and I_t = incident and transmitted light intensities at wavelength λ.

ϵ_λ = molar absorptivity at a wavelength λ.

l = light path, in cm.

[A] = molar concentration of the species A.

Mixtures of species A, B, ... usually give additive absorbances,

$$\frac{D}{l} = \epsilon_\text{A}[\text{A}] + \epsilon_\text{B}[\text{B}] + \cdots \qquad (3.18)$$

and so it is possible to analyze changes in the concentrations of specific reactants or products from absorbance changes in the reaction mixture.

It is not difficult to show that the optical absorbance, or other properties for that matter, can be used directly to measure rate constants, without converting to concentrations.   Consider the first-order reaction

$$\text{A} \rightarrow \text{B} \qquad (3.19)$$

Omitting brackets to denote concentrations, we find:

At zero time, $D_0 = \epsilon_\text{A} A_0 + \epsilon_\text{B} B_0$ $\qquad (3.20)$

At time t, $D_t = \epsilon_\text{A} A_t + \epsilon_\text{B} B_t$ $\qquad (3.21)$

At equilibrium, $D_\text{e} = \epsilon_\text{B} B_\text{e} = \epsilon_\text{B}(A_0 + B_0) = \epsilon_\text{B}(A_t + B_t)$ $\qquad (3.22)$

Therefore,

$$A_0 = \frac{(D_0 - D_\text{e})}{\epsilon_\text{A} - \epsilon_\text{B}} \qquad A_t = \frac{(D_t - D_\text{e})}{\epsilon_\text{A} - \epsilon_\text{B}} \qquad (3.23)$$

$$\ln \frac{A_0}{A_t} = \ln \frac{(D_0 - D_\text{e})}{(D_t - D_\text{e})} = kt \qquad (3.24)$$

and a semilog plot of $(D_t - D_\text{e})$ vs t is linear with slope $-k/2.3$.   More difficult situations are discussed elsewhere.[79]   See also Prob. 2a.

Most commercial spectrophotometers read out optical absorbance directly, and combined with recorders, give a continuous record of absorbance, and therefore concentration changes, as the reaction proceeds. The application of spectral monitoring to the flow and relaxation methods is less straightforward, although still easy to use in practice (Sec. 3.6.3).

Visible and ultraviolet monitoring is particularly useful since few, if any, reactions of transition metal complexes are unaccompanied by absorption spectral changes in these regions.   There are distinct advantages in using absorbance in the visible region since there is less likelihood of interference from buffers and added electrolytes, which are usually transparent in this region.   However, the molar absorptivities of complex ions are often much higher in the ultraviolet, since they are based on charge transfer rather than on d–d transitions.   Consequently, lower concentrations of reactants with ultraviolet monitoring will, as the reaction proceeds, give absorbance changes that are comparable with the absorbance changes when the visible region is used.   A lower concentration means a greater economy in materials, but sometimes more important, a longer $t_{1/2}$ for all but first-order reactions.   Thus by working with μM concentrations of reactants and monitoring in the ultraviolet, it is possible to study the second-order redox reactions between Fe^{2+} and $Co(C_2O_4)_4{}^{3-}$ and Cr^{2+} and $Co(NH_3)_5X^{2+}$ by conventional[51] and by flow methods[57] respectively.

Low molar absorptivities may be accentuated by using long optical paths (increasing the value of l in (3.17)).   Indeed path lengths as long as 80 cm have been produced by a multiple reflection technique for the study of certain rapid reactions of the hydrated electron.[80]

A special and important application of spectrometry is in the measurement of rates of $[H^+]$ changes that accompany many reactions, by incorporating an indicator in the reaction mixture (Sec. 3.7(b)).

3.6.2   Isosbestic Points

The collection of a family of spectra as the reaction proceeds can be very informative.   *Isosbestic points* may be observed at one or more wavelengths, indicating that absorbance at these points remains constant as the reactant and product composition changes.   The occurrence of isosbestic points (preferably two or more) during a reaction strongly suggests that the original reactant is being replaced by *one* product, or if by more than one product, that these are always in a strictly constant ratio.   The absence of appreciable amounts of reaction intermediates can thus be implied.   A beautiful illustration of this is in the occurrence of seven isosbestic points in the relatively fast reaction of HgTPP with Zn(II) in pyridine (TPP = tetraphenylporphine) (Fig. 3.7).   The seven isosbestic points show that HgTPP converts to ZnTPP without formation of appreciable amounts of free TPP base, which has a different spectrum from either complex.[81]

The concept of the isosbestic point has been effectively used by Ingold and Tobe and their co-workers in their series of studies of hydrolysis of

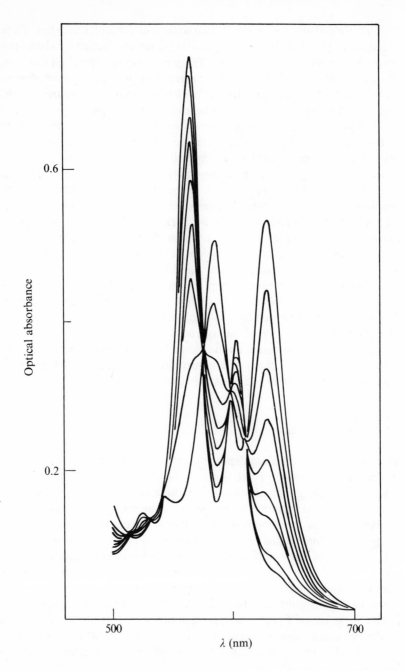

FIGURE 3.7   Seven isosbestic points observed during reaction of Zn(II) with HgTPP.[81]

cobalt(III) complexes, and more recently by Garner and his school in some corresponding studies of chromium(III) complexes.

In the hydrolysis of cis-$Cr(NH_3)_4(H_2O)Cl^{2+}$ in 1 M $HClO_4$, three sharp isosbestic points are observed, for at least 85% reaction, at 503 nm ($\epsilon = 35.5$), 433 nm ($\epsilon = 10.6$), and 368 nm ($\epsilon = 28.1$). This almost proves that the primary product ($\geqslant 95\%$) is cis-$Cr(NH_3)_4(H_2O)_2^{3+}$, which has ϵ values at 501 nm, 432 nm, and 368 nm, of 35.2, 10.0, and 27.5 respectively. It indicates that no significant amounts of $trans$-$Cr(NH_3)_4(H_2O)Cl^{2+}$ or $trans$-$Cr(NH_3)_4(H_2O)_2^{3+}$ are formed.[82]

The absence of isosbestic points in a series of reaction spectra that intersect at varying wavelengths may indicate the type of reaction complexity, for example, that it is a consecutive reaction,

$$A \to B \to C \qquad (3.25)$$

rather than (or as well as) a concurrent one,

$$A \overset{\nearrow B}{\underset{\searrow C}{}} \qquad (3.26)$$

The ratio [B]/[C] will vary in the former situation and remain constant in the latter.[6]

Somewhat esoteric discussions of the conditions for the occurrence of isosbestic points have been given.[83,84] Obviously the isosbestic principle is more easily applied to slow reactions since repetitive spectral scans of such reactions can easily be made. Rapid responding monochromators are now available and allow a series of spectral curves, albeit of poor resolution, even at intervals as short as 10 msec.[44]

Even in the absence of a spectral scan, reaction complexity can often show up (and be resolved) by studying the reaction at more than one wavelength, when different rate patterns may be observed.

The reaction of Fe^{2+} with $Co(C_2O_4)_3^{3-}$ (3.9) shows a simple optical absorbance decrease at 600 nm (Fig. 3.8), corresponding to a loss of $Co(C_2O_4)_3^{3-}$, which has a maximum at this wavelength, where no other reactant or product absorbs significantly. Now, examining this reaction at 310 nm shows that there are two steps (Fig. 3.8). The fast increase and slower decrease in absorbance correspond to the production and loss of an intermediate, $Fe(C_2O_4)^+$, which has a higher molar absorptivity at 310 nm than reactants or products:[85]

$$Fe^{2+} + Co(C_2O_4)_3^{3-} \xrightarrow{H^+} Fe(C_2O_4)^+ + Co^{2+} + 2H_2C_2O_4 \quad (3.27)$$

$$Fe(C_2O_4)^+ \xrightarrow{H^+} Fe^{3+} + H_2C_2O_4 \quad (3.28)$$

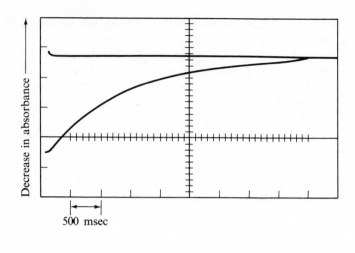

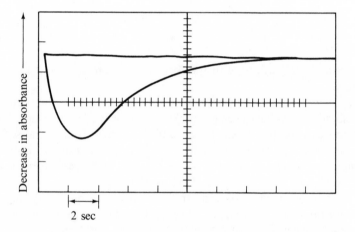

FIGURE 3.8   Stopped-flow traces in reaction of $Co(C_2O_4)_3^{3-}$ with
Fe^{2+}. $[Co(C_2O_4)_3^{3-}] = 1.0 \times 10^{-3} M$, $[Fe^{2+}] = 2.5 \times 10^{-2} M$,
$[HClO_4] = 0.92 M$, ionic strength $= 1.0 M$.   Upper curve shows
the disappearance of $Co(C_2O_4)_3^{3-}$; wavelength 600 nm; abscissa
scale, 500 msec per major division.   Lower curve shows the
formation and disappearance of the intermediate $FeC_2O_4^+$: wavelength, 310 nm; abscissa scale, 2 sec per major division.[85]

3.6.3   Spectral Monitoring of Rapid Reactions

In the usual electronic arrangement for monitoring spectral changes in a
reaction, monochromatic light, after traversing the reaction cell, impinges

upon a photomultiplier (Figs. 3.3 and 3.4). The current generated is converted into voltage (usually with amplification) and registered as a deflection of the y ordinate on an oscilloscope. This deflection is thus proportional to the light *transmitted* through the reaction solution. Most oscilloscope traces reported so far for flow and relaxation experiments thus denote a change of light transmitted with time (x ordinate on an oscilloscope) (see Fig. 3.8, for example). For small changes in transmittance these data can be used directly as a measure of concentration (see Prob. 2c). A commercial apparatus has a log amplifier incorporated so that transmittance can be automatically converted into absorbance, if desired. By placing a second logarithmic amplifier in series with the first, one can convert exponential curves for first-order reactions into a straight line, from which kinetic data can be obtained directly. This is equivalent to making the semilog plot.[86]

In recent developments, voltage output from the photomultiplier is interfaced with a computer to produce absorbance/time data and calculate rate constants.[39,87]

The deadtime of a flow apparatus (Sec. 3.3.5) represents a loss of reactants before an observation can be made. For a first-order reaction, this represents no problem, but it must be taken into account in converting oscilloscope traces into second- or other-order reaction rate constants. Since deadtimes are a few milliseconds, this loss is important only in the most rapid reactions, however.[88]

In a limited number of cases the spectral change accompanying a reaction may be too small to be useful, in which case fluorescent or polarimetric monitoring may then be feasible.

3.6.4 Fluorescence

The method is important in the study of reactions involving proteins because of the fluorescence quenching of certain residues, for example, tryptophan in the protein.[31,40] Thus the reaction of carbonic anhydrase with a wide variety of sulfonamides results in a substantial quenching of the fluorescence of the native protein. This attenuation of fluorescence can be used as a sensitive monitor for the progress of the reaction. Even reactant concentrations as low as 0.5–2.5 μM can be detected, thus bringing the reaction rates into the stopped-flow region, even although second-order rate constants as high as 10^7 are involved.[89] Fluorescence monitoring has been little used in the study of simpler complex-ion reactions, although its enhanced sensitivity, compared with sensitivity of spectral monitoring, could be an important consideration, particularly for following reactions involving aromatic-type ligands.

A nitromethane solution of Euterpy$_3$ (ClO$_4$)$_3$ fluoresces at 595 nm when irradiated at about 360 nm. This fluorescence decays when Tb^{3+} is added, and the rate of the reaction

$$\text{Euterpy}_3^{3+} + \text{Tb}^{3+} \rightarrow \text{Euterpy}_2^{3+} + \text{Tbterpy}^{3+} \qquad (3.29)$$

can be measured from the rate of fluorescence decay.[90]

3.6.5 Polarimetry

The polarimetric method naturally must be used when the stereochemical behavior of an optically active reactant is being investigated. The observation of isorotatory points (constant degree of rotation at specific wavelengths) can in principle give information similar to that obtained with isosbestic points (See. 3.6.2), although it has been little used.[91,92]

Polarimetry can also be used as an analytical means of following the course of a reaction in certain specific instances. The environment, and therefore optical rotatory power, of a resolved ligand will change during a chemical reaction and the rate of change of the rotation will be a measure of the reaction rate.[93]

The polarimetric method may sometimes be used to study an exchange reaction in which a rotational, but no net chemical, change is involved:[94]

$$\text{D-Co}^{\text{III}}(-)\text{PDTA}^- + \text{L-Co}^{\text{II}}(+)\text{PDTA}^{2-} \rightleftharpoons$$

$$\text{D-Co}^{\text{II}}(-)\text{PDTA}^{2-} + \text{L-Co}^{\text{III}}(+)\text{PDTA}^- \qquad (3.30)$$

The stereospecific coordination of $(+)$ or $(-)$PDTA to metal ions ensures that the optical rotation of Co(II)- and Co(III)-complexed ligands will differ substantially at some wavelengths. Complete racemization occurs when equivalent amounts of D-Co(III)$(-)$PDTA$^-$ and the $(+)$-PDTA complex of Co(II) are mixed.[94] For a description of a rate study involving a Perking-Elmer 141 photoelectric polarimeter with a potentiometric readout of optical rotation linked to a recorder, the reader is referred to Ref. 93.

3.6.6 Infrared Region

Direct monitoring by infrared absorption is not commonly used for the study of complex-ion reactions in water, because the solvent and dissolved electrolytes often absorb in this region. Infrared analysis has found some use however in studying H–D exchange processes in both substitution and redox reactions, using D_2O as the solvent since this does not absorb extensively in the near infrared. The exchange of deuterium for hydrogen in a series of metal ammine complexes has been studied in D_2O by monitoring the decrease of the N–H peak at 1.53 μm or the increase of the OH solvent band at 1.65 or 1.40 μm.[95]

$$Co(NH_3)_6{}^{3+} + D_2O \rightleftharpoons Co(NH_3)_5(NH_2D)^{3+} + HDO \qquad (3.31)$$

The large differences in the infrared absorption of $Ru(NH_3)_6{}^{2+}$ and $Ru(NH_3)_6{}^{3+}$ ions (Fig. 3.9) and the transparency of the deuterated forms in the same region form the basis for following the electron-transfer process:

$$Ru(NH_3)_6{}^{2+} + Ru(ND_3)_6{}^{3+} \rightleftharpoons Ru(ND_3)_6{}^{2+} + Ru(NH_3)_6{}^{3+} \qquad (3.32)$$

The reaction is monitored at 1.55 μm in acidic D_2O.[96] In this medium, exchange between coordinated ligands and solvent, that is, the reaction analogous to (3.31), is too slow to interfere. In principle, the nmr method can also be used to study these exchanges (see next section) but larger concentrations of reactants must be used and this can occasionally cause problems.[96]

Infrared monitoring is a most valuable means of tracing the progress of organometallic reactions in nonaqueous solvents. The CO, NC, and NO stretches in carbonyl, isonitrile, and nitrosyl compounds are very sensitive to the metal environment, and substitution reactions involving

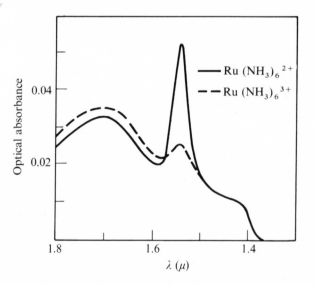

FIGURE 3.9 The near infrared spectra of $Ru(NH_3)_6{}^{2+}$ and $Ru(NH_3)_6{}^{3+}$ in D_2O.[96] μ represents microns (= micrometers).

such compounds are often accompanied by substantial infrared spectral changes. An early example of such a use is in the study of the reactions

$$Ni(CO)_2(PR_3)_2 \xrightarrow{PR'_3} Ni(CO)_2(PR_3)(PR'_3) \xrightarrow{PR'_3} Ni(CO)_2(PR'_3)_2 \quad (3.33)$$

in acetonitrile, from the carbonyl frequency changes.[97]

Similarly, the rates of the reaction (L = substituted pyridines) in CCl_4,

$$[Re(CO)_2(NO)Cl_2]_2 + 2L \rightarrow 2Re(CO)_2(NO)Cl_2L \quad (3.34)$$

have been determined by following the disappearance of the NO stretch at 1803 cm^{-1} due to the dimeric compound. The analogous band of the reaction product occurs at lower frequencies.[98]

Exchange of carbon monoxide between carbonyls and free CO can be examined by using the C–O stretching region:[99]

$$Ni(C^{16}O)_4 + C^{18}O \rightleftharpoons Ni(C^{16}O)_3(C^{18}O) + C^{16}O \quad (3.35)$$

These experiments are complicated by subsequent isotopic substitution leading to $Ni(C^{16}O)_2(C^{18}O)_2$ but this problem can be overcome. The advantages of in situ monitoring of this and similar exchanges over the use of a ^{14}CO radioisotope procedure are well documented.[100] The experimental advantages are, however, somewhat offset by the need of a good deal of spectroscopic theory for unequivocal interpretation of the data.[101]

3.6.7 Nmr Region

Nmr can be used simply as an analytical tool in which the strength of the signal is a measure of the concentration of a particular species. In principle, many chemical reactions could be studied by nmr, although it is likely to be inferior to the UV-visible spectral method. Its real advantage lies in the study of exchange processes, of which there have been a number of splendid examples. In particular, it has proven popular for studying H–D exchange between a complexed N–H grouping and D_2O.

The rate of deuteration of H in the sarcosine N–H group in $Co(NH_3)_4(NH(CH_3)CH_2COO)^{2+}$ can be measured by the rate of growth of the singlet up through a doublet at 2.45 ppm (Fig. 3.10). The doublet is assigned to the methyl group, which is split by the sarcosine N–H but not the N–D grouping. A semilog plot of the singlet-peak height vs time yields a value for k_D, the first-order deuteration rate constant (1.154).[102] There may be some concomitant D_2O exchange with the coordinated NH_3 but this does not interfere, emphasizing the advantage over the older approach that would measure total exchangeable hydrogen.[103] Similarly,

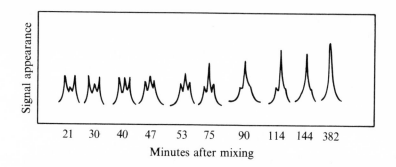

FIGURE 3.10   Deuteration at the sarcosine N in $Co(NH_3)_4$-$(NH(CH_3)CH_2COO)^{2+}$ ion. A 10% solution of the complex in $4.4 \times 10^{-4}\ M\ D_2SO_4$ at 33° was used. The growth of the singlet up through a doublet is used to measure the deuteration rate constant.[102]

the exchange of hydrogen between $Pt(NH(CH_3)CH_2CH_2NH_2)(NH_3)_2^{2+}$ and D_2O can be followed from the collapse of the methyl doublet as deuteration occurs. This spectral region is well separated from the spectra due to other protons.[104]

The exchange of metal-coordinated ligand with free ligand (which may also be solvent) can be measured by nmr in certain instances. The cis-$Coen_2(DMSO)_2^{3+}$ exchange with D_6–DMSO is measured from the rate of change of the area of CH_3-proton resonances of coordinated DMSO,[105] and the $Cr(H_2O)_6^{3+}$–H_2O exchange is estimated from the decrease of peak height of the ^{17}O peak in enriched H_2O.[106] (See Prob. 1, Chap. 4). The $NiEDTA^{2-}$–D_8-EDTA exchange is monitored by the area increase of the signal due to uncomplexed EDTA produced:

$$NiEDTA^{2-} + D_8\text{–}EDTA \rightleftharpoons Ni(D_8\text{–}EDTA)^{2-} + EDTA \quad (3.36)$$

Ni-coordinated EDTA protons are removed from the region of interest by the large metal paramagnetic contact shift.[107]

The exchange of EDTA with the labile Ca, Cd, Pb, and Sr EDTA complexes is very rapid,[107] and so if the previous approach were tried with these systems any changes would be complete after mixing and before examination in the sample tube. Another approach to determining these rates can be made, however, by nmr line-broadening measurements. These will be dealt with next, and represent an entirely different principle from the one used above.

The study of exchange processes by nmr has the tremendous advantage that it can be made in situ, circumventing the separation and laborious assay techniques that were used previously. It appears to have displaced the infrared method, at least in its application to diamagnetic complexes. One disadvantage of the method is the high concentrations (~ 0.5 to $1.0\ M$) of solute that must normally be used, which poses problems of solubility or stability.   More sensitive and more stable equipment now allows solutions to be used that are more dilute.

3.6.8   Nmr Line Broadening

The determination of the rates for fast exchange processes by nmr line-broadening experiments is playing a significant role in the understanding of the mechanisms of complex-ion reactions, particularly of substitution processes and stereochemical rearrangement.   There have been several comprehensive accounts of the application of nmr to the measurement of exchange rates.[108]

The same nucleus (say methyl protons) in different chemical environments A and B will generally have nuclear magnetic resonances at different frequencies.   If the exchange of protons between A and B is sufficiently slow, sharp lines corresponding to A and B will be recorded.   As the exchange rate increases however, it is observed that at first there is an initial broadening of the signals; this is followed by their coalescing, and finally, at high exchange rates, narrowing of the single signal occurs.

This behavior is well typified by the exchange[109]

$$Pt[P(OEt)_3]_4 + P(OEt)_3 \rightleftharpoons Pt[P(OEt)_3]_4 + P(OEt)_3 \qquad (3.37)$$

The methyl nmr of $Pt[P(OEt)_3]_4$ has a well-resolved triplet similar to that in the free ligand but shifted slightly downfield.   At temperatures below $40°$, the spectra of mixtures are additive and exchange is too slow to affect the signals.   Above $50°$ however, as exchange becomes important, the lines broaden until they coalesce at $70°$, and above $70°$ the methyl triplet appears at the average position but is still broadened.   Eventually at $90°$ and above, where exchange is very fast, the linewidth no longer decreases. The region between $50°$ and near to $70°$ is termed the *slow-exchange region*. That around the coalescence temperature is the *intermediate-exchange region*, and the region above $\sim 75°$ is the *fast-exchange region*.   Only the temperature region between $50°$ and about $85°$ can be used to assess exchange rates (see following discussion).

(*a*)   *Slow-Exchange Region.*   If the exchange rate is very slow, the lines due to A and B in the mixture correspond to the lines of the single components in both position and linewidth.

The broadening of the signal, say due to A, as the exchange rate increases, is the difference in full linewidth at half height between the exchange-broadened signal W_A^E, and the signal in the absence of exchange W_A^0. If the broadening of the lines is still much smaller than their separation and the widths are expressed in cps, or Hertz, then in this, *the slow-exchange region,*[110]

$$W_A^E - W_A^0 = (\pi\tau_A)^{-1} \tag{3.38}$$

The width W is related to the transverse relaxation time T_2 by the expression[111]

$$W = (\pi T_2)^{-1} \tag{3.39}$$

Now τ_A is the required kinetic information, since it represents the mean lifetime of the nucleus (for example, a proton) in the environment A.

$$\tau_A = \frac{[A]}{d[A]/dt} \tag{3.40}$$

τ_A^{-1} is the first-order rate constant k_A for transfer of the nucleus out of site A. Similarly for the signal due to B,

$$W_B^E - W_B^0 = (\pi\tau_B)^{-1} \tag{3.41}$$

$$\tau_B = \frac{[B]}{d[B]/dt} \tag{3.42}$$

and $$\frac{\tau_A}{\tau_B} = \frac{[A]}{[B]} = \frac{k_B}{k_A} \tag{3.43}$$

The slow-exchange region has been most useful in studying the rates of complex-ion reactions. It was used early to study the fast electron-transfer processes involving Cu(I)–Cu(II),[112] VO^{2+}–VO_2^+,[113] and MnO_4^-–MnO_4^{2-} [114,115] couples. This last exchange had been previously examined by quenched flow using radioactive manganese (Sec. 1.9 and Table 1.3).[26] The agreement in the results from the studies is good. Other more recent examples of the use of the slow-exchange region are the studies of the exchange of multidentate ligands between the free and complexed states[116] as well as ligand exchange in tetrahedral complexes,[117] optical inversion rates in Co(III) chelates,[118] and an impressive number of exchanges of solvent molecules between solvated cations and the bulk solvent (Table 4.15). In many of these systems, a paramagnetic species broadens the signal due to a diamagnetic one via the chemical exchange. Often only the diamagnetic species will have a signal because the paramagnetic one is broadened completely by the interaction of unpaired electron or electrons and the nucleus. The sole signal can still be used for rate analysis, however.

(b) Intermediate-Exchange Region. In the intermediate-exchange region, the separation of the peaks is still discernible. This separation (the chemical shift in cps) $\Delta\omega$ is compared with the separation in the *absence* of exchange $\Delta\omega_0$. With the conditions of equal populations of A and B, that is, $P_A = P_B$ and $P_A + P_B = 1$, $\tau_A = \tau_B$, and no spin coupling between sites:

$$\tau^{-1} = 2^{1/2}\pi(\Delta\omega_0{}^2 - \Delta\omega^2)^{1/2} = \tau_A{}^{-1} + \tau_B{}^{-1} \qquad (3.44)$$

Coalescence of lines occurs at

$$\tau^{-1} = 2^{1/2}\pi\,\Delta\omega_0 \qquad (3.45)$$

The use of the intermediate region to determine rate constants is less straightforward, although it is relatively simple to obtain an approximate rate constant at the coalescence temperature.[119,120] By fitting nmr traces to computer-generated curves for doublet collapse near coalescence, it has been possible to study the exchange of hydrogen between H_2O and some Pt(II) complexes of diamines and amino acids.[121]

(c) Fast-Exchange Region. The two lines have now coalesced to a single line. Exchange is still slow enough to contribute to the width, however. Eventually, when the exchange is very fast, a limiting single-line width is reached. In certain conditions in the fast-exchange region[122]

$$\tau^{-1} = 4\pi P_A P_B(\Delta\omega_0)^2(W^E - W^0)^{-1} \qquad (3.46)$$

where W^E and W^0 are the widths of the single broadened and final lines respectively.

A number of studies have used the slow-, intermediate-, and fast-exchange regions with consistent results.[116] Both the slow- and the fast-exchange regions were used to analyze the exchange between $Pt[P(OEt)_3]_4$ and $P(OEt)_3$ (3.37) with very good agreement between the resultant activation parameters. The intermediate region was not useful because of serious overlap of lines.[109] The most reliable method involves matching observed spectra with a series of computer-calculated spectra with a given set of input parameters including τ.[123]

The values of τ, τ_A, or τ_B, and the manner in which they vary with the concentrations of A and B, yield information on the rate law and rate constants.

Suppose that the mechanism for exchange between A and B is a dissociative one:

$$A \rightleftharpoons B + C \qquad k_1, k_{-1} \qquad (3.47)$$

$$V = \frac{\pm d[B]}{dt} = \frac{\pm d[A]}{dt} = k_1[A] \qquad (3.48)$$

Combined with (3.40) and (3.43), this yields

$$(\tau_A)^{-1} = k_1 \qquad (3.49)$$

and
$$(\tau_B)^{-1} = k_1 \frac{[A]}{[B]} \qquad (3.50)$$

The broadening of the line A from (3.38) will be independent of the concentrations of reactants and will equal k_1/π. The broadening of the line due to B from (3.41) will give a linear plot vs [A]/[B] of slope k_1/π.[124]

The problems in relating relaxation times to rate constants for more complicated exchanges is exemplified by the treatment of the methyl exchange between $Al_2(CH_3)_6$ and $Ga(CH_3)_3$.[125]

(d)   Chemical Exchange Involving a Paramagnetic Ion.   When the nuclei examined can exist in two environments, one of which is close to a paramagnetic ion, then the paramagnetic contribution to relaxation is extremely useful for determining the exchange rate of the nuclei between the two environments. This is undoubtedly the area on which nmr line broadening technique has had its greatest impact in transition metal chemistry, particularly in studying the exchange of solvent between metal coordinated and free (bulk) solvent.[126]   A variety of paramagnetic metal ions in aqueous and nonaqueous solvents have been studied.[127]

When a paramagnetic ion is dissolved in a solvent there will be, in principle, two resonance lines (due perhaps to ^{17}O or ^{1}H) resulting from the two types of solvent, coordinated and free. The conditions for separate signals are often not met however, and instead only a single line due to bulk solvent will be observed.[128]   The broadening of the line will follow the sequence outlined above as the temperature of the solution is raised.   A rigorous treatment of two-site exchange, considering the effects of a relaxation time and a chemical shift, has been made by Swift and Connick,[129] with some later modifications.[130]

The relaxation time is given by

$$\pi(W_A^E - W_A^0) = \frac{1}{T_2} - \frac{1}{T_{2A}} = \frac{P_M}{\tau_M} \left\{ \frac{\dfrac{1}{T_{2M}^2} + \dfrac{1}{\tau_M T_{2M}} + \Delta\omega_M^2}{\left[\dfrac{1}{T_{2M}} + \dfrac{1}{\tau_M}\right]^2 + \Delta\omega_M^2} \right\} \qquad (3.51)$$

where T_{2A}, T_2 = transverse relaxation times for bulk solvent nuclei alone, and with solute (concentration [M]), respectively.

T_{2M} = relaxation time in the environment of the metal.

τ_M = average residence time of the solvent molecule in the metal coordination sphere (coordination number n).

P_M = mole fraction of solvent that is coordinated to the metal $\sim n[M]/[\text{solvent}]$ for dilute solutions; $P_M/\tau_M = 1/\tau_A$.

$\Delta\omega_M$ = chemical shift between the two environments.

The subscripts A and M refer to bulk and coordinated solvent.

We can obtain the exchange regions outlined previously by considering various terms in (3.51) dominant.

(a)   If the chemical exchange is slow compared with the relaxation mechanism (which is incorporated in the terms $\Delta\omega_M$ or T_{2M}), that is,

$$\tau_M^{-2}, \quad T_{2M}^{-2} \ll \Delta\omega_M^2 \tag{3.52}$$

or
$$\tau_M^{-2}, \quad \Delta\omega_M^{-2} \ll T_{2M}^{-2} \tag{3.53}$$

then in either case

$$\frac{1}{T_2} - \frac{1}{T_{2A}} = \frac{P_M}{\tau_M} \tag{3.54}$$

Relaxation is thus controlled by ligand exchange between bulk and coordinated ligand. This, the slow-exchange region (II in Fig. 3.11), is most useful for obtaining kinetic data. Since $\tau_M^{-1} = k_1$, the pseudo first-order exchange rate constant, then a semilog plot of $1/P_M(1/T_2 - 1/T_{2A})$ vs $1/T$ will give an Arrhenius-type plot, from which k_1 at any temperature, and the activation parameters for exchange, may be directly determined.

$$\tau_M^{-1} = \frac{kT}{h} \exp\left(\frac{-\Delta H^{\ddagger}}{RT} + \frac{\Delta S^{\ddagger}}{R}\right) \tag{3.55}$$

It is clearly shown, for example, in Fig. 3.11, that at $T = 25\,°C$ $(1/T = 3.36 \times 10^{-3})$, $k_1 \simeq 3 \times 10^3\,\text{sec}^{-1}$.

(b)   If relaxation is controlled by the difference in precessional frequency between the free and coordinated states, that is, if

$$\tau_M^{-2} \gg \Delta\omega_M^2 \gg (\tau_M T_{2M})^{-1} \tag{3.56}$$

then
$$\frac{1}{T_2} - \frac{1}{T_{2A}} = P_M \tau_M \Delta\omega_M^2 \tag{3.57}$$

Now the linewidths *decrease* rapidly with decreasing τ_M (increasing temperature) and the anti-Arrhenius behavior is shown (Region III). Nevertheless the exchange rate constant can be determined if $\Delta\omega_M$ is known.

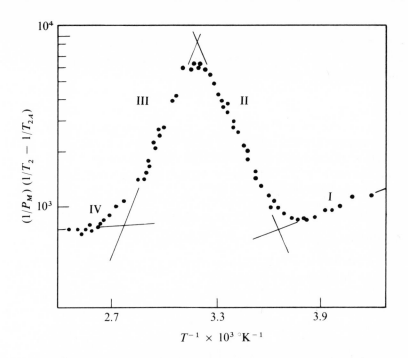

FIGURE 3.11   Temperature dependence of $(1/P_M)(1/T_2 - 1/T_{2A})$ for protons in CH_3CN solutions of $Ni(CH_3CN)_6{}^{2+}$ at 56.4 MHz. [From D. K. Ravage, T. R. Stengle, and C. H. Langford, *Inorg. Chem.*, **6**, 1252 (1967).]

(c)   If the T_{2M} process controls relaxation, that is,

$$(T_{2M}\tau_M)^{-1} \gg T_{2M}{}^{-2}, \quad \Delta\omega_M{}^2 \tag{3.58}$$

then
$$\frac{1}{T_2} - \frac{1}{T_{2A}} = \frac{P_M}{T_{2M}} \tag{3.59}$$

Now the linewidths no longer depend on the exchange rate and only vary slightly with temperature (Region IV).

Only rarely is the complete behavior that is depicted in Fig. 3.11 displayed by a single system. Caution must be exercised in the use of the approximate forms,[131] and computer fitting of the experimental data to the full equation is advisable.[132]

Although the treatment has been used mostly to study solvent exchange, obviously any exchange of an appropriate rate between free ligand and ligand coordinated to a paramagnetic metal may be measured by nmr line broadening.[117,133]

The chemical shift as well as the linewidth changes as chemical exchange becomes important. Chemical shift is used less frequently to estimate exchange rates with paramagnetic systems but is important in the study of diamagnetic ones.[126,129]

3.6.9 Epr Region

Electron paramagnetic resonance (epr) has found restricted use as an analytical method. It can be valuable when paramagnetic species are being consumed or formed, without marked electronic spectral changes, as in the acid-catalyzed reactions

$$Cr(CN)_2(NO)(H_2O)_3 + H_2O \xrightarrow{\text{H}^+} Cr(CN)(NO)(H_2O)_4{}^+ + HCN \quad (3.60)$$

$$Cr(CN)(NO)(H_2O)_4{}^+ + H_2O \xrightarrow{\text{H}^+} Cr(NO)(H_2O)_5{}^{2+} + HCN \quad (3.61)$$

Each chromium species gives characteristic narrow signals and the height of these are followed with time.[134]

Epr appears to be useful in distinguishing species such as $Ni(III)TPP^+$ cation from the isomer $Ni(II)TPP.^+$, in which the unpaired electron is associated with the ligand π-system (TPP = tetraphenylporphine). The slow decomposition of $Ni(III)TPP^+$ to the stable $Ni(II)TPP$ complex, via $Ni(II)TPP.^+$ can be followed by a combination of epr and optical spectroscopy.[135]

Epr is most effective in the study of mechanism by detecting free radicals that may occur as intermediates in oxidation and reduction reactions involving transition metal ions. Since these transients are invariably quite labile, epr is combined with the flow method to effect their detection.[136]

3.6.10 Epr Line Broadening

Another example of the use of spectral line broadening for rate measurement is by epr, although the method has been little used. It covers only a range of very short lifetimes, 10^{-4}–10^{-10} sec. The very rapid interaction of ligands with square-planar complexes at the axial positions are suited for treatment by epr line broadening, and examples include the reaction of $VOacac_2$ with py ($k = 1.0 \times 10^9 \ M^{-1} sec^{-1}$) and py derivatives,[137] solvent exchange at the axial position of $VO(DMF)_5{}^{2+}$,[138] and interaction of **3** with py ($k = 1.5 \times 10^9 \ M^{-1} sec^{-1}$) and other bases.[139]

$$(n\text{-Bu})_2N\text{---}C \underset{S}{\overset{S}{<}} Cu \underset{S}{\overset{S}{>}} C\text{---}N(n\text{-Bu})_2 + base \rightleftharpoons \text{5-coordinate adduct} \quad (3.62)$$

3

3.7　[H⁺] CHANGES

Except for direct spectrophotometry, the method of [H⁺] changes is the most versatile in use. Many complex-ion reactions are accompanied by a change in the hydrogen ion concentration. This may be as a direct result of the reaction under study or because of fast concomitant secondary reactions that monitor the primary reaction. The change of [H⁺] with time may therefore be used *qualitatively*, to give insight into the number of changes occurring during a reaction,[140] or as is more usual, *quantitatively*, to measure the rate of the reaction or reactions. There are basically two ways in which [H⁺] changes are measured in kinetic studies.

(a) Glass Electrode. The relationship

$$\text{pH} = -\log a_{\text{H}^+} \tag{3.63}$$

means that pH values read from a meter must usually be converted from activities into concentrations of H^+, $[H^+]$, by using activity coefficients, calculated, for example, from Davies' equation[141]

$$\log \gamma_\pm = \frac{-[A]z_1 z_2 I^{1/2}}{1 + I^{1/2}} + BI \tag{3.64}$$

At $I = 0.1\ M$, $A = 0.507$ and $B = 0.1$, and therefore

$$-\log [H^+] = \text{pH} - 0.11 \tag{3.65}$$

For experiments in D_2O, $pD = pH + 0.40$,[142] while for work in mixed aqueous solvents, an operational pH scale has been used.[143]

A small correction must therefore be made in estimating [H⁺] or [OH⁻] from the pH, when these concentrations have to be used for calculating the rate constants in [H⁺]-dependent rate laws. However, $d[\text{pH}]/dt$ can be used directly as a measure of $d[H^+]/dt$ provided that only small pH changes are involved in the reaction. Since the rates of many reactions are pH-sensitive, it is obviously sensible in any case to avoid a large pH change. Specialized apparatus has been developed that will measure a change as small as 0.001 pH unit in an overall change of 0.05 pH unit during the reaction. Such equipment has been successfully employed in the study of certain enzyme reactions.[144] An accurate pH meter and recorder can be used to study the interaction of metal ions and apocarbonic anhydrase, which is attended by small pH changes.[145] Obviously, the reaction must be sufficiently slow so that the meter or recorder response does not become rate-limiting. In certain cases, it may be necessary to add a small amount of buffer to keep the pH change reasonably small.

In a clever variation of the use of a pH change to monitor rate, the pH change is minimized by the controlled and registered addition of acid or base to maintain a constant pH during the reaction. The rate of addition of reagent is thus a measure of the pH change and the reaction rate.[146] The so-called pH-*stat method* has been exploited by the inorganic kineticist only in recent years. It has the decided advantage that reactions can be studied at a constant pH without recourse to buffers. It can only be used for reaction half-lives in the range 10 sec to a few hours, because of the slow response time, and possible electrode drift, over longer times.

The types of reaction for which pH monitoring is useful include:

1. Base hydrolysis of complex ions at pH $\geqslant$ 7, where the product is usually the hydroxo complex,[147]

$$Coen_2(RNH_2)Cl^{2+} + OH^- \rightarrow Coen_2(RNH_2)OH^{2+} + Cl^- \quad (3.66)$$

2. Formation or dissociation of complexes containing basic ligands, for example,[148]

$$Nien(H_2O)_4^{2+} \rightleftharpoons Ni(H_2O)_6^{2+} + en \quad (3.67)$$

$$en \xrightarrow{H^+} enH^+ \xrightarrow{H^+} enH_2^{2+} \quad (3.68)$$

The dissociation of $Ni(NH_3)(H_2O)_5^{2+}$ at $-30°$ was one of the earliest studies by pH-stat methods.[54]

3. Spontaneous and metal-ion-catalyzed base hydrolysis of esters, amides, and so on,[2,149,150]

$$\quad (3.69)$$

(b)   Indicators. It may be more convenient, or even essential in certain cases, to avoid the glass electrode and register $d[H^+]/dt$ using an appropriate acid-base indicator. This is usually necessary in the study of rapid reactions, although glass electrodes have been incorporated into continuous-flow apparatus (Sec. 3.3.2). The acid-base equilibrium involving the indicator is usually established rapidly and will not be rate-limiting with flow measurements, but may have to be considered with temperature-jump experiments, carried out at the shortest times. Some useful indicators that have been used are bromochlorophenol blue ($pK = 4.0$), bromocresol green (4.7), chlorophenol red (6.0), bromothymol blue (7.1), and phenol red (7.5). The figure in parenthesis is the pK, and therefore the optimum pH value at which the indicators may be used.

3.8 CATION AND ANION CONCENTRATION CHANGES

Electrodes are now available for the selective determination of the concentration of a large number of cations and several anions.[35] The reactions

$$Fe^{3+} + F^- \rightleftharpoons FeF^{2+} \tag{3.70}$$

$$\textit{trans-}Pt(CN)_4Br_2{}^{2-} + OH^- \rightarrow \textit{trans-}Pt(CN)_4Br(OH)^{2-} + Br^- \tag{3.71}$$

have been followed using fluoride- or bromide-sensitive electrodes,[151] with results that compare well with those obtained by other means. The relatively slow response of glass and liquid membrane electrodes, and also their inability to withstand abrupt stoppage, require that they be used in a continuous-flow arrangement if they are to be used to monitor fast reactions. Stopped flow may be used with solid crystal membrane electrodes.

Ion-selective electrodes may have particular utility in the study of reactions with low spectral absorbance changes and in the assay of ions difficult to analyze otherwise, namely alkali metals and alkaline earth metals, and F^-, $NO_3{}^-$, or $ClO_4{}^-$ ions.

3.9 CONDUCTIVITY

The conductivity method of monitoring has not been widely used but it has occasionally been valuable for studying specific reactions. It can cope with a wide variety of rates. Conductivity is a colligative effect and rarely shows up the fine reaction detail possible with spectral measurements. It is fairly convenient to use in flow methods, and has decided value in relaxation techniques since in these the changes of concentration of reactants are usually small and conductivity is a very sensitive and rapidly registered property. High concentrations of nonreacting electrolyte are to be avoided, since otherwise the conductivity changes would be relatively small, superimposed on a large background conductivity. In addition, the use of conductivity monitoring in nonaqueous solution is sometimes precluded because of complicating ionic association, an important factor in this medium.[152]

A good example of use of the conductivity method is in the study of the hydrolysis of cobalt(III) complexes,[38,153] for example,

$$CotrienCl_2{}^+ + H_2O \rightarrow Cotrien(H_2O)Cl^{2+} + Cl^- \tag{3.72}$$

In a typical run the total resistance change would be 45 ohms, measurable to ± 0.01 ohm with a precision conductance bridge.[153]

3.10 THERMAL CHANGES

If a reaction is accompanied by a change in ΔH, then the temperature of that reaction sensed with time is a measure of the extent of the reaction with time, that is, the rate. The difference between the temperature of a reaction mixture and a reference solution is monitored with sensitive thermistors. The reference solution is identical to the reaction mixture solution except for absence of one of the reactants. Both solutions are contained in identical vessels. Heat changes of 1 millidegree and reaction times as short as 2 sec can be measured in an apparatus that is described for determining the rate of the reaction[154]

$$MgCyDTAH^- + Pb^{II} \rightarrow PbCyDTA^{2-} + Mg^{II} + H^+ \qquad (3.73)$$

The method has been linked with flow techniques for measuring rapid reactions and for determining ΔH values associated with rapid pre-equilibria (see Sec. 3.3.4).

3.11 POLAROGRAPHY

For polarography to be potentially useful, one of the species in the reaction must give a polarographic wave, and this is less likely than that one of the reactants will have some useful spectral feature. The limiting current at a given potential is a measure of the concentration of the species involved and so the change of waveheight with time is recorded. The reactions[155,156]

$$Cr(NH_3)_5Br^{2+} + H_2O \longrightarrow Cr(NH_3)_5H_2O^{3+} + Br^- \qquad (3.74)$$

$$Cr(CN)_5NO^{3-} + H_2O \xrightarrow{H^+} Cr(CN)_4(H_2O)NO^{2-} + HCN \qquad (3.75)$$

as well as a large number of substitution reactions of polyaminocarboxylate complexes studied particularly by Tanaka and other Japanese schools[157] illustrate the types of system amenable to the polarographic approach. Zuman has tabulated the polarograms that might arise in a variety of reaction schemes.[158] The polarographic method rarely has any obvious advantages over other methods, although it is straightforward to use.

Polarographic probes that respond specifically to concentrations of O_2, CO_2, or SO_2 are available. Their use is limited to slow reactions or the continuous-flow approach, governed by the relatively long response time of the probe (for example, 90% in 10 sec for O_2 probe). These probes have, however, decided advantages over the more clumsy mano-metric monitoring.

　　The polarographic technique can be used to measure the rates of rapid reactions.[158]　Because an "internal" process is examined, the problem of mixing is avoided, as it is in relaxation methods.

　　The rate of diffusion of a species (which can be oxidized or reduced) to an electrode surface competes with the rate of a chemical reaction of that species, for example,

$$Cd + 4CN^- \xrightleftharpoons[\text{electrode}]{2e} Cd(CN)_4{}^{2-} \underset{k_{-1}}{\overset{k_1}{\rightleftharpoons}} Cd(CN)_3{}^- + CN^- \quad (3.76)$$

Values of k_1 and k_{-1} may be extracted from the polarographic data.　The treatment of the results is complex, and occasionally leads to absurdly high rate constants.

　　There are a number of different ways in which the method may be used, including reflection spectroscopy at optically transparent electrodes. In this way, the rate constant k_1 for the reaction

$$Ta_6Br_{12}{}^{2+} + Ta_6Br_{12}{}^{4+} \rightleftharpoons 2Ta_6Br_{12}{}^{3+} \quad k_1, k_{-1} \quad (3.77)$$

has been determined ($6.9 \times 10^7 \, M^{-1} \sec^{-1}$ at 25°).[159]

3.12　PRESSURE CHANGES

Reactions accompanied by gas evolution or absorption may be followed by measuring the change in pressure in a sealed vessel equipped with a manometer.　A sketch and description of such an apparatus, simple in design, has been given.[160,161]　Other useful apparatus is described in the studies of the decarboxylation of dimethyloxaloacetic acid[162] and the decomposition of hydrogen peroxide[163] (both reactions catalyzed by metal complexes), the reactions of CO with Ru(II)–Cl complexes,[164] and the homogeneous reduction of transition metal complexes by H_2.[165]　It is essential to check that the rate of equilibration between dissolved gas in and above the solution or the manipulation times in using the manometer, or both, are not being measured and thus mistaken for a (faster) reaction rate.[166]

3.13　BATCH METHODS

All the methods described above have been amenable to continuous monitoring as the reaction proceeded.　In the remaining methods, the batch method must be used, in which aliquots of the reaction mixture are removed at various times and analyzed.

3.13.1   Chemical Methods

In years past, the hydrolysis of ions such as $Co(NH_3)_5Cl^{2+}$ or cis-$Coen_2F_2^+$ has been studied by volumetric analysis of liberated chloride or fluoride ions respectively.   Such purely chemical methods of assay have been largely superseded by continuous monitoring of the hydrolyzed substrate, based on some physical property.   Chemical methods do have the advantage, however, of analyzing *specific* reactants, usually after a separation, and should always be used (at least in one run) to check the stoichiometry of the reaction if this is in doubt, and to monitor reactions that may have irritating side reactions.   An excellent example of the technique is in the analysis of the rate of the base hydrolysis of carboxylatopentaminecobalt(III) ions.[167]

3.13.2   Radioisotopic Assay

The use of radioisotopes as an analytical tool, although somewhat laborious, has decided value.   Because of the high sensitivity of radioisotope assay, mM or less concentrated solutions of complexes can be examined, and in this way the effect on the rate of low ionic strengths (for which the Debye-Hückel treatment is most applicable) or low concentration of ions can be assessed.   The rates of hydrolysis of $Co(NH_3)_5Cl^{2+}$ and $Cr(NH_3)_5Cl^{2+}$ have been very carefully measured by radioisotopic monitoring.[168]   The radioactive Cl^- liberated by hydrolysis of the chloride-labeled complexes is radioassayed in the effluent after separation from the cation complexes using cation exchange paper or resin.   The reaction

$$Co(NH_3)_5PO_4 + H_2O \rightleftharpoons Co(NH_3)_5H_2O^{3+} + PO_4^{3-} \qquad (3.78)$$

has been studied using 32-phosphorus-labeled complexes.[169]   The spectral changes are insufficient for easy analysis.

3.13.3   Isotopic Exchange

The study of an exchange reaction (Sec. 1.9) in which an atom or group of atoms X is transferred from one environment in AX to another in BX is made possible by using labeled X.   Before 1934, only exchange reactions involving heavy elements, which had naturally occurring radioactive isotopes, could be studied by tracer methods.   The production of artificial radioisotopes in 1934, and later the development of the atomic energy program and the production of electronic equipment, stimulated a good deal of study of isotopic exchange reactions by radiotracers in the period 1945–1960.[103]

History has now completed a full circle with renewed interest in the naturally occurring isotopes such as ^{2}H and ^{17}O. We have already alluded to the use of infrared and nmr monitoring for studying exchange reactions in situ. In using radioisotopes to study exchange processes, we must necessarily use the batch method.

Consider the exchange

$$CrN_3{}^{2+} + *Cr^{2+} \rightleftharpoons *CrN_3{}^{2+} + Cr^{2+} \tag{3.79}$$

in which *Cr is transferred from Cr^{2+} to the monoazide complex of Cr(III).[170] Chromium(III) perchlorate containing a small amount of $^{51}Cr^{3+}$ is reduced with Zn/Hg. This solution is mixed with $CrN_3{}^{2+}$, and at various times after mixing, aliquots of the reaction mixture are withdrawn and the exchange stopped by converting Cr(II) to Cr(III) with Fe(III). The $CrN_3{}^{2+}$ is separated from Cr^{3+} by ion exchange and the specific activity of the former determined. Ion-exchange separation is preferred to methods involving precipitation or extraction, since the latter often "induce" exchange.[171]

3.14 COMPETITION METHODS[172]

Occasionally it is as useful to obtain *relative* rate constants for a series of reactants acting on a common substrate as it is to have actual rate values. Relative rate constants are obtained by competition methods, which avoid the kinetic approach entirely. The method is well illustrated[173] by considering the second-order reactions of two Co(III) complexes Co_A^{III} and Co_B^{III}, which might, for example, be $Co(NH_3)_5Cl^{2+}$ and $Co(NH_3)_5Br^{2+}$, with a common reductant Cr(II), leading in this case to $CrCl^{2+}$ and $CrBr^{2+}$, respectively:

$$Co_A^{III} + Cr^{II} \rightarrow Co^{II} + Cr_A^{III} \qquad k_A \tag{3.80}$$

$$Co_B^{III} + Cr^{II} \rightarrow Co^{II} + Cr_B^{III} \qquad k_B \tag{3.81}$$

If Cr(II) is used in deficiency, that is, if the starting conditions are $[Cr^{II}]_0 < [Co_A^{III}] + [Co_B^{III}]$, then when the reaction is complete it is clear that the ratio of Co(III) complexes remaining, $[Co_A^{III}]_e/[Co_B^{III}]_e$, will be related to their relative reactivities, since

$$\frac{-d[Co_A^{III}]}{dt} = k_A[Co_A^{III}][Cr^{II}] \tag{3.82}$$

$$\frac{-d[Co_B^{III}]}{dt} = k_B[Co_B^{III}][Cr^{II}] \tag{3.83}$$

$$\log \frac{[Co_B^{III}]_e}{[Co_B^{III}]_0} = \frac{k_B}{k_A} \log \frac{[Co_A^{III}]_e}{[Co_A^{III}]_0} \tag{3.84}$$

In practice, a solution containing both Co(III) species is added rapidly with very good stirring to the Cr(II) solution. After reaction, the solution is analyzed and the percentage of Co(III) species remaining is assessed. It is convenient if $[Co_A^{III}]_0 = [Co_B^{III}]_0 = [Cr^{II}]_0$ so that (3.84) becomes

$$\log \frac{[Co_B^{III}]_e}{[Co_B^{III}]_0} = \frac{k_B}{k_A} \log \left\{ 1 - \frac{[Co_B^{III}]_e}{[Co_B^{III}]_0} \right\} \tag{3.85}$$

Thus if 86% of the Co(III) remaining is assigned to Co_B^{III}, $k_B/k_A = 0.08$.

The method is useful for obtaining comparative rate constants for fast reactions without recourse to sophisticated equipment and with results probably as accurate as by the direct method.[174] In addition, the variation of the product ratios with temperature allows accurate determination of *small* differences in the heats of activation for two processes.[175]

3.14.1 Isotope Fractionation

Probably the most powerful application of the competition method is in *isotope fractionation experiments*. These allow determination of the relative rates of reactants with different isotopic composition. Co_A^{III} in (3.80) might be $Co(NH_3)_5H_2{}^{16}O^{3+}$ and Co_B^{III} in (3.81) might be $Co(NH_3)_5H_2{}^{18}O^{3+}$. By examining the $^{16}O/^{18}O$ contents of the Co(III) complex remaining after all the other reactant (Cr(II) or V(II), for example) has disappeared, one can determine $k_{^{16}O}/k_{^{18}O}$, their relative rate constants, obtaining thereby the isotopic fractionation factor f. Since the rate constants are so close (the value of f is 1.020 for V(II) reduction[176]), separate studies of the two reactions could not possibly yield the desired accuracy. The $^{16}O/^{18}O$ ratio in the complex, converted to H_2O by heating and thence equilibrating with CO_2 for assay, can however be accurately determined by mass spectrometry. An accurate value for f can thence be obtained, although the treatment and procedure are complicated.

In the reaction of a cobalt(III) aqua complex containing ^{16}O and ^{18}O with another reagent,[177]

$$f = \frac{k_{^{16}O}}{k_{^{18}O}} = \frac{d \ln [^{16}O]}{d \ln [^{18}O]} = \frac{[^{18}O]}{[^{16}O]} \cdot \frac{d[^{16}O]}{d[^{18}O]} \tag{3.86}$$

It can be shown that[178]

$$f = \frac{\ln \alpha (1 - N_t)/(1 - N_0)}{\ln \alpha (N_t/N_0)} \sim \frac{\log \alpha}{\log \alpha (N_t/N_0)} \tag{3.87}$$

where $\alpha = [Co(III)]_t/[Co(III)]_0$, the fraction of complex sample left unreduced at time t, which may conveniently be designated when all the other reagent is consumed.

$N_t, N_0 =$ mole fractions of ^{18}O in complex after partial reduction and initially.

TABLE 3.4. Oxygen Isotopic Fractionation in the Reaction of *trans*-$Cr(NH_3)_4(H_2O)Cl^{2+}$ with Cr^{II} at $25°$[179]

α	N_t/N_0	k_{16_O}/k_{18_O}
0.283	1.0216	1.0174
0.218	1.0270	1.0178
0.214	1.0266	1.0173
0.197	1.0277	1.0171
0.195	1.0274	1.0168
0.190	1.0291	1.0176
0.177	1.0271	1.0157
0.159	1.0333	1.0182
0.118	1.0355	1.0168

NOTE: [Complex] = 0.28 M; $[H^+]_i = 2.0\ M$; $I = 2.8$; $T = 15°$.

In the reduction of *trans*-$Cr(NH_3)_4(H_2O)Cl^{2+}$ by Cr^{2+}, there is substantial fractionation of ^{16}O in the ligated water, so that N_t/N_0 increases steadily as the extent of the reaction increases (Table 3.4).[179] The computed value of $f(1.0172)$ remains constant however. If ^{18}O-enriched complex were used, allowance would have to be made for any exchange of it with H_2O of normal composition.[179]

REFERENCES

1. A. Samuni and G. Czapski, *J. Chem. Soc., A*, 487 (1973); G. Davies and B. Warnquist, *Coordn. Chem. Rev.*, **5**, 349 (1970).
2. R. W. Hay and L. J. Porter, *J. Chem. Soc., A*, 127 (1969).
3. D. E. Tallman and D. L. Leussing, *J. Amer. Chem. Soc.*, **91**, 6253, 6256 (1969).
4. D. D. Perrin and J. G. Sayce, *Talanta*, **14**, 833 (1967).
5. J. M. Veigel and C. S. Garner, *Inorg. Chem.*, **4**, 1569 (1965).
6. K. S. Mok and C. K. Poon, *Chem. Commun.*, 1358 (1971).
7. R. Koren and B. Perlmutter-Hayman, *Israel J. Chem.*, **8**, 1 (1970).
8. K. G. Brandt, P. C. Parks, G. H. Czerlinski, and G. P. Hess, *J. Biol. Chem.*, **241**, 4180 (1966).
9. J. F. Bunnett, in Friess, Lewis, and Weissberger, Chap. 6, directs attention to the various points that should be considered before and after a kinetic study.
10. J. Veprek-Siska and A. Hasneoll, *Chem. Commun.*, 1167 (1968).

11. D. L. Ball and J. O. Edwards, *J. Amer. Chem. Soc.*, **78**, 1125 (1956).
12. J. Veprek-Siska and V. Ettel, *J. Inorg. Nucl. Chem.*, **31**, 789 (1969).
13. S. C. Chan and C. W. Fung, *J. Inorg. Nucl. Chem.*, **33**, 569 (1971).
14. a. J. G. Pritchard and F. A. Long, *J. Amer. Chem. Soc.*, **79**, 2365 (1957).
    b. N. F. Good, G. D. Winget, W. Winter, T. N. Connolly, S. Izawa, and R. M. M. Singh, *Biochem.*, **5**, 467 (1966).
15. S. F. Lincoln and D. R. Stranks, *Aust. J. Chem.*, **21**, 1745 (1968).
16. T. J. Williams and C. S. Garner, *Inorg. Chem.*, **9**, 2058 (1970).
17. E. J. Hart, S. Gordon, and J. K. Thomas, *J. Phys. Chem.*, **68**, 1271 (1964).
18. R. A. Bauer and F. Basolo, *Inorg. Chem.*, **8**, 2237 (1969).
19. J. R. Graham and R. J. Angelici, *Inorg. Chem.*, **6**, 2082 (1967).
20. J. H. Swinehart and G. W. Castellan, *Inorg. Chem.*, **3**, 278 (1964); J. H. Swinehart, *J. Chem. Educ.*, **44**, 524 (1967), gives a full description of the study of the equilibrium $Cr_2O_7^{2-} + H_2O \rightleftharpoons 2HCrO_4^-$ by changing the total concentration of Cr(VI) and watching the concomitant spectral changes on a recording spectrophotometer.
21. J. E. Taylor and S. L. Arora, *Chem. Instr.*, **1**, 353 (1969).
22. R. Thompson and G. Gordon, *J. Sci. Instrum.*, **41**, 408 (1964); B. Perlmutter-Hayman and H. A. Wolff, *Israel J. Chem.*, **3**, 155 (1965); R. C. Patel, G. Atkinson, and R. J. Boe, *J. Chem. Educ.*, **47**, 800 (1970).
23. In addition to the Selected Bibliography, see Q. Gibson, *Ann. Rev. Biochem.*, **35**, 435 (1966), and L. I. Budarin and K. B. Yatsimirski, *Russ. Chem. Rev.*, **37**, 209 (1968).
24. F. J. W. Roughton, in Friess, Lewis, and Weissberger, Chap. 14. Even a three-way capillary T-tap may make an effective mixer for reactions with $t_{1/2} \geqslant 10$ msec.
25. H. Baldwin and H. Taube, *J. Chem. Phys.*, **33**, 206 (1960).
26. J. C. Sheppard and A. C. Wahl, *J. Amer. Chem. Soc.*, **79**, 1020 (1957).
27. R. J. Campion, C. F. Deck, P. King, Jr., and A. C. Wahl, *Inorg. Chem.*, **6**, 672 (1967).
28. P. Hurwitz and K. Kustin, *Trans. Faraday Soc.*, **62**, 427 (1966).
29. M. R. Chakrabarty, J. F. Stephens, and E. S. Hanrahan, *Inorg. Chem.*, **5**, 1617 (1966).
30. B. M. Gordon and A. C. Wahl, *J. Amer. Chem. Soc.*, **80**, 273 (1958).
31. H. Gutfreund, in *Methods in Enzymology*, Chap. 7.
32. S. C. Chan and M. L. Tobe, *J. Chem. Soc.*, 4531 (1962).
33. R. C. Bray, G. Palmer, and H. Beinert, *J. Biol. Chem.*, **239**, 2667 (1964); V. Massey, P. E. Brumby, and H. Komai, *J. Biol. Chem.*, **244**, 1682 (1969).
34. J. A. Sirs, *Trans. Faraday Soc.*, **54**, 207 (1958).
35. G. A. Rechnitz, *Accounts Chem. Research*, **3**, 69 (1970).
36. D. C. Borg, *Nature*, **201**, 1087 (1964).
37. R. G. Pearson, R. E. Meeker, and F. Basolo, *J. Amer. Chem. Soc.*, **78**, 709 (1956); J. J. Pescatore, M. Cefola, and J. J. Casazza, Jr., *J. Chem. Educ.*, **47**, 86 (1970).

38. Rapid mixing and sampling techniques in biochemistry: G. Dulz and N. Sutin, *Inorg. Chem.*, **2**, 917 (1963); Q. H. Gibson and L. Milnes, *Biochem. J.*, **91**, 161 (1964). J. I. Morrow, *Chem. Instr.*, **2**, 375 (1970).

39. Q. H. Gibson, in *Methods in Enzymology*, Chap. 6.

40. P. Zuman, in *Methods in Enzymology*, Chap. 5.

41. J. L. Sudmeier and J. J. Pesek, *Inorg. Chem.*, **10**, 860 (1971); J. Grimaldi, J. Baldo, C. McMurray, and B. D. Sykes, *J. Amer. Chem. Soc.*, **94**, 7641 (1972).

42. P. E. Sørensen and A. Jensen, *Acta Chem. Scand.*, **24**, 1483 (1970).

43. J. D. Ellis, K. L. Scott, R. K. Wharton, and A. G. Sykes, *Inorg. Chem.*, **11**, 2565 (1972), who observe optical density changes when 1 *M* acid solutions are mixed with water in a Durrum-Gibson stopped-flow apparatus. Such traces could be incorrectly assigned to chemical reactions.

44. S. G. Smith and J. Billet, *J. Amer. Chem. Soc.*, **89**, 6948 (1967); R. E. DeSimone, M. W. Penley, L. Charbonneau, S. G. Smith, J. M. Wood, H. A. O. Hill, J. M. Pratt, S. Ridsdale, and R. J. P. Williams, *Biochem. Biophys. Acta*, **304**, 851 (1973).

45. G. Schwarzenbach and G. Geier, *Helv. Chim. Acta*, **46**, 906 (1963).

46. R. C. Splinter, S. J. Harris, and R. S. Tobias, *Inorg. Chem.*, **7**, 897 (1968).

47. A. Lifshitz and B. Perlmutter-Hayman, *J. Phys. Chem.*, **65**, 2098 (1961).

48. Y. S. Chiang, J. Craddock, D. Mickewich, and J. Turkevich, *J. Phys. Chem.*, **70**, 3509 (1966). M. R. Arick and S. I. Weissman, *J. Amer. Chem. Soc.*, **90**, 1654 (1968); W. T. Dixon and R. O. C. Norman, *J. Chem. Soc.*, 3119 (1963).

49. G. Czapski, *J. Phys. Chem.*, **75**, 2957 (1971).

50. A. Samuni and G. Czapski, *Israel J. Chem.*, **8**, 551, 563 (1970); D. Meisel, G. Czapski, and A. Samuni, *J. Amer. Chem. Soc.*, **95**, 4148 (1973).

51. J. Barrett and J. H. Baxendale, *Trans. Faraday Soc.*, **52**, 210 (1956).

52. M. J. Carter and J. K. Beattie, *Inorg. Chem.*, **9**, 1233 (1970).

53. J. Bjerrum and K. G. Poulsen, *Nature*, **169**, 463 (1952).

54. C. S. Garner and J. Bjerrum, *Acta Chem. Scand.*, **15**, 2055 (1961).

55. Caldin, p. 47.

56. B. M. Gordon, L. L. Williams, and N. Sutin, *J. Amer. Chem. Soc.*, **83**, 2061 (1961).

57. J. P. Candlin and J. Halpern, *Inorg. Chem.*, **4**, 766 (1965).

58. H. Gerischer, J. Holzworth, D. Seifert, and L. Strohmaier, *Ber. Bunsenges. Gesellschaft*, **73**, 952 (1969).

59. A. F. Pearlmutter and J. Stuehr, *J. Amer. Chem. Soc.*, **90**, 858 (1968).

60. R. M. Krupka, H. Kaplan, and K. J. Laidler, *Trans. Faraday Soc.*, **62**, 2754 (1966).

61. J. R. Pladziewicz and J. H. Espenson, *Inorg. Chem.*, **10**, 634 (1971).

62. G. H. Czerlinski and M. Eigen, *Z. Elektrochem.*, **63**, 652 (1959).

63. G. G. Hammes and P. Fasella, *J. Amer. Chem. Soc.*, **84**, 4644 (1962); D. W. Margerum and H. M. Rosen, *J. Amer. Chem. Soc.*, **89**, 1088

(1967); F. Accascina, F. P. Cavasino, and E. Di Dio, *Trans. Faraday Soc.*, **65**, 489 (1969); G. C. Kresheck, E. Hamori, G. Davenport, and H. A. Scheraga, *J. Amer. Chem. Soc.*, **88**, 246 (1966); T. C. French and G. G. Hammes, in *Methods in Enzymology*, Chap. 1.

64. R. D. Farina and J. H. Swinehart, *J. Amer. Chem. Soc.*, **91**, 568 (1969).

65. K. Kustin, I. A. Taub, and E. Weinstock, *Inorg. Chem.*, **5**, 1079 (1966).

66. J. V. Beitz, G. W. Flynn, D. H. Turner, and N. Sutin, *J. Amer. Chem. Soc.*, **92**, 4130 (1970), **94**, 1554, (1972).

67. H. Rüppel and H. T. Witt, in *Methods in Enzymology*, Chap. 9.

68. G. G. Hammes, *Accounts Chem. Research*, **1**, 321 (1968).

69. H. Strehlow and H. Wendt, *Inorg. Chem.*, **2**, 6 (1963).

70. S. Ljunggren and O. Lamm, *Acta Chem. Scand.*, **12**, 1834 (1958).

71. M. T. Takahashi and R. A. Alberty, in *Methods in Enzymology*, Chap. 2.

72. G. Macri and S. Petrucci, *Inorg. Chem.*, **9**, 1009 (1970).

73. M. Eigen and E. M. Eyring, *Inorg. Chem.*, **2**, 636 (1963); L. C. M. De Maeyer, in *Methods in Enzymology*, Chap. 4; D. T. Rampton, L. P. Holmes, D. L. Cole, R. P. Jensen, and E. M. Eyring, *Rev. Sci. Instrum.*, **38**, 1637 (1967).

74. T. M. Schuster and G. Ilgenfritz, "Studies on the Mechanism of Oxygen Binding to Hemoglobin," in *Symmetry and Function of Biological Systems at the Macromolecular Level* (Wiley-Interscience, New York, 1969).

75. H. Diebler, M. Eigen, G. Ilgenfritz, G. Maass, and R. Winkler, *Pure Appl. Chem.*, **20**, 93 (1969).

76. B. Perlmutter-Hayman, *J. Chem. Educ.*, **47**, 201 (1970), for a simple presentation.

77. F. Eggers and K. Kustin in *Methods in Enzymology*, Chap. 3. For a full description of one apparatus and its application, see S. Petrucci, *J. Phys. Chem.*, **71**, 1174 (1967); P. Hammes and S. Petrucci, *J. Phys. Chem.*, **72**, 3986 (1968).

78. M. Eigen and K. Tamm, *Ber. Bunsenges. Gesellschaft*, **66**, 107 (1962); LeRoy G. Jackopin and E. Yeager, *J. Phys. Chem.*, **74**, 3766 (1970).

79. Frost and Pearson, Chap. 3; Harris, p. 45.

80. J. Rabani and M. S. Matheson, *J. Amer. Chem. Soc.*, **86**, 3175 (1964).

81. C. Grant, Jr., and P. Hambright, *J. Amer. Chem. Soc.*, **91**, 4195 (1969).

82. D. W. Hoppenjans, J. B. Hunt, and C. R. Gregoire, *Inorg. Chem.*, **7**, 2506 (1968).

83. D. Kling and H. L. Schläfer, *Ber. Bunsenges. Gesellschaft*, **65**, 142 (1961).

84. M. D. Cohen and E. Fischer, *J. Chem. Soc.*, 3044 (1962).

85. A. Haim and N. Sutin, *J. Amer. Chem. Soc.*, **88**, 5343 (1966).

86. Durrum Instrument Corporation, Palo Alto, California 94303, have developed a number of accessories for use with the Gibson-Durrum stopped-flow technique.

87. B. G. Willis, J. A. Bittikofer, H. L. Pardue, and D. W. Margerum, *Anal. Chem.*, **42**, 1340 (1970); H. L. Fritz and J. H. Swinehart, *Inorg. Chem.*, **12**, 1259 (1973).

88. D. W. Carlyle and J. H. Espenson, *J. Amer. Chem. Soc.*, **90**, 2272 (1968).

89. P. W. Taylor, R. W. King, and A. S. V. Bergen, *Biochem.*, **9**, 2638, 3894 (1970).

90. G. H. Frost and F. A. Hart, *Chem. Commun.*, 836 (1970).

91. K. Garbett, R. D. Gillard, and P. J. Staples, *J. Chem. Soc.*, *A*, 201 (1966).

92. K. Garbett and R. D. Gillard, *J. Chem. Soc.*, *A*, 204 (1966).

93. P. E. Reinbold and K. H. Pearson, *Inorg. Chem.*, **9**, 2325 (1970).

94. Y. Ae Im and D. H. Busch, *J. Amer. Chem. Soc.*, **83**, 3362 (1961).

95. F. Basolo, J. W. Palmer, and R. G. Pearson, *J. Amer. Chem. Soc.*, **82**, 1073 (1960).

96. T. J. Meyer and H. Taube, *Inorg. Chem.*, **7**, 2369 (1968).

97. L. S. Meriwether and M. L. Fiene, *J. Amer. Chem. Soc.*, **81**, 4200 (1959).

98. F. Zingales, A. Trovati, and P. Uguagliati, *Inorg. Chem.*, **10**, 510 (1971).

99. J. P. Day, F. Basolo, and R. G. Pearson, *J. Amer. Chem. Soc.*, **90**, 6927 (1968).

100. H. D. Kaesz, R. Bau, D. Hendrickson, and J. M. Smith, *J. Amer. Chem. Soc.*, **89**, 2844 (1967); B. F. G. Johnson, J. Lewis, J. R. Miller, B. H. Robinson, P. W. Robinson, and A. Wojcicki, *J. Chem. Soc.*, *A*, 522 (1968).

101. A. Berry and T. L. Brown, *Inorg. Chem.*, **11**, 1165 (1972).

102. B. Halpern, A. M. Sargeson, and K. R. Turnbull, *J. Amer. Chem. Soc.*, **88**, 4630 (1966).

103. D. R. Stranks and R. G. Wilkins, *Chem. Rev.*, **57**, 743 (1957).

104. J. B. Goddard and F. Basolo, *Inorg. Chem.*, **8**, 2223 (1969).

105. I. R. Lantzke and D. W. Watts, *Aust. J. Chem.*, **20**, 173 (1967).

106. Mohammed Alei, Jr., *Inorg. Chem.*, **3**, 44 (1964).

107. J. D. Carr and C. N. Reilley, *Anal. Chem.*, **42**, 51 (1970).

108. See Selected Bibliography on fast reactions.

109. M. Meier, F. Basolo, and R. G. Pearson, *Inorg. Chem.*, **8**, 795 (1969).

110. These and subsequent equations are treated in J. A. Pople, W. C. Schneider, and J. H. Bernstein, *High-Resolution Nuclear Magnetic Resonance* (McGraw-Hill, New York, 1959), Chap. 10.

111. Sometimes W' is used, which is half the width at half height, expressed in radians sec^{-1} = 2π cps. Now W' = T_2^{-1}.

112. H. M. McConnell and H. E. Weaver, *J. Chem. Phys.*, **25**, 307 (1956).

113. C. R. Giuliau and H. M. McConnell, *J. Inorg. Nucl. Chem.*, **9**, 171 (1959).

114. O. E. Myers and J. C. Sheppard, *J. Amer. Chem. Soc.*, **83**, 4739 (1961).

115. A. D. Britt and W. M. Yen, *J. Amer. Chem. Soc.*, **83**, 4516 (1961).

116. D. L. Rabenstein and R. J. Kula, *J. Amer. Chem. Soc.*, **91**, 2492 (1969); A. Bryson and I. S. Fletcher, *Aust. J. Chem.*, **23**, 1095 (1970).

117. L. H. Pignolet and W. D. Horrocks, Jr., *J. Amer. Chem. Soc.*, **90**, 922 (1968).

118. G. N. La Mar, *J. Amer. Chem. Soc.*, **92**, 1806 (1970).
119. F. F. L. Ho and C. N. Reilley, *Anal. Chem.*, **42**, 600 (1970).
120. G. E. Glass, W. B. Schwabacher, and R. S. Tobias, *Inorg. Chem.*, **7**, 2471 (1968).
121. L. E. Erickson, A. J. Dappen, and J. C. Uhlenhopp, *J. Amer. Chem. Soc.*, **91**, 2510 (1969).
122. A. Allerhand, H. S. Gutowsky, J. Jones, and R. A. Meinzer, *J. Amer. Chem. Soc.*, **88**, 3185 (1966).
123. K. C. Williams and T. L. Brown, *J. Amer. Chem. Soc.*, **88**, 4134 (1966); D. E. Clegg, J. R. Hall, and N. S. Ham, *Aust. J. Chem.*, **23**, 1981 (1970).
124. T. L. Brown, *Accounts Chem. Research*, **1**, 25 (1968).
125. D. S. Matteson, *Inorg. Chem.*, **10**, 1555 (1971).
126. T. R. Stengle and C. H. Langford, *Coord. Chem. Rev.*, **2**, 349 (1967), for a very readable account.
127. J. P. Hunt, *Coord. Chem. Rev.*, **7**, 1 (1971); H. P. Bennetto and E. F. Caldin, *J. Chem. Soc.*, A, 2198 (1971).
128. R. E. Connick and D. Fiat, *J. Chem. Phys.*, **44**, 4103 (1966).
129. T. J. Swift and R. E. Connick, *J. Chem. Phys.*, **37**, 307 (1962).
130. Z. Luz and S. Meriboom, *J. Chem. Phys.*, **40**, 1058, 2686 (1964); R. Murray, H. W. Dodgen, and J. P. Hunt, *Inorg. Chem.*, **3**, 1576 (1964); H. H. Glaeser, H. W. Dodgen, and J. P. Hunt, *Inorg. Chem.*, **4**, 1061 (1965).
131. J. E. Letter, Jr., and R. B. Jordan, *J. Amer. Chem. Soc.*, **93**, 864 (1971).
132. A. G. Desai, H. W. Dodgen, and J. P. Hunt, *J. Amer. Chem. Soc.*, **91**, 5001 (1969); A. G. Desai, H. W. Dodgen, and J. P. Hunt, *J. Amer. Chem. Soc.*, **92**, 798 (1970).
133. P. W. Taylor, J. Feeney, and A. S. V. Burgen, *Biochem.*, **10**, 3866 (1971), describe exchange of formate or acetate (using ^{1}H) and fluoro-acetate (^{19}F) between free and ligand bound to carbonic anhydrase.
134. J. Burgess, B. A. Goodman, and J. B. Raynor, *J. Chem. Soc.*, A, 501 (1968).
135. A. Wolberg and J. Manassen, *Inorg. Chem.*, **9**, 2365 (1970); A. Wolberg and J. Manassen, *J. Amer. Chem. Soc.*, **92**, 2982 (1970).
136. H. B. Brooks and F. Sicilio, *Inorg. Chem.*, **10**, 2530 (1971).
137. F. A. Walker, R. L. Carlin, and P. H. Rieger, *J. Chem. Phys.*, **45**, 4181 (1966).
138. R. B. Jordan and N. S. Angerman, *J. Chem. Phys.*, **48**, 3983 (1968).
139. B. J. Corden and P. H. Rieger, *Inorg. Chem.*, **10**, 263 (1971); J. B. Farmer, F. G. Herring, and R. L. Tapping, *Can. J. Chem.*, **50**, 2079 (1972).
140. C. H. Sorum, F. S. Charlton, J. A. Neptune, and J. O. Edwards, *J. Amer. Chem. Soc.*, **74**, 219 (1952).
141. C. W. Davies, *J. Chem. Soc.*, 2093 (1938); R. G. Bates, *Determination of pH* (Wiley, New York, 1964), p. 74.
142. P. K. Glasoe and F. A. Long, *J. Phys. Chem.*, **64**, 188 (1960).

143. R. G. Bates, M. Paabo, and R. A. Robinson, *J. Phys. Chem.*, **67**, 1833 (1963); B. B. Hasinoff, H. B. Dunford, and D. G. Horne, *Can. J. Chem.*, **47**, 3225 (1969).

144. Gutfreund, p. 141.

145. R. G. Wilkins, *Pure Appl. Chem.*, **33**, 583 (1973).

146. H. V. Malmstadt and E. H. Piepmeier, *Anal. Chem.*, **37**, 34 (1965).

147. R. W. Hay and P. L. Cropp, *J. Chem. Soc.*, *A*, 42 (1969).

148. A. K. Shamsuddin Ahmed and R. G. Wilkins, *J. Chem. Soc.*, 3700 (1959).

149. H. L. Conley, Jr. and R. B. Martin, *J. Phys. Chem.*, **69**, 2923 (1965).

150. R. W. Hay and S. J. Harvie, *Aust. J. Chem.*, **18**, 1197 (1965).

151. C. E. Skinner and M. M. Jones, *J. Amer. Chem. Soc.*, **91**, 1984 (1969); K. Srinivasan and G. A. Rechnitz, *Anal. Chem.*, **40**, 1818 (1968).

152. D. W. Watts, *Rec. Chem. Prog.*, **29**, 131 (1968).

153. A. M. Sargeson and G. H. Searle, *Inorg. Chem.*, **6**, 2172 (1967).

154. T. Meites, L. Meites, and J. N. Jaitly, *J. Phys. Chem.*, **73**, 3801 (1969); T. Meites and L. Meites, *J. Amer. Chem. Soc.*, **92**, 37 (1970).

155. M. A. Levine, T. P. Jones, W. E. Harris, and W. J. Wallace, *J. Amer. Chem. Soc.*, **83**, 2453 (1961).

156. D. I. Bustin, J. E. Earley, and A. A. Vlcek, *Inorg. Chem.*, **8**, 2062 (1969).

157. N. Tanaka and Y. Sakuma, *Bull. Chem. Soc. Jap.*, **32**, 578 (1959); H. Ogina, T. Saba, and N. Tanaka, *Bull. Chem. Soc.*, *Jap.*, **42**, 1578 (1969); M. Kimura, *Bull. Chem. Soc. Jap.*, **42**, 2844 (1969).

158. P. Zuman, in *Methods in Enzymology*, Chap. 5.

159. N. Winograd and T. Kuwana, *J. Amer. Chem. Soc.*, **92**, 224 (1970).

160. J. E. Taylor, *J. Chem. Educ.*, **42**, 618 (1965).

161. R. W. Hay and K. N. Leong, *J. Chem. Soc.*, *A*, 3639 (1971).

162. K. G. Claus and J. V. Rund, *Inorg. Chem.*, **8**, 59 (1969).

163. V. S. Sharma and J. Schubert, *J. Amer. Chem. Soc.*, **91**, 6291 (1969).

164. B. C. Hui and B. R. James, *Can. J. Chem.*, **48**, 3613 (1970).

165. R. G. Dakers and J. Halpern, *Can. J. Chem.*, **32**, 969 (1954).

166. E. R. Allen, J. Cartlidge, M. M. Taylor, and C. F. H. Tipper, *J. Phys. Chem.*, **13**, 1437, 1442 (1959).

167. W. E. Jones and J. D. R. Thomas, *J. Chem. Soc.*, *A*, 1481 (1966).

168. S. H. Laurie and C. B. Monk, *J. Chem. Soc.*, 724 (1965); J. B. Walker and C. B. Monk, *J. Chem. Soc.*, *A*, 1372 (1966).

169. S. F. Lincoln and D. R. Stranks, *Aust. J. Chem.*, **21**, 37, 67 (1968).

170. R. Snellgrove and E. L. King, *Inorg. Chem.*, **3**, 288 (1964).

171. J. R. Paxson and D. S. Martin, Jr., *Inorg. Chem.*, **10**, 1551 (1971).

172. G. A. Russell, in Freiss, Lewis, and Weissberger, Chap. 8; Hammett, Chap. 4.

173. P. B. Wood and W. C. E. Higginson, *J. Chem. Soc.*, *A*, 1645 (1966); M. C. Moore and R. N. Keller, *Inorg. Chem.*, **10**, 747 (1971).

174. R. W. Taft, Jr., and E. H. Cook, *J. Amer. Chem. Soc.*, **81**, 46 (1959); G. B. Smith and G. V. Downing, Jr., *J. Phys. Chem.*, **70**, 977 (1966); T. J. Williams and C. S. Garner, *Inorg. Chem.*, **10**, 975 (1971).

175. H. L. Bott and A. J. Poë, *J. Chem. Soc., A*, 205 (1967).
176. H. Diebler, P. H. Dodel, and H. Taube, *Inorg. Chem.*, **5**, 1688 (1966).
177. F. A. Posey and H. Taube, *J. Amer. Chem. Soc.*, **79**, 255 (1957).
178. I. Dostrovsky and F. S. Klein, *Anal. Chem.*, **24**, 414 (1952).
179. Sr. M. J. DeChant and J. B. Hunt, *J. Amer. Chem. Soc.*, **90**, 3695 (1968).

SELECTED BIBLIOGRAPHY

The Experimental Study of Rapid Reactions

CALDIN, E. F. *Fast Reactions in Solution.* Blackwell, Oxford, 1964. The most complete account available.

CHANCE, B., EISENHARDT, R. H., GIBSON, Q. H., and LONBERG-HOLM, K. K., eds. *Rapid Mixing and Sampling Techniques in Biochemistry.* Academic, New York, 1964. A series of authoritative papers covering all aspects of flow techniques.

CROOKS, J. E. "Relaxation Techniques." In *Chemical Kinetics*, edited by J. C. Polyanyi. Butterworths, London, 1972.

KUSTIN, K., ed. "Fast Reactions." In *Methods of Enzymology*, vol. 16. Academic, New York, 1969. Excellent accounts of all fast reaction techniques, including commercial sources of components and equipment.

NOTE: See also works indicated in Chap. 1.

PROBLEMS

1. **a.** Calculate the half-life for reaction (3.10) at pH = 3.

   b. How would you verify that the intermediate in the Fe^{2+}, $Co(C_2O_4)_3{}^{3-}$ reactions (3.27) and (3.28) is $FeC_2O_4{}^+$ ion?

   c. A number of Co(III) complexes, such as $CoEDTA^-$ and $Cophen_3{}^{3+}$, can be resolved into optical isomers and are extremely stable towards racemization. The Co(II) analogs are configurationally labile and resolution has proved impossible. Suggest how with a double mixing apparatus it might be possible to obtain half-lives in the 10^{-3}-to-1-sec range for the first-order racemization of the Co(II) complexes. [E. Blinn, C. F. V. Pearce, and R. G. Wilkins, Proceedings 10th I.C.C.C., Israel.]

2. **a.** The second-order rate constants k for the base hydrolysis of a number of cobalt(III) complexes were measured with a simple flow apparatus using conductivity as a monitoring device. Equal concentrations (A_0) of reactants were used. Show that a plot of $R_t/R_e - R_t$ vs time is linear, having slope s, and that

$$k = \frac{(R_e - R_0)s}{R_0 A_0}$$

where R_0, R_t, and R_e are the resistance of the solution at times 0 and t and at equilibrium, respectively. [R. G. Pearson, R. E. Meeker, and F. Basolo, *J. Amer. Chem. Soc.*, **78**, 709 (1956); and Frost and Pearson, p. 37.]
b. For a first-order reaction

$$\ln \frac{D_0 - D_e}{D_t - D_e} = kt$$

where D_0, D_t, and D_e are optical absorbances at times 0, t, and e (3.24). The importance of an accurate value for D_e can be reduced by using Guggenheim's modification. In this, readings are taken at times t_1, t_2, and so on, and at $t_1 + \Delta t$, $t_2 + \Delta t$, and so on, where Δt is a constant interval.

$$D_{t_1} - D_e = (D_0 - D_e)e^{-kt_1} \tag{A}$$

$$D_{t_1 + \Delta t} - D_e = (D_0 - D_e)e^{-k(t_1 + \Delta t)} \tag{B}$$

Subtracting (B) from (A), we obtain

$$D_{t_1} - D_{t_1 + \Delta t} = (D_0 - D_e)(1 - e^{-k\Delta t})e^{-kt_1}$$

$$\ln(D_{t_1} - D_{t_1 + \Delta t}) = -kt_1 + \ln[(D_0 - D_e)(1 - e^{-k\Delta t})]$$

Generally, from a $\log(D_{t_1} - D_{t_1 + \Delta t})$ vs t_1 plot, k can be obtained. Develop a relation by *dividing* (A) by (B), and show how an appropriate linear plot can give k. How might this modification (P. C. Mangelsdorf, *J. Appl. Phys.*, **30**, 443 (1959)) be superior? [D. Margerison, in C. H. Banford and C. F. H. Tipper, eds., *Comprehensive Chemical Kinetics*, vol. 1, p. 388.]
c. The concentration of an absorbing material is related to the transmittance T of light by the Beers-Lambert law:

$$T = \frac{I_t}{I_0} = \exp(-\epsilon'_\lambda l[A])$$

$$D = \log \frac{1}{T} = \epsilon_\lambda l[A] \qquad \epsilon_\lambda = 0.43\epsilon'_\lambda$$

Show that for small (specify) changes in $\log(I_0/I_t)$

$$\frac{\Delta(I_0/I_t)}{\Delta[A]} \approx \frac{\Delta\log(I_0/I_t)}{\Delta[A]}$$

and that transmittance data can be used directly as a measure of [A] without conversion to absorption. (This is oscilloscope trace information in spectral monitoring of rapid reactions.) [J. E. Stewart, Durrum Application Notes, No. 5, Durrum Instrument Corporation, Palo Alto, California 94303.]
d. Show that in the successive reactions (B in excess)

$$A + B \xrightarrow{k_1} C \xrightarrow{k_2} D$$

a maximum in the absorbance-vs-time curve will be observed at

$$t_{\max} = \frac{1}{k_2 - k_1[B]} \ln \frac{\epsilon_c k_2}{\epsilon_A[k_2 - k_1[B]] + \epsilon_c k_1[B]}$$

[D. P. Fay and N. Sutin, *Inorg. Chem.*, **9**, 1291 (1970).]

3. The proton nmr spectra of solutions of $Ni(DMF)_6(ClO_4)_2$ in DMF were recorded over a range of temperatures in which, on the nmr time scale, the exchange of coordinated solvent with bulk solvent is slow. From the accompanying data, evaluate the rate constant for solvent exchange at 298 °K and the enthalpy and entropy of activation. [R. G. Little, unpublished results (I am grateful to Dr. Little for providing this problem).]

$T\,°K$	$(\pi T_2)^{-1}$	$(\pi T_{2A})^{-1}$	P_M
297.08	16.60	3.23	8.73
291.93	19.13	3.17	14.2
289.65	12.85	3.70	8.73
286.96	10.62	3.81	8.73
282.00	8.53	3.33	8.73
282.00	11.38	3.33	14.2

4. Suggest a suitable method (other than uv-vis spectral) for monitoring the following reactions and give details:

a.

$$en_2Co\underset{OH}{\overset{OH}{\diagup\!\!\!\diagdown}}Coen_2^{4+} \xrightarrow{\;2OH^-\;} 2Coen_2(OH)_2^{\,+}$$

[A. A. El-Awady and Z. Z. Hugus, Jr., *Inorg. Chem.*, **10**, 1415 (1971).]

b. $Pd(PR_3)_2CH_3Cl + py \xrightarrow{\;MeOH\;} Pd(PR_3)_2CH_3py^+ + Cl^-$

[F. Basolo, J. Chatt, H. B. Gray, R. G. Pearson, and B. L. Shaw, *J. Chem. Soc.*, 2207 (1961).]

c. $Cd(PDTA)^{2-} + H_2PDTA^{2-} \rightarrow Cd(PDTA)^{2-} + H_2PDTA^{2-}$

[B. Bosnich, F. P. Dwyer, and A. M. Sargeson, *Aust. J. Chem.*, **19**, 2213 (1966).]

d. $Mo(CO)_6 + Ph_3As \xrightarrow{\;decalin\;} Mo(CO)_5Ph_3As + CO$

[J. R. Graham and R. J. Angelici, *Inorg. Chem.*, **6**, 2082 (1967).]

e. Zn^{2+} + apocarbonic anhydrase $\rightarrow$ carbonic anhydrase (this is the regeneration of the enzyme from the demetallated form and zinc ion). [R. W. Henkens and J. M. Sturtevant, *J. Amer. Chem. Soc.*, **90**, 2669 (1968).]

5. The yields of hydrogen from the reaction of sodium amalgam (forget the mercury) with dilute acid are reduced by the prior addition of certain substances (S). It is found that

$$\frac{V_0}{V} = 1 + \frac{A[S]}{[H^+]}$$

where V and V_0 indicate the volumes of hydrogen evolved at STP per gram of sodium in the presence and absence respectively of S. Discuss the significance of these results, and of the values of A:

$$\begin{array}{ll} S = Co(NH_3)_6{}^{3+} & A = 9.3 \\ Cu^{2+} & 1.2 \\ Zn^{2+} & 1.0 \\ Fe(CN)_6{}^{3-} & 0.56 \end{array}$$

Decide what further experiments might confirm your ideas. [G. Hughes and R. J. Roach, *Chem. Commun.*, 600 (1965).]

PART II

Results

In Part II, the mechanistic behavior of transition metal complexes will be extensively surveyed. Substitution, redox, and stereochemical change will be examined, as well as reactions involving the coordinated ligands themselves, bringing us to the borders of organic and biological chemistry. In this Part, the principles and concepts developed in Part I will be extensively used.

Chapter 4

Substitution Reactions

4.1 METAL ION–LIGAND INTERACTIONS

Before any consideration of the mechanisms of complex-ion reactions, the nature of metal ions and complexes in solution will be briefly reviewed. The types and abbreviations of ligands that have been used in kinetic studies have been tabulated at the beginning of the book.

4.1.1 Solvated Metal Ion

A metal ion has a primary solvation sheath, which comprises solvent molecules near to the metal ion.[1] These have lost their translational degrees of freedom and move as one entity with the metal ion in solution. Although the residence time is quite short, a matter of microseconds or less, for a solvent molecule in the coordination sphere of some of the most labile transition metal ions such as Zn^{2+} and Cu^{2+}, these times can be measured by relaxation techniques, particularly nmr and ultrasonics (Chap. 3), and may be distinguished from the even shorter residence times of solvent molecules adjacent to others in the bulk of the solvent. By lowering the temperature of the solvent, one may slow the exchange process

$$M(solv)_n^{m+} + {}^*solv \rightleftharpoons M(solv)_{n-1}({}^*solv)^{m+} + solv \qquad (4.1)$$

sufficiently so that the value of n can be determined—from the ratio of areas of the nmr peaks due to coordinated and free solvent, or from simple isotopic analysis. The solvation numbers of many of the labile and inert transition metal ions in water and several other solvents have now been determined.[2] Solvent exchange rate studies have played a key role in our understanding of substitution mechanisms.

Solvent in the solvated ion can be replaced by other ligands, which may occupy one (unidentate) or more (multidentate ligand) of the solvent positions; for example, in the simple case of a neutral unidentate ligand L replacing H_2O,

$$M(H_2O)_n{}^{m+} + L \rightleftharpoons M(H_2O)_{n-1}L^{m+} + H_2O \qquad (4.2)$$

leading eventually to

$$M(H_2O)L_{n-1}^{m+} + L \rightleftharpoons ML_n{}^{m+} + H_2O \qquad (4.3)$$

All these species are termed *inner-sphere* complexes. The forward reaction is a *formation* reaction, or *anation* if L is anionic. The reverse reaction is variously referred to as *solvation, solvolysis,* or *dissociation.* Formation constants,

$$K_1 = \frac{[M(H_2O)_{n-1}L^{m+}]}{[M(H_2O)_n{}^{m+}][L]} \qquad (4.4)$$

have been measured for many metal-ligand interactions, and a knowledge of their values is often essential in interpreting the kinetics of metal complex reactions.[3]

There is a secondary interaction of an inner-sphere complex with free ligands in solution (which may be solvent, the *secondary solvation shell*) to give an outer-sphere complex.[4] This residual affinity is most effective between oppositely charged species (*ion pairs*). The presence of an outer-sphere complex is easily demonstrated in a number of systems.

Rapid spectral changes in the 200–300-nm region, which can be ascribed to outer-sphere complexing, occur on addition of a number of anions to $M(NH_3)_5H_2O^{3+}$, where $M = Cr$ or Co,[5,6,7,8] *long* before final equilibration to the inner-sphere complex occurs. For example,

$$Co(NH_3)_5H_2O^{3+} + N_3{}^- \underset{}{\overset{K_0}{\rightleftharpoons}} \underset{\text{Outer-sphere complex}}{Co(NH_3)_5H_2O^{3+} \cdots N_3{}^-} \rightleftharpoons$$

$$\underset{\text{Inner-sphere complex}}{Co(NH_3)_5N_3{}^{2+}} + H_2O \quad (4.5)$$

The separation of the two stages is easier to discern when the rates of the two processes are so different, but it can also be seen in the ultrasonic spectra of metal-sulfate systems (see Fig. 3.6). Absorption peaks can be attributed to formation of outer-sphere complexes (at higher frequency, shorter τ) and collapse of outer-sphere to inner-sphere complexes (at lower frequency).

There are several methods for estimating K_0, the outer-sphere complexity constant.[4] These may emerge as a result of kinetic studies, they may be obtained directly from spectral, polarimetry, or nmr measurements, and they may be calculated using theoretically deduced expressions:[9]

$$K_0 = \frac{4\pi N a^3}{3000} \exp - \frac{U(a)}{kT} \tag{4.6}$$

where $U(a)$ is the Debye-Hückel interionic potential

$$U(a) = \frac{z_1 z_2 e^2}{aD} - \frac{z_1 z_2 e^2 \kappa}{D(1 + \kappa a)} \tag{4.7}$$

$$\kappa^2 = \frac{8\pi N e^2 I}{1000 D k T} \tag{4.8}$$

where N = Avogadro's number.

a = distance of closest approach of two ions.

k = Boltzmann's constant.

e = charge of an electron in esu units.

D = bulk dielectric constant.

I = ionic strength.

z_1, z_2 = charge of reactants.

The calculation has been applied to cationic-anionic,[10] cationic–zero-charged species,[11] and cationic-cationic interactions[12,13] (Table 4.1). Agreement between calculated and experimentally determined values is fair.

The difference between K_0 and K_1 (for entry 2, $K_1 = 830\ M^{-1}$ at $25°$) emphasizes the relative weakness of outer-sphere complexes in these cases; with other systems however, the ratio of outer- to inner-sphere complexes in the equilibrium mixture may exceed unity. In both cases, the outer-sphere complex may play an important role in both substitution and redox reactions. This becomes particularly relevant in nonaqueous solution, where outer-sphere complexing is larger (see (4.6)).[14,15]

TABLE 4.1. Some Values of K_0 (M^{-1}; M, Ionic Strength) at $25°$

System	Spectral	Kinetic	Theoretical
$Co(NH_3)_5H_2O^{3+} + N_3^{-a}$	0.18 (3.6)	0.26[e] (2.0)	...
$Ni(H_2O)_6^{2+} + MePO_4^{2-b}$	...	41 (0.1)	14 (0.1)
$Ni(H_2O)_6^{2+} + NH_3^c$	...	0.15 (0.1)	0.15
$Fe(H_2O)_5OH^{2+} + Fe(H_2O)_5OH^{2+d}$	...	...	1.2×10^{-3} (0.0)

[a] Ref. 8   [b] Refs. 10, 44   [c] Ref. 11   [d] Ref. 13   [e] At 45°.

4.1.2 The Characteristics of Substitution Reactions

Substitution embraces the replacement of a ligand coordinated to a metal by a free ligand in solution, or the replacement of the coordinated ion by a free metal ion. No change of oxidation state of the metal occurs during the substitution; a change may take place as a result of the substitution. The kinetics of the process has been studied with all the important stereochemistries but most intensely investigated with octahedral and square-planar complexes. A very wide span of rates is found, ranging from the extremely slow exchange of NH_3 with $Co(NH_3)_6^{3+}$ ion in aqueous ammonia solution (no exchange in 162 days)[16] to the almost diffusion-controlled exchange of H_2O between $Cu(H_2O)_6^{2+}$ and water ($t_{1/2} \sim 10^{-8}$ sec).[17] Thus the whole armory of techniques must be used to measure the substitution rate constants. Metal ions or complexes that generally react rapidly (within a matter of seconds) are termed *labile*, whereas if they substitute slowly, taking minutes or longer for completion, they are considered *inert*.[18]

The substitution process permeates the whole realm of coordination chemistry. It is not infrequently the first step in a redox process,[12,19,20] or in a dimerization or a polymerization reaction.[13] An understanding of the kinetics of substitution can be important for defining the best conditions for a preparative or analytical procedure in coordination chemistry.[21] The process is undoubtedly important in the reactions of metal or metal-activated enzymes, for example, in the inhibition by ligands of the catalytic function of metal enzymes,[22] and the transport of metal ions through cell membranes.[23] In addition to the ligand interchange reactions shown in (4.2) and (4.3), there is the replacement of one ligand by another without the direct intervention of solvent, for example,

$$PtdienBr^+ + Cl^- \rightleftharpoons PtdienCl^+ + Br^- \qquad (4.9)$$

Such ligand interchange in metal complexes can occur in two ways, either (1) by a combination of solvolysis and anation or (2) by simple interchange. The former appears to be the method much preferred by tetrahedral and octahedral complexes, whereas both routes are used by square-planar complexes. Implicit in these statements is the generalization that octahedral and tetrahedral complexes react by dissociative-type mechanisms with bond breaking in the transition state of primary importance. With square-planar complexes, on the other hand, the entering ligand plays an important "active" role, with bond making a feature of the activated complex. This situation could perhaps be predictable in view of the available space and orbitals of the correct energy lying on either side of the plane.[24] It is thus apparent that studies of octahedral (and tetrahedral) complexes will invariably be concerned with the individual steps of solvolysis and solvent replacement, whereas these are only part of the total picture in the replacement reactions of square-planar complexes.

4.2 SUBSTITUTION IN OCTAHEDRAL COMPLEXES

The replacement of one unidentate ligand by another is the simplest situation to envisage and this process has been used extensively to investigate the mechanism of substitution. Later we shall discuss substitution in chelates of increasing complexity. Since direct replacement appears rare with octahedral complexes of the Werner type, at least one of the unidentate ligands will be a solvent molecule. It is immaterial which of the directions in (4.2) is studied, since these are intimately related (Sec. 2.3.2), and evidence about octahedral substitution can emerge from either study, particularly in conjunction with solvent exchange studies. Most of the examinations of solvolysis have been made with the inert complexes, particularly of cobalt(III), since it is often easier to produce specific starting species in these cases. The ligation of both labile and inert metal complex ions has been investigated, since complexes containing at least one replaceable solvent molecule are readily available. Most studies concern an aqueous medium, although increasing attention is being paid to protic and dipolar aprotic (Sec. 2.8.3) solvents with both the inert[14] and labile[25,26] complexes. The relative simplicity of behavior in aqueous solution (see below) appears usually not to be duplicated in other solvents. The earlier studies of the Werner-type complexes have now been augmented by investigations of organometallic complexes, particularly of the metal carbonyls and related derivatives, although we shall not deal specifically with these.

4.3 THE KINETICS OF REPLACEMENT OF COORDINATED WATER BY UNIDENTATE LIGAND

Commonly, such reactions as

$$M\text{—}OH_2 + L \rightarrow M\text{—}L + OH_2 \tag{4.10}$$

are studied with excess ligand L, and pseudo first-order rate constants k are measured for the loss of $M\text{—}OH_2$. The values of k are invariably proportional to the concentration of L, when this is low, so that $k/[L]$ will be a second-order rate constant. In a few systems, as the concentration of L becomes higher, deviations from constancy for the function $k/[L]$

are observed, and eventually a point may be reached in which k is a constant, no longer dependent on [L], Fig. 4.1[27] (Sec. 1.6.3):

$$\frac{-d[\text{M}-\text{OH}_2]}{dt} = k[\text{M}-\text{OH}_2] = \frac{a[\text{M}-\text{OH}_2][\text{L}]}{1 + b[\text{L}]} \qquad (4.11)$$

4.3.1 Dissociative Mechanisms

This kinetic behavior shown in (4.11) by certain systems, and other considerations to be detailed subsequently, rule out a *compact* associative mechanism for these replacements. In this, there would be an intermediate or activated complex of increased coordination number.

There are two main contenders for a dissociative type of mechanism. One of these is an S_N1 (lim),[28] or D type,[29] in which a five-coordinated intermediate is generated with a sufficient lifetime to discriminate between different nucleophiles that may be present:[30]

$$\text{M}-\text{OH}_2 \rightleftharpoons \text{M} + \text{OH}_2 \qquad k_1, k_{-1} \qquad (4.12)$$

$$\text{M} + \text{L} \rightarrow \text{ML} \qquad k_2 \qquad (4.13)$$

The derived rate law, assuming stationary state concentrations for M,

$$\frac{-d[\text{M}-\text{OH}_2]}{dt} = \frac{k_1 k_2[\text{M}-\text{OH}_2][\text{L}]}{k_{-1}[\text{H}_2\text{O}] + k_2[\text{L}]} \qquad (4.14)$$

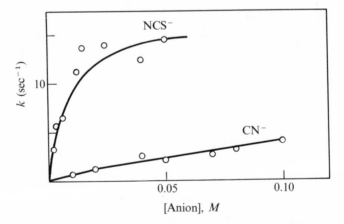

FIGURE 4.1   Pseudo first-order rate constant (k, sec^{-1}) vs [anion] for replacement of H_2O in Co(III) hematoporphyrin IX(H_2O)$_2$ by CN^- and NCS^- (Ref. 27). The limiting rate with NCS^- is clearly shown but the deviation from linearity is barely discernible with CN^-.

is of the form (4.11), with

$$a = \frac{k_1 k_2}{k_{-1}[H_2O]} \quad \text{and} \quad b = \frac{k_2}{k_{-1}[H_2O]} \tag{4.15}$$

Another mechanism leads to a similar kinetic expression. In this, the ion-pair $S_N 1IP$[28] or interchange I_d mechanism,[29] there is a dissociative interchange of H_2O and L within an outer-sphere complex or ion pair, which is *rapidly* formed from the reactants

$$M-OH_2 + L \rightleftharpoons M-OH_2 \cdot L \qquad K_0 \tag{4.16}$$

$$M-OH_2 \cdot L \rightarrow M-L + OH_2 \qquad k_0 \tag{4.17}$$

For this mechanism,

$$\frac{-d[M-OH_2]}{dt} = \frac{k_0 K_0[M-OH_2]_0[L]_0}{1 + K_0[L]_0} \tag{4.18}$$

where the subscript 0 indicates the total (starting) concentration of the species. Equation (4.18) is once again of the form (4.11), with $a = K_0 k_0$ and $b = K_0$. The expressions (4.14) and (4.18) differ only in that the former contains an $[H_2O]$ term, but since this is invariant it is not diagnostically useful. Occasionally, (4.10) is reversible and the reverse rate constant k_{-2} or k_{-0} has to be included in the full rate law.[31]

4.3.2   Characteristics of the Mechanisms

In the limiting $S_N 1$ reaction, second-order kinetics are obtained when $k_2[L] < k_{-1}[H_2O]$, that is, when the intermediate is much more effectively scavenged by H_2O than by the ligand L. This leads to a second-order rate constant equivalent to $k_1 k_2 / k_{-1}[H_2O]$. At high ligand concentrations, L may effectively compete with H_2O for the intermediate, and the loss of $M-OH_2$ will be governed simply by the first-order step k_1. The value of k_2 / k_{-1} will be a measure of the relative affinity of L and H_2O for the five-coordinate species M.

In the *interchange mechanism*, second-order kinetics hold when $K_0[L] < 1$. Here there is a very small buildup of the outer-sphere complex and the second-order rate constant is equivalent to $k_0 K_0$. At high [L], when (4.16) is complete, $K_0[L]_0 > 1$ and the reaction being studied is the interchange within the outer-sphere complex, rate constant $= k_0$.

4.3.3   The Limiting First-Order Rate Constant

The observations of (1) deviations from second-order kinetics and (still better) (2) the limiting first-order kinetics are very informative. They have been obtained mostly with the inert complexes, since the rapidity of reaction of the labile complexes largely precludes operating at the high ligand concentrations usually necessary to reach the $b[L] \geqslant 1$ region. The limiting first-order rate constants for the $S_N 1$ (lim) and interchange mechanisms might reasonably be equated to the exchange rate constant for the process

$$\text{M—OH}_2 + \text{*OH}_2 \rightleftharpoons \text{M—*OH}_2 + \text{OH}_2 \qquad k_{\text{exch}} \qquad \textbf{(4.19)}$$

in the absence and presence, respectively, of the entering ligand. The evidence available indicates that outer-sphere complexing of the M–OH$_2$ entity does not markedly alter the value of k_{exch}.[6,32] Thus the experimental limiting first-order rate constant is unlikely to be useful for distinguishing the preferred path, k_1 in (4.12) and k_0 in (4.17), but in any case its value should be close to the value of k_{exch}. Table 4.2 indicates that this is the case with reactions of Co(NH$_3$)$_5$H$_2$O^{3+}.[33]

In examining the labile ions, we can usually determine only the second-order rate constant, $k_1 k_2/k_{-1}[\text{H}_2\text{O}]$ in (4.14) and $k_0 K_0$ in (4.18). We have no way of assessing k_2/k_{-1} for a particular reaction but we can sometimes determine K_0 experimentally or estimate it from theoretical considerations (see (4.6)) and thus calculate k_0. Some values for k_0 for reactions of Ni^{2+} ion with a variety of unidentate ligands (Table 4.3) calculated in this manner are reasonably constant, and once again satisfyingly close to the water exchange rate constant. It was this type of evidence that Eigen used to propose the ion-pair mechanism for the reactions of a number of bivalent metal ions.[34-36] The probable importance of outer-sphere complexes in substitution processes had however been recognized by Werner[4] and later by Taube and his associates.[5]

TABLE 4.2. Limiting Rate Constants (k_1, sec^{-1}) for Anation by L^{n-} and Water Exchange (k_e, sec^{-1}) of Co(NH$_3$)$_5$H$_2$O^{3+} at 45° ($I = 0.6$ to $2.0\ M$)

L^{n-}	$10^6 \times k_1$	k_1/k_e
NCS$^-$	16	0.16
H$_2$PO$_4$$^-$	0.77[a]	0.13
Cl$^-$	21	0.21
N$_3$$^-$	100	1.0
SO$_4$$^{2-}$	24	0.24
H$_2$O	100	...
H$_2$O	5.8[a]	...

SOURCE: Tables in Refs. 7 and 8.
[a] At 25°.

Table 4.3. Computed Values for k_0 from Second-Order Rate Constants $(K_0 k_0)$ for the Formation of Nickel(II) Complexes from Unidentate Ligands at 25°

L^{n-}	$10^{-3} \times K_0 k_0$ $M^{-1} sec^{-1}$	K_0, M^{-1}	$10^{-4} \times k_0$ sec^{-1}
$CH_3PO_4^{2-}$	290	40	0.7
CH_3COO^-	100	3	3
NCS^-	6	1	0.6
F^-	8	1	0.8
HF	3	0.15	2
H_2O	...	...	3
NH_3	5	0.15	3
C_5H_5N	~4	0.15	~3
$C_4H_4N_2^a$	2.8	0.15	2
$NH_2(CH_2)_2NMe_3^+$	0.4	0.02	2

Source: Ref. 83.
[a] J. M. Malin and R. E. Shepherd, *J. Inorg. Nucl. Chem.*, **34**, 3203 (1972).

4.3.4 The Second-Order Rate Constant

For a single substrate reacting with a series of ligands, the second-order rate constant is a measure of k_2 for mechanism (4.12) (since k_1 and k_{-1} are constants) and $K_0 k_0$ for mechanism (4.16). For similarly charged ligands, the values of $K_0 k_0$ are likely to remain fairly constant,[37] whereas the values of k_2, reflecting the nucleophilicity of the ligand, might be expected to vary widely.

The formation rate constants are extremely similar for the reactions of cobalamins with negatively charged ligands, Table 4.4,[38] whereas a

TABLE 4.4. Rate Constants $(k, M^{-1} sec^{-1})$ for Reaction of Cobalamin with Ligands L^{n-} at 25° and $I = 0.5$ M[38]

L^{n-}	$10^{-2} \times k$	$\Delta H^{\ddagger}$
SCN^-	23	17.0
I^-	14	14.0
Br^-	10	...
N_3^-	12	...
NCO^-	4.7	15.7
HSO_3^-	1.7	15.6
$S_2O_3^{2-}$	2.0	15.0
SO_3^{2-}	$\lessgtr 2.0$	...

wide range of second-order rate constants (or discriminating values of k_2/k_{-1}) is the substitution pattern of a number of other cobalt(III) complexes, Table 4.5.[39-41]

The behavior denoted in Tables 4.4 and 4.5 would correspond to an I_d and D mechanism, respectively, and constitutes a reasonable basis for their differentiation.

4.3.5 The Nature of the Intermediate

The presence of an outer-sphere complex, a feature of the interchange mechanism, can be demonstrated in a number of ways (Sec. 4.1.1). The formation of outer-sphere complexes is near-diffusion-controlled, for example,[42]

$$Co(NH_3)_6^{3+} + SO_4^{2-} \rightleftharpoons Co(NH_3)_6^{3+} \cdots SO_4^{2-} \qquad k_1, k_{-1} \qquad (4.20)$$

Outer-sphere complexes are observed in the study of the interaction of Fe(III) with Br^- ions by flow methods,[43] and assumed from temperature-jump data (see discussion of (1.142) and (1.143)) on the $Ni^{2+}-CH_3PO_4^{2-}$ system[44] and ultrasonic absorption spectra on a number of $M^{2+}-SO_4^{2-}$ systems.[36,45]

TABLE 4.5. Discrimination Factors for Intermediates in Reactions of Co(III) Complexes

Reaction	Intermediate	Relative reactivity of nucleophile towards intermediate		Ref.
$Co(NH_3)_4SO_3X + Y$	$Co(NH_3)_4SO_3$	NH_3	1	40
		SCN^-	30	
		CN^-	43	
		NO_2^-	70	
		OH^-	8×10^3	
$Co(CN)_5H_2O^{2-} + Y$	$Co(CN)_5^{2-}$	H_2O^a	1	39
		Br^-	0.10	
		NH_3	0.15	
		N_3^-	0.53	
		OH^-	3×10^3	
$Coen_2SO_3H_2O^+ + Y$	$Coen_2SO_3^+$	H_2O^a	1	41
		SO_3^{2-}	9×10^3	
		OH^-	$\geqslant 4.5 \times 10^5$	

^{a} Assuming $H_2O = 55\ M$.

Unfortunately, establishing the existence of the outer-sphere complex in a reacting system does not necessitate its being in the direct pathway for the formation of the inner-sphere complex (see Sec. 1.6.4),[19,46] although it is an attractive candidate for such a role.

By comparison, it is extremely difficult to obtain evidence for the five-coordinated intermediate M of (4.12). Indeed, doubt has been expressed, because of the necessary high energies, that such a species could be produced, although it has also been pointed out that five-coordinated complexes are quite common.[47] Further, a five-coordinated intermediate is well established in base hydrolysis (see Sec. 4.5.3). Few serious attempts to detect this type of intermediate in a substitution reaction have so far been made. The spectral change accompanying the reaction of $Co(NH_3)_5NO_3^{2+}$ with a large excess of SCN^- ion in acid solution can be fully accounted for in terms of an aqua intermediate $Co(NH_3)_5H_2O^{3+}$.

$$Co(NH_3)_5NO_3^{2+} + H_2O \rightarrow Co(NH_3)_5H_2O^{3+} \xrightarrow{\ SCN^-\ } Co(NH_3)_5NCS^{2+}$$
$$\underset{\overline{}/\!/}{\qquad\qquad} Co(NH_3)_5^{3+} \underline{}\uparrow \qquad (4.21)$$

This suggests strongly the absence of any $Co(NH_3)_5^{3+}$ intermediate during the reaction, since the latter might be expected to react directly with SCN^- to give the final product $Co(NH_3)_5NCS^{2+}$, even at early times, and this is not observed.[48]

The most telling evidence so far for a five-coordinated intermediate comes from scavenging experiments in CH_3OH/H_2O mixtures. Hydrolysis in a variety of ways of a series of complexes $Cr(H_2O)_5X^{2+}$ in a specific mixed solvent (Table 4.6) produces common proportions of $Cr(H_2O)_5(CH_3OH)^{3+}$ and $Cr(H_2O)_6^{3+}$, irrespective of the nature of X

TABLE 4.6. Values of [Bound CH_3OH]/[Total Cr(III)] in the Cr(III) Species Produced in Various Ways at 25° and 0.1 M $HClO_4$[49]

Reaction	Z [a]			
	0.28	0.46	0.64	0.87
CrI^{2+} + Tl^{3+}	0.20	0.32	0.46	0.74
CrI^{2+} + Hg^{2+}	0.20	0.33	0.47	0.72
CrI^{2+} + Ag^+	0.21	0.32	0.47	0.74
CrI^{2+} + solvent [b]	0.21	0.29	0.49	...
$CrCl^{2+}$ + Hg^{2+}	0.19	0.34	0.47	0.72

[a] Z = (moles of methanol)/(moles of methanol + moles of water).
[b] Values are from extrapolation to zero extent of reaction.

and of the means of promoting hydrolysis. This is compelling evidence for a common intermediate, likely $Cr(H_2O)_5^{3+}$, occurring in all these reactions,[49] although the conclusion is equivocal.[50]

It is obviously difficult to differentiate between the dissociative mechanisms and this is not surprising since the distinction is fine: dissociation within or apart from an outer-sphere complex. Both mechanisms surely operate and may be of comparable importance in certain systems.

(a)　The Shape of the Five-Coordinated Intermediate. Irrespective of the details of the dissociative mechanism, the geometry of the five groups around the central metal in the intermediate has to be examined. There are, almost certainly, only slight energy differences between the square-pyramid and the trigonal-bipyramidal forms. A number of factors—steric effects, π bonding, or solvation, for example—may favor one over the other.

Most insight into the five-coordinate geometry comes from an examination of the stereochemical course of a reaction. Those that proceed with retention of configuration, such as the aquation of *cis*-$CoL_4(A)Cl^{n+}$, and most reactions of Rh(III) and Ir(III), are considered to go via a square-pyramid intermediate, although solvent attack adjacent to the leaving group is also consistent with the results. These have generally negative values for $\Delta S^{\ddagger}$, in contrast to the reactions that proceed with substantial stereochemical change and for which a trigonal-bipyramid intermediate is suggested (Sec. 2.6).

4.3.6　Replacement of Coordinated Ligand by Water

All the considerations so far have been directed towards formation reactions. Establishment of a rate law and suggestion of a mechanism for this process automatically defines the rate law for the reverse reaction (microscopic reversibility, Sec. 2.3.2). For example, the reaction.

$$Cr(H_2O)_6^{3+} + SCN^- \rightarrow Cr(H_2O)_5NCS^{2+} + H_2O \qquad k_f, k_r, K \qquad \textbf{(4.22)}$$

is governed by the rate law

$$V = \{k_1 + k_2[H^+]^{-1} + k_3[H^+]^{-2}\}[Cr^{3+}][SCN^-] \qquad \textbf{(4.23)}$$

The reverse rate (for hydrolysis) must be of the form

$$V = \{k_{-1} + k_{-2}[H^+]^{-1} + k_{-3}[H^+]^{-2}\}[CrNCS^{2+}] \qquad \textbf{(4.24)}$$

with rate constants for the forward and reverse directions related by values of K and hydrolysis constants for $Cr(H_2O)_6^{3+}$.[51]

4.3.7 Consequences of a Dissociative Mechanism—LFER

In this section we shall deal with kinetic data that can be regarded either as evidence for a dissociative mechanism or as a consequence of such a mechanism. The approximate constancy for the formation rate constants $k_1{}^1$, $k_1{}^2$, and so forth for a series of substitutions of a complex system M–OH$_2$ by similar-type ligands L$_1$, L$_2$, and so forth,

$$M—OH_2 + L_1 \rightleftharpoons M—L_1 + H_2O \qquad k_1{}^1, k_{-1}{}^1, K_1{}^1 \qquad (4.25)$$

$$M—OH_2 + L_2 \rightleftharpoons M—L_2 + H_2O \qquad k_1{}^2, k_{-1}{}^2, K_1{}^2 \qquad (4.26)$$

requires that any differences in the formation constants, $K_1{}^1$, $K_1{}^2$, ... should reside in differences in $k_{-1}{}^1$, $k_{-1}{}^2$, ... since

$$K_1{}^1 = \frac{k_1{}^1}{k_{-1}{}^1} \qquad K_1{}^2 = \frac{k_1{}^2}{k_{-1}{}^2} \qquad \cdots \qquad (4.27)$$

This corollary was early recognized.[52] It was demonstrated in a striking manner as an LFER between the hydrolysis rate constant (k_{-1}) and the hydrolysis constant $(K_1)^{-1}$ for a series of reactions (Sec. 2.5)[53]

$$Co(NH_3)_5X^{2+} + H_2O \rightarrow Co(NH_3)_5H_2O^{3+} + X^- \qquad k_{-1}, k_1, (K_1)^{-1}$$
$$(4.28)$$

$$\log k_{-1} = A \log (K_1)^{-1} + B \qquad (4.29)$$

With $A = 1.0$, this was interpreted as meaning that (1) the state of X$^-$ in the activated complex is similar to the state of X$^-$ in the product, that is, solvated anion, and (2) entering water is weakly bound in the activated complex. Both of these features are obviously in harmony with a dissociative mechanism.[37] Linear free-energy relationships have also been constructed for the hydrolysis of $Co(NH_3)_5X^+$,[37] $Co(tet–a)X_2{}^+$,[54] $CrX(OH)^+$,[55] and CrX^{2+}.[56] All values of A are near unity, except in the last case $A = 0.56$, this deviation arising from a nonconstancy of k_f (Table 4.7). The transition state is considered to resemble $Cr(H_2O)_6{}^{3+}$ and X$^-$ to a moderate degree, but such a formulation obviously raises interpretive problems. Taken in conjunction with ΔV considerations (Sec. 2.7.1), it may mean that bond making and bond breaking are synchronous, and that an I$_a$ mechanism (below) operates.[50]

When the pK_a of HX is linearly related to K_1, plots of $\log k_{-1}$ vs pK_a are linear, as with the hydrolysis of $Ni(H_2O)_5py–X^{2+}$ and $Cr(NH_3)_5X^{2+}$ ions.[57,58]

Since the transition state approximates the products in many respects for a dissociative mechanism, linear relationship between other activation parameters with their corresponding reaction parameters would be expected. There is a linear relation between $\Delta H^{\ddagger}$ and ΔH,[56] and a similarity

Table 4.7. Rate Constants (k, M^{-1} sec^{-1}) and Associated Activation Parameters for Reaction of $Cr(H_2O)_6^{3+}$ and $Cr(H_2O)_5OH^{2+}$ with Ligands L^{n-} at 25°

L^{n-}	$Cr(H_2O)_6^{3+}$			$Cr(H_2O)_5OH^{2+}$		
	$10^8 \times k$	$\Delta H^{\ddagger}$	$\Delta S^{\ddagger}$	$10^5 \times k$	$\Delta H^{\ddagger}$	$\Delta S^{\ddagger}$
SO_4^{2-}	1100	29.1	+16	39	25.5	+11
Cl^-	2.9	30.3	+ 9	2.8	26.0	+ 8
Br^-	0.9	28.9	+ 2	1.7	22.8	− 4
I^-	0.08	30.6	+ 6	0.26	27.0	+11
NCS^-	180	25.1	+ 1	4.9	22.8	− 1
SCN^-	0.4	29.6	+ 2	0.5	24.5	− 1
NO_3^-	73	26.1	+ 1	9.0	20	− 10
HSO_4^-	13	28.2	+ 5	627	14.2	− 21
HF	56	24.2	− 6	29	19	− 11
H_2O	250[a]	26.1	...	< 10[a]	...	...
$HgCl^+$	0.13[b]	...	...	...	...	...

SOURCE: Tables in Ref. 63.
[a] sec^{-1}.
[b] Ref. 142.

between $\Delta S^{\ddagger}$ and ΔS^5 and between $\Delta S^{\ddagger}$ and S_{corr}^0 of X^- (Sec. 2.6.1) for the hydrolysis of CrX^{2+}, and, most convincing, a close correspondence between $\Delta V_0^{\ddagger}$ and ΔV for reaction (4.28) (Sec. 2.7.1). These correlations have been obtained with a quite restricted series of complexes and it is hoped that these approaches can be extended so that a broader understanding may be reached of the factors influencing the degree of participation of the entering reactant in substitution reactions.

4.3.8 Associative Mechanisms

Dissociative mechanisms are promoted by strong labilizing groups such as CH_3, CN^-, or SO_3^{2-} in the complex. In certain cases, reaction times are reduced to seconds from the hours normal with Co(III)[59,60] and Pt(IV).[61,62] The rate constants for reaction of $Fe(H_2O)_6^{3+}$ and $Cr(H_2O)_6^{3+}$ with a variety of ligands are wider spread than the rate constants for $FeOH^{2+}$ and $CrOH^{2+}$ (Tables 2.1 and 4.7). It is possible that this may result from the coordinated hydroxy group promoting dissociation through π bonding.[63] The ligand dependency would be more pronounced, however, were it not for compensating $\Delta H^{\ddagger}$ and $\Delta S^{\ddagger}$ values (see Fig. 2.11 and Sec. 2.6.3).[64]

Although a dissociative mechanism is favored in a number of the reactions of octahedral complexes, evidence is growing for a contribution by the attacking ligand in selected systems. Now there is a problem in distinguishing between an associative A[29] or $S_N2(lim)$[28] mechanism and an I_a process,[29] in which there is an element of bond making within an outer-sphere complex during the reaction.

Direct replacement of one ligand by another, without solvent participation, has been observed in the reaction

$$Ru(NH_3)_6{}^{3+} + NO + H^+ \rightarrow Ru(NH_3)_5NO^{3+} + NH_4{}^+ \qquad (4.30)$$

which takes place *much* more rapidly than could be explained by aquation of the hexammine as a first step.[65] A bimolecular mechanism with a seven-coordinated intermediate or transition state might appear more likely with such a d^5 system, in which there are available orbitals for attack by an entering ligand.

The lower values for $\Delta H^{\ddagger}$ (23.9 kcal/mole) and $\Delta S^{\ddagger}$ (-3 eu) for the exchange of H_2O between $Rh(NH_3)_5H_2O^{3+}$ and water[32] compared with the corresponding quantities for water exchange with $Co(NH_3)_5H_2O^{3+}$ (26.6 kcal/mole and 7 eu)[66] have been construed as evidence for a bimolecular character for the Rh(III) reactions.[32] More compelling, however, is that for the reactions

$$Rh(NH_3)_5H_2O^{3+} + X^{n-} \rightarrow Rh(NH_3)_5X^{(3-n)+} + H_2O \qquad k_X \qquad (4.31)$$

The ratio $k_X/k_{H_2O} = 1.0$, 2.6, and 4.9 for $X = SO_4{}^{2-}$, Cl^-, and Br^-, respectively. This indicates an element of bond making during the anation.[67] These ratios, which are higher than those normally encountered for reaction of Co(III) aqua complexes (Table 4.2) have been observed for other Rh(III) anations[68] and for the chloride anation of the $Ir(NH_3)_5H_2O^{3+}$ ion.[69]

It is difficult to examine the mechanism of hydrolysis except indirectly. Negative values for $\Delta V^{\ddagger}$ for water exchange of $Cr(H_2O)_6{}^{3+}$, $Cr(NH_3)_5$-H_2O^{3+}, and $Rh(NH_3)_5H_2O^{3+}$, in contrast to a slightly positive one for $Co(NH_3)_5H_2O^{3+}$, are interpreted in terms of an I_a mechanism (Sec. 2.7.1).[70]

Finally, it should be mentioned that substitution in transition metal π complexes of coordination number six is often associative in character. The types of ligand involved include acetylenes, olefines, and π-arene, π-allyl, and cyclopentadienyl compounds.[71] Substitution reactions of $Mo(CO)_6$ with phosphines (L)

$$M(CO)_6 + L \rightarrow Mo(CO)_5L + CO \qquad (4.32)$$

depend in their rate on the concentration of L,

$$V = k_1[Mo(CO)_6] + k_2[Mo(CO)_6][L] \qquad (4.33)$$

and, in behavior reminiscent of square complexes (see Sec. 4.1), this indicates direct ligand attack on an octahedral complex, as a basis for the k_2 term.[72a] An I_d mechanism cannot, however, be excluded.[72b]

4.3.9 Summary

Since we shall not obtain the comparable amount of detailed information from the study of more complicated substitutions (next section) it might be worthwhile to summarize here the salient features of substitution in Werner-type octahedral complexes.[73]

1. Relatively small influence of entering group on kinetics.
2. Parallel rate constants for substitution and water exchange for a large number of metal systems, with the former rarely exceeding the latter.
3. Correlation of hydrolysis rate with the binding tendencies of the leaving group, leading to a variety of LFER.
4. Decrease of rate with an increase in the charge of the complex.
5. Increase of rate with increasing steric crowding within the complex (Table 2.5).

4.4 REPLACEMENT REACTIONS INVOLVING MULTIDENTATE LIGANDS

There is no reason to believe that replacement of water by the donor groups of a chelating agent is fundamentally different from replacement when only unidentate ligands are involved. However, the multiplicity of steps may increase the difficulty in understanding the detailed mechanism, and mainly for this reason the simpler bidentate ligands have been most studied.

4.4.1 The Formation of Chelates

The successive steps in the replacement of two coordinated waters by a bidentate ligand L–L is represented as

$$
\begin{array}{c}
\overset{|}{\underset{|}{M}}\!\!\!\!\begin{array}{c}OH_2\\ \\OH_2\end{array} + L-L \rightleftharpoons \overset{|}{\underset{|}{M}}\!\!\!\!\begin{array}{c}OH_2\\ \\L-L\end{array} + OH_2 \qquad k_1, k_{-1} \qquad (4.34)
\end{array}
$$

$$M(OH_2)_2$$

$$
\overset{|}{\underset{|}{M}}\!\!\!\!\begin{array}{c}OH_2\\ \\L-L\end{array} \rightleftharpoons \overset{|}{\underset{|}{M}}\!\!\!\!\begin{array}{c}L\\ \\L\end{array} + OH_2 \qquad k_2, k_{-2} \qquad (4.35)
$$

$$M(L_2)$$

Assuming stationary-state conditions for the intermediate, in which L–L is acting as a unidentate ligand, we find

$$\frac{d[M(L_2)]}{dt} = k_f[M(OH_2)_2][L\text{—}L] - k_d[M(L_2)] \qquad (4.36)$$

with $$k_f = \frac{k_1 k_2}{(k_{-1} + k_2)} \qquad k_d = \frac{k_{-1} k_{-2}}{(k_{-1} + k_2)} \qquad (4.37)$$

The function k_2/k_{-1} will dominate the kinetics of bidentate chelation. If $k_2 \gg k_{-1}$, then $k_f = k_1$, and the overall rate of chelate formation will be determined by the rate of formation of the M–L–L entity (Fig. 2.3(1)), a process we can assume controlled by the same factors that apply with the entry of unidentate ligands. The relationship would be anticipated when the first bond formed is relatively strong so that the tendency for the bond to break (measured by k_{-1}) is much less than the tendency to complete the formation of the ring (k_2). Normal substitution is indicated when, in rate constants for reaction, the bidentate (or multidentate) ligand resembles the appropriate unidentate ligand, for which only the first step is meaningful (Table 4.8). The behavior was indicated in some early studies, which showed a common log k vs pH plot for the reaction of Cr(III) with a variety of carboxylates, uni- and bidentate (Fig. 4.2[74]). Very occasionally, the two stages in schemes (4.34) and (4.35) can be isolated:

$$trans\text{-Coen}_2(H_2O)OH^{2+} + HPO_4^{2-} \xrightarrow{\text{rapid}}$$
$$trans\text{-Coen}_2(H_2O)OH^{2+} \cdots HPO_4^{2-} \qquad (4.38)$$

$$trans\text{-Coen}_2(H_2O)OH^{2+} \cdots HPO_4^{2-} \xrightleftharpoons[\sim 10^{-8}]{7.7 \times 10^{-5}}$$
$$Coen_2(OH)OPO_3H \xrightleftharpoons[2.5 \times 10^{-5}]{8.3 \times 10^{-4}} Coen_2PO_4 \qquad (4.39)$$

The rate constants are all in sec^{-1} at 22.5°.[75]

TABLE 4.8. Some Examples of Normal Substitution by Multidentate Ligands

Ligand	Metal ion	$10^{-3} \times k_f(25°)$ M^{-1} sec^{-1}	k_{-2} (25°) sec^{-1}
py	Ni^{2+}	~4	40
bipy		1.5	...
terpy		1.4	...
NH$_3$		5.0	6
en		400	0.14
CH$_3$CO$_2^-$		100	5×10^3
$^-$O$_2$CCH$_2$CO$_2^-$		850	1×10^2
HCOOH	FeOH^{2+}	7^a	10^a
$^-$O$_2$CCO$_2$H		20^a	3×10^{-3a}

SOURCE: Tables in Ref. 83.
^{a} E. G. Moorhead and N. Sutin, *Inorg. Chem.*, **5**, 1866 (1966).

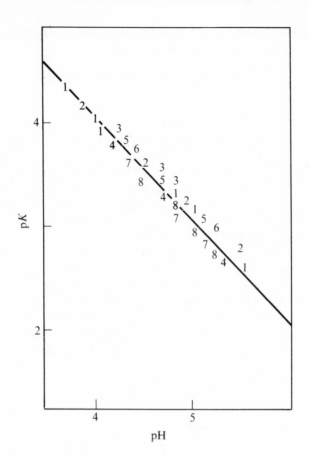

Key to ligands:

(1) malonate, (2) citrate, (3) acetate, (4) tartrate,
(5) oxalate, (6) phthalate, (7) glycolate, (8) lactate.

FIGURE 4.2   Plot of $-\log k$ vs pH at $25°$ for reaction of Cr(III) with a variety of carboxylates. All the points for unidentate and multidentates are near a line slope -1. This indicates a common mechanism for reaction in which water replacement from the Cr(III) ion is rate-limiting.[74]

The establishment of the first bond appears to signal rapid successive ring closures with most of the multidentate ligands also, and all the ligands containing strong nitrogen donors that have so far been examined (Table 4.8). See also Table 4.13. In certain cases it can be shown that the later stages of ring closure are quite rapid. Thus the ion **1**, containing trien bound as a bidentate ligand, is converted into **2**, containing terdentate trien, simply by leaving at pH 7–8 for less than 5 min at 0° and then acidifying.[76]

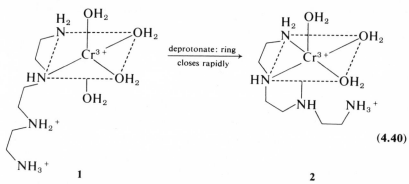

(4.40)

When $k_2 \leqslant k_{-1}$ (Fig. 2.3(2) and (3)), an overall formation constant that is composite will result. This is likely to arise in the following circumstances:

1. When the complex containing the bidentate ligand attached at only one end, en′, is not particularly stable:

$$\text{Nien}_2(\text{H}_2\text{O})_2{}^{2+} + \text{en} \underset{k_{-1}}{\overset{k_1}{\rightleftharpoons}} \text{Nien}_2\text{en}'(\text{H}_2\text{O})^{2+} \overset{k_2}{\rightleftharpoons} \text{Nien}_3{}^{2+} \quad (4.41)$$

We could guess that $K_1(k_1/k_{-1}) \sim 1$, and if we assume that $k_2 \sim k_1$ (both water-exchange-controlled), then $k_{-1} \sim k_2$. This reasoning agrees with data from relaxation experiments.[77]

2. When the completion of the ring entails steric hindrance or strain. The rate constant for reaction of β-alanine, forming a six-membered ring, is less than the rate constant for reaction of glycine, forming a five-membered ring, particularly with the more labile ions.[78] The reaction of cis-Coen$_2$(H$_2$O)$_2{}^{3+}$ with SO$_4{}^{2-}$ ion stops at the formation of Coen$_2$(H$_2$O)-OSO$_3{}^+$, showing the reluctance of SO$_4{}^{2-}$ to form a strained four-membered ring.[79]

3. When there is some inhibition to ring closure because the closing arm is protonated, and a proton has to be lost prior to coordination. The effect is likely to be important only with the most reactive metal ions, for which substitution rate constants can be comparable to those of protonation and deprotonation[80,81]

$$\text{Cu}^{2+} + \text{NH}_2(\text{CH}_2)_2\text{NH}_3{}^+ \rightleftharpoons \text{Cu–NH}_2(\text{CH}_2)_2\text{NH}_3{}^{3+} \rightleftharpoons$$

$$\text{Cu–NH}_2(\text{CH}_2)_2\text{NH}_2 + \text{H}^+$$

$$\Updownarrow \qquad (4.42)$$

$$\text{Cu}\overset{\text{NH}_2}{\underset{\text{NH}_2}{\diagup\diagdown}}(\text{CH}_2)_2$$

4. When a hydroxy group rather than an aqua group has to be replaced by the closing arm. $Coen_2(OH)C_2O_4$ only *very* slowly converts to $Coen_2C_2O_4{}^+$ in base, in contrast to the rapid conversion of $Coen_2(H_2O)-C_2O_4{}^+$ ion in acid solution.[82]

4.4.2 The Hydrolysis of Chelates

The data from studies of the hydrolysis of chelates may complement data obtained from examination of the reverse reaction, or may represent new information. Some values of the rate constant (k_{-2}) for opening of chelate ring of a number of nickel(II) complexes are given in Table 4.8.[83] One is impressed by the somewhat lowered value of k_{-2} of these five-membered chelates compared with the dissociation rate constant for the appropriate unidentate ligand. These differences can be attributed to the necessity for twisting an aliphatic chain and rotating the donor atom away from the metal atom in the bidentate chelate.

In the case of some strained four-membered rings produced by oxyanions, however, the reverse may hold; for example, the hydrolysis of *cis*-$Coen_2SO_4{}^+$ or $Coen_2PO_4$ is much faster than the hydrolysis of *cis*-$Coen_2(H_2O)SO_4{}^+$ or of $Coen_2(OH)(OPO_3H)$.[75,79] The chelated carbonate complex $Co(NH_3)_4CO_3{}^+$ smoothly ring-opens in water, whereas there is no evidence for hydrolysis of $Co(NH_3)_5CO_3{}^+$.[84] It is not easy to compare the behavior of these oxyion chelates, however, since there is a lack of information on the values of the activation parameters and there is also the possibility of Co–O or O–C (O–P or O–S) bond cleavage during the hydrolysis.

The strain resident in multi-ring complexes is clearly demonstrated by some hydrolysis rate studies of nickel(II) and chromium(III) complexes. The $\Delta H^{\ddagger}$ values for the *first* bond rupture for Ni(II)–polyamine complexes fall neatly into groups. It is highest for en, containing the most strain-free ring (~ 20 kcal mol^{-1}), ca. 18 kcal mol^{-1} for complexes with terdentate ligands, and only 15 kcal mol^{-1} for complexes with quadridentate and quinquedentate amines and with NH_3 itself.[85] The effect of strain on the rate constants for hydrolysis is also illustrated in an extensive series of studies of chromium(III) ammines.[86] The data (Table 4.9) show that the aquation of 1,2,6-$Crdien(H_2O)_3{}^{3+}$ is 300 times faster than aquation of the less strained 1,2,3-$Crdien(H_2O)_3{}^{3+}$ and that further aquation of these complexes is successively slower with larger $\Delta H^{\ddagger}$ values, a behavior paralleled by the Cr(III)–trien and –tetren complexes.[87] These studies by Garner and his colleagues are model examples of the care and approach that should be taken in this type of work.

The competition between bond rupture, and re-formation, which

TABLE 4.9.   Rate Parameters for Aquation of Some Cr(III) Amine Complexes at 60° in 1 M HClO$_4$[86]

Complex	Cr–N bonds	$10^6 \times k$, sec^{-1}	$\Delta H^{\ddagger}$	$\Delta S^{\ddagger}$
1,2,6-Crdien(H$_2$O)$_3{}^{3+}$	3	1.6×10^4	18.6	-11
1,2,3-Crdien(H$_2$O)$_3{}^{3+}$	3	59	23.7	-7
CrdienH(H$_2$O)$_4{}^{4+}$	2	22	23.4	-10
Cren(H$_2$O)$_4{}^{3+\,a}$	2	3.0	27.1	-3
CrdienH$_2$(H$_2$O)$_5{}^{5+}$	1	2.6	25.9	-6
CrenH(H$_2$O)$_5{}^{4+\,a}$	1	1.9	24.8	-11

[a] 3 M HClO$_4$.

attends the complete cleavage of a multidentate ligand, is the basic reason for the high kinetic stability that resides in the chelate. This situation is altered when the released donor atom can be prevented from reattaching (see subject of accelerated substitution).

4.4.3   The Formation of Macrocyclic Complexes

Macrocyclic complexes should be considered for their intrinsic interest and importance rather than for their value in illuminating the mechanism of chelation. This is probably the least-studied area of chelation; most of the work has concerned the incorporation of metal ions M(II) into the porphyrin molecule PH$_2$,[88]

$$M^{II} + PH_2 \rightleftharpoons M^{II}P + 2H^+ \qquad (4.43)$$

These are slow reactions, easily followed spectrally because of the high characteristic absorption coefficients of the complexes and free porphyrins (see Fig. 3.7). The reactions have been usually investigated in non-aqueous solution. A number of rate laws have been observed for the incorporation of M(II) into PH$_2$.[89] These include

$$V = k[M][PH_2] \qquad (4.44)$$

$$V = k'[M]^2[PH_2] \qquad (4.45)$$

$$V = k''[PH_2] \qquad (4.46)$$

or any combination of these rate terms. The rate constants k, k', or k'' may contain $[H^+]^{-1}$ terms arising from participation of deprotonated metal ion or porphyrin species.

It has been suggested that such variety of behavior might be accommodated by a general mechanism:[90]

$$M + PH_2 \rightleftharpoons M \cdots P \cdots H_2 \tag{4.47}$$

$$M \cdots P \cdots H_2 \rightleftharpoons [MP]_1 + 2H^+ \tag{4.48}$$

$$[MP]_1 \rightleftharpoons [MP]_2 \tag{4.49}$$

$$[MP]_2 + M \rightleftharpoons MP + M \tag{4.50}$$

Different rate-determining steps, with (4.48) the most popular, will lead to different rate laws. $[MP]_1$ and $[MP]_2$ are different forms of the final product MP. The role of one metal ion may be to deform the porphyrin nucleus sufficiently to ease attack by another metal ion from the other side.[91]

Incorporation of metal ions into the rigid porphyrin is easily followed spectrally and it is much slower than reaction with simpler ligands. Nevertheless, the reactivity orders are very similar, for example, for bivalent ions towards tetrapyridylporphine:[91]

$$Cu > Zn > Mn > Co > Fe > Ni > Cd \tag{4.51}$$

(See Table 4.13 for order towards simpler ligands.)

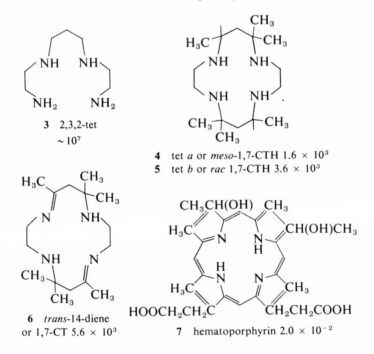

3   2,3,2-tet
~ 10^7

4   tet a or $meso$-1,7-CTH 1.6×10^3
5   tet b or rac 1,7-CTH 3.6×10^3

6    $trans$-14-diene
or 1,7-CT 5.6×10^3

7   hematoporphyrin 2.0×10^{-2}

The constraints imposed by a macrocycle on complex formation are well illustrated by a comparison of metal ion sequestering by a flexible chain polyamine, a flexible macrocycle ligand, and a rigid porphyrin.[92] The second-order rate constants in $M^{-1} sec^{-1}$ at 25° for reaction with Cu(II) in 0.5 M NaOH (probably present as $Cu(OH)_3^-$ and $Cu(OH)_4^{2-}$) are given below the formulas. They show that a chain polyamine 3 allows easy stepwise replacement of coordination H_2O and OH groups and reacts $\sim 10^9$ times faster than the rigid porphyrin 7, where simultaneous multiple desolvation of the metal ion is mandatory. With ligands 4–6, some twisting or folding of the ligand is possible and the rate constants lie between those of 3 and 7. It is apparent that the mechanisms must differ appreciably.

The incorpration of metal ions into macrocycles has important implications in the phenomenon of biological carriers.[23] There have been some interesting studies with some rate data[93] on the inclusion of cations in the cavity of macrobicyclic ligands ("artificial cryptates").[94]

Only qualitative information on the hydrolysis of metalloporphyrins and macrocycle complexes exists. The enhanced stability of macrocycles over noncyclic complexes[92] has been used in a variety of ways—corrin synthesis,[95] and the production of unusual oxidation states, for example, Ni(I), Co(I), Cu(III), and Ni(III) by intact reduction and oxidation,[96] to name but two.

4.5   ACCELERATED SUBSTITUTION

Reagents such as H^+, OH^-, and certain metal ions, particularly Hg^{2+} and Ag^+, may alter the rate of replacement of one ligand by another. These reagents act either by modifying the structure of one of the reactants, or by direct participation in the transition state (and the difference may be a subtle one and difficult to diagnose; see Sec. 2.3.2). It is always important to establish that these reagents are producing another reaction pathway and not simply promoting a medium effect (see Sec. 2.8.2).

4.5.1   Acid-Assisted Removal of Unidentates

Studies on the removal of unidentates by acid have been made mainly with inert complexes. It might be expected that the removal of ligands that retain some basicity, even when coordinated, would be acid-catalyzed. Table 4.10 shows that H^+ aids in the removal of a number of X groups from

$Cr(H_2O)_5X^{n+}$. In acid medium, a protonated form of the complex is considered to be formed and this is more labile than the unprotonated:

$$CrX^{2+} + H^+ \rightleftharpoons CrXH^{3+} \qquad K, \Delta H_1 \qquad (4.52)$$

$$CrX^{2+} + H_2O \rightarrow Cr^{3+} + X^- \qquad k_0, \Delta H_0^\ddagger \qquad (4.53)$$

$$CrXH^{3+} + H_2O \rightarrow Cr^{3+} + HX \qquad k_1, \Delta H_1^\ddagger \qquad (4.54)$$

The experimental value of $\Delta H^\ddagger$ for the proton-assisted path will include a ΔH_1 term for protonation since $\Delta H^\ddagger = \Delta H_1 + \Delta H_1^\ddagger$. Since ΔH_1 appears to be quite small (X = OCOCH$_3$,[97] X = CN[98]), it can be seen from Table 4.10 that $\Delta H_1^\ddagger$ for hydrolysis of the protonated form is usually less than $\Delta H_0^\ddagger$ for the acid-independent hydrolysis. Placing a proton on the ligand must weaken the Cr–X bond and show up as a reduced enthalpy of activation. In the cases of X = ONO and OCOCH$_3$,[97] the $\Delta H_1^\ddagger$ values are much less than those normally associated with Cr–O bond fission (for example, 26.1 for the $Cr(H_2O)_6^{3+}$–H_2O exchange). This might suggest that protonation is weakening the O–N or O–C bonds and that these are cleaved during reaction, especially since for a reaction such as

$$CH_3OAc + H^+ \rightarrow CH_3OH + AcOH \qquad (4.55)$$

the value of $\Delta H^\ddagger = 16.4$.[97] This is an argument that must be viewed with caution however, when it is recalled that for acid-catalyzed aquation of cis-Coen$_2$(OAc)$_2^+$, $\Delta H^\ddagger$ is quite low (18.4) although it is certain from [18]O studies that Co–O fission occurs in this case.[99]

If the coordinated X group is sufficiently basic, appreciable amounts of protonated form may build up (1.163)

$$\frac{-d[CrX]_{\text{TOTAL}}}{dt} = k[CrX]_{\text{TOTAL}} \qquad (4.56)$$

where

$$k = \frac{k_0 + k_1 K[H^+]}{1 + K[H^+]} \qquad (4.57)$$

This behavior is observed in the aquation of CrCN^{2+}[98] and CrOCOCH$_3^{2+}$.[97]

Normally, the removal of unidentate ammonia or amine ligands from metal complexes is not catalyzed by acid since the nitrogen is coordinately saturated. An important exception to this generalization concerns the ruthenium(II) complexes Ru(NH$_3$)$_6^{2+}$ and Ru(NH$_3$)$_5$py^{2+}, whose hydrolyses are H$^+$-assisted. Attack by H$^+$ is believed to occur at the metal ion, and in this process one of the three electron pairs of the low-spin d^6 system is engaged by the proton.[100]

4.5.2 Acid-Assisted Dechelation

Certain bidentate ligands retain sufficient basicity that their removal from chelates is acid-catalyzed. Now, however, a problem arises in the interpre-

TABLE 4.10. Activation Parameters for Hydrolysis of CrX^{2+} Ion at 25°

X^{n-}	k_0, sec^{-1}	$\Delta H_0^{\ddagger}$	$\Delta S_0^{\ddagger}$	Kk_1, M^{-1}sec^{-1}	$\Delta H^{\ddagger}$	$\Delta S^{\ddagger}$	Ref.
ONO^-	...	...	...	2.0	19.8	+9	a
$OCOCH_3^-$	...	...	-13	7.7×10^{-6}	18.6	-15	b
SO_4^{2-}	6.1×10^{-7}	21.9	...	1.1×10^{-7}	26.5	-1	c
$H_2PO_2^-$	...	...	...	1.4×10^{-6}	18.1	-24	d
N_3^-	2.6×10^{-8}	32.4	16	9.3×10^{-7}	23.2	-8	e
NCS^-	7.2×10^{-9}	27.5	-3	...	...	...	f
F^-	6.2×10^{-10}	28.7	-4	1.4×10^{-8}	24.5	-12	g
Cl^-	2.8×10^{-7}	24.3	-7	...	...	...	g
Br^-	2.3×10^{-6}	23.8	-4	...	...	...	h
I^-	8.4×10^{-5}	23.0	0	...	...	...	g
ONO_2^-	7.2×10^{-5}	21.5	6	...	...	...	i
CN^-	1.1×10^{-5}	26.9	9	5.9×10^{-4}	20.2	-6	j
SCN^-	1.7×10^{-5}	23.5	1	...	...	...	k
C_5H_5N	1.2×10^{-8}	27.2	-4	...	...	...	l

[a] T. C. Matts and P. Moore, J. Chem. Soc., 1997 (1969).
[b] E. Deutsch and H. Taube, Inorg. Chem., 7, 1532 (1968).
[c] J. E. Finholt and S. M. Deming, Inorg. Chem., 6, 1533 (1967).
[d] J. H. Espenson and D. E. Binau, Inorg. Chem., 5, 1365 (1966).
[e] T. W. Swaddle and E. L. King, Inorg. Chem., 3, 234 (1964).
[f] C. Postmus and E. L. King, J. Phys. Chem., 59, 1216 (1955).
[g] T. W. Swaddle and E. L. King, Inorg. Chem., 4, 532 (1965).
[h] F. A. Guthrie and E. L. King, Inorg. Chem., 3, 916 (1964).
[i] T. W. Swaddle, J. Amer. Chem. Soc., 89, 4338 (1967); M. Ardon and N. Sutin, Inorg. Chem., 6, 2268 (1967).
[j] J. P. Birk and J. H. Espenson, Inorg. Chem., 7, 991 (1968); D. K. Wakefield and W. B. Schaap, Inorg. Chem., 8, 512 (1969).
[k] M. Orhanovic and N. Sutin, J. Amer. Chem. Soc., 90, 4286 (1968).
[l] A. Bakac and M. Orhanovic, Inorg. Chem., 10, 2443 (1971).

tation of the mechanism. Does the protonation produce a reactive protonated species that hydrolytically cleaves more easily (as shown in the previous section), or does the proton, in a kinetically equivalent manner, function by aiding ring opening in the rate-determining step?

There is evidence for the latter view in the hydrolysis of cobalt(III) complexes, $CoL_4CO_3^+$,

$$L_4Co\underset{O}{\overset{O}{\diagup\!\!\!\diagdown}}C{=}O^+ + H_3O^+ \rightarrow cis\text{-}L_4Co\underset{OCO_2H}{\overset{OH_2}{\diagup\!\!\!\diagdown}}{}^{2+} \qquad (4.58)$$

$$cis\text{-}L_4Co\underset{OCO_2H}{\overset{OH_2}{\diagup\!\!\!\diagdown}}{}^{2+} + H_3O^+ \rightarrow cis\text{-}L_4Co(H_2O)_2^{3+} + CO_2 \qquad (4.59)$$

The first step occurs with Co–O bond breakage and the second with C–O rupture. There is a marked effect of the basicity of L on the rate of the first step.[101]

In contrast, the acid-catalyzed ring opening of $Coen_2PO_4$ arises from production of a protonated species ($pK \sim 4$), $Coen_2PO_4H^+$,[102] while the ring opening of $Co(C_2O_4)_3^{3-}$ probably results from intervention of H^+ in the ring-opened species.[103] The latter behavior is similar to that frequently met with organic chelates, which usually have N-donor atoms. These chelates have their potential basic sites tied up by coordination. Therefore, the acid catalysis almost certainly operates by H^+ scavenging of the released ligand, after "spontaneous" (or water-induced) ligand-metal bond rupture. Numerous examples of this behavior exist. It was first observed in the H^+-catalyzed hydrolysis of $Febipy_3^{2+}$ ion.[104] Since there is no change in the spectra of the complex between neutral and strong acid solutions, it is unlikely that direct protonation of the intact chelate occurs; and H^+ must interact with the cleaved chelate.[105] The rigid phenanthroline ligand cannot enter into "half-bonded" structures and no H^+ effect is observed.[106] Similar results are obtained with bipy and phen complexes of other metals. Even more pronounced effects of pH on the hydrolysis rate constants have been observed for $Fe(terpy)_2^{2+}$ and $Fe(TPTZ)_2^{2+}$, which contain terdentate ligands.[107]

4.5.3 Base-Assisted Removal of Unidentates

The hydroxide ion can modify the reactivity of a system even in acid medium. This was long ago[108] recognized in the hydrolysis

$$Co(NH_3)_4(H_2O)NO_3^{2+} + H_2O \rightleftharpoons Co(NH_3)_4(H_2O)_2^{3+} + NO_3^- \qquad (4.60)$$

for which

$$V = (k_0 + k_1 K[H^+]^{-1})[Co(NH_3)_4(H_2O)NO_3{}^{2+}] \qquad (4.61)$$

and k_0 is the hydrolysis rate constant for the aqua species (dissociation constant K), and k_1 is the hydrolysis rate constant for the hydroxy complex (1.168). This type of rate law often arises in the replacement of a group X from a complex containing also an aqua ligand, for example, $Cr(H_2O)_5X^{2+}$,[109] since a hydroxo ligand usually labilizes the X group.

The ability of hydroxide to modify a reactant probably finds its most important example in the base-catalyzed hydrolysis of metal ammine and amine complexes containing anionic ligands.[110] The overwhelming bulk of these studies have been with Co(III), for example,

$$Co(NH_3)_5X^{2+} + OH^- \rightarrow Co(NH_3)_5OH^{2+} + X^- \qquad (4.62)$$

and these will be considered first. The kinetics are straightforward, invariably second-order,[111]

$$V = k[Co^{III}][OH^-] \qquad (4.63)$$

which is maintained up to 1 M OH$^-$, a region where flow methods must be used to follow the rapid rates.[112,113,114] There are, however, a number of mechanisms that can account for these simple kinetics, although there is overwhelming support for a conjugate base mechanism for the majority of systems studied.

(a) The Conjugate Base Mechanism. As originally proposed by Garrick,[115] base removes a proton from the ammonia or amine ligand in a rapid preequilibrium to form a substitutionally labile amide complex

$$Co(NH_3)_5X^{2+} + OH^- \rightleftharpoons Co(NH_3)_4(NH_2)X^+ + H_2O \qquad k_1, k_{-1}, K_1$$
$$(4.64)$$

Unimolecular solvolysis of this conjugate base, steps (4.65) and (4.66), produces an aqua amide complex that rapidly converts to the final product (4.67):

$$Co(NH_3)_4(NH_2)X^+ \rightarrow Co(NH_3)_4NH_2{}^{2+} + X^- \qquad k_2 \qquad (4.65)$$

$$Co(NH_3)_4NH_2{}^{2+} + H_2O \rightarrow Co(NH_3)_4NH_2(H_2O)^{2+} \qquad \text{fast} \qquad (4.66)$$

$$Co(NH_3)_4NH_2(H_2O)^{2+} \rightarrow Co(NH_3)_5OH^{2+} \qquad \text{fast} \qquad (4.67)$$

This mechanism (termed S_N1CB) was developed by Basolo and Pearson and their group in the 1950s[116] in the face of a good deal of healthy opposition from Ingold, Nyholm, Tobe, and their workers,[116] who favored a straightforward S_N2 attack by OH^- ion on the complex (q.v.). For an S_N1CB mechanism:

$$V = \frac{K_1 k_2 [Co^{III}][OH^-]}{1 + K_1[OH^-]} \tag{4.68}$$

The absence of any deviation from linearity for the $V/[OH^-]$ plot indicates $K_1[OH^-] \ll 1$,

$$V = K_1 k_2 [Co(NH_3)_5 X^{2+}][OH^-] \tag{4.69}$$

Since $K_1 = K_a/K_w$, $pK_a > 15$, which is reasonable in view of the very weak acidity of the ammine hydrogen.[117]

Some of the evidence for the various steps proposed in the conjugate base mechanism will now be considered:

1. The base-catalyzed exchange of hydrogen between the cobalt ammines and water demanded by equilibrium (4.64) has been amply demonstrated. Normally all the exchange will proceed by (4.64), but when k_2 and k_{-1} are similar in magnitude, the amount of exchange of H between solvent and reactant will be less than amount of exchange between solvent and product. The latter is apparently rare, but has been observed (using deuterium and infrared or nmr, Secs. 3.6.6 and 3.6.7).[118] As expected from (4.68), there appears to be a relation between increasing acidity of the N–H bonds (larger K_a), anticipated with increased chelation,[119] and an increased base hydrolysis rate constant[120] (Table 4.11).

Table 4.11. Rate Parameters for Aquation, Base Hydrolysis, and Hg(II)-Induced Hydrolysis of Chloropentaminecobalt(III) Complexes at 25°, Variable I

Complex	k_{H_2O} sec^{-1}	k_{OH^-} M^{-1} sec^{-1}	$k_{Hg^{2+}}$ M^{-1} sec^{-1}
$Co(NH_3)_5Cl^{2+}$	$1.7 \times 10^{-6\,a}$	0.85^c	0.12^c
cis-$Coen_2(NH_3)Cl^{2+}$	$1.4 \times 10^{-6\,b}$ (35°)	3.3^c	$1.4 \times 10^{-2\,c}$
cis-β_2-$Cotrien(NH_3)Cl^{2+}$	...	$2.1 \times 10^{4\,c}$	...
β_2-$Cotrien(glyOEt)Cl^{2+}$	...	$2.2 \times 10^{5\,c}$	$1.0 \times 10^{-2\,c}$
α-$Co(tetren)Cl^{2+}$	$4 \times 10^{-7\,b}$ (35°)	$3.5 \times 10^{4\,b}$	...
cis-$Coen_2(Pr^iNH_2)Cl^{2+}$	...	50^d	...
$Co(MeNH_2)_5Cl^{2+}$	$3.7 \times 10^{-5\,a}$	$2.6 \times 10^{3\,a}$	...
$Co(Bu^iNH_2)_5Cl^{2+}$	$1.8 \times 10^{-4\,a}$	$1.5 \times 10^{5\,a}$	...

[a] D. A. Buckingham, B. M. Foxman, and A. M. Sargeson, *Inorg. Chem.*, **9**, 1790 (1970).
[b] T. L. Ni and C. S. Garner, *Inorg. Chem.*, **6**, 1071 (1967).
[c] D. A. Buckingham, D. M. Foster, L. G. Marzilli, and A. M. Sargeson, *Inorg. Chem.*, **9**, 11 (1970).
[d] R. W. Hay and P. L. Cropp, *J. Chem. Soc.*, A, 42 (1969).

2. An intermediate $Co(NH_3)_4NH_2^{2+}$ is postulated in (4.65), the reactions of which should be independent of the nature of the X group in the starting material. Thus the constant isotope fractionation factors for base hydrolysis (X = Cl, Br, and NO_3) support a common intermediate reacting in an $H_2^{16}O/H_2^{18}O$ mixture to give constant proportions of $Co(NH_3)_5^{16}OH^{2+}$ and $Co(NH_3)_5^{18}OH^{2+}$ ions.[121] Similarly, if base hydrolysis is carried out in solutions containing another nucleophile Y^- that can also attack the intermediate, then a constant ratio $[Co(NH_3)_5Y^{2+}]/[Co(NH_3)_5OH^{2+}]$ should be obtained (Sec. 2.2.1(b)).

The base hydrolysis of $Co(NH_3)_5Cl^{2+}$ in 0.1 M NaOH and 1 M NaSCN produces, in addition to $Co(NH_3)_5OH^{2+}$, the intermediates $Co(NH_3)_5NCS^{2+}$ and $Co(NH_3)_5SCN^{2+}$, which then slowly hydrolyze to the final product $Co(NH_3)_5OH^{2+}$.[122]

3. There is strong evidence for a dissociative type of mechanism for base hydrolysis from at least three pieces of data. We would expect steric crowding in the reactants to be reduced in the transition state for a dissociative mechanism. *Steric acceleration* has been strikingly demonstrated in the $\sim 10^5$-fold rate enhancement for hydrolysis of $Co(RNH_2)_5Cl^{2+}$ relative to $Co(NH_3)_5Cl^{2+}$.[123] The effect is much smaller ($\sim 10^2$) in aquation and implies that bond breaking is less important here than in base hydrolysis.[123] The steric acceleration factor is very much smaller when there is only *one* hindered coordinated amine[124] (Table 4.11),

$$cis\text{-}Coen_2(RNH_2)Cl^{2+} + OH^- \rightarrow cis\text{-}Coen_2(RNH_2)OH^{2+} + Cl^- \quad \textbf{(4.70)}$$

Secondly, there is an LFER between $\log k_{OH}$ and $-\log K_{OH}$ for the hydrolysis of a series of $Co(NH_3)_5X$ complexes. The slope (1.0) is similar to the slope for the analogous plot involving aquation and indicates a common mode of activation, that is, dissociative (Sec. 4.3.7).[125]

Finally, the heat contents for the activated complexes for the reactions (X = Cl, Br, I, and NO_3)

$$Co(NH_3)_5X^{2+} + OH^- \rightarrow Co(NH_3)_5OH^{2+} + X^- \quad \textbf{(4.71)}$$

are all 32.0 ± 0.9. This similarity, suggests a common structure with marked dissociation of X in the activated state.[126]

(b)   The Shape of the Five-Coordinated Intermediate.   It is not easy to arrive at any firm conclusions about the geometry of the five-coordinated intermediate of the conjugate base mechanism.[110] The base hydrolysis of a number of octahedral cobalt(III) and chromium(III) complexes, particularly of the type Men_2XY^{n+}, is accompanied by stereochemical change and has invariably large positive $\Delta S^{\ddagger}$ values. It is not unreasonable to suppose that in such reactions there is a rearranged (trigonal-bipyramidal) intermediate, and Basolo and Pearson[127] and Nordmeyer[128] have attempted to explain the steric course of these reactions on the basis of such an intermediate and certain assumptions about the direction of attack of the water on the amido intermediate.

Stereochemical change is not observed in the base hydrolysis of less simple cobalt(III) complexes,[110] or of ruthenium(III)[129] and rhodium(III) complexes, which suggests a square-pyramidal intermediate in these cases. Additionally, a group *trans* to the leaving ligand is important in influencing the reaction path in these cases, whereas its identity would be lost if a trigonal-bipyramidal arrangement were produced.

The extreme lability of the amido conjugate base must arise from strong labilizing effects of the NH_2^- residue, which in turn may be due to the ability of this group to π-bond to the metal as in **8** (which would arise from $M(NH_3)_5X^{2+}$), or to its strong basicity. The former view has lost support in view of recent experiments (Sec. 7.7).

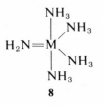

8

(c) *Other Mechanisms.* We are certain that there is not a universal mechanism for base hydrolysis. *Trans*-$Pt(CN)_4Br_2^{2-}$ undergoes base hydrolysis;[130] acetate ion fails to accelerate the hydrolysis of *trans*-$Coen_2(p\text{-}MeC_6H_4CO_2)_2^+$ in acetic acid.[131] In both reactions an S_N1CB mechanism cannot be invoked. It is essential therefore to consider other mechanisms and their likely occurrence. These must account for a transition complex of the composition $[Pt(IV), OH^-]^\ddagger$ or $[Co(III), OH^-]^\ddagger$ in the examples above.

1. One mechanism that appears to come close to a conjugate base mechanism, and that is strongly reminiscent of the interchange mechanism, is the ion-pair mechanism, S_N1IP or S_N2IP, which gives a rate expression identical to (4.68).[132]

$$Co(NH_3)_5X^{2+} + OH^- \rightleftharpoons Co(NH_3)_5X^{2+} \cdot OH^- \qquad K_1, \text{fast} \qquad \textbf{(4.72)}$$

$$Co(NH_3)_5X^{2+} \cdot OH^- \rightarrow Co(NH_3)_5OH^{2+} \cdot X^- \qquad k_2 \qquad \textbf{(4.73)}$$

$$Co(NH_3)_5OH^{2+} \cdot X^- \rightleftharpoons Co(NH_3)_5OH^{2+} + X^- \qquad \text{fast} \qquad \textbf{(4.74)}$$

If $K_1 < 0.05$ (in 4.68), then strictly second-order kinetics once again hold.

It has been pointed out that the preequilibria could be quite similar for the two mechanisms, that is,

$$\text{Co---NH}_2 + \text{OH}^- \rightleftharpoons \text{Co---N}^- \cdots \text{H---OH} \qquad \text{CB} \qquad (4.75)$$

$$\text{Co---NH}_2 + \text{OH}^- \rightleftharpoons \text{Co---N}_2\text{---H} \cdots \text{OH}^- \qquad \text{IP} \qquad (4.76)$$

and that the subsequent steps would also resemble each other if they were dissociative in nature.[133] Obviously they are not easy to distinguish.

2. A radically different mechanism involves an electron transfer in the rate-determining step:[134]

$$\text{Co(NH}_3)_5\text{X}^{2+} + \text{OH}^- \rightarrow \text{Co}^{II}(\text{NH}_3)_5\text{X}^+ + \text{OH}\cdot \qquad \text{slow} \qquad (4.77)$$

$$\text{Co}^{II}(\text{NH}_3)_5\text{X}^+ \rightarrow \text{Co(NH}_3)_5^{2+} + \text{X}^- \qquad \text{rapid} \qquad (4.78)$$

$$\text{Co(NH}_3)_5^{2+} + \text{OH}\cdot \rightarrow \text{Co(NH}_3)_5\text{OH}^{2+} \qquad \text{rapid} \qquad (4.79)$$

Oxidation of OH^- to OH radicals by complex ions is known, for example, by $Febipy_3^{3+}$.[135,136] This ingenious mechanism, although able to correlate a certain amount of cobalt(III) chemistry, fails in a number of important points. It is hard to understand, for example, why the rate of aquation of $Co(NH_3)_5NO_3^{2+}$ is unaffected by large amounts of Cl^-, I^-, or HO_2^-, all of which are better reducing agents than OH^-, unless there is specific interaction with the latter ion.[125] Further, the rapid base hydrolysis of Cr(III) and Ru(III) complexes is difficult to interpret in terms of redox processes.

3. There appear to be circumstances when base solvolysis has some associative character. Solvolysis of the conjugate base may be bimolecular, that is, (4.65) and (4.66) are combined in an S_N2CB mechanism.[121] It is possible to explain a large amount of kinetic data by a simple S_N2 mechanism but this is unable to account satisfactorily for a number of critical-type observations especially related to the competitive experiments described in part (a) of this section. Concerted attack by *two* OH^- ions has, however, been postulated to explain second-order dependence on $[OH^-]$ in some base hydrolyses.[111]

4.5.4   Base-Assisted Dechelation

There have been relatively few studies of the alkaline hydrolysis of chelates. All the ions $Coen_2CO_3^+$, $Coen_2PO_4^+$, and $Coen_2C_2O_4^+$ undergo a second-order ring cleavage in base, for example,

$$\text{Coen}_2\text{CO}_3^+ + \text{OH}^- \rightarrow \text{Coen}_2\text{CO}_3(\text{OH}) \qquad (4.80)$$

$Coen_2SO_4^+$ cleaves too easily in base for conventional study. A lack of activation parameters, plus varying degrees of Co–O bond cleavage during the hydrolysis of the three complexes thwarts a discussion of the factors influencing the rates.[111,137]

The base-catalyzed hydrolysis of a number of iron(II) complexes with ligands of the bipyridine type has been observed.[138] However, interpretation of these results are complicated by the observation that the presence of O_2 is required to promote hydrolysis in basic solution.[139] Significantly, the dissociation of $Niphen_3^{2+}$ (which is not expected to take part in a redox process) is almost independent of pH from 7 to 13.

4.5.5 Metal-Assisted Removal of Unidentates

Certain coordinated ligands can be attacked by metal ions, of which Hg^{2+} is by far the most studied and most effective, and the removal of the ligand from the complex is thus accelerated (Table 4.11).[140] Since these reactions appear to involve displacement of one electron-deficient species by another, these are termed *electrophilic substitution reactions* S_E. The ligands that can be removed in this way are often ones (N_3^-, CN^-) whose removal is also H^+-catalyzed (Sec. 4.5.1) and also an additional type (NCS^-, Cl^-) that shows a strong tendency to form bridged binuclear complexes. The majority of these induced aquations follow simple second-order kinetics. At high inducing-metal-ion concentration, deviations might be expected as (rapid) appearance of the adduct occurs (exactly as is sometimes observed with H^+ catalysis). This has been noted, for example, in the Hg^{2+}-catalyzed aquation of cis-$Coen_2Cl_2^+$. Two mechanisms, interaction of the two reactants via the adduct (steps (4.81) and (4.82)) and interaction extraneous to adduct formation (steps (4.81) and (4.83)), are not easily distinguished since they lead to the same kinetics (Sec. 1.6.4):[141]

$$cis\text{-}Coen_2Cl_2^+ + Hg^{2+} \rightleftharpoons Coen_2Cl_2Hg^{3+} \qquad K \quad (4.81)$$

$$Coen_2Cl_2Hg^{3+} \rightarrow cis\text{-}Coen_2(H_2O)Cl^{2+} + HgCl^+ \qquad k_2 \quad (4.82)$$

$$cis\text{-}Coen_2Cl_2^+ + Hg^{2+} \rightarrow cis\text{-}Coen_2(H_2O)Cl^{2+} + HgCl^+ \qquad k_3 \quad (4.83)$$

$$V = \frac{A[Hg^{2+}][Co^{III}]}{1 + K[Hg^{2+}]} \qquad (4.84)$$

where $A = k_2K$ on the basis of (4.81) + (4.82), and $A = k_3$ with (4.81) + (4.83).

It has been argued that since $trans$-$Coen_2Cl_2^+$ does not form an adduct with Hg(II), that formed with the *cis* isomer must be doubly bridged. It is not easy to visualize how such a species would easily break down to products, $Coen_2(H_2O)Cl^{2+}$, without further intervention of Hg^{2+}. From this point of view, the second mechanism is favored. Adduct formation between $CrNCS^{2+}$ and Hg^{2+} is quite strong, so that it is possible to measure the unequivocal breakdown of $CrNCSHg^{4+}$, and thus reaction through the adduct can be established as a route for Hg^{2+}-catalyzed aquation of $CrNCS^{2+}$ ion.[142]

Thallium(III) is generally less effective than Hg(II) in promoting aquation. In one of the few kinetic studies, it is found that Tl(III)-catalyzed hydrolysis of $Co(NH_3)_5Cl^{2+}$ and cis- and trans-$Coen_2Cl_2^+$ are second-order reactions over a wide [Tl(III)] range. Its effect lies in 4–6 units lower $\Delta H^{\ddagger}$ and $\Delta S^{\ddagger}$ values compared with spontaneous aquation. Towards these cobalt(III) substrates,[143]

$$Hg^{2+} \sim HgCl^+ > Tl^{3+} \sim TlOH^{2+} > TlCl^{2+} \qquad (4.85)$$

in effectiveness. Both Hg(II) and Tl(III) can effect S_E2 displacements of Au(I), Au(III), Co(III), Cr(III), Fe(II), and Hg(II) σ-bonded organometallic compounds,[144] for example,

$$(H_2O)_5CrCH_2C_5H_4NH^{3+} + Hg^{2+} \rightarrow Cr(H_2O)_6^{3+} + HgCH_2C_5H_4NH^{2+}$$

$$(4.86)$$

4.5.6 Metal-Induced Hydrolysis and Other Processes

There is substantial evidence that Hg^{2+}-catalyzed reactions do not require the incoming H_2O to bond appreciably in the transition state. Since aquation also allows for a minor role for incoming H_2O, the established parallelism between the rate constants for Hg^{2+}-catalyzed and spontaneous aquation $k_{Hg^{2+}}$ and k_{H_2O} for a number of cobalt(III) and chromium(III) complexes can be understood.[141,145] Therefore, Hg^{2+} is useful for generating five-coordinated intermediates and thus indirectly shedding light on the mechanism of spontaneous aquation. When the removal of coordinated halides is speeded up, products not normally obtained in aquation may result. With Hg^{2+}, trans-$CotrienCl_2^+$ produces trans-$Cotrien(H_2O)Cl^{2+}$, which isomerizes to β-cis-$Cotrien(H_2O)Cl^{2+}$. The cis complex is the only observed product of noncatalyzed aquation.[146] Mercury(II) is also useful for producing chelated esters, for hydrolytic examination (Sec. 6.4.1).

Mercuric ion-catalyzed aquation and metal-ion reduction of a common substrate have formally similar activated complexes, for example,

$$CrCl^{2+} + Hg^{2+} \rightarrow [Cr—Cl—Hg^{4+}]^{\ddagger} \qquad (4.87)$$

and $\qquad CrCl^{2+} + Cr^{2+} \rightarrow [Cr—Cl—Cr^{4+}]^{\ddagger} \qquad (4.88)$

Earlier-expected similar reaction parameters have not materialized[147] (Table 4.12). In general, there are lowered values of $\Delta H^{\ddagger}$ and more

TABLE 4.12. Comparison of Activation Parameters for Catalyzed Aquation and Reduction by Metal Ions, M^{2+}

Substrate	Aquation			Reduction			Ref.
	$\Delta H^{\ddagger}$	$\Delta S^{\ddagger}$	M^{2+}	$\Delta H^{\ddagger}$	$\Delta S^{\ddagger}$	M^{2+}	
$CrCl^{2+}$	18	-5	Hg^{2+}	8	-27	Cr^{2+}	a
trans-$CrCl_2^+$	13.5	-6	Hg^{2+}	5	-30	Cr^{2+}	b
$Co(EDTA)Cl^{2-}$	23	11	Cd^{2+}	11	-22	Fe^{2+}	c

[a] R. V. James and E. L. King, *Inorg. Chem.*, **9**, 1301 (1970).
[b] J. P. Birk, *Inorg. Chem.*, **9**, 735 (1970).
[c] A large number of metal ions have the ability to catalyze this ring-closure reaction (2.131).[148,149]

negative $\Delta S^{\ddagger}$ for the reduction, and this has been ascribed to extra weakening of the Cr–Cl bond and more stringent geometrical requirements in the activated complex.[148,149] Further, there is a poor correlation between rate constants for reactions of Fe^{2+} (inner-sphere) and Hg^{2+} with $Coen_2$-ACl^{n+} ions.[141]

4.5.7 Shape of the Intermediate

Reaction of trans-$Co(NH_3)_4(ND_3)N_3^{2+}$ and trans-$Co(NH_3)_4(ND_3)$-$OCONH_2^{2+}$ with NO^+ and of trans-$Co(NH_3)_4(ND_3)X^{2+}$, X = Br or Cl, with Hg^{2+} gives trans-$Co(NH_3)_4(ND_3)H_2O^{3+}$. If a dissociative mechanism is operative, the intermediate must be square-pyramidal.[150] Competition studies tend to support this formulation.[151]

On the other hand, reactions of cis-$Coen_2Cl_2^+$ with Hg^{2+} and cis-$Coen_2Cl(N_3)^+$ with HNO_2 give the same product (80% cis- and 20% trans-$Coen_2(H_2O)Cl^{2+}$) and this result suggests a common trigonal-bipyramidal intermediate.[152] The difference in behavior between the ethylenediamine and ammonia complexes may result from enhanced stability of the trigonal bipyramid in the $Coen_2X$ system.[152]

4.5.8 Metal-Assisted Dechelation

Metal ions can assist also in the dissociation (or hydrolysis) of complexes containing multidentate ligands. The metal ion may not necessarily complex with the detached ligand, for example, in the metal-assisted acid-catalyzed aquation of $Cr(C_2O_4)_3^{3-}$.[153] Usually, however, the metal ion removes and complexes the ligand as in

$$ML + M' \rightarrow M'L + M \tag{4.89}$$

The reactions have been followed spectrally, or polarographically (when M' is monitored), or by isotope exchange (M' an isotopic form of M).[154] Among the earliest kinetic studies of complex ions, they are commonly second-order, with the second-order rate constant k often dependent on $[H^+]$ and $[M]$, for example,[155]

$$\frac{d[M'L]}{dt} = k[ML][M'] \tag{4.90}$$

with

$$k = k_1 + k_2[H^+] + k_3[H^+][M]^{-1} \tag{4.91}$$

The three terms in the rate law correspond to paths I, II, and III:

$$ML + M' \rightarrow M'L + M \qquad k_I \qquad (I) \tag{4.92}$$

$$ML + H^+ \rightleftharpoons MLH^+ \qquad K_{II} \qquad (II) \tag{4.93}$$

$$MLH^+ + M' \rightarrow M'LH^+ + M \qquad k_{II} \tag{4.94}$$

$$ML + H^+ \rightleftharpoons M + LH \qquad K_{III} \qquad (III) \tag{4.95}$$

$$LH + M' \rightarrow M'LH \qquad k_{III} \tag{4.96}$$

with $k_1 = k_I$; $k_2 = K_{II}k_{II}$; $k_3 = K_{III}k_{III}$.

Since K_{III} is often known from thermodynamic data, k_{III} can be estimated from the experimental data, and this approach has been very useful in evaluating the high rate constants for complexation by labile metal ions.

It has been supposed that binuclear intermediates occur in all the paths and that the stability of these greatly influences the rates.[155,156] We have already seen that it is relatively easy to partially unwind chelates and sequester the end with a proton; the situation is analogous, although more complicated, with these reactions. The most studied systems are those involving EDTA complexes. The rate law shown in (1.153) is typical, each term representing paths for the metal interchange. Electrophilic reactions involving CyDTA complexes—for example, M = Ni, M' = Cu, L = CyDTA, in Eq. (4.89)—interestingly have zero dependence on the entering metal concentration, since the rigidity of the CyDTA molecule precludes bonding of two metals to the iminodiacetate segments of one CyDTA molecule.[157] The same situation arises in ligand-accelerated dechelation (see Sec. 4.5.10).

In metal interchange reactions involving even rigid macrocycles, such as the porphyrin (P) complexes,

$$M^{II}P + *M^{II} \rightarrow *M^{II}P + M^{II} \tag{4.97}$$

the entering metal plays an important role. Some qualitative and quite limited quantitative data for metallophorphyrin complexes already indicate a variety of behavior.[88,90] Rate laws containing $[*M(II)]$,

$[*M(II)]^2$, or even $[*M(II)]^{-1}$ terms have been found, but this may simply mean differing rate-determining steps in a general scheme (see Sec. 4.4.3).[90] In the relatively fast reaction of Zn(II) with HgTPP in pyridine at 25° (TPP = tetraphenylporphine), the occurrence of isosbestic points (Fig. 3.7) and a very slow Zn(II)–TPP reaction observed indicate that the free base is not an intermediate and that these substitutions are definitely S_E2 in character.[90,91]

4.5.9 Ligand-Assisted Removal of Unidentates

Anions can promote hydrolysis of complex cations by producing ion pairs of enhanced reactivity (see (2.178)).[158] There are a few examples, rather special in nature, of induced aquation of unidentate ligands. These include the accelerated removal of an azide or a carbamate group by NO^+ (nitrous acid),[30] and removal of coordinated iodide by iodine,[159] both probably proceeding through some reactive adduct, for example, in the HNO_2-induced aquation of $Co(NH_3)_5N_3^{2+}$ ion:

$$V = k[Co(NH_3)_5N_3^{2+}][HNO_2][H^+] \qquad \textbf{(4.98)}$$

the suggested mechanism is

$$HNO_2 + H^+ \rightleftharpoons H_2NO_2^+ \qquad \textbf{(4.99)}$$

$$H_2NO_2^+ \rightleftharpoons NO^+ + H_2O \qquad \textbf{(4.100)}$$

$$Co(NH_3)_5N_3^{2+} + NO^+ \rightarrow [Co(NH_3)_5N_3NO^{3+}] \xrightarrow[\text{rapid}]{H_2O} Co(NH_3)_5H_2O^{3+}$$
$$\textbf{(4.101)}$$

A remarkable replacement reaction proceeding rapidly and with retention of configuration involves the interchange of Br^- with Cl^- when Cl_2 reacts with $Coen_2(X)Br^+$ ions.[160] The interchange occurs without formation of a five-coordinate intermediate.[160]

Probably the only important means whereby a ligand may accelerate the removal of a coordinated ligand is entering the metal coordination sphere with it and thereby labilizing it towards hydrolysis. The ions HSO_3^- and NO_2^- induce the aquation of Cr(III) complexes containing halide or halide-type ligands.[161,162] The suggested mechanism involves rapid H_2O–NO_2^- interchange in (1) and (3):

$$Cr(H_2O)_5Br^{2+} \xrightarrow[(1)]{NO_2^-} Cr(H_2O)_4(ONO)Br^+ \xrightarrow[(2)]{H_2O}$$

$$Cr(H_2O)_5ONO^{2+} \xrightarrow[(3)]{H_2O} Cr(H_2O)_6^{3+} \qquad \textbf{(4.102)}$$

and the rate-determining removal of Br^- in (2), this being more rapid than hydrolysis of $Cr(H_2O)_5Br^{2+}$, perhaps by the operation of a neighboring group effect, as in **9**:

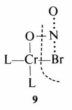

9

This idea is supported by the effect being observed with the *cis* but not the *trans* isomer of the $Cr(NH_3)_4(H_2O)Cl^{2+}$ ion.[162]

4.5.10   Ligand-Assisted Dechelation

In this category are the well-studied ligand exchange reactions of EDTA and polyamine complexes, a typical one of which (charges omitted) is

$$CuEDTA + trien \rightleftharpoons Cutrien + EDTA \qquad (4.103)$$

which may be studied in either direction depending on the pH conditions and reactant concentrations.[163]

    The rate in the forward direction is first-order in CuEDTA and first-order in total trien (T). The contribution of the amine forms T, TH^+, and TH_2^{2+} may be resolved from a rate/pH profile.

$$V = \{k_1[T] + k_2[TH^+] + k_3[TH_2^{2+}]\}[CuEDTA] \qquad (4.104)$$

    Interchange involving multidentate ligands is obviously even less likely to be direct than interchange involving unidentate ligands. However, when solvent is available on the complex (or part of the coordinated ligand is very rapidly replaceable by solvent), the incoming ligand can gain a "coordination foothold."[164] Substantial evidence exists for a mechanism in which three nitrogen atoms of the polyamine bond to the metal **10** before the rds of M–N cleavage, which leads to the final products:

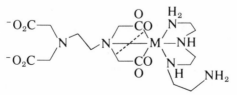

10

In the fast reaction of $Ni(dien)(H_2O)_3^{2+}$ with EDTA, giving $NiEDTA^{2-}$, various intermediates with decreasing chelation of dien can be detected by the stopped-flow method.[165] Significantly, the rate constants resemble those for H^+ stripping of the $Ni(dien)(H_2O)_3^{2+}$ ion.[85] In this sense, the EDTA simulates H^+ by preventing reclosing as the Ni–N bonds are successively broken.

A similar type of sequence has been used to explain ligand exchange in MEDTA complexes.[166,167] Intermediates involve two partially bonded EDTA ligands for each metal atom. The critical stage is reached when the symmetrical intermediate **11** is formed.

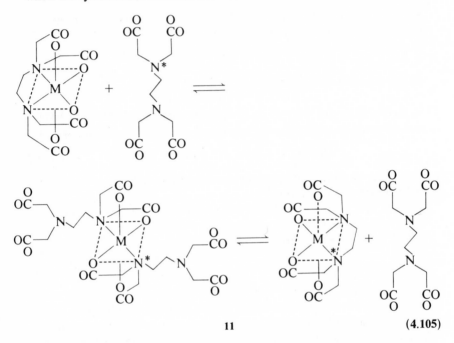

11   (4.105)

The various steps leading to **11** have been considered for $NiEDTA^{2-}/$ EDTA exchange[166] and the results compared with the formally similar $NiEDTA^{2-}/Ni^{2+}$ exchange.[168]

4.6 REACTION RATES AND THE ELECTRONIC CONFIGURATION OF THE METAL

There has been some success in understanding the rates of substitution in octahedral complexes in terms of properties of metal ion, specifically, charge and electron configuration.

TABLE 4.13. Rate Constants ($\log k$, M^{-1} sec^{-1}) for Reaction of Aquated Bivalent Metal Ions with Ligands at 25°

Ligand	Metal Ion and Electron Configuration[a]									
	V^{2+} d^3	Cr^{2+} hsd^4	Mn^{2+} hsd^5	Fe^{2+} hsd^6	Ru^{2+} lsd^6	Co^{2+} hsd^7	Ni^{2+} d^8	Cu^{2+} d^9	Zn^{2+} d^{10}	Cd^{2+} d^{10}
H_2O[b]	2.0	8.5	7.5	6.5	...	6.3	4.3	9.3	7.5	8.2
NH_3	...	...	...	...	...	5.1	3.7	8.3[g]	6.6	...
phen	0.5	8.0	~5.4	5.9	...	5.3	3.4	7.9	6.8	>7.0
X^-	1.5[c]	...	6.5[d]	6.0[d]	–2.0[e]	5.3[d]	3.9[d]	8.7[d]	...	...
$EDTAH^{3-}$	...	...	8.7[f]	...	...	7.1	5.3	9.3	~9	9.6

SOURCE: Tables in Refs. 83 and 173.

[a] hs = high spin, ls = low spin.
[b] Water exchange in log sec^{-1} units, from nmr or ultrasonics.
[c] X = NCS.
[d] X = F.
[e] X = Cl, Br, and I, Ref. 174.
[f] With NTA^{3-}.
[g] H. Diebler and P. Rosen, Ber. Bunsenges. Phys. Chem., 76, 1031 (1972).

Bjerrum and Poulsen as the result of a number of rate measurements in MeOH at $-75°$ drew attention to some rules governing reactivity,[169] while the electron configuration was used to explain the rates of CN^- exchange with several cyanide complexes.[170] It was Taube who first rationalized the rates and electronic configuration of a number of octahedral complexes, using qualitative observations almost exclusively.[18] Since then, these ideas have been placed on a semiquantitative basis by CF and MO theory.[171] The crystal field stabilization energy (CFSE) has been calculated for octahedral and five-coordinated geometries. If a dissociative mechanism is assumed, the latter will approximate the activated complex for such a reaction. The difference in CFSE, the activation energy, CFAE, will represent the loss of stabilization energy. The higher the CFAE, the more the likelihood of a slower reaction in a series where the other contributions to the overall activation energy might be considered constant. The calculations have since been refined,[172] but all lead to the idea that metal ions with certain electron configurations will react more slowly than other similarly charged metal ions. Electron configurations with positive CFAE are d^3, low spin d^4, d^5, and d^6, and d^8.

These predictions have been amply borne out, as examination of Tables 4.13 and 4.14[173] for reactions of bivalent and tervalent metal complexes reveals.

The relative inertness of the V^{2+}, Ru^{2+}, and Ni^{2+} triad are striking in Table 4.13. The CFAE for V^{2+} and Ni^{2+} is $2Dq$,[171] which should lead to a value for $k_{Ni}/k_V \sim 25$. The experimental value, nearer to 300, does show up the qualitative nature of the theory however.[12] Further, the inertness of Cr(III) relative to V(III), Fe(III), and Ti(III) (Table 4.14) is anticipated, but once again the $\geqslant 10^8$-fold difference is larger than would be expected on CF ideas alone.[12] However, the slower reactions of $Ru(H_2O)_6^{3+}$, t_{2g}^5, compared with $Fe(H_2O)_6^{3+}$, $t_{2g}^3 e_g^2$ are exactly as would be expected.

When ions have the same electron configuration but different charges, the higher-charged species will react more slowly.[169] This would be anticipated for a dissociative mechanism,[171] and is supported by data for Ru^{2+} vs Rh^{3+},[174] Mn^{2+} vs Fe^{3+}, and V^{2+} vs Cr^{3+}

4.7 SUBSTITUTION IN NONAQUEOUS SOLVENTS

Attention is now being paid to substitution behavior in nonaqueous solution. Rate constants are remarkably similar for the exchange of the solvated cation in a number of solvents (Table 4.15). Although this is suggestive of a common (dissociative) mechanism for exchange, there is however a wide range of activation parameters forming an isokinetic

TABLE 4.14. Rate Constants (log k, M^{-1} sec^{-1}) for Reaction of Aquated Tervalent Metal Ions with Ligands at 25°

Ligand	Metal Ion and Electron Configuration[a]							
	Ti^{3+} d^1	V^{3+} d^2	Cr^{3+} d^3	Mn^{3+} hsd^4	Fe^{3+} hsd^5	Ru^{3+} lsd^5	Co^{3+} hsd^6	Rh^{3+} lsd^6
H$_2$O[b]	5.0	...	-5.7	...	4.3	...	...	...
HN$_3$	...	-0.4[g]	...	...	0.4[g]	...	...	-7.5
X$^-$	3.6[c]	2.1[c], 3.1[h]	-5.7[c]	≤ 4[d]	2.1[c]	-6[e]	1.9[cf]	...

SOURCE: Tables in Ref. 173.
[a] hs = high spin, ls = low spin.
[b] Water exchange in log sec^{-1} units from nmr.
[c] X = NCS.
[d] X = F.
[e] Ref. 174.
[f] G. Davis and K. O. Watkins, *Inorg. Chem.*, **9**, 2735 (1970), see Table 5.18.
[g] J. H. Espenson and J. R. Pladziewicz, *Inorg. Chem.*, **9**, 1380 (1970).
[h] X = HC$_2$O$_4^-$, R. C. Patel and H. Diebler, *Ber. Bunsenges. Phys. Chem.*, **76**, 1035 (1972).

TABLE 4.15. Exchange Rate Parameters (log k, sec^{-1}) for Transition Metal Ions at 25°

Solvent	Mn^{2+}			Fe^{2+}			Co^{2+}			Ni^{2+}		
	log k	$\Delta H^{\ddagger}$	$\Delta S^{\ddagger}$	log k	$\Delta H^{\ddagger}$	$\Delta S^{\ddagger}$	log k	$\Delta H^{\ddagger}$	$\Delta S^{\ddagger}$	log k	$\Delta H^{\ddagger}$	$\Delta S^{\ddagger}$
H$_2$O	7.5	8.1	+ 3	6.5	7.7	− 3	6.4[a]	10.4[a]	+ 5[a]	4.5	13.9[f]	+ 9[f]
CH$_3$OH	5.6	6.2	−12	4.7	12.0	+ 3	4.3	13.8	+ 7	3.0	15.8	+ 8
DMSO	...	...	...	...	...	...	5.5[b]	12.2[b]	+10[b]	3.5[b]	13.0[b]	+ 1[b]
CH$_3$CN	7.1	7.3	− 2	5.6[d]	9.7[d]	0[d]	5.5[e]	11.4[e]	+ 5[e]	3.4	11.7	− 4
										3.3	16.4[d]	+12[d]
DMF	...	...	...	5.7	5.3	−15	5.3 or 5.8	7.1 or 13.4	−10 or +13	3.8[c]	14.0[c]	+ 6[c]

SOURCE: Ref. 25 except where noted.
[a] P. E. Haggard, H. W. Dodgen, and J. P. Hunt, *Inorg. Chem.*, **10**, 959 (1971).
[b] L. S. Frankel, *Inorg. Chem.*, **10**, 814 (1971).
[c] Ref. 176.
[d] R. J. West and S. F. Lincoln, *Aust. J. Chem.*, **24**, 1169 (1971).
[e] R. J. West and S. F. Lincoln, *Inorg. Chem.*, **11**, 1688 (1972).
[f] J. W. Neely and R. E. Connick, *J. Amer. Chem. Soc.*, **94**, 3419, 8646 (1972).

plot (Sec. 2.6.3).[25,26] Values for rate constants and activation parameters for ligand substitution of bivalent metal ions in nonaqueous solution do not agree with values predicted on the basis of (4.18). Further, the situation of first bond formation controlling chelation in aqueous solution (Sec. 4.4.1) does not persist in the few studies in nonaqueous solution.[175] It appears that solvent structure, probably modified by solute, plays an important role in the substitution process.[25,26,176]

Rate parameters for the exchange of DMF between $Ni(DMF)_6^{2+}$ and DMF/CD_3NO_2 mixtures are however independent of the composition of the solvent mixture.[177] This observation, duplicated in other solvent mixtures,[178] does constitute strong evidence for the operation of a dissociative mechanism.[47]

4.8   SUBSTITUTION IN SQUARE-PLANAR COMPLEXES

There are a number of metals, particularly with a low spin d^8 configuration, that form four-coordinated square-planar complexes. Of these, the Pt(II) complexes have been the most intensively investigated. They are therefore representatives of this geometry, much as Co(III) complexes epitomize octahedral behavior—and for precisely the same reasons, namely that they have been previously well characterized and studied, particularly by Russian workers, and that they react slowly. There have never been any problems therefore in the initiation and the rate measurement of these reactions. The variety of square-planar Rh(I), Ir(I), Pd(II), Ni(II), Cu(II), and Au(III) complexes suitable for study is more limited, and the measurement of their reaction rates usually requires flow methods.

Many of the Pt(II) complexes, unlike most octahedral complexes, are soluble in aprotic solvents and therefore this has been a possible examining medium. The ultraviolet spectral method and, less commonly, conductivity and radioactive isotopic exchange have been the methods most commonly employed for monitoring the rates.

4.9   THE KINETICS OF REPLACEMENT INVOLVING UNIDENTATE LIGANDS

Most studies have been concerned with replacement of one unidentate ligand by another, and the rules and patterns of behavior that have evolved are based mainly on this simple type of substitution reaction. The complex ion $PtdienX^+$ has proved a popular Pt(II) substrate, with the dien acting as a nonremovable terdentate ligand, and the X group replaceable by a variety of negative and neutral ligands:[179]

$$PtdienX^+ + Y^{n-} \rightleftharpoons PtdienY^{(2-n)+} + X^- \qquad (4.106)$$

The rate law governing substitution in planar complexes usually consists of two terms, one first-order in the metal complex (M) alone and the other first-order in both M and the entering ligand Y:

$$V = \frac{-d[M]}{dt} = k_1[M] + k_2[M][Y] \qquad (4.107)$$

The experiments are invariably carried out using excess Y and therefore with pseudo first-order conditions. The experimental first-order rate constant k is given by

$$V = k[M] \qquad (4.108)$$

Therefore $\qquad\qquad k = k_1 + k_2[Y] \qquad (4.109)$

A plot of k vs [Y] will have an intercept k_1 and a slope k_2. Two examples are shown in Figs. 4.3[180] and 4.4. For different nucleophiles reacting with the same complex, the value of k_1 is the same, whereas the value of k_2 usually will be different.

(a) Significance of k_1. The term containing k_1 resembles octahedral complexes in their substitution behavior where it represents ligand-ligand replacement via the solvated complex:

$$-\overset{|}{\underset{|}{M}}-X \underset{\text{X slow}}{\overset{\text{S}}{\rightleftharpoons}} -\overset{|}{\underset{|}{M}}-S \underset{\text{S fast}}{\overset{\text{Y}}{\rightleftharpoons}} -\overset{|}{\underset{|}{M}}-Y \qquad (4.110)$$

As with solvolysis reactions of octahedral complexes, the rate-determining step may be solvolytic or dissociative;[181,182] in any case, it is independent of the concentration of Y:

$$-\overset{|}{\underset{|}{M}}-X \quad\begin{matrix} \overset{k_D}{\diagup}\negmedspace\negmedspace\negmedspace\diagdown_{k_{-D}} \\ \underset{k_{-S}}{\diagdown}\negmedspace\negmedspace\negmedspace\diagup^{k_S} \end{matrix}\quad \begin{matrix} -\overset{|}{\underset{|}{M}} + X \xrightarrow[+Y]{k_D{}^Y} -\overset{|}{\underset{|}{M}}-Y + X \\[2em] -\overset{|}{\underset{|}{M}}-S + X \xrightarrow[+Y]{k_S{}^Y} -\overset{|}{\underset{|}{M}}-Y + S + X \end{matrix} \qquad (4.111)$$

Setting up stationary-state conditions for $-\overset{|}{\underset{|}{M}}$ and $-\overset{|}{\underset{|}{M}}-S$ yields

$$k_1 = \frac{k_D{}^Y k_D[Y]}{k_D{}^Y[Y] + k_{-D}[X]} + \frac{k_S{}^Y k_S[S][Y]}{k_S{}^Y[Y] + k_{-S}[X]} \qquad (4.112)$$

which, when the step involving Y is fast, reduces to

$$k_1 = k_D + k_S[S] \qquad (4.113)$$

On the basis of either interpretation, k_1 should equal the solvolysis rate constant and if MS is an isolatable intermediate, it should be shown to

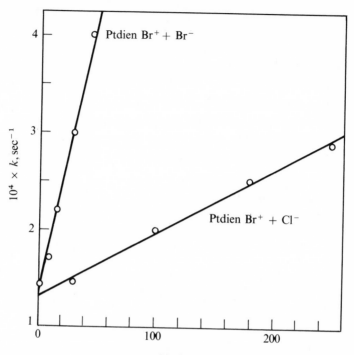

FIGURE 4.3   Plots of pseudo first-order rate constant (k, sec^{-1} at 25°) vs [anion] for reactions of Ptdien Br$^+$ with Br$^-$ and Cl$^-$ ions in H$_2$O.   Intercepts (k_1) are identical; the (different) slopes are values for k_2.[180]

react rapidly with Y.   Both consequences have been realized in certain systems.   Thus the value for the rate constant for hydrolysis of PtdienBr$^+$ (1.3×10^{-4} sec^{-1})[183] is identical to that (k_1) for the intercept in Fig. 4.3 (1.3×10^{-4} sec^{-1}).   The rate constant for the reaction of PtdienH$_2$O^{2+} with Y exceeds the rate constant for the replacement of X by Y in PtdienX$^+$ by at least a factor of 20.[184]   Although there is no doubt about the general occurrence of a k_1 path, in a few cases it cannot be distinguished experimentally from zero.[185]   If

$$\text{PtdienNO}_2{}^+ + \text{I}^- \rightleftharpoons \text{PtdienI}^+ + \text{NO}_2{}^- \qquad (4.114)$$

is treated as a reversible reaction, then the forward rate constant k_f is given by

$$k_f = k_1 + k_2[\text{I}^-] \qquad (4.115)$$

Making allowance for the $k_2[\text{I}^-]$ term leaves $k_1 \sim 0$.[186]

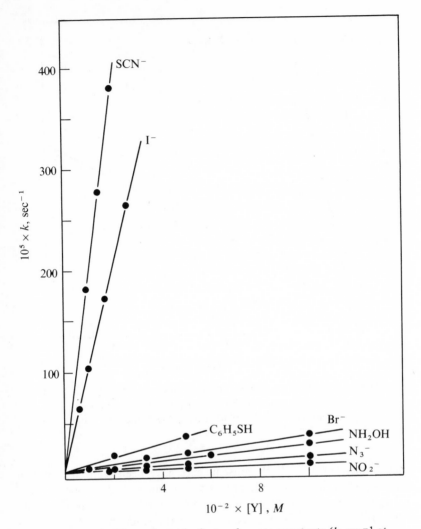

FIGURE 4.4   Plots of pseudo first-order rate constants (k, sec^{-1} at 30°) vs [nucleophile] for reactions of *trans*-Ptpy$_2$Cl$_2$ in methanol.[198]

(b) Significance of k_2. It is generally accepted that the key rate term in substitution in square-planar complexes involves nucleophilic S$_N$2[28] or A[29] attack of the entering nucleophile Y on the metal complex. It follows from this that the bond-making as well as the bond-breaking process will be important, and it can be expected that there will be varying degrees of participation by both. All attempts, however, to observe an intermediate in the bimolecular reactions of Pt(II) have failed, even with the most favorable situation, that is, using a strong entering ligand and a weak leaving one.[186]   A five-coordinated intermediate has been reported in a substitution reaction of Rh(I); and in one of the few studies of substitution in Ni(II) planar complexes, the formation of an intermediate is rapid compared with the subsequent processes, and therefore is easily discernible.[187]   Since the characteristics of the k_1 and k_2 terms are similar, an associative path is commonly favored for k_1, that is, $k_S[S]$, also.

4.9.1   Activation Parameters

Examination of Table 4.16 and other data[188] shows that substitution in Pt(II) complexes, for which there are the most data, is largely $\Delta H^{\ddagger}$-controlled.   The reactions are invariably attended by large negative values for $\Delta S^{\ddagger}$.   This latter fact is consistent with a net increase in bonding in an ordered and charged transition state.   These considerations apply to both the k_1 and the k_2 terms.[188,189]   Large negative $\Delta V_1^{\ddagger}$ and $\Delta V_2^{\ddagger}$ terms also indicate that bond formation is dominant in the transition state for both the solvolytic and the bimolecular paths.[190]

TABLE 4.16.   Activation Parameters for Substitution in Pt(II) Complexes in Water at 30°, $I = 0.1$ [189]

Complex	Reagent	k, M^{-1} sec^{-1}	$\Delta H^{\ddagger}$	$\Delta S^{\ddagger}$
PtdienCl$^+$	H_2O	2×10^{-7} a	20	-18
	Cl$^-$	1.4×10^{-3}	21	-4
		4.2×10^{-4} b		
	N$_3^-$	5×10^{-3}	16	-17
	Br$^-$	7×10^{-3}	13	-25
	I$^-$	0.170	11	-25
	NCS$^-$	0.270	10	-28
	SC(NH$_2$)$_2$	0.580	8.5	-31
PtdienBr$^+$	H_2O	3.6×10^{-6} a	19.5	-17
		2.2×10^{-6} a,b	20	-13
	Cl$^-$	6.0×10^{-4} b	18	-11
	Br$^-$	6.0×10^{-3} b	16	-15
	I$^-$	0.32	11	-25
	NCS$^-$	0.68	9.5	-27
	SC(NH$_2$)$_2$	1.3	8.5	-29

[a] First-order rate constant corrected to second-order by dividing by $[H_2O] = 55.5$ M.
[b] At 25°, J. R. Paxson and D. S. Martin, Jr., *Inorg. Chem.*, **10**, 1551 (1971).

4.10   LIGAND EFFECTS ON THE RATE

There is naturally an overriding interest in the shape of the five-coordinated intermediate, or transition, state. General considerations of the shape in which there will be least mutual interaction of five ligands and of the available orbitals[24,191] support a trigonal bipyramid. Much replacement behavior can be rationalized on the basis of a trigonal-bipyramidal species. It has been suggested, however, that both square-pyramid and trigonal-bipyramid geometries are developed in the course of the replacement:[188]

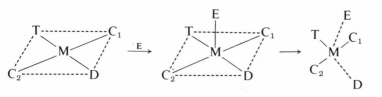

(T, D, and E in equatorial plane)

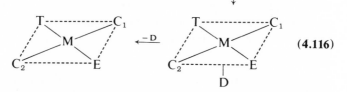

                                                     (4.116)

The departing ligand D is replaced by the entering E. The ligands C_1 and C_2 are *cis*, and T is *trans* to D. Since substitution rates are quite sensitive to steric effects in D, it seems very likely that E must approach at an angle rather than normal to the plane.[192]

     One of the consequences of an associative mechanism is the decided importance of the ligands—entering, leaving, and remaining—on the rate of the process. This feature, as well as an often pronounced solvent effect, distinguishes planar from octahedral substitution.

     There have therefore been a large number of studies of substitution in which systematic variations are made in the character of T, C_1, C_2, E, and D. Interpretation has been helped by the fact that complete retention of configuration during substitution has been consistently observed with Pt(II). It is difficult to assess whether this is universally true with square-planar complexes of other metals, since these have marked configurational lability.

4.10.1   Effects of Ligands Already Present

The group *trans* to the leaving ligand appears to have a more pronounced influence than the two *cis* to it on the rate of its departure.[193,194] A limited number of studies indicate an order in *trans*-Pt(PEt₃)₂XCl:[193]

$$H^- > CH_3^- > C_6H_5^- > p\text{-}CH_3OC_6H_4^- > Cl^- \qquad \textbf{(4.117)}$$

and in cis-$Pt(NH_3)XCl_2$:[188]

$$C_2H_4 \gg NO_2^- > Br^- > Cl^- \qquad (4.118)$$

for the effect on Cl^- replacement by py. The sequence is, however, not completely independent of the nature of the entering group.[182]

It has been known for many years that a ligand can be assigned an order of *trans effect*, which denotes its tendency to direct an incoming group in the position *trans* to itself. In Pt(II) complexes, this power decreases approximately in the order[181]

$$CN, C_2H_4, CO, NO > R_3P \sim H^- \sim SC(NH_2)_2 > CH_3^- > C_6H_5^-$$

$$> SCN^- > NO_2^- > I^- > Br^- > Cl^- > NH_3 > OH^- > H_2O$$

$$\qquad (4.119)$$

The effect has played an important role in preparing Pt(II) complexes of specific geometry,[195,196] and comparison of the two series—(4.117) and (4.118) with (4.119)—indicates that the greater *trans* effect is associated with a larger rate constant for elimination.[197]

The *trans*-directing group may lower the activation energy for substitution in two ways. It may destabilize the ground state of the complex; and older theories of the *trans* effect emphasized the weakening of the *trans* bond. Alternatively, the activated complex may be stabilized; and this aspect of the *trans* effect is incorporated in more recent explanations suggested for the *trans* effect.[191,197] The *trans* ligand, in addition to its effect on the rate of the reaction, also plays a role in the discrimination of various entering groups.[188]

Ligands *cis* to the leaving group have a relatively small effect on the rates of replacement unless steric effects are important.[188] They are considered to occupy the axial positions in the trigonal-bipyramidal transition complex.

4.10.2   Effect of Entering Ligand

There have been extensive studies of the influence of an entering ligand on its rate of entry into a Pt(II) complex.[198,199] The rate constants for reaction of a large number and variety of ligands with $trans$-$Ptpy_2Cl_2$ have been measured (Fig. 4.4 and Table 4.17). It is the large range in reactivities for entering ligands that is a feature of the associative mechanism, and that differentiates it from the behavior of octahedral complexes. The order of nucleophilic reactivity is not, however, completely independent of the nature of the substrate.

The softness or polarizability of the nucleophile rather than its basicity is important in determining its effectiveness. This is apparent when one considers that olefines, phosphines, and so forth, are strong while

TABLE 4.17.   Rate Constants (k, $M^{-1}\,sec^{-1}$) for Reaction of $trans$-$Ptpy_2Cl_2$ with a Number of Nucleophiles in CH_3OH[198,199]

Nucleophile	$10^3 \times k$	n_{Pt}	Nucleophile	$10^3 \times k$	n_{Pt}
CH_3OH	0.00027	0.0	I^-	107[a]	5.46
CH_3O^-	Very slow	< 2.4	$(CH_3)_2Se$	148	5.70
Cl^-	0.45[a]	3.04	SCN^-	180[a]	5.75
NH_3	0.47[a]	3.07	SO_3^{2-}	250[a]	5.79
C_5H_5N	0.55[a]	3.19	Ph_3Sb	1,810	6.79
NO_2^-	0.68[a]	3.22	Ph_3As	2,320	7.68
$C_3H_3N_2$	0.74	3.44	CN^-	4,000	7.14
N_3^-	1.6[a]	3.58	$SeCN^-$	5,150[a]	7.11
N_2H_4	2.9[a]	3.86	$SC(NH_2)_2$	6,000[a]	7.17
Br^-	3.7[a]	4.18	Ph_3P	249,000	8.93
$(CH_3)_2S$	21.9	4.87			

[a] Kinetic data at 30°.

OH^- and OEt^- are weak nucleophiles. The reactivity order resembles that for the decreasing ability of these ligands to labilize the $trans$ position in the complex. This might be anticipated since in the five-coordinated intermediate the entering nucleophile and the $trans$ ligand both occupy positions in the trigonal plane (see (4.116)) and both may influence the energetics of the transition state in similar ways.

Values of $\Delta F^{\ddagger}$ parallel $\Delta H^{\ddagger}$ for a limited series of reactions.[189] Rate constants may therefore be used to set up some quantitative relationships (Sec. 2.5.4). It is found that for a variety of reactions of Pt complexes in different solvents,[198,199]

$$\log k_Y = sn_{Pt} + \log k_S \qquad (4.120)$$

where k_Y = second-order rate constant for reaction of Y.

k_S = rate constant for solvent reaction/[solvent].

s = nucleophilic discriminating factor.

n_{Pt} = nucleophilic reactivity constant, defined as equal to $\log(k_Y/k_S)$ for reaction of $trans$-$Ptpy_2Cl_2$ in CH_3OH.

The terms s and k_S depend only on the Pt complex and not on the entering ligand. This relationship holds in methanol and other solvents, and with few exceptions the order of n_{Pt} is not dependent on the nature of the solvent. It has not been found possible to correlate n_{Pt} with other parameters such as n_{CH_3I},[200] basicity (see above), and so on. The main value of the relationship is found in correlating kinetic data and in discussing effects in terms of the discriminating factor s.[188] With Au(III), relative reactivities appear very substrate-dependent, and even an approximate series cannot be assigned.

4.10.3 Effect of Leaving Group

Reactions of the type

$$\text{PtdienX}^+ + \text{py} \rightarrow \text{Ptdienpy}^{2+} + \text{X}^- \qquad (4.121)$$

in aqueous solution have been used to study the effect of X on the rate of the reactions.[184,201] Now, the groups with a pronounced ability to trans-labilize are replaced the least easily. The members of the series

$$\text{CN}^- < \text{NO}_2^- < \text{SCN}^- < \text{N}_3^- \ll \text{I}^- < \text{Br}^- < \text{Cl}^- < \text{H}_2\text{O} < \text{NO}_3^-$$
$$(4.122)$$

differ in rate constant by as much as 10^6 from the slowest (CN^-) to the fastest (NO_3^-) removed. It is fairly clear from these observations, therefore, that metal-ligand bond breakage must be significant, even in a predominantly associative reaction. Generally, the second-order rate constant increases with decreasing basicity of the leaving group, and LFER exist. A rare example, where the nature of the leaving group also controls the mechanism, is shown in the reactions of $\text{Pd}(\text{Et}_4\text{dien})\text{X}^+$ with Br^- ion in DMF. When $X = -\text{SCN}$, only the k_1 term is observed (see Sec. 4.12). With $X = -\text{SeCN}$, however, the two-term rate law applies.[202]

4.10.4 Effect of Solvent

Solvent plays a much more important role in planar substitution than with octahedral complexes, although the solubility of the latter is often restricted to polar solvents so that the effect of a range of solvents often cannot be examined. The solvent acts as a nucleophile in the reaction path represented by k_1. A large value of k_1 relative to k_2 is observed in solvents capable of coordinating strongly to the metal so that *generally* the order

$$\text{DMSO} > \text{MeNO}_2, \text{H}_2\text{O} > \text{ROH} \qquad (4.123)$$

is observed,[203] although the spread of rate constants is not large.[204] Conversely, in solvents that are poor coordinators, such as C_6H_6 and CCl_4, the k_2 value dominates. However, the order of nucleophilicities does not change in different solvents.

Additionally, the solvent is the reaction medium and as such, by solvating the ground and activated states, will influence profoundly the energetics of the activated process.[205] This is probably more important with square complexes because of the pronounced solvation at the axial positions.

4.10.5 Reaction Profiles

The tendency for enhanced rates of substitution usually encountered for metals other than Pt(II) presumably resides in the stronger ability of these metals to form five-coordinated species. With these metals, then, bond making is much more in evidence, a characteristic reaching a limit with Rh(I), and particularly with Ni(II), where the k_1 term is unimportant and five-coordinate intermediates can be detected.[187]

If the mechanism is accepted as an associative one, then there will probably be a minimum somewhere along the reaction profile. The energy corresponding to the associated intermediate will usually be above the energies of reactant and products (Fig. 4.5), and the highest energy level determines the *major* transition state. If we exaggerate the situations likely to occur in practice, we can depict two extreme cases in which (1) bond breaking is rate-determining (Fig. 4.5(a)) and (2) bond making is

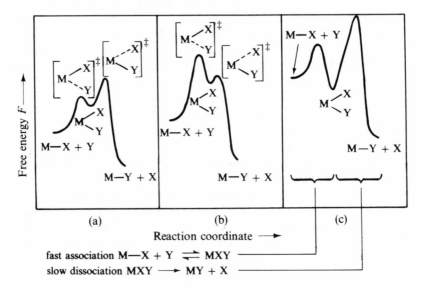

FIGURE 4.5 Reaction profiles for various situations in the associative mechanism for substitution in square-planar complexes, focusing attention on the replacement M–X + Y → M–Y + X: (a) M–X bond breaking rate-determining; (b) M–Y bond making rate-determining. In (a) and (b) there is an unstable intermediate containing the M⟨X Y entity; in (c) a stable intermediate is produced.[188,197]

rate-determining (Fig. 4.5(b)). Obviously, the nature of the X group will have a much less pronounced effect on the rate in situation (b) than in (a). If a five-coordinated intermediate is detected, as in certain Rh(I) and Ni(II) reactions, the energy of this will be between the energies of reactants and products and the major transition state will follow the minor transition state, Fig. 4.5(c).

4.11 CHELATION IN SQUARE-PLANAR COMPLEXES

As with substitution in octahedral complexes, in chelation in square-planar complexes the formation of the first bond is usually rate-determining, although much less data are available.[206–209] Thus, in the reaction (N–N = bipyridine)

$$
\begin{array}{c}
\underset{Cl}{\overset{C_2H_4}{>}}Pt\underset{Cl}{\overset{Cl^-}{<}} + N{-}N \xrightarrow{\;-Cl^-\;}
\underset{Cl}{\overset{C_2H_4}{>}}Pt\underset{N-N}{\overset{Cl}{<}} \xrightarrow[\text{fast}]{\;-Cl^-\;}
\underset{Cl}{\overset{C_2H_4}{>}}Pt\underset{N}{\overset{N^+}{<}}
\end{array}
\tag{4.124}
$$

in methanol, containing sufficient HCl to prevent hydrolysis products from interfering, the first step is rate-determining.[207]

It is possible to compare the ring closure with a process involving only unidentate ligands (rate constants at 25°):

$$
\underset{Cl}{\overset{H_2N(CH_2)_2H_2N}{>}}Pt\underset{NH_2(CH_2)_2NH_2}{\overset{Cl}{<}} \xrightarrow{\;10.4\ \text{sec}^{-1}\;}
$$

$$
\underset{Cl}{\overset{H_2N(CH_2)_2H_2N}{>}}Pt\underset{NH_2}{\overset{NH_2\ \ +}{<}}(CH_2)_2 \xrightarrow{\;0.73\ \text{sec}^{-1}\;}
(H_2C)_2\ Pt\ (CH_2)_2 \quad
\underset{H_2N}{\overset{H_2N\qquad NH_2\ \ 2+}{}}\underset{NH_2}{} \tag{4.125}
$$

$$
\underset{Cl}{\overset{H_3N}{>}}Pt\underset{NH_3}{\overset{Cl}{<}} + NH_3 \xrightarrow[M^{-1}\,\text{sec}^{-1}]{\;5.7\times10^{-3}\;}
$$

$$
\underset{Cl}{\overset{H_3N}{>}}Pt\underset{NH_3}{\overset{NH_3\ \ +}{<}} \xrightarrow[M^{-1}\,\text{sec}^{-1}]{\;5.4\times10^{-4}\;}
\underset{H_3N}{\overset{H_3N}{>}}Pt\underset{NH_3}{\overset{NH_3\ \ 2+}{<}} \tag{4.126}
$$

Ring closures are over 10^3 times faster than unidentate replacement in $1\ M\ NH_3$. When a slightly greater nucleophilicity of ethylenediamine over ammonia is allowed for, a nearly 10^3-fold enhancement in rate attends chelation.[208]   Although part of this effect resides in a higher effective concentration of $-NH_2$ nearer the replaced chloride in (4.125) compared with (4.126), other more specific effects probably play a role.

Such a specific influence has been described in comparing the rate characteristics of the reactions

$$\text{bipy Pt} \diagup^{\text{Cl}}_{\diagdown\text{Cl}} + L \rightarrow \text{bipy Pt} \diagup^{\text{Cl}}_{\diagdown\text{L}} \qquad (4.127)$$

$$\text{bipy Pt} \diagup^{\text{Cl}}_{\diagdown\text{Cl}} + \text{L—L} \rightarrow \text{bipy Pt} \diagup^{\text{L}}_{\diagdown\text{L}} \qquad (4.128)$$

in CH_3OH.[209]   Only one slow stage is discerned in (4.128), so that once again formation of Pt–L–L is rate-determining.   This is further supported by similar rate constants for (4.127) and (4.128).   However, the activation parameters for (4.127) and (4.128) are quite different, ranging from 15 to 17 kcal mole^{-1} ($\Delta H^{\ddagger}$) and -12 to -17 eu ($\Delta S^{\ddagger}$) for (4.127), and 11 to 12 kcal mole^{-1} and -27 to -28 eu respectively for (4.128), Table 4.18. These differences are ascribed to increased bonding and compactness in the transition complex **12** associated with (4.128):

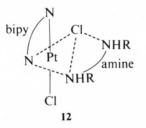

12

TABLE 4.18.   Rate Constant (k, M^{-1} sec^{-1}) and Activation Parameters for Reaction of PtbipyCl$_2$ with Unidentate and Bidentate Ligands in CH_3OH at 25°[209]

Ligand	$10^3 \times k$	$\Delta H^{\ddagger}$	$\Delta S^{\ddagger}$
py	5.3	16.3	-15
4-Mepy	5.4	15.6	-17
n-BuNH$_2$	25	15.7	-14
en	60	11.2	-28
tn	53	11.7	-27
piperazine	15	12.2	-28
N,N,N',N'-tetrameen	0.14	17.9	-18

The k_1 term in (4.107) often is missing, or at least negligible, compared with k_2, in the first step of a number of chelations. This may arise from the comparative rapidity of the solvolytic path over chelation,[210] or may be associated with unreactivity of the solvolysis species (Prob. 6a).[211]

Ring opening of chelates appears to occur at only a slightly slower rate than cleavage of unidentates from the metal.[208] Comparison of data for $Pten_2{}^{2+}$ and $Pt(NH_3)_4{}^{2+}$ indicates that the enhanced stability of chelated en over NH_3 complexes resides largely (10^3) in enhanced ring closure and only slightly (10) in decreased cleavage (ring opening).[208]

Because of the nature of substitution in square complexes, some effects are possible in ring opening that are not observed with octahedral complexes. The rate-determining step in the replacement of $C_6H_5S(CH_2)_2$-SC_6H_5 from Pd(II) by py is ring opening by the entering nucleophile. When the py has two *ortho* substituents, the rate-determining step is switched to displacement of the second sulfur.[212]

A proton may aid in the removal of chelating ligands in a manner similar to that of octahedral complexes, although second-order reaction paths are possible:

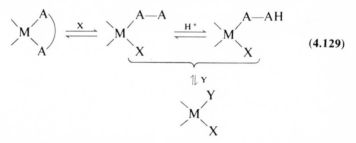

$$(4.129)$$

X and Y may be H_2O or halide groups. A number of reactions of Pd(II) appear to fit this scheme.[213]

4.12   SUBSTITUTION IN PSEUDO-OCTAHEDRAL COMPLEXES

If bulky ligands in the plane of a four-coordinated metal complex spill over and hinder the apical positions, a pseudo-octahedral complex results.[214] This will resemble the octahedral complex in reactivity characteristics while retaining some features of a square-planar complex. We can illustrate by comparing nucleophilic substitution in the planar complexes $Pt(PEt_3)_2ClR$, where $R = CH_3$ or C_6H_5[182] (normal square-planar complexes) and $R = o$-mesityl (pseudo-octahedral complex, with the o-CH_3 groups interacting with the apical positions).[215] Figures 4.6 and 4.7 show that with the latter there is steric retardation.[216] Only the strongest

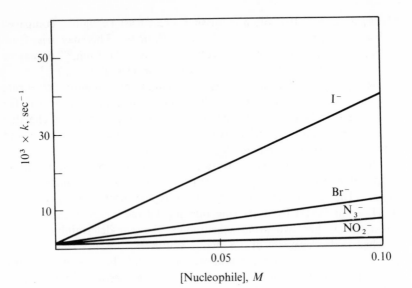

FIGURE 4.6   Plots of pseudo first-order rate constants (k, sec^{-1} at 30°) for reaction of Pt(PEt$_3$)$_2$(CH$_3$)Cl with nucleophiles in methanol.[182]

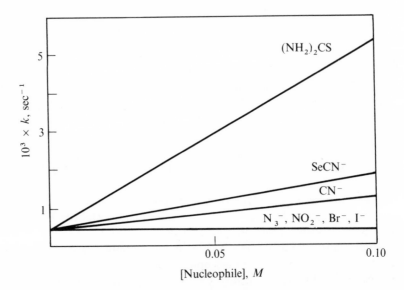

FIGURE 4.7   Plots of pseudo first-order rate constants (k, sec^{-1} at 30°) for reaction of Pt(PEt$_3$)$_2$(mesityl)Cl with nucleophiles in methanol.[215]

entering nucleophiles contribute to the rate, and with most nucleophiles only the k_1 path is important, that is,

$$V = k_1[Pt^{II}]$$ (4.130)

This is a rate law that would be observed with the octahedral analog. It might be expected that the k_1 term would arise from a dissociative interchange mechanism between complex and solvent since the associative path is suppressed. Support for this lies in the fact that the k_1 value is greatly *reduced* in going from a protic solvent to a dipolar aprotic one.[217]

An interesting group of pseudo-octahedral complexes of the type $M(Et_4dien)X^{n+}$, where $M = Pd(II),$[218,219] $Pt(II),$[116] or $Au(III),$[220] all display the characteristics outlined above, and are quite different from the unsubstituted analogs $M(dien)X^{n+}$. The sequence for the interchange of X and Y,

$$Pd(Et_4dien)X^+ + H_2O \xrightarrow{k_1} Pd(Et_4dien)H_2O^{2+} \xrightarrow[\text{fast}]{Y^-} Pd(Et_4dien)Y^+$$ (4.131)

has been shown to be feasible by demonstrating the rapidity of the second step. The rate constants for this second step (anation) have been measured by stopped flow. The range of values for a variety of anions (Table 4.19) suggests the operation of an S_N2IP or I_a mechanism (Sec. 4.3.8).[218]

The same type of steric effect also arises when bulky entering groups are involved. In a study of the reaction

$$\textit{trans-}Pt(PPr_3{}^n)(NH(^{14}C_2H_5)_2)Cl_2 + amine \rightleftharpoons$$
$$\textit{trans-}Pt(PPr_3{}^n)(amine)Cl_2 + (^{14}C_2H_5)_2NH \quad (4.132)$$

in CH_3OH, using radioactivity monitoring, it was found that both k_1 and k_2 in the normal two-term rate law were markedly depressed when the amine was hindered. The value of k_2 is determined by the effective size of the entering ligand, decreasing in the sequence primary > secondary > tertiary (for which $k_2 \sim 0$), Fig. 4.8.[221]

TABLE 4.19. Rate Constants (k, M^{-1} sec^{-1}) for the Reaction of $Pd(Et_4dien)H_2O^{2+}$ with Different Ligands, Y^{n-}, at 25°[218]

Y^{n-}	k	Y^{n-}	k
$S_2O_3{}^{2-}$	1.8×10^3	Br^-	6.0
$HSO_3{}^-$	5.1×10^2	I^-	4.5
SCN^-	72	CH_3COO^-	2.2
$NO_2{}^-$	13	$SC(NH_2)_2$	1.4
Cl^-	7.4		

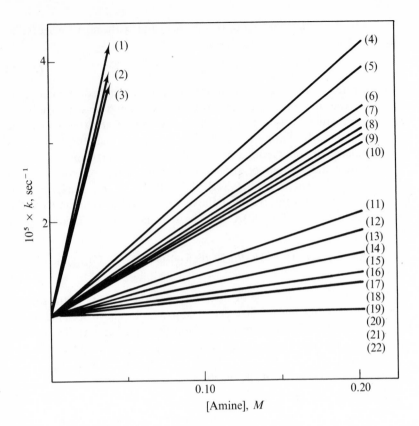

(1) 4-methylpyridine, (2) 3-methylpyridine,
(3) pyridine, (4) methylamine, (5) aziridine,
(6) ethylamine, (7) isobutylamine, (8) pyr-
rolidine, (9) *n*-butylamine, (10) ammonia,
(11) isopropylamine, (12) *s*-butylamine,
(13) 2-methylpyridine, (14) piperidine,
(15) dimethylamine, (16) 2, 4, 6-trimethylpyridine,
(17) *t*-butylamine, (18) diethylamine,
(19) di-isobutylamine, (20) and (21) di-isobutylamine, (22) 2, 4, 6-trimethylpiperidine.

FIGURE 4.8   Plots of pseudo first-order rate constants (k, sec^{-1} at
25°) for reaction (4.132) with various entering amines, in methanol.[221]

4.13   SUBSTITUTION IN FIVE-COORDINATED COMPLEXES

Replacement reactions involving five-coordinated complexes have been little studied kinetically. They may be regarded as intermediate between the planar complexes, which are open to nucleophilic attack, and the octahedral ones, which are not. They thus take on the character of pseudo-octahedral complexes.[222]

The exchange of $Co(2,6\text{-lutidine-N-oxide})_5$ with free ligand in a $CD_3NO_2/(CD_3)_2CO$ medium has been studied by nmr methods. The exchange rate is independent of the concentration of the free ligand.[223a]

Substitution in $Co(III)(mnt)_2Ph_3P^-$ by uni- and bidentate ligands have dissociative and associative paths,[223b] for example, for unidentate ligand entry

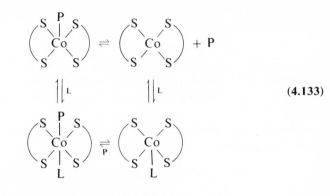

$$(4.133)$$

where   S—S = mnt (maleonitriledithiolate).

$P = Ph_3P.$

$L = Ph_3PO_2.$

Entry by a bidentate ligand L–L is initially identical. The noncoordinated end of L–L then attacks the planar position:

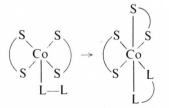

$$(4.134)$$

Reaction in the reverse direction, in which L–L is replaced by P, has been studied with internally consistent results (See Prob. 6d).[224]

4.14 SUBSTITUTION IN TETRAHEDRAL COMPLEXES

One of the earliest studies of substitution in tetrahedral complexes was concerned with the exchange reaction

$$Ni(CO)_2(PR_3)_2 + PR_3' \rightleftharpoons Ni(CO)_2(PR_3)(PR_3') + PR_3 \quad \textbf{(4.135)}$$

for which

$$V = k\,[Ni(CO)_2(PR_3)_2] \quad \textbf{(4.136)}$$

and a dissociative mechanism was proposed.[225] This behavior has been consistently observed in the few studies of tetrahedral complexes of metals of zero oxidation state. An associative mechanism may be deterred because of strong mutual repulsion of the entering nucleophile and the filled d orbitals of the d^{10} system. The enthalpies of activation for ligand exchange of $M(P(OEt)_3)_4$[226] follow an order (Table 4.20)

$$Pt > Ni > Pd \quad \textbf{(4.137)}$$

quite unlike the behavior of the planar M(II) complexes. It is suggested that appreciable π bonding in the Ni(O) complex confers enhanced kinetic stability.[227]

On the other hand, the exchange reactions (M = Fe, Co, and Ni; Ar = Ph or p-tolyl)

$$M(PAr_3)_2Br_2 + PAr_3 \rightleftharpoons M(PAr_3)_2Br_2 + PAr_3$$

studied in $CDCl_3$ by nmr linewidth techniques are all second-order (Table 4.21).[228] The lability trend Fe > Ni > Co resides mainly in a $\Delta H^{\ddagger}$ effect. Ligand field arguments indicate that the tetrahedral d^6 ground state and five-coordinated d^6 transition state are both stabilized to a lesser extent than the d^7 and d^8 counterparts. These effects would make Fe(II) more reactive and less reactive, respectively, than Co(II) and Ni(II), so that presumably ground-state destabilization is the more important.[228,229]

TABLE 4.20. Rate Constants (k, sec^{-1}) and Activation Parameters for Ligand Exchange of $M[P(OC_2H_5)_3]_4$ in Toluene at 25°[226]

M	k	$\Delta H^{\ddagger}$	$\Delta S^{\ddagger}$
Ni	9.9×10^{-7}	26.2	2
Pd	2.1×10^3	22.0	30
Pt	2.6×10^{-2}	27.5	27

TABLE 4.21. Rate Constants (k, M^{-1} sec^{-1}) and Activation Parameters for Ligand Exchange of $M(PPh_3)_2Br_2$ in $CDCl_3$ at $25°$[228]

M	k	$\Delta H^{\ddagger}$	$\Delta S^{\ddagger}$
Fe	2.0×10^5	3.8	-22
Co	8.7×10^2	7.7	-19
Ni	6.9×10^3	4.7	-25

REFERENCES

1. H. Taube, in *Progr. in Stereochem.*, **3**, 95 (1962); J. P. Hunt, *Metal Ions in Aqueous Solution* (W. A. Benjamin, New York, 1963).
2. S. F. Lincoln, *Coordn. Chem. Revs.*, **6**, 309 (1971).
3. S. J. Ashcroft and C. T. Mortimer, *Thermochemistry of Transition Metal Complexes* (Academic, London, 1970); J. J. Christiansen and R. M. Izatt, *Handbook of Metal Ligand Heats* (M. Dekker, New York, 1970); *Stability Constants* (The Chemical Society, London, 1971). Values from these compilations will be used in calculations throughout this book.
4. This term was first coined by A. Werner, 1913. M. T. Beck, *Coordn. Chem. Revs.*, **3**, 91 (1968) for a review of outer-sphere complexes.
5. H. Taube and F. A. Posey, *J. Amer. Chem. Soc.*, **75**, 1463 (1953).
6. N. V. Duffy and J. E. Earley, *J. Amer. Chem. Soc.*, **89**, 272 (1967).
7. C. H. Langford and W. R. Muir, *J. Amer. Chem. Soc.*, **89**, 3141 (1967).
8. T. W. Swaddle and G. Guastalla, *Inorg. Chem.*, **8**, 1604 (1969).
9. R. M. Fuoss, *J. Amer. Chem. Soc.*, **80**, 5059 (1958); M. Eigen, *Z. Phys. Chem.* (Frankfurt), **1**, 176 (1954).
10. R. G. Pearson and P. Ellgen, *Inorg. Chem.*, **6**, 1379 (1967).
11. By equating the exponential term to unity and setting $a = 4A$ arbitrarily, $K_0 = 2.5 \times 10^{21}a^3 \sim 0.15\ M^{-1}$. See also J. E. Prue, *J. Chem. Soc.*, 7534 (1965); D. B. Rorabacher, *Inorg. Chem.*, **5**, 1891 (1966).
12. W. Kruse and D. Thusius, *Inorg. Chem.*, **7**, 464 (1968).
13. H. Wendt, *Inorg. Chem.*, **8**, 1527 (1969).
14. D. W. Watts, *Rec. Chem. Progr.*, **29**, 131 (1968).
15. M. L. Tobe, *Adv. Chem. Series*, **49**, 7 (1965).
16. D. R. Llewellyn, C. J. O'Connor, and A. L. Odell, *J. Chem. Soc.*, 196 (1964).
17. T. J. Swift and R. E. Connick, *J. Chem. Phys.*, **37**, 307 (1962); **41**, 2553 (1964).
18. H. Taube, *Chem. Rev.*, **50**, 69 (1952).
19. E. Chaffee and J. O. Edwards, in *Inorganic Reaction Mechanisms*, Part I, p. 205.

20. J. Halpern and L. E. Orgel, *Disc. Faraday Soc.*, **29**, 32 (1960).

21. J. L. Burmeister and F. Basolo, *Prep. Chem. React.*, **5**, 1 (1968).

22. A. S. Mildvan, "Metals in Enzyme Catalysis," in *The Enzymes*, Chap. 9.

23. H. Diebler, M. Eigen, G. Ilgenfritz, G. Maass, and R. Winkler, *Pure Appl. Chem.*, **20**, 93 (1969).

24. J. Chatt, L. A. Duncanson, and L. M. Venanzi, *J. Chem. Soc.*, 4456 (1955); L. E. Orgel, *J. Inorg. Nucl. Chem.*, **2**, 137 (1956).

25. H. P. Bennetto and E. F. Caldin, *J. Chem. Soc.*, A, 2191, 2198, 2207 (1971); H. P. Bennetto, *J. Chem. Soc.*, A, 2211 (1971).

26. P. K. Chattopadhyay and J. F. Coetzee, *Inorg. Chem.*, **12**, 113 (1973).

27. E. B. Fleischer, S. Jacobs, and L. Mestichelli, *J. Amer. Chem. Soc.*, **90**, 2527 (1968).

28. Terms used by F. Basolo and R. G. Pearson, in *Mechanisms of Inorganic Reactions*.

29. Terms used by C. H. Langford and H. B. Gray, in *Ligand Substitution Processes*.

30. A. Haim and H. Taube, *Inorg. Chem.*, **2**, 1199 (1963).

31. R. Grassi, A. Haim, and W. K. Wilmarth, *Inorg. Chem.*, **6**, 237 (1967).

32. F. Monacelli and E. Viel, *Inorg. Chim. Acta.*, **1**, 467 (1967).

33. A value of $k_1/k_e \sim 0.2$ might arise in the ion-pair mechanism if the complexed anion is held randomly around the octahedral complex, and only loss of water near to the anion will lead to anion entry. Although values far removed from this[6,8] might be capable of being rationalized, they are not predictable and this must be recognized as a weakness in this approach.

34. M. Eigen, *Ber. Bunsenges. Phys. Chem.*, **64**, 115 (1960).

35. M. Eigen and K. Tamm, *Ber. Bunsenges. Phys. Chem.*, **66**, 107 (1962).

36. M. Eigen, *Advances in the Chemistry of Coordination Compounds* (Macmillan, New York, 1961), p. 371.

37. A. Haim, *Inorg. Chem.*, **9**, 426 (1970).

38. D. Thusius, *J. Amer. Chem. Soc.*, **93**, 2629 (1971).

39. A. Haim, R. J. Grassi, and W. K. Wilmarth, *Adv. Chem. Series*, **49**, 31 (1965).

40. J. Halpern, R. A. Palmer, and L. M. Blackley, *J. Amer. Chem. Soc.*, **88**, 2877 (1966).

41. D. R. Stranks and J. K. Yandell, *Inorg. Chem.*, **9**, 751 (1970).

42. A. Elder and S. Petrucci, *Inorg. Chem.*, **9**, 19 (1970), who find from ultrasonics, $k_1 = 2.4 \times 10^{11} \, M^{-1} \sec^{-1}$ and $k_{-1} = 2.0 \times 10^8 \sec^{-1}$ at $25°$.

43. D. W. Carlyle and J. H. Espenson, *Inorg. Chem.*, **8**, 575 (1969).

44. H. Brintzinger and G. G. Hammes, *Inorg. Chem.*, **5**, 1286 (1966).

45. P. Hemmes and S. Petrucci, *J. Phys. Chem.*, **72**, 3986 (1968).

46. J. Halpern, *J. Chem. Educ.*, **45**, 372 (1968).

47. C. H. Langford and H. G. Tsiang, *Inorg. Chem.*, **9**, 2346 (1970).

48. R. G. Pearson and J. W. Moore, *Inorg. Chem.*, **3**, 1335 (1964).

49. S. P. Ferraris and E. L. King, *J. Amer. Chem. Soc.*, **92**, 1215 (1970).

50. G. Guastalla and T. W. Swaddle, *Can. J. Chem.*, **51**, 821 (1973).

51. C. Postmus and E. L. King, *J. Phys. Chem.*, **59**, 1216 (1955).
52. R. G. Wilkins, *Quart. Rev.*, **16**, 316 (1962).
53. C. H. Langford, *Inorg. Chem.*, **4**, 265 (1965).
54. J. A. Kernohan and J. F. Endicott, *Inorg. Chem.*, **9**, 1504 (1970).
55. L. R. Casey, W. E. Jones, and T. W. Swaddle, *Inorg. Chem.*, **10**, 1566 (1971).
56. T. W. Swaddle and G. Guastalla, *Inorg. Chem.*, **7**, 1915 (1968).
57. P. Moore and R. G. Wilkins, *J. Chem. Soc.*, 3454 (1964).
58. T. P. Jones and J. K. Phillips, *J. Chem. Soc.*, *A*, 674 (1968).
59. T. Sakurai, J. P. Fox, and L. L. Ingraham, *Inorg. Chem.*, **10**, 1105 (1971).
60. A. L. Crumbliss and W. K. Wilmarth, *J. Amer. Chem. Soc.*, **92**, 2593 (1970).
61. D. E. Clegg, J. R. Hall, and N. S. Ham, *Aust. J. Chem.*, **23**, 1981 (1970) and references.
62. G. E. Glass, W. B. Schwabacher, and R. S. Tobias, *Inorg. Chem.*, **7**, 2471 (1968).
63. J. H. Espenson, *Inorg. Chem.*, **8**, 1554 (1969).
64. D. Thusius, *Inorg. Chem.*, **10**, 1106 (1971).
65. J. N. Armor, H. A. Scheidegger, and H. Taube, *J. Amer. Chem. Soc.*, **90**, 5928 (1968); S. D. Pell and H. Taube, *J. Amer. Chem. Soc.*, **95**, 7625 (1973).
66. H. R. Hunt and H. Taube, *J. Amer. Chem. Soc.*, **80**, 2642 (1958). These and $\Delta V^{\ddagger}$ values have been used to support a dissociative mechanism in which Co–OH$_2$ bond *stretching* occurs to a critical distance, at which point bonding is made to the incoming H$_2$O.
67. F. Monacelli, *Inorg. Chim. Acta*, **2**, 263 (1968).
68. H. L. Bott, A. J. Poe, and K. Shaw, *J. Chem. Soc.*, *A*, 1745 (1970).
69. F. Borghi and F. Monacelli, *Inorg. Chim. Acta*, **5**, 211 (1971).
70. T. W. Swaddle and D. R. Stranks, *J. Amer. Chem. Soc.*, **94**, 8357 (1972).
71. A. Z. Rubezhov and S. P. Gubin, *Adv. Organom.*, **10**, 347 (1972).
72. a. R. J. Angelici and J. R. Graham, *J. Amer. Chem. Soc.*, **88**, 3658 (1966).
    b. W. D. Covey and T. L. Brown, *Inorg. Chem.*, **12**, 2820 (1973).
73. C. H. Langford and T. R. Stengle, *Ann. Rev. Phys. Chem.*, **19**, 193 (1968).
74. R. E. Hamm, R. L. Johnson, R. H. Perkins, and R. E. Davis, *J. Amer. Chem. Soc.*, **80**, 4469 (1958).
75. S. F. Lincoln and D. R. Stranks, *Aust. J. Chem.*, **21**, 1745 (1968).
76. R. L. Wilder, D. A. Kamp, and C. S. Garner, *Inorg. Chem.*, **10**, 1393 (1971).
77. J. P. Jones and D. W. Margerum, *J. Amer. Chem. Soc.*, **92**, 470 (1970).
78. K. Kustin, R. F. Pasternack, and E. M. Weinstock, *J. Amer. Chem. Soc.*, **88**, 4610 (1966).
79. C. G. Barraclough and R. S. Murray, *J. Chem. Soc.*, 7047 (1965).
80. V. S. Sharma and D. L. Leussing, *Inorg. Chem.*, **11**, 138 (1972).
81. D. L. Rabenstein and R. J. Kula, *J. Amer. Chem. Soc.*, **91**, 2492 (1969).

82. S. C. Chan and G. M. Harris, *Inorg. Chem.*, **10**, 1317 (1971).
83. R. G. Wilkins, *Accounts Chem. Research*, **3**, 408 (1970).
84. K. V. Krishnamurty, G. M. Harris, and V. S. Sastri, *Chem. Rev.*, **70**, 171 (1970).
85. G. Melson and R. G. Wilkins, *J. Chem. Soc.*, 2662 (1963).
86. D. K. Lin and C. S. Garner, *J. Amer. Chem. Soc.*, **91**, 6637 (1969).
87. D. A. Kamp, R. L. Wilder, S. C. Tang, and C. S. Garner, *Inorg. Chem.*, **10**, 1396 (1971); S. J. Ranney and C. S. Garner, *Inorg. Chem.*, **10**, 2437 (1971).
88. P. Hambright, *Coord. Chem. Rev.*, **6**, 247 (1971).
89. J. Weaver and P. Hambright, *Inorg. Chem.*, **8**, 167 (1969) and references.
90. C. Grant, Jr. and P. Hambright, *J. Amer. Chem. Soc.*, **91**, 4195 (1969).
91. R. Khosropour and P. Hambright, *Chem. Commun.*, 13 (1972).
92. D. K. Cabbiness and D. W. Margerum, *J. Amer. Chem. Soc.*, **92**, 2151 (1970).
93. J. M. Lehn, J. P. Savage, and B. Dietrich, *J. Amer. Chem. Soc.*, **92**, 2916 (1970).
94. J. J. Christensen, J. O. Hill, and R. M. Izatt, *Science*, **174**, 459 (1971).
95. A. Eschenmoser, *Pure Appl. Chem.*, **20**, 93 (1969).
96. D. C. Olson and J. Vesilevskis, *Inorg. Chem.*, **8**, 1611 (1969); **10**, 1228 (1971).
97. E. Deutsch and H. Taube, *Inorg. Chem.*, **7**, 1532 (1968).
98. D. K. Wakefield and W. B. Schaap, *Inorg. Chem.*, **8**, 512 (1969).
99. T. P. Dasgupta and M. L. Tobe, *Inorg. Chem.*, **11**, 1011 (1972); T. J. Przystas, J. R. Ward, and A. Haim, *Inorg. Chem.*, **12**, 743 (1973).
100. P. C. Ford, J. R. Kuempel, and H. Taube, *Inorg. Chem.*, **7**, 1976 (1968).
101. T. P. Dasgupta and G. M. Harris, *J. Amer. Chem. Soc.*, **93**, 91 (1971); D. J. Francis and R. B. Jordan, *J. Amer. Chem. Soc.*, **11**, 461 (1972).
102. S. F. Lincoln and D. R. Stranks, *Aust. J. Chem.*, **21**, 57 (1968).
103. J. Aggett and A. L. Odell, *J. Chem. Soc.*, A, 1415 (1968); J. A. Broomhead, I. Lauder, and P. Nimmo, *Chem. Commun.*, 652 (1969).
104. J. H. Baxendale and P. George, *Trans. Faraday Soc.*, **46**, 736 (1950).
105. F. Basolo, J. C. Hayes, and H. M. Neumann, *J. Amer. Chem. Soc.*, **76**, 3807 (1954).
106. R. G. Pearson and D. A. Gansow, *Inorg. Chem.*, **7**, 1373 (1963), and refs.
107. R. Farina, R. Hogg, and R. G. Wilkins, *Inorg. Chem.*, **7**, 170 (1968); G. K. Pagenkopf and D. W. Margerum, *Inorg. Chem.*, **7**, 2514 (1968).
108. J. N. Brønsted, *Z. Phys. Chem.*, **122**, 383 (1926).
109. J. P. Birk and J. H. Espenson, *Inorg. Chem.*, **7**, 991 (1968).
110. M. L. Tobe, *Accounts Chem. Research*, **3**, 377 (1970).
111. R. B. Jordan and H. Taube, *J. Amer. Chem. Soc.*, **88**, 4406 (1966); N. S. Angerman and R. B. Jordan, *Inorg. Chem.*, **6**, 379 (1967); R. Davies, G. B. Evans, and R. B. Jordan, *Inorg. Chem.*, **8**, 2025 (1969); M. E. Farago and C. F. V. Mason, *J. Chem. Soc.*, A, 3100 (1970). In the hydrolysis of a few complexes, a second term in the rate law

k'[Co(III)][OH$^-$]^2 is observed. This is believed to arise from a concerted attack on the cobalt complex by two OH$^-$ ions, an event not easy to visualize.

112. M. R. Wendt and C. B. Monk, *J. Chem. Soc.*, *A*, 1624 (1969).
113. D. A. Buckingham, I. I. Olsen, and A. M. Sargeson, *Inorg. Chem.*, **7**, 174 (1968).
114. R. W. Hay and D. J. Barnes, *J. Chem. Soc.*, *A*, 3337 (1970).
115. F. J. Garrick, *Nature (London)*, **139**, 507 (1937).
116. Basolo and Pearson, p. 177–93; C. K. Ingold, R. S. Nyholm, and M. L. Tobe, *Nature (London)*, **194**, 344 (1962).
117. There is spectral and nmr evidence for a pK ~ 14.2 for the protons of Coen$_3$$^{3+}$. G. Navon, R. Panigel, and D. Meyerstein, *Inorg. Chim. Acta*, **6**, 299 (1972); J. Wilinski and R. J. Kurland, *Inorg. Chem.*, **12**, 2202 (1973).
118. G. Marangoni, M. Panayotou, and M. L. Tobe, *J. Chem. Soc.*, Dalton, 1989 (1973).
119. This appears to be the case from some limited data with platinum ammines, L. E. Erickson, *J. Amer. Chem. Soc.*, **91**, 6284 (1969).
120. R. G. Pearson, R. E. Meeker, and F. Basolo, *J. Amer. Chem. Soc.*, **78**, 709 (1956); T–L, Ni, C. S. Garner, *Inorg. Chem.*, **6**, 1071 (1967).
121. M. Green and H. Taube, *Inorg. Chem.*, **2**, 948 (1963).
122. D. A. Buckingham, I. I. Creaser, and A. M. Sargeson, *Inorg. Chem.*, **9**, 655 (1970).
123. D. A. Buckingham, B. M. Foxman, and A. M. Sargeson, *Inorg. Chem.*, **9**, 1790 (1970).
124. R. W. Hay and P. L. Cropp, *J. Chem. Soc.*, *A*, 42 (1969).
125. W. E. Jones, R. B. Jordan, and T. W. Swaddle, *Inorg. Chem.*, **8**, 2504 (1969).
126. D. A. House and H. K. J. Powell, *Inorg. Chem.*, **10**, 1583 (1971).
127. F. Basolo and R. G. Pearson, *Inorg. Chem.*, **4**, 1522 (1965).
128. F. R. Nordmeyer, *Inorg. Chem.*, **8**, 2780 (1969).
129. J. A. Broomhead and L. Kane-Maguire, *Inorg. Chem.*, **8**, 2124 (1969).
130. C. E. Skinner and M. M. Jones, *J. Amer. Chem. Soc.*, **91**, 1984 (1969).
131. A. W. Chester, *Inorg. Chem.*, **9**, 1743, 1746 (1970).
132. S. C. Chan and F. Leh, *J. Chem. Soc.*, *A*, 126 (1966).
133. F. Aprile, F. Basolo, G. Illuminati, and F. Maspero, *Inorg. Chem.*, **7**, 519 (1968).
134. R. D. Gillard, *J. Chem. Soc.*, *A*, 917 (1967).
135. W. W. Brandt, F. P. Dwyer, and E. C. Gyarfas, *Chem. Revs.*, **54**, 959 (1954).
136. G. Nord and O. Wernberg, *J. Chem. Soc.*, *A*, 866 (1972).
137. D. J. Francis and R. B. Jordan, *J. Amer. Chem. Soc.*, **91**, 6626 (1969).
138. D. W. Margerum, *J. Amer. Chem. Soc.*, **79**, 2728 (1957).
139. G. Nord, *Acta Chem. Scand.*, **27**, 743 (1973).
140. A comprehensive list of metal-ion-assisted substitution reactions has been discussed in terms of the hard, soft–acid, base concept. M. M. Jones and H. R. Clark, *J. Inorg. Nucl. Chem.*, **33**, 413 (1971).

141. C. Bifano and R. G. Linck, *Inorg. Chem.*, **7**, 908 (1968).
142. J. N. Armor and A. Haim, *J. Amer. Chem. Soc.*, **93**, 867 (1971).
143. S. W. Foong, B. Kipling, and A. G. Sykes, *J. Chem. Soc.*, *A*, 118 (1971); J. H. Espenson and J. P. Birk, *Inorg. Chem.*, **4**, 527 (1965); J. H. Espenson, *Inorg. Chem.*, **5**, 686 (1966).
144. D. Dodd, M. D. Johnson, and N. Winterton, *J. Chem. Soc.*, *A*, 910 (1971); M. D. Johnson, *Rec. Chem. Progr.*, **31**, 143 (1970).
145. D. A. Loeliger and H. Taube, *Inorg. Chem.*, **5**, 1376 (1966).
146. A. M. Sargeson and G. H. Searle, *Inorg. Chem.*, **6**, 2172 (1967).
147. L. C. Falk and R. G. Linck, *Inorg. Chem.*, **10**, 215 (1971).
148. A. Pidcock and W. C. E. Higginson, *J. Chem. Soc.*, 2798 (1963).
149. S. P. Tanner and W. C. E. Higginson, *J. Chem. Soc.*, *A*, 1164 (1969).
150. D. A. Buckingham, I. I. Olsen, and A. M. Sargeson, *Aust. J. Chem.*, **20**, 597 (1967).
151. D. A. Buckingham, I. I. Olsen, A. M. Sargeson, and H. Satrapa, *Inorg. Chem.*, **6**, 1027 (1967).
152. D. A. Buckingham, I. I. Olsen, and A. M. Sargeson, *Inorg. Chem.*, **6**, 1807 (1967).
153. H. Kelm and G. M. Harris, *Inorg. Chem.*, **6**, 1743 (1967).
154. D. W. Margerum, *Rec. Chem. Progr.*, **24**, 237 (1963).
155. T. R. Bhat, D. Radhamma, and J. Shankar, *Inorg. Chem.*, **5**, 1132 (1966).
156. D. W. Margerum, D. L. Jones, and H. M. Rosen, *J. Amer. Chem. Soc.*, **87**, 4463 (1965).
157. D. W. Margerum and T. J. Bydalek, *Inorg. Chem.*, **2**, 683 (1963).
158. K. Cummins and T. P. Jones, *Chem. Commun.*, 638 (1970).
159. J. H. Espenson, *Inorg. Chem.*, **4**, 1834 (1965).
160. J. F. Renar, D. E. Pennington, and A. Haim, *Inorg. Chem.*, **4**, 1832 (1965); D. A. Buckingham, D. M. Foster, and A. M. Sargeson, *J. Amer. Chem. Soc.*, **90**, 6032 (1968).
161. D. W. Carlyle and E. L. King, *Inorg. Chem.*, **9**, 2333 (1970).
162. T. C. Matts and P. Moore, *J. Chem. Soc.*, *A*, 1632 (1971).
163. J. D. Carr, R. A. Libby, and D. W. Margerum, *Inorg. Chem.*, **6**, 1083 (1967).
164. D. B. Rorabacher and D. W. Margerum, *Inorg. Chem.*, **3**, 382 (1964).
165. D. W. Margerum and H. M. Rosen, *Inorg. Chem.*, **7**, 299 (1968).
166. J. D. Carr and C. N. Reilley, *Anal. Chem.*, **42**, 51 (1970).
167. A. Bryson and I. S. Fletcher, *Aust. J. Chem.*, **23**, 1095 (1970).
168. C. M. Cook, Jr., and F. A. Long, *J. Amer. Chem. Soc.*, **80**, 33 (1958).
169. J. Bjerrum and K. G. Poulsen, *Nature*, **169**, 463 (1952).
170. A. W. Adamson, J. P. Welker, and W. B. Wright, *J. Amer. Chem. Soc.*, **73**, 4786 (1951); A. W. Adamson, *J. Amer. Chem. Soc.*, **73**, 5710 (1951).
171. Basolo and Pearson, Chaps. 2 and 3.
172. N. S. Hush, *Aust. J. Chem.*, **15**, 378 (1962); K. Breitschwerdt, *Ber. Bunsenges. Phys. Chem.*, **72**, 1046 (1968); A. L. Companion, *J. Phys. Chem.*, **73**, 739 (1969).
173. Compilations of rate data in M. Eigen and R. G. Wilkins, *Adv. Chem.*

Series, **49**, 55 (1965); D. J. Hewkin and R. H. Prince, *Coordn. Chem. Rev.*, **5**, 45 (1970); K. Kustin and J. Swinehart, *Inorganic Reaction Mechanisms*, ed. J. O. Edwards, p. 107; A. McAuley and J. Hill, *Quart. Rev.*, **23**, 18 (1969).

174. T. W. Kallen and J. E. Earley, *Inorg. Chem.*, **10**, 1149, 1152 (1971).
175. M. W. Buck and P. Moore, *Chem. Commun.*, 60 (1974).
176. H. P. Bennetto and E. F. Caldin, *J. Solution Chem.*, **2**, 217 (1973).
177. L. S. Frankel, *Inorg. Chem.*, **10**, 2360 (1971) and references.
178. M. L. Yount and S. S. Zumdahl, *Inorg. Chem.*, **10**, 1212 (1971); R. W. Kluiber, R. Kukla, and W. D. Horrocks, Jr., *Inorg. Chem.*, **9**, 1319 (1970).
179. H. B. Gray, *J. Amer. Chem. Soc.*, **84**, 1548 (1962).
180. J. E. Teggins and D. S. Martin, Jr., *Inorg. Chem.*, **6**, 1003 (1967); D. S. Martin, Jr., *Inorg. Chem.*, **6**, 1653 (1967).
181. F. Basolo, *Adv. Chem. Series*, **49**, 81 (1965).
182. U. Belluco, M. Graziani, and P. Rigo, *Inorg. Chem.*, **5**, 1123 (1966).
183. Hydrolysis of PtdienBr$^+$ is reversible. The reaction is driven to completion by OH$^-$ ion, which does not, however, accelerate the rate. See Ref. 179.
184. H. B. Gray and R. J. Olcott, *Inorg. Chem.*, **1**, 481 (1962).
185. S. C. Chan, *J. Chem. Soc.*, A, 1000 (1966).
186. P. Haake, S. C. Chan, and V. Jones, *Inorg. Chem.*, **9**, 1925 (1970).
187. R. G. Pearson and D. A. Sweigart, *Inorg. Chem.*, **9**, 1167 (1970).
188. L. Cattalini, "Mechanism of Square-Planar Substitution," in *Inorganic Reaction Mechanisms*, ed. J. O. Edwards, p. 266.
189. U. Belluco, R. Ettorre, F. Basolo, R. G. Pearson, and A. Turco, *Inorg. Chem.*, **5**, 591 (1966).
190. T. Taylor and L. R. Hathaway, *Inorg. Chem.*, **8**, 2135 (1969).
191. S. S. Zumdahl and R. S. Drago, *J. Amer. Chem. Soc.*, **90**, 6669 (1968).
192. A. L. Odell and H. A. Raethel, *Chem. Commun.*, 87 (1969).
193. F. Basolo, J. Chatt, H. B. Gray, R. G. Pearson, and B. L. Shaw, *J. Chem. Soc.*, 2207 (1951).
194. G. Carturan and D. S. Martin, Jr., *Inorg. Chem.*, **9**, 258 (1970).
195. F. Basolo and R. G. Pearson, *Progr. Inorg. Chem.*, **4**, 318 (1962).
196. R. G. Wilkins and M. J. G. Williams, in *Modern Coordination Chemistry*, Chap. 3.
197. Langford and Gray, p. 24 f.
198. U. Belluco, L. Cattalini, F. Basolo, R. G. Pearson, and A. Turco, *J. Amer. Chem. Soc.*, **87**, 241 (1965).
199. R. G. Pearson, H. Sobel, and J. Songstad, *J. Amer. Chem. Soc.*, **90**, 319 (1968).
200. C. S. Swain and C. B. Scott, *J. Amer. Chem. Soc.*, **75**, 141 (1953).
201. F. Basolo, H. B. Gray, and R. G. Pearson, *J. Amer. Chem. Soc.*, **82**, 4200 (1960).
202. J. L. Burmeister and J. C. Lim, *Chem. Commun.*, 1154 (1969).
203. R. G. Pearson, H. B. Gray, and F. Basolo, *J. Amer. Chem. Soc.*, **82**, 787 (1960).

204. U. Belluco, A. Orio, and M. Martelli, *Inorg. Chem.*, **5**, 1370 (1966).
205. P. Haake and R. M. Pfeiffer, *J. Amer. Chem. Soc.*, **92**, 5243 (1970).
206. P. Haake and P. A. Cronin, *Inorg. Chem.*, **2**, 879 (1963); W. J. Louw and W. Robb, *Inorg. Chim. Acta*, **3**, 29, 303 (1969).
207. P. Uguagliati, U. Belluco, U. Croatto, and R. Pistropaolo, *J. Amer. Chem. Soc.*, **89**, 1336 (1967).
208. M. J. Carter and J. K. Beattie, *Inorg. Chem.*, **9**, 1233 (1970).
209. L. Baracco, L. Cattalini, J. S. Coe, and E. Rotondo, *J. Chem. Soc.*, A, 1800 (1971), and references.
210. D. E. Schwab and J. V. Rund, *Inorg. Chem.*, **11**, 499 (1972).
211. J. E. Teggins and T. S. Wood, *Inorg. Chem.*, **7**, 1424 (1968).
212. L. Cattalini, M. Martelli, and G. Marangoni, *Inorg. Chim. Acta*, **2**, 405 (1968).
213. J. S. Coe and J. R. Lyons, *J. Chem. Soc.*, A, 829 (1971) and refs.
214. W. H. Baddley and F. Basolo, *J. Amer. Chem. Soc.*, **86**, 2075 (1964).
215. G. Faraone, V. Ricevuto, R. Romeo, and M. Trozzi, *Inorg. Chem.*, **8**, 2207 (1969).
216. First demonstrated in Ref. 193.
217. C. Faraone, V. Ricevuto, R. Romeo, and M. Trozzi, *Inorg. Chem.*, **9**, 1525 (1970).
218. J. B. Goddard and F. Basolo, *Inorg. Chem.*, **7**, 936 (1968).
219. J. B. Goddard and F. Basolo, *Inorg. Chem.*, **7**, 2456 (1968).
220. C. F. Weick and F. Basolo, *Inorg. Chem.*, **5**, 576 (1966).
221. A. L. Odell and H. A. Raethel, *Chem. Commun.*, 1323 (1968).
222. R. G. Pearson, M. M. Muir, and L. M. Venanzi, *J. Chem. Soc.*, 5521 (1965).
223. a. P. M. Enriquez, S. S. Zumdahl, and O. L. Forshey, *Chem. Commun.*, 1527 (1970).
      b. D. A. Sweigart and D. G. DeWit, *Inorg. Chem.*, **9**, 1582 (1970).
224. D. G. DeWit, M. J. Hynes, and D. A. Sweigart, *Inorg. Chem.*, **10**, 196 (1971).
225. L. S. Meriwether and M. L. Fiene, *J. Amer. Chem. Soc.*, **81**, 4200 (1959).
226. M. Meier, F. Basolo, and R. G. Pearson, *Inorg. Chem.*, **8**, 795 (1969).
227. R. D. Johnston, F. Basolo, and R. G. Pearson, *Inorg. Chem.*, **10**, 247 (1971).
228. L. H. Pignolet, D. Forster, and W. DeW. Horrocks, Jr., *Inorg. Chem.*, **7**, 828 (1968).
229. L. H. Pignolet and W. DeW. Horrocks, Jr., *J. Amer. Chem. Soc.*, **90**, 922 (1968).

SELECTED BIBLIOGRAPHY

General Accounts

BASOLO, F. and PEARSON, R. G. *Mechanisms of Inorganic Reactions.* Wiley, New York, 1967.

BENSON, D. *Mechanisms of Inorganic Reactions in Solution.* McGraw-Hill, London, 1968.

CANDLIN, J. P., TAYLOR, K. A., and THOMPSON, D. T. *Reactions of Transition Metal Complexes.* Elsevier, Amsterdam, 1968.

EDWARDS, J. O., ed. *Inorganic Reaction Mechanisms.* Wiley-Interscience, New York, 1970, Part I, 1972, Part 2.

EDWARDS, J. O. *Inorganic Reaction Mechanisms.* Benjamin, New York, 1964.

SYKES, A. G. *Kinetics of Inorganic Reactions.* Pergamon, Oxford, 1966.

TOBE, M. L. *Inorganic Reaction Mechanisms.* Nelson, London, 1972.

Substitution Reactions

LANGFORD, C. H. and GRAY, H. B. *Ligand Substitution Processes.* Benjamin, New York, 1965.

LANGFORD, C. H. and PARRIS, M. "Reactions of Inert Complexes and Metal Organic Compounds." In *Comprehensive Chemical Kinetics,* edited by C. H. Bamford and C. F. H. Tipper, vol. 7. Elsevier, Amsterdam, 1972.

LANGFORD, C. H. and SASTRI, V. S. "Mechanism and Steric Course of Octahedral Substitution." In *Reaction Mechanisms in Inorganic Chemistry,* edited by M. L. Tobe. Butterworths, London, 1972.

CATTALINI, L. "Mechanism of Square-Planar Substitution." In *Reaction Mechanisms in Inorganic Chemistry,* edited by M. L. Tobe. Butterworths, London, 1972.

PROBLEMS

1. A Cr(III) perchlorate solution containing 10.5 millimoles of Cr in H_2O of ordinary ^{17}O abundance (0.04%) is added to a large amount of H_2O enriched to $\sim 1\%$ in ^{17}O (total water = 229 millimoles). The height of the ^{17}O nmr peak for solvent water is initially measured as 65 mm. When exchange between solvent and coordinated water is complete, the signal height is reduced to 48 mm. Calculate the number of water molecules held by each Cr(III) in aqueous solution. [M. Alei, *Inorg. Chem.,* **3**, 44 (1964).]

2. Speculate on the relative merits of the dissociative and interchange mechanisms to explain each of the following observations.

    a. Aquation of $Cr(H_2O)_5X^{2+}$ (X = Br, I, NO_3, and NCS) in 1.0 M HCl produces different ratios of $[CrCl^{2+}]/[Cr^{3+}]$. [L. R. Carey, W. E. Jones, and T. W. Swaddle, *Inorg. Chem.,* **10**, 1566 (1971).]

    b. Rate data for the reaction of SCN^- with *trans*-Cocyclam(H_2O)Cl^{2+} lead to a value for $K_0 = 880\ M^{-1}$ (60°) and for reaction with the *cis* isomer a value for $K_0 = 7.7\ M^{-1}$ (25°) on the basis of the interchange mechanism. [C. K. Poon and M. L. Tobe, *J. Chem. Soc., A,* 2069 (1967); 1549 (1968).]

c. If the results for the reaction

$$cis\text{-}Coen_2(H_2O)_2{}^{3+} + H_2C_2O_4 \rightarrow Coen_2C_2O_4{}^+ + 2H_3O^+$$

are interpreted on the basis of a D mechanism, k_2/k_{-1} (4.15) = 13 at 40°. [P. M. Brown and G. M. Harris, *Inorg. Chem.*, **7**, 1872 (1968).]

d. In the anation reaction

$$trans\text{-}Coen_2(H_2O)OH^{2+} \rightarrow Coen_2(OH)HPO_4$$

the variation of the anation pseudo first-order rate constant k_{an} in excess of reactant concentration is similar whether the cobalt(III) complex or phosphate is used in excess. At low reactant concentration, k_{an} is proportional to [reactant]; it then reaches a limiting value at higher [reactant]. [S. F. Lincoln and D. R. Stranks, *Aust. J. Chem.*, **21**, 1745 (1968).]

3. Rationalize the following facts:

a. Although the rate constants for reaction of Zn^{2+} with most ligands are in the range 10^7 to 10^9 M^{-1} sec^{-1}, that for reaction with $HN^+(CH_2COO^-)_3$ is 5.1×10^5. [D. L. Rabenstein and R. J. Kula, *J. Amer. Chem. Soc.*, **91**, 492 (1969).]

b. Hydrolysis of $Coen_2(NH_2CH_2COOR)^{3+}$ leads smoothly to $Coen_2$-$(NH_2CH_2COO)^{2+}$ whereas $Co(NH_3)_5OCOCH_3{}^{2+}$ loses acetate rapidly. [J. K. Hurst and H. Taube, *J. Amer. Chem. Soc.*, **90**, 1174 (1968).]

c. Carbon dioxide catalyzes the aquation of $Cr(NH_3)_5OH^{2+}$ but not the aquation of $Cr(NH_3)_6{}^{3+}$ or $Co(NH_3)_5OH^{2+}$. [J. E. Earley and W. Alexander, *J. Amer. Chem. Soc.*, **92**, 2294 (1970).]

d. Hg^{2+} and Pb^{2+} ions give a rapid precipitation of the metal carbonates on treatment with $Co(NH_3)_5CO_3{}^+$. (How might ^{18}O be used to check your answer?) [R. B. Jordan, A. M. Sargeson, and H. Taube, *Inorg. Chem.*, **5**, 486 (1966).]

e. Although VO^{2+} is a d^1 system, it reacts about as slowly as Ni^{2+}, a d^8 system with a positive CFAE. [K. Wuthrich and R. E. Connick, *Inorg. Chem.*, **6**, 583 (1967).]

f. The aquation of $Co(NH_3)_5Br^{2+}$ has a $\Delta S^{\ddagger} = -4$ eu. [D. L. Gay and G. C. Galor, *J. Chem. Soc.*, 1181 (1966).]

4. What light do the following results throw on the mechanism of base hydrolysis of cobalt(III) complexes?

$trans\text{-}[Coen_2N_3(NCS)]^+$	$+ OH^- \rightarrow 70\%$ $cis\text{-}[Coen_2NCS(OH)]^+$
$trans\text{-}[Coen_2Cl(NCS)]^+$	$+ OH^- \rightarrow 76\%$ $cis\text{-}[Coen_2NCS(OH)]^+$
$trans\text{-}[Coen_2Br(NCS)]^+$	$+ OH^- \rightarrow 79\%$ $cis\text{-}[Coen_2NCS(OH)]^+$
$trans\text{-}[Coen_2Br(OH)]^+$	$+ OH^- \rightarrow 90\%$ $cis\text{-}[Coen_2(OH)_2]^+$
$trans\text{-}[Coen_2Cl(OH)]^+$	$+ OH^- \rightarrow 94\%$ $cis\text{-}[Coen_2(OH)_2]^+$
$trans\text{-}[Coen_2Cl(Br)]^+$	$+ OH^- \rightarrow 5\%$ $cis\text{-}[Coen_2Cl(OH)]^+$
$trans\text{-}[Coen_2Cl_2]^+$	$+ OH^- \rightarrow 5\%$ $cis\text{-}[Coen_2Cl(OH)]^+$
$cis\text{-}[Coen_2Cl(NH_3)]^{2+}$	$+ OH^- \rightarrow 84\%$ $cis\text{-}[Coen_2NH_3(OH)]^{2+}$
$cis\text{-}[Coen_2Br(NH_3)]^{2+}$	$+ OH^- \rightarrow 85\%$ $cis\text{-}[Coen_2NH_3(OH)]^{2+}$
$cis\text{-}[Coen_2NO_3(NH_3)]^{2+}$	$+ OH^- \rightarrow 86\%$ $cis\text{-}[Coen_2NH_3(OH)]^{2+}$
$cis\text{-}[Coen_2N_3Cl]^+$	$+ OH^- \rightarrow 59\%$ $cis\text{-}[Coen_2N_3(OH)]^+$
$cis\text{-}[Coen_2(N_3)_2]^+$	$+ OH^- \rightarrow 55\%$ $cis\text{-}[Coen_2N_3(OH)]^+$

[R. B. Jordan and A. M. Sargeson, *Inorg. Chem.*, **4**, 433 (1965).]

5. There have been a number of studies of the kinetics of interaction of Ni(II) complexes with CN^- ion.

   a. The rate law for the reaction of Ni^{2+} and $Nitrien(H_2O)_2^{2+}$ with CN^- to give $Ni(CN)_4^{2-}$ is $V = k[Ni^{II}][CN^-]^2[HCN]^2$ between pH 5.5 and 7.5. Suggest a mechanism, and the reason for a larger value for k with the trien complex. What form will the rate law take for dissociation of $Ni(CN)_4^{2-}$ in this pH range?

   b. The rate law for the reaction between $NiEDTA^{2-}$ and CN^- at pH 10.8 is $V = k[NiEDTA^{2-}][CN^-]^n$, where n varies from 3 at low $[CN^-]$ to 1 at high $[CN^-]$. Suggest a mechanism, and the reason for the very slow reaction between $NiCyDTA^{2-}$ and CN^-. [G. B. Kolski and D. W. Margerum, *Inorg. Chem.*, **7**, 2239 (1968); **8**, 1125 (1969); L. C. Coombs, D. W. Margerum, and P. C. Nigam, *Inorg. Chem.*, **9**, 2081 (1970).]

6. **a.** What form will the rate law for substitution in square-planar complexes take if the solvolysis of the complex is rapid compared with ligand substitution? (This occurs in reactions of $PtCl_4^{2-}$ with $*Cl^-$, bipy, and phen.) [F. A. Palocsay and J. V. Rund, *Inorg. Chem.*, **8**, 524 (1969).]

   b. In the relationship $\log k_y = sn_{Pt} + \log k_s$, why, and under what conditions, might an inverse correlation between s and k_s be anticipated? [V. Belluco, L. Cattalini, F. Basolo, R. G. Pearson, and A. Turco, *J. Amer. Chem. Soc.*, **87**, 241 (1965).]

   c. Predict the effect of $[OH^-]$ on the rate constant for replacement of Cl in Pd dien Cl^+, $Pd(Et_4dien)Cl^+$, and $Pd(Me_5dien)Cl^+$. [J. B. Goddard and F. Basolo, *Inorg. Chem.*, **7**, 936 (1968).]

   d. Derive the relation between the observed rate constant and the rate constants for the individual steps in the uni- and bidentate ligand entry into $Co(mnt)_2Ph_3P^-$ (Sec. 4.13). [D. A. Sweigart and D. G. DeWit, *Inorg. Chem.*, **9**, 1582 (1970).]

Chapter 5

Oxidation-Reduction Reactions

5.1 GENERAL CHARACTERISTICS

Oxidation-reduction (redox) reactions of the transition metal complexes are probably the best understood of the types of processes we are concerned with. In redox reactions, the oxidation state of at least two reactants changes. A variety of such reactions are shown in Table 5.1.

A net chemical change does not necessarily occur as a result of the redox reaction. Reactions 1 and 2 (Table 5.1) involve an interchange of electrons between two similar metal complex ions. Such isotopic exchange reactions were the subject of a sizable number of studies in the late forties and fifties,[1] and the novelty at that time of working with radioactive isotopes attracted many physical chemists to inorganic reaction mechanisms. Reactions 1 and 2[2,3] emphasize the wide variation in rates encountered here, as in substitution. One of the challenges we must face is rationalizing these large differences in rate constants (15 orders of magnitude), as well as interpreting smaller more subtle disparities. Reaction 3 indicates that isotopic exchange may not involve merely electron transfer but also movement of atoms (chlorine in this case).

Redox reactions usually lead, however, to a marked change in the species, as reactions 4–6 indicate. An important reaction involves the oxidation of inorganic and organic substrates by oxidizing complex ions. Here the substrate often has ligand properties, and the first step in the overall process appears to be complex formation between the metal and substrate species. After this the redox reaction can occur in a variety of ways,[4] of which a direct intramolecular electron transfer within the adduct is the most obvious. Redox reactions will often then be phenomenologically associated with substitution.

TABLE 5.1. Some Types of Redox Reactions

	Redox reaction	Characteristics	Ref.
1	$*Co(NH_3)_6^{2+} + Co(NH_3)_6^{3+} \rightleftharpoons *Co(NH_3)_6^{3+} + Co(NH_3)_6^{2+}$	Exchange rate extremely slow, $k_{exch} < 10^{-8}$ M^{-1} sec^{-1}.	2
2	$*Fephen_3^{2+} + Fephen_3^{3+} \rightleftharpoons *Fephen_3^{3+} + Fephen_3^{2+}$	Exchange rate too fast to measure, even by nmr line-broadening methods, $k_{exch} \geqslant 10^7$ M^{-1} sec^{-1}.	3
3	$*Cr^{2+} + CrCl^{2+} \rightleftharpoons *CrCl^{2+} + Cr^{2+}$	Second-order isotopic exchange, $k = 9\ M^{-1}$ sec^{-1} at 0°.	27
4	$Cr^{2+} + Co(NH_3)_5Cl^{2+} + 5H^+ \rightarrow CrCl^{2+} + Co^{2+} + 5NH_4^+$	Early example of an inner-sphere redox reaction, $k = 6 \times 10^5\ M^{-1}$ sec^{-1}.	10
5	$2MnEDTA(H_2O)^- + 2N_3^- \rightarrow 2MnEDTA(H_2O)^{2-} + 3N_2$	Kinetics of formation and decomposition of azide complex measured.	a
6	$H_2A + 2Fe^{3+} \rightarrow 2Fe^{2+} + 2H^+ + A$	H_2A = ascorbic acid. Reaction proceeds through ferric ascorbate complex(es).	b

[a] M. A. Suwyn and R. E. Hamm, *Inorg. Chem.*, **6**, 2150 (1967).
[b] G. S. Laurence and K. J. Ellis, *J. Chem. Soc.*, *A*, 1667 (1972) and refs.

Spectrophotometry has been a popular means of monitoring redox reactions, augmented increasingly with flow techniques. The majority of redox reactions, even those with involved stoichiometry, have second-order characteristics. Less straightforward kinetics may arise with redox reactions that involve metal complex or radical intermediates,[5] or multi-electron transfer, as in the reduction of Cr(VI) to Cr(III).[6] Reactants with differing equivalences (noncomplementary reactions), as in the reaction[7]

$$2Fe^{II} + Tl^{III} \rightarrow 2Fe^{III} + Tl^{I} \tag{5.1}$$

often give rise to complicated kinetic rate laws.

Proton-accelerated rates are often observed when the net reaction involves protons since some of these will have been lost or gained at the transition state. This is the situation with a large number of reactions of oxyions,[8a,9] exemplified by the $VO_2{}^+ \rightarrow VO^{2+}$ and $HCrO_4{}^- \rightarrow Cr(H_2O)_6{}^{3+}$ conversions.

5.2   CLASSIFICATION OF REDOX REACTIONS

The most important single development in the understanding of the mechanism of redox reactions has probably been the recognition and establishment of *outer-sphere* and *inner-sphere* processes.[10] Outer-sphere electron transfer involves intact (although not completely undisturbed) coordination shells of the reactants. In inner-sphere redox reactions, there are marked changes in the coordination spheres of the reactants in the formation of the activated complex.

Reaction 2 in Table 5.1 must qualify for an outer-sphere redox category since the phenanthroline could not become detached, even by just one end of the bidentate ligand, from the inert iron(II) or iron(III) centers during the course of the rapid redox reaction. There is thus no bond breaking or making during the electron transfer, a situation making them ideal for treatment by the theoretical chemist (Sec. 5.10).

Reaction 4 in Table 5.1, on the other hand, was one of the first-established examples of an inner-sphere redox reaction.[10] The rapid reaction gives $CrCl^{2+}$ as a product, characterized spectrally after separation by ion exchange from the remainder of the species in solution. It is clear that since $CrCl^{2+}$ could not possibly be produced from Cr^{3+} and Cl^- ions during the brief time for reaction and ion-exchanger manipulation, it must arise from the redox process per se. Thus an activated complex or intermediate of the composition **1** must arise from the penetration of the chromium(II) ion by the coordinated chloride of the cobalt(III):

$$(NH_3)_5CoCl^{2+} + Cr(H_2O)_6{}^{2+} \rightarrow (NH_3)_5CoClCr(H_2O)_5{}^{4+} \tag{5.2}$$
1

Within **1**, an intramolecular electron transfer from Cr(II) to Co(III) must occur, producing Cr(III) and Co(II). The adduct then breaks up and the Cr(III) takes along the chloride as the species $CrCl^{2+}$:

$$(NH_3)_5\,CoClCr(H_2O)_5^{4+} \xrightarrow{\text{H}^+} Co^{2+} + 5NH_4^+ + Cr(H_2O)_5Cl^{2+} \quad (5.3)$$

This scheme implies that at no time does chloride ion break free of the influence of at least one of the metals, and in support of this there is no incorporation of ^{36}Cl in $CrCl^{2+}$ when the reaction takes place in the presence of $^{36}Cl^-$ ion.[10]

5.3 CHARACTERIZATION OF MECHANISM

The characterization of a redox reaction as inner-sphere or outer-sphere is a primary preoccupation of the redox kineticist. The assignment is sometimes obvious, but often difficult and in certain cases impossible!

(a) *From the Nature of the Products.* The *eventual* products from reaction 4, Table 5.1, are Cr^{3+}, $CrCl^{2+}$, Co^{2+}, Cl^-, and NH_4^+ ions. These could arise from an outer- or an inner-sphere process:[11]

Outer-sphere $Cr^{2+} + Co(NH_3)_5Cl^{2+} \xrightarrow[\text{transfer}]{e} Cr^{3+} + Co(NH_3)_5Cl^+$ (5.4)

$$Co(NH_3)_5Cl^+ \xrightarrow[\text{rapid}]{\text{H}^+} Co^{2+} + 5NH_4^+ + Cl^- \quad (5.5)$$

$$Cr^{3+} + Cl^- \xrightleftharpoons{\text{slow}} CrCl^{2+} \quad (5.6)$$

Inner-sphere $Cr^{2+} + Co(NH_3)_5Cl^{2+} \xrightarrow[\text{mechanism}]{\text{bridged}} CrCl^{2+} + Co(NH_3)_5H_2O^{2+}$

$$(5.7)$$

$$Co(NH_3)_5H_2O^{2+} \xrightarrow[\text{rapid}]{\text{H}^+} Co^{2+} + 5NH_4^+ + H_2O$$

$$(5.8)$$

$$CrCl^{2+} \xrightleftharpoons{\text{slow}} Cr^{3+} + Cl^- \quad (5.9)$$

The relative stability of $CrCl^{2+}$ and the labilities of Cr^{2+} and Co^{2+} (in part responsible for the rapidity of the intermediate formation and the breakup steps) were thus cleverly exploited to provide unambiguous proof for the operation of the inner-sphere process.[10] Since most redox reactions involving Cr^{2+} are rapid, and the hydrolyses of most Cr(III) complexes slow, it is not difficult to detect the intermediate CrX^{n+}, for example,

$$Cr^{2+} + M^{III}X^{n+} \rightarrow Cr^{III}X^{n+} + M^{2+} \quad (5.10)$$

and, in so doing, characterize the reaction as inner-sphere. This has been demonstrated in the Cr(II) reductions of a large number of Co(III), Cr(III), and Fe(III) oxidants.[12]

The only other common reducing agents that can lead to products leisurely characterizable, because they hydrolyze extremely slowly, are $Co(CN)_5^{3-}$ [13a] and $Ru(NH_3)_5H_2O^{2+}$,[13b] for example,

$$Co(CN)_5^{3-} + Co(NH_3)_5N_3^{2+} \rightarrow Co(CN)_5N_3^{3-} + Co^{2+} + 5NH_3 \quad \textbf{(5.11)}$$

With the other common reducing agents, Fe^{2+}, V^{2+}, Eu^{2+}, and Cu^+, any product will hydrolyze rapidly, for example,

$$M^{2+} + Co(NH_3)_5X^{2+} \xrightarrow{\text{H}^+} MX^{2+} + Co^{2+} + 5NH_4^+ \quad \textbf{(5.12)}$$

$$MX^{2+} \rightleftharpoons M^{3+} + X^- \qquad \text{rapid} \qquad \textbf{(5.13)}$$

It will be very difficult to detect Cu(II)X and Eu(III)X as intermediates because of their marked lability, and therefore hard to characterize Cu^+ and Eu^{2+} as inner-sphere reductants by product identification. It is easier to detect Fe(III) and V(III) species, by flow methods; and a number of reactions of Fe^{2+} with Co(III) complexes[14-16] and V^{2+} with V(IV), Co(III), and Cr(III) complexes, Table 5.2,[17,18] have been shown to progress via the intermediate required of an inner-sphere reaction.

Closer examination of the reaction between Fe^{2+} and $Co(C_2O_4)_3^{3-}$ (Sec. 3.6.2), for example, shows the formation and decay of an intermediate $FeC_2O_4^+$ ion,[15]

$$Fe^{2+} + Co(C_2O_4)_3^{3-} \xrightarrow{\text{H}^+} FeC_2O_4^+ + Co^{2+} + 2H_2C_2O_4 \quad \textbf{(5.14)}$$

$$FeC_2O_4^+ \xrightarrow{\text{H}^+} Fe^{3+} + H_2C_2O_4 \qquad \textbf{(5.15)}$$

Obviously, for success in this approach, the redox step producing the intermediate must not be appreciably slower than the decomposition of the intermediate.[19] The reaction between $Co(NH_3)_5SCN^{2+}$ and Fe^{2+} ion proceeds in two discernible stages.[16]

$$Fe^{2+} + Co(NH_3)_5SCN^{2+} \xrightarrow{\text{H}^+} FeNCS^{2+} + Co^{2+} + 5NH_4^+ \quad \textbf{(5.16)}$$

$$FeNCS^{2+} \rightleftharpoons Fe^{3+} + SCN^- \qquad \textbf{(5.17)}$$

In contrast, the redox step between $Co(NH_3)_5NCS^{2+}$ and Fe^{2+} is so much slower that any intermediate would break up before it could be detected.[20]

(b) By the Detection of a Bridged Species. The detection of a bridged complex comparable to **1** does not prove (although it may suggest) that it is an intermediate in an inner-sphere redox process (see Sec. 1.6.4 and Fig. 5.5). The bridged species could be in equilibrium with the reactants, and the products form directly from reactants by an outer-sphere process.

TABLE 5.2. Rate Parameters (k, $M^{-1} sec^{-1}$) and Characteristics of Some Reactions of V(II) at 25°

Reactant	k	$\Delta H^{\ddagger}$	$\Delta S^{\ddagger}$
Inner-sphere redox, intermediate detected			
$CrSCN^{2+}$	8.0	13.0	-11
VO^{2+}	1.6	12.3	-17
$Co(NH_3)_5SCN^{2+}$	30	16.4	6
$Co(NH_3)_5C_2O_4^{+}$	45	12.3	-10
cis-$Coen_2(N_3)_2^{+}$	33	...	...
$Co(CN)_5N_3^{3-}$	112	...	...
$Co(CN)_5SCN^{3-}$	140	...	...
Probably inner-sphere redox			
Cu^{2+}	27	11.4	-14
$Co(NH_3)_5N_3^{2+}$	13	11.7	-14
$Co(NH_3)_5SO_4^{+}$	26	11.6	-13
$Co(NH_3)_5OCOR^{2+}$	$1-21$[a]	$11-12.2$[a]	-13 to -17[a]
$Co(CN)_5X^{3-}$	$120-280$[b]	...	...
Probably outer-sphere redox			
$Co(NH_3)_5Cl^{2+}$	10	7.5	-29
$Co(NH_3)_5H_2O^{3+}$	0.63	8.2	-32
$Co(NH_3)_6^{3+}$	0.004	9.1	-40
$RuCl^{2+}$	1.9×10^3	...	...
Fe^{3+}	1.8×10^4	...	...
FeX^{2+}	$(4.6-6.6) \times 10^5$[c]		
Replacement reaction			
NCS^-	28	13.5	-7
H_2O	90[d]	16.4	6

SOURCE: Tables in Refs. 17 and 18.
[a] Variety of R groups; see Table 5.10.
[b] $X = Cl^-$, Br^-, I^-, and H_2O.
[c] $X = Cl^-$, N_3^-, and NCS^-.
[d] First-order rate constant (sec^{-1}) for water exchange.

The possible oxidation states of the metals in **1** itself are either Cr(II) and Co(III) or Cr(III) and Co(II). In both cases, one of the components is quite labile, and the binuclear species will respectively either return to reactants or dissociate to products rather than exist independently for any length of time. When both partners in the bridged intermediate are inert, however, there is every chance that it will be detected, or at least its presence inferred from the form of the rate law, or the magnitude of the activation parameter (Sec. 5.5). A number of such systems are shown in Table 5.3. The oxidation states of the detected species are deduced from spectral or chemical considerations. In only one case are

TABLE 5.3. Some Bridged Species Arising from Redox Reactions

Reactants	Species [h]	Ref
Cr^{III} + Ru^{III}chloro complexes	Cr^{III}–Cl–Ru^{II}	a
Cr^{II} + $IrCl_6^{2-}$	Cr^{III}–Cl–Ir^{III}	b
$Co(CN)_5^{3-}$ + $IrCl_6^{2-}$	Co^{III}–Cl–Ir^{III}	c
$Co(CN)_5^{3-}$ + $Fe(CN)_6^{3-}$	Co^{III}–NC–Fe^{II}	d
$CoEDTA^{2-}$ + $Fe(CN)_6^{3-}$	Co^{III}–NC–Fe^{II}	e
Fe^{II} + $Co(NH_3)_5NTA$	Fe^{II}–NTA–Co^{III}	f
Cr^{II} + V^{IV}	Cr^{III}–$(OH)_2$–V^{III}	g

[a] D. Seewald, N. Sutin, and K. O. Watkins, *J. Amer. Chem. Soc.*, **91**, 7307 (1969); W. G. Movius and R. G. Linck, *J. Amer. Chem. Soc.*, **92**, 2677 (1970).
[b] A. G. Sykes and R. N. F. Thorneley, *J. Chem. Soc.*, *A*, 232 (1970).
[c] B. Grossman and A. Haim, *J. Amer. Chem. Soc.*, **92**, 4835 (1970).
[d] A. Haim and W. K. Wilmarth, *J. Amer. Chem. Soc.*, **83**, 509 (1961).
[e] A. W. Adamson and E. Gonick, *Inorg. Chem.*, **2**, 129 (1963); D. H. Huchital and R. G. Wilkins, *Inorg. Chem.*, **6**, 1022 (1967).
[f] R. D. Cannon and J. Gardiner, *J. Amer. Chem. Soc.*, **92**, 3800 (1970).
[g] This is one of a number of examples in which a binuclear complex with an –O–, $(OH)_2$, or OH bridge results from interaction of oxyions.[21,22]
[h] The oxidation states are assigned from spectral considerations.

the oxidation states of the metals in the bridged complex the same as the oxidation states of the reactants.

(c) *From Rate Data.* Both inner- and outer-sphere redox reactions are usually second-order,

$$V = k[\text{oxidant}][\text{reductant}] \tag{5.18}$$

Only in a limited number of instances will the value of k and its associated parameters be useful in diagnosing mechanism.

The activation parameters for substitution in V^{2+} and for its reaction with certain oxidants are very similar (Table 5.2). An inner-sphere redox reaction, controlled by the replacement of the coordinated water of V^{2+}, is favored in these cases.[22,23] This is confirmed in certain instances by the detection of a vanadium complex as an intermediate. When the redox rate is faster than substitution within either reactant, as it is with a number of other oxidants towards V^{2+}, we can be quite certain that an outer-sphere mechanism holds (Table 5.2). Although the rate constants for reaction of $Co(NH_3)_5Cl^{2+}$ and $Co(NH_3)_5H_2O^{3+}$ with V^{2+} (Table 5.2) could be accommodated in the inner-sphere range of values, the much lower $\Delta H^{\ddagger}$ and $\Delta S^{\ddagger}$ may justify an outer-sphere classification. There is independent evidence for this assignment with the aqua complex, based on isotopic fractionation results (see Sec. 3.14.1).[24]

Other methods of distinguishing between the two basic mechanisms must also necessarily be indirect. They are based on patterns of reactivity often constructed from data for authentic inner-sphere and outer-sphere processes. The role of the bridging group is most important in these considerations.

5.4 THE BRIDGING LIGAND

The early work of Taube and his co-workers opened several interesting avenues of approach, most of which have been fully exploited. One of the most obvious is to examine the requirements for a good bridging group and determine the effects of this bridge on the rate of the inner-sphere redox reaction. It has been estimated that almost 200 different bridges were examined in the 1960s.[25] Attendant changes of redox rates by more than eight orders of magnitude were observed. Much data have been obtained on reactions of the type

$$Cr^{2+} + Co(NH_3)_5 L^{n+} \xrightarrow{5H^+} CrL^{n+} + Co^{2+} + 5NH_4^+ \quad \textbf{(5.19)}$$

and these, together with reduction by other metal ions and complexes, may be used for discussion purposes (Table 5.4).[26] Oxidation by Cr(III) and Ru(III) also provides useful information, and isotopic exchanges of the type

$$*Cr^{2+} + CrX^{2+} \rightleftharpoons *CrX^{2+} + Cr^{2+} \quad \textbf{(5.20)}$$

which cannot be outer-sphere, were early explored[27] (Table 5.5).

Examination of the data for (5.19) and (5.20) shows that there is some general order of reactivity for the various L ligands. Containing an unshared electron pair *after coordination* appears a minimum requirement for a ligand to be a potential bridging group, for it has to function as a Lewis base towards two metal cations. Thus $Co(NH_3)_6^{3+}$ and $Co(NH_3)_5 py^{3+}$ oxidize Cr^{2+} by an outer-sphere mechanism, giving Cr^{3+} as the product, at a much slower rate than for the inner-sphere reactions.

There is evidence, furthermore, that bridging electron transfer will not occur even through an NH_2 group in a ligand despite its having an electron pair. There is no evidence of ligand transfer, and the rate constants are small, for the reactions with Cr^{2+} of $Co(NH_3)_5OC(NH_2)_2^{3+}$ and $Co(NH_3)_5OCHNH_2^{3+}$ ions. The lone pair of the nitrogen is apparently drawn into the $O{=}C{-}N$ π system by the $Co(NH_3)_5^{3+}$ entity (Sec. 6.3) and is not available for attack by the Cr(II).[28]

TABLE 5.4. Rate Constants (k, M^{-1} sec^{-1}) for the Reduction of $Co(NH_3)_5L^{n+}$ by a Variety of Reductants at 25°

L	Cr^{2+}	V^{2+}	Fe^{2+}	Eu^{2+}	Cu^+	$Co(CN)_5^{3-}$	$Crbipy_3^{2+}$	$Ru(NH_3)_6^{2+}$
NH_3	8.0×10^{-5} A	3.7×10^{-3}		2×10^{-2} G		8×10^{4a} O	6.9×10^2 G	1.1×10^{-2} Q
py	4.1×10^{-3} B	0.24 I						
H_2O	$\leqslant 0.1$ C	0.53 E		0.15 G	1.0×10^{-3} N		2×10^3 (4°) P	3.0 Q
$OC(NH_2)_2$	1.9×10^{-2} D							
$OCHNH_2$	8.5×10^{-3} D							
$OCOCH_3$	0.35 E	1.2 E	<0.05 K	0.18 G		1.1×10^{4a} O	1.2×10^3 G	
$OCOCOOH$	1.0×10^{-2} E	12.5 E	$\leqslant 5 \times 10^{-4}$ K					0.6 E
F^-	2.5×10^5 F	2.6 G	7.6×10^{-3} K, L	2.6×10^4 G	1.1 N	1.8×10^3 O	1.8×10^3 G	
Cl^-	6×10^5 F	10 E	1.6×10^{-3} K, L	3.9×10^2 G	4.9×10^4 N	$\sim 5 \times 10^7$ O	8×10^5 G	2.6×10^2 Q
Br^-	1.4×10^6 F	25 E	9.2×10^{-4} K, L	2.5×10^2 G	4.5×10^5 N		5×10^6 G	1.6×10^3 Q
I^-	3×10^6 F	1.2×10^2 G		1.2×10^2 G				6.7×10^3 Q
OH^-	1.5×10^6 C				3.8×10^2 N	9.3×10^4 O	1×10^3 (4°) P	0.04 Q

L	Cr^{2+}	V^{2+}	Fe^{2+}	Eu^{2+}	Cu^+	$Co(CN)_5^{3-}$	$Crbipy_3^{2+}$	$Ru(NH_3)_6^{2+}$
N_3^-	$\sim 3 \times 10^5$ G	13 G	8.8×10^{-3} K	1.9×10^2 G	1.5×10^3 N	1.6×10^6 O	4.1×10^4 G	1.2 Q
NCS^-	19^b G	0.3 G	$<3 \times 10^{-6}$ K	~ 0.7 G	~ 1 N	1.1×10^6 O	1.1×10^4 G	
SCN^-	$1.9 \times 10^{5\,b}$ $0.8 \times 10^{5\,c}$ H	30 J	0.12 M					
$NHCHO^-$	1.7 D							
$N{=}C{=}NH^-$	3.3×10^3 D							

[a] $M^{-2}\,sec^{-1}$, outer-sphere reduction by $Co(CN)_6^{3-}$.
[b] Remote attack.
[c] Adjacent attack.

A. A. Zwickel and H. Taube, *J. Amer. Chem. Soc.*, **83**, 793 (1961).
B. Ref. 50.
C. Ref. 31.
D. Ref. 28.
E. Tables 5.2 and 5.10.
F. Refs. 34, 57.
G. Ref. 38.
H. C. Shea and A. Haim, *J. Amer. Chem. Soc.*, **93**, 3055 (1971).
I. C. Norris and F. R. Nordmeyer, *Inorg. Chem.*, **10**, 1235 (1971).

J. Ref. 16.
K. Ref. 20.
L. Ref. 40.
M. Ref. 16.
N. O. J. Parker and J. H. Espenson, *J. Amer. Chem. Soc.*, **91**, 1968 (1969).
O. Ref. 13a.
P. A. Zwickel and H. Taube, *Disc. Faraday Soc.*, **29**, 42 (1960).
Q. Ref. 39.

TABLE 5.5. Rate Parameters (k, M^{-1} sec^{-1}) for Cr(II)–Cr(III) Exchange Reactions (5.20) at 25°

Exchange partners	k	$\Delta H^{\ddagger}$	$\Delta S^{\ddagger}$
$Cr^{2+} + Cr^{3+}$	$\leqslant 2 \times 10^{-5}$	...	...
$Cr^{2+} + CrOH^{2+}$	0.7	12.8	−16
$Cr^{2+} + CrNCS^{2+}$	1.4×10^{-4}	...	...
$Cr^{2+} + CrSCN^{2+}$	40	...	...
$Cr^{2+} + CrN_3^{2+}$	6.1	9.6	−23
$Cr^{2+} + CrF^{2+}$	2.4×10^{-3} [a]	13.7	−20
$Cr^{2+} + CrCl^{2+}$	9 [a]	...	...
$Cr^{2+} + CrBr^{2+}$	> 60 [a]	...	...
$Cr^{2+} + CrCN^{2+}$	7.7×10^{-2} [b]	9.3	−32
$Cr^{2+} + cis\text{-}Cr(N_3)_2^{+}$	60	...	...

SOURCE: Ref. 21, except where noted.
[a] At 0°.
[b] J. P. Birk and J. H. Espenson, *J. Amer. Chem. Soc.*, **90**, 2266 (1968).

The bridging group is often supplied by the oxidizing agent because this is invariably the inert reactant. In these cases, the bridging ligand normally transfers from oxidant to reductant during the reaction. This, however, is not an essential feature of an inner-sphere redox reaction. The cyanide bridge is supplied by $Fe(CN)_6^{4-}$ in some reductions and remains with the iron after electron transfer and breakup.[29]

The different types of bridging ligands will now be discussed, and the varying patterns of associated redox reactions will be developed.

(a) Hydroxide and Water. With oxidants containing a coordinated water group, for example $Co(NH_3)_5H_2O^{3+}$, a term in the rate law containing an $[H^+]^{-1}$ dependency for their reaction is often found. This may make a significant contribution to the rate, and mask any $[H^+]$-independent term. The inverse term is usually ascribed to reduction of the hydroxy species, for example $Co(NH_3)_5OH^{2+}$, offering a very effective OH bridge in an inner-sphere process.[30-32] Reactions in which the aqua and hydroxy forms have similar reactivities and in which no other bridging group is present are probably outer-sphere,[22] and assignment of mechanism on this basis is illustrated in Table 5.6.

There has been a continuing discussion of whether the aqua group acts as a (weak) bridge in the situations where the corresponding hydroxo complex reacts inner-sphere. The interesting point has been made that the ratios of rate constants for reduction by Cr^{2+} and V^{2+} of "authentic" outer-sphere oxidants—for example $Co(NH_3)_6^{3+}$—and of $Co(NH_3)_5$-H_2O^{3+}, Fe^{3+}, and Hg^{2+} are similar, thus tending to place the last three also in the outer-sphere category (Table 5.7).[31]

TABLE 5.6. Assignment of Mechanism, Inner-Sphere (is) or Outer-Sphere (os), to Reactions of Hydroxy Species on the Basis of Rate Constants for Reaction of Aqua and Hydroxy Forms

Reductant	Oxidant	k_{H_2O} [a]	k_{OH} [b]	Mechanism
Cr^{2+}	$Co(NH_3)_5H_2O^{3+}$	$\leqslant 0.1$	1.5×10^6	is, from ^{18}O experiments.[32]
	$Co(\text{tet } a)(H_2O)_2^{3+}$	$\leqslant 10^2$	7×10^6	is
	$Fe(H_2O)_6^{3+}$	$\leqslant 5.7 \times 10^2$	4.4×10^6	is
V^{2+}	$Co(NH_3)_5H_2O^{3+}$	0.53	<4	os (see Table 5.2)
	$Co(\text{tet } a)(H_2O)_2^{3+}$	1.8×10^3	8.5×10^3	Magnitude and relative values suggest os
	$Fe(H_2O)_6^{3+}$	1.8×10^4	$<4 \times 10^5$	os
$Ru(NH_3)_6^{2+}$	$Co(NH_3)_5H_2O^{3+}$	3.0	0.04	os
	$Co(\text{tet } a)(H_2O)_2^{3+}$	3.0×10^3	5×10^2	os
$Crbipy_3^{2+}$	$Co(NH_3)_5H_2O^{3+}$	$2 \times 10^3 \ (4°)$	$1 \times 10^3 \ (4°)$	os
Eu^{2+}	$Co(NH_3)_5H_2O^{3+}$	7.4×10^{-2}	$<2 \times 10^3$	Probably os

SOURCE: Refs. 30 and 31, and Table 5.4.
a Rate constant M^{-1} sec^{-1} at 25° for reaction of aqua form.
b Rate constant for reaction of hydroxy form.

TABLE 5.7. Rate Constants (k, M^{-1} sec^{-1}) for Reduction by Cr(II) and V(II) at $25°$[31]

Oxidant	$k_{Cr^{2+}}$	$k_{V^{2+}}$	$k_{Cr^{2+}}/k_{V^{2+}}$
$Co(NH_3)_6^{3+}$	8.0×10^{-5}	3.7×10^{-3}	0.024
$Co(NH_3)_5py^{3+}$	4.1×10^{-3}	2.4×10^{-1}	0.018
$Ru(NH_3)_5py^{3+}$	3.4×10^{3}	1.2×10^{5}	0.028
$Co(NH_3)_5H_2O^{3+}$	$\leqslant 0.1$	5.3×10^{-1}	$\leqslant 0.2$
$Fe(H_2O)_6^{3+}$	$\leqslant 5.7 \times 10^{2}$	1.8×10^{4}	$\leqslant 0.03$
Hg^{2+}	5.7×10^{-2}	1.3	0.044

(b) **Halides.** The reduction of halide complexes has featured prominently in the development of redox chemistry. Rates invariably vary monotonically from F to I but not in a consistent manner. In authentic inner-sphere reductions by Cr^{2+} of $Co(NH_3)_5X^{2+}$,[33,34] $Cr(NH_3)_5X^{2+}$,[35] CrX^{2+},[27] and FeX^{2+};[12] by $Co(CN)_5^{3-}$ of $Co(NH_3)_5X^{2+}$;[13a] and by Pt(II) of Pt(IV) substitutions,[36,37] the rate increases with increasing size of the halogen. This ("normal") order persists, however, in the outer-sphere reductions by $Cr(bipy)_3^{2+}$ and $Ru(NH_3)_6^{2+}$.[38,39] The order is inverted ("inverse-order") (F > I) in some reductions by Fe^{2+} and Eu^{2+} (Table 5.4; also Refs. 12, 20, 38, 40) although it is probable that these are inner-sphere. From reactivity behavior alone it is clear that the halide order is not a useful criterion for distinguishing between these mechanisms. It has been suggested that the inverse order is determined by the driving force for the reaction,[33,38,40] and Haim has allowed for differing free energies of the ground states by calculating formal equilibrium constants for halide interchange *in the transition state* for various redox reactions.[41] The equilibrium constant for

$$[(NH_3)_5CoFCr^{4+}]^{\ddagger} + I^- \rightleftharpoons [(NH_3)_5CoICr^{4+}]^{\ddagger} + F^- \qquad K_1 \quad (5.21)$$

can be calculated knowing the rate and equilibrium constants for

$$Co(NH_3)_5F^{2+} + Cr^{2+} \rightleftharpoons [(NH_3)_5CoFCr^{4+}]^{\ddagger} \qquad k_2 \quad (5.22)$$

$$Co(NH_3)_5I^{2+} + Cr^{2+} \rightleftharpoons [(NH_3)_5CoICr^{4+}]^{\ddagger} \qquad k_3 \quad (5.23)$$

$$Co(NH_3)_5H_2O^{3+} + F^- \rightleftharpoons Co(NH_3)_5F^{2+} + H_2O \qquad K_4 \quad (5.24)$$

$$Co(NH_3)_5H_2O^{3+} + I^- \rightleftharpoons Co(NH_3)_5I^{2+} + H_2O \qquad K_5 \quad (5.25)$$

since $K_1 = k_3K_5/k_2K_4 = 0.064$.[42]

The value of $K_1 < 1$ for this Cr(II) reduction, as with the reactions of Fe(II), Eu(II), and V(II), indicates that the substitution of bridging F by I is unfavorable in the bridged transition complex in all these cases. The two sets of reactivity patterns noted above thus no longer exist. For the outer-sphere reductions by $Crbipy_3^{2+}$ and $Ru(NH_3)_6^{2+}$ of $Co(NH_3)_5X^{2+}$, the stability order of transition states is $F < Cl < Br < I$ (that is, $K_1 > 1$), and thus they parallel the reactivity order. In the reactions of CrX^{2+} with Cr^{2+}, and FeX^{2+} with Fe^{2+}, and in Cr^{2+} and Eu^{2+} reductions of FeX^{2+},[12] the activated complex containing the lighter halogen is the more stable once again for these inner-sphere reactions, and the comparison of the stability of transition states for the halide series may afford a means of diagnosing mechanism. It should be appreciated that this treatment is a rationalization rather than an explanation for the halide effects.[42]

(c) *Ambidentate Ligands.* The use in the oxidant of a polyatomic bridging ligand that presents more than one potential donor site towards the reducing metal ion introduces the concept of *remote* and *adjacent* attack.[43] This can be illustrated by the reaction scheme[44]

$$\text{Co(NH}_3)_5\text{SCN}^{2+} \begin{array}{l} \xrightarrow[\text{Cr}^{2+}]{\text{remote attack by}} [(NH_3)_5CoSCNCr^{4+}]^{\ddagger} \rightarrow CrNCS^{2+} \quad (5.26) \\ \qquad\qquad\qquad\qquad\qquad\qquad \text{Stable (purple) form} \\ \\ \xrightarrow[\text{Cr}^{2+}]{\text{adjacent attack by}} \left[\begin{array}{c} (NH_3)_5CoSCr^{4+} \\ C \\ N \end{array} \right]^{\ddagger} \rightarrow CrSCN^{2+} \\ \qquad\qquad\qquad\qquad\qquad \text{Unstable linkage} \\ \qquad\qquad\qquad\qquad\qquad \text{(green) isomer} \end{array}$$

Different products might result from attack by Cr^{2+} at centers remote and adjacent to the metal. Analysis for $CrSCN^{2+}$ and $CrNCS^{2+}$ in the products can be made by ion-exchange separation and spectral identification. This procedure indicates that about 30% of the reaction goes by the adjacent attack path in $1\ M\ H^+$ at 25°. Reduction of $Co(NH_3)_5NCS^{2-}$ by Cr^{2+}, in contrast, proceeds much more slowly and quantitatively by remote attack, leading to the unstable isomer $CrSCN^{2+}$. This preference for reaction via sulfur, even although it leads to an unstable isomer, may reside in the high electron-mediating ability of S bound to an oxidizing center.[45] It is generally found that $MSCN^{2+}$ is about 10^4 times more reactive than $MNCS^{2+}$, $M = Co(NH_3)_5$ and $Cr(H_2O)_5$, in its reaction with Fe(II) and Cr(II), Table 5.8. With V(II), the ratio is much less, and this supports the idea that the $V(II)-Co(NH_3)_5SCN^{2+}$ reaction is substitution-controlled.[16] Redox reactions of the type outlined above have been used to prepare linkage isomers (Sec. 7.3).

The azide bridging ligand cannot offer the interesting dual possibilities of the thiocyanate group. Because it is symmetrical and presents a nitrogen donor atom, which is favored over sulfur for most incipient tervalent metal centers, $Co(NH_3)_5N_3^{2+}$ is likely to be a more effective oxidant than $Co(NH_3)_5NCS^{2+}$ if the reaction goes by an inner-sphere mechanism; it is not likely to be much different in an outer-sphere reaction. This has been a useful diagnostic tool[27,46,47] (see Table 5.8).

It is not easy to distinguish remote from adjacent attack when the

TABLE 5.8. Rate Constants (k, M^{-1} sec^{-1}) for Reduction of N- and S-Bonded Co(III) complexes by V(II), Cr(II), Fe(II), and Crbipy$_3{}^{2+}$ at 25°

Oxidant	V^{II}	Cr^{II}	Fe^{II}	Crbipy$_3{}^{2+}$
$Co(NH_3)_5SCN^{2+}$	30	1.9×10^5 [a] 0.8×10^5 [b]	0.12	...
$Co(NH_3)_5N_3{}^{2+}$	13	$\sim 3 \times 10^5$	8.8×10^{-3}	4.1×10^4
$Co(NH_3)_5NCS^{2+}$	0.3	19	$< 3 \times 10^{-6}$	1.0×10^4
Type of Reaction	is	is	is	os

Source: Refs. 16, 38.
[a] Remote attack.
[b] Adjacent attack.

ambidentate ligand is symmetrical. This has been a particularly vexing problem in the inner-sphere redox reactions of the type

$$a \downarrow$$

$$Cr^{2+} + Co(NH_3)_5O\cdot C\cdot R^{2+} + 5H^+ \rightarrow CrOCOR^{2+} + Co^{2+} + 5NH_4{}^+$$

$$\underset{\underset{b}{\uparrow}}{\overset{\parallel}{O}}$$

$$(5.27)$$

The site of attack (a or b) is still uncertain,[48] although there is evidence for attack at the carbonyl O in the reaction of the Ru(III) analog.[49] Inductive effects of R in (5.27) are relatively unimportant compared with steric factors, since log (k/k_0) (k_0 for R = CH$_3$) vs σ^* is linear for a number of R groups and $\rho^* = -0.37$. Where R = pivalato and formato groups, data deviate from the linear plot, reflecting abnormal steric hindrance to attack from Cr^{2+} based on a model **2** for the activated complex[48] (Fig. 5.1).

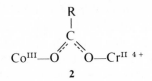

2

(d) *Extended (Organic) Ligands.* The identification of the primary product of the reaction

$$(NH_3)_5CoN\!\!\!\!\bigcirc\!\!\!\!-CONH_2{}^{3+} + Cr^{2+} \xrightarrow[H^+]{high}$$

$$HN\!\!\!\!\bigcirc\!\!\!\!-C\!\!\begin{array}{c}OCr^{4+}\\ NH_2\end{array} + Co^{2+} + 5NH_4{}^+ \quad (5.28)$$

3

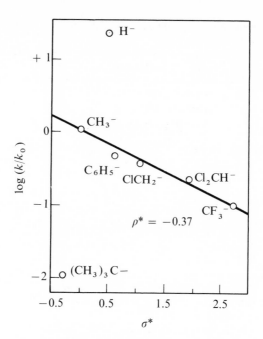

FIGURE 5.1 Taft plot for the reaction (5.27) indicating the importance of steric factors in R on the rate constant.[48]

by a number of methods **3** unequivocally demonstrates remote attack.[50] It is therefore a much more rapid reaction than that with the (unsubstituted) py derivative, $Co(NH_3)_5py^{3+}$ (Tables 5.4 and 5.9). This type of reaction has been useful in answering (at least in part) the interesting question, What is the detailed mechanism of electron transfer when remote attack occurs through an extended bond system? There are two important ways in which this may occur:

1. By the passage of electrons to the bridging group to give a radical ion, which passes an electron further to the oxidant center.[25,51,52] This transfer of an electron might be regarded also as a concurrent process.[52]

$$M^{III}L + Cr^{II} \rightarrow M^{III} \cdot L \cdot Cr^{II} \rightarrow M^{III} \cdot L^{-} \cdot Cr^{III} \rightarrow M^{II} \cdot L \cdot Cr^{III}$$
$$\rightarrow M^{II} + Cr^{III}L \qquad (5.29)$$

2. By action of the bridging group to increase the probability of electron transfer by tunneling, termed resonance transfer.[52]

The chemical mechanism (1) is not likely to occur when L^- is F^- or some other singly charged ion, since F^{2-}, for example, would be produced and this is energetically unfavorable. With an aromatic extended bond

TABLE 5.9. Some Comparisons of the Behavior of Co(III), Cr(III), and Ru(III) Complexes at 25°

Reductant	Oxidant	k, M^{-1} sec^{-1}
Cr^{2+}	$Co(NH_3)_5F^{2+}$	2.5×10^5
	$Cr(H_2O)_5F^{2+}$	2.6×10^{-2}
Cr^{2+}	$Co(NH_3)_5OCOCH_3^{2+}$	0.35
	$Cr(H_2O)_5OCOCH_3^{2+}$	$<10^{-4}$
Cr^{2+}	$(NH_3)_5Co\!-\!N$⟨pyridine⟩$-CONH_2$	17.4
	$(H_2O)_5Cr\!-\!N$⟨pyridine⟩$-CONH_2$	1.8
	$(NH_3)_5Ru\!-\!N$⟨pyridine⟩$-CONH_2$	3.9×10^5
Eu^{2+}	$(NH_3)_5Co\!-\!N$⟨pyridine⟩$-CONH_2$	0.85

SOURCE: Data from Refs. 50, 53, and 55, and Tables 5.4 and 5.5.

system, however, it is much more probable, and indeed very likely in certain instances. The similar rate constants for reaction (5.28) when Cr(III) replaces Co(III), which is a very unusual situation (Table 5.9), strongly suggests mechanism (1), in which the rds is a transfer of electrons from Cr(II) to L.[50] This is a process that is not likely to be much affected by the nature of the distant oxidizing M(III) center. For reaction (5.28), when a Ru(III) complex is the oxidant, however, much higher rate constants ($\sim 10^4$-fold) (Table 5.9) are determined in spite of little difference in driving force compared with the Co(III)–Cr(III) pair of reactions.[53] This suggests that a direct rather than a stepwise passage of electrons occurs. This difference has been rationalized as follows. Electron transfer from Cr^{2+} occurs to a low-lying π orbital of the ligand. Ruthenium(III), t_{2g}^5, has an acceptor orbital of π symmetry, whereas the oxidants with t_{2g}^3 and t_{2g}^6 configurations employ an e_g acceptor orbital of σ symmetry (Fig. 5.2).[54] The matching of Cr(II) with Ru(III) is more likely to lead to resonance transfer, without a stepwise feature. For this to occur with the Cr(II), Cr(III) and Cr(II), Co(III) pairs of systems would require a distortion of the coordination sphere of the oxidant to lower its energy and provide

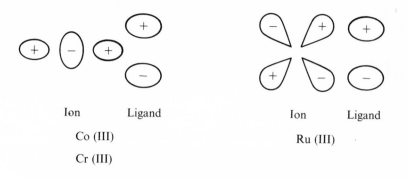

FIGURE 5.2   Acceptor and carrier orbital symmetries for Cr(III), Co(III), and Ru(III) complexes.[54]

overlap with the ligand system before the electron could pass over. It is easy to see how in these cases (1) might be favored.[54]   There is indirect but compelling evidence for a radical intermediate also in the Eu(II) reductions of pentamminecobalt(III) isonicotinamide complexes, that is, (5.28) with Eu(II) in place of Cr(II).[55]

5.4.1   Reducibility of Ligands

It is perhaps not surprising that the intrinsic reducibility of the ligand may play a role in moderating the redox rate constants. Some puzzling differences in behavior of similar coordinated ligands may be rationalized on this basis.   The rate of reduction by Cr^{2+} is higher for $Co(NH_3)_5$-$OCOCHO^{2+}$ compared with $Co(NH_3)_5OCOCH_3^{2+}$ and $Co(NH_3)_5$-$OCOCH_2OH^{2+}$ by a factor of over 10^4 (Table 5.10) and this may arise from a difference in reducibility of the two types of ligands. The former has an unoccupied orbital lying at lower energy and therefore more readily available for an electron.

5.5   FURTHER DETAILS OF THE REDOX PROCESS: ACTIVATION PARAMETERS

Another pertinent aspect of the details of the mechanism is the question whether the bridged species in the inner-sphere reaction is an activated complex or an unstable intermediate.   To consider this and related points, we must dissect a redox reaction into its individual steps.[26,46,52,56]

TABLE 5.10. Activation Parameters for Reduction of Co(NH$_3$)$_5$L Complexes, L Carboxylate, and Related Ligands, at 25°

L	Cr^{2+}			V^{2+}			Ru(NH$_3$)$_6^{2+}$		
	k $M^{-1}\,sec^{-1}$	$\Delta H^{\ddagger}$	$\Delta S^{\ddagger}$	k $M^{-1}\,sec^{-1}$	$\Delta H^{\ddagger}$	$\Delta S^{\ddagger}$	k $M^{-1}\,sec^{-1}$	$\Delta H^{\ddagger}$	$\Delta S^{\ddagger}$
O=CH	7.2	8.3	−27	3.6	13.9	−13			
O=CCH$_3$	0.35	8.2	−33	1.2	11.6	−19			
O=CC$_6$H$_5$	0.15	9.0	−32	0.63	12.4	−18			
O=CCH$_2$Cl	0.12	8.9	−33						
O=CCHCl$_2$	0.075	8.1	−36						
O=CCF$_3$	0.017	9.3	−35						
O=CC(CH$_3$)$_3$	0.007	11.1	−31						
O=CCH$_2$OH	3.1	9.0	−26						

L	Cr²⁺			V²⁺			Ru(NH₃)₆²⁺		
	k $M^{-1}\,sec^{-1}$	$\Delta H^{\ddagger}$	$\Delta S^{\ddagger}$	k $M^{-1}\,sec^{-1}$	$\Delta H^{\ddagger}$	$\Delta S^{\ddagger}$	k $M^{-1}\,sec^{-1}$	$\Delta H^{\ddagger}$	$\Delta S^{\ddagger}$
$\overset{O\;O}{\overset{\|\;\|}{OCCH}}$	$>7 \times 10^3$			8.2	11.0	−17	0.09	13.1	−20
$\overset{O\;O}{\overset{\|\;\|}{OCCOH}}$	1.0×10^2			12.5	12.2	−13	0.50	16.1	− 6
$\overset{O\;O}{\overset{\|\;\|}{OCCO^-}}$	4.6×10^4	2.3	−20	45	...	...	0.10	6.4	−41
$\overset{O\;O}{\overset{\|\;\|}{OCCNH_2}}$	1.9×10^2	8.8	−19	21	11.6	−14	0.22	11.0	−24
$\overset{O\;O}{\overset{\|\;\|}{OCCCH_3}}$	1.1×10^4	5.8	−21	11	11.6	−15	0.20	15.9	− 8
$\overset{O\;O}{\overset{\|\;\|}{OCCC(CH_3)_3}}$	9.3×10^3	2.9	−31	2.1	11.9	−17	0.39	13.1	−17

SOURCE: Ref. 48.

271

Specifically, we study the reaction of $Cr(H_2O)_6{}^{2+}$ with $Co(III)(NH_3)_5L$. The first step is the diffusion-controlled formation of a collision complex **4** with the reactants trapped in the solvent matrix (charges omitted).

$$(H_2O)_6Cr^{II} + LCo^{III}(NH_3)_5 \rightleftharpoons (H_2O)_6Cr^{II}\cdots LCo^{III}(NH_3)_5 \qquad (5.30)$$
$$\mathbf{4}$$

The entity **4** can then progress either through an inner-sphere path (5.31) and (5.32), giving precursor **5** and successor **6** complexes:

$$(H_2O)_6Cr^{II}\cdots LCo^{III}(NH_3)_5 \rightleftharpoons (H_2O)_5Cr^{II}LCo^{III}(NH_3)_5 + H_2O \quad (5.31)$$
$$\mathbf{5}$$

$$(H_2O)_5Cr^{II}LCo^{III}(NH_3)_5 \rightleftharpoons (H_2O)_5Cr^{III}LCo^{II}(NH_3)_5 \qquad (5.32)$$
$$\mathbf{6}$$

and products:

$$(H_2O)_5Cr^{III}LCo^{II}(NH_3)_5 \rightleftharpoons (H_2O)_5Cr^{III}L + Co^{II}(NH_3)_5 \qquad (5.33)$$

or through an outer-sphere mechanism:

$$(H_2O)_6Cr^{II}\cdots LCo^{III}(NH_3)_5 \rightleftharpoons (H_2O)_6Cr^{III}\cdots LCo^{II}(NH_3)_5$$
$$\rightleftharpoons \text{products} \qquad (5.34)$$

The binuclear species will be termed an intermediate only if its lifetime exceeds characteristic vibration times, and obviously in these situations the observed second-order rate constant and the associated activation parameters $\Delta H^{\ddagger}$ and $\Delta S^{\ddagger}$ will be composite values. Precursor complex formation, intramolecular electron transfer, or successor complex decomposition may severally be rate-limiting. The associated reaction profiles are shown in Fig. 5.3.[56,57]

Negative values for $\Delta H^{\ddagger}$ for reaction of Cr^{2+} with a number of Co(III) complexes (Table 5.11) are powerful evidence for precursor complexes, since $\Delta H_1^{\circ} + \Delta H_2^{\circ} + \Delta H_3^{\ddagger} < 0$ only can explain these values.[26] Similarly, a value of $\Delta H^{\ddagger} \sim 0$ for the outer-sphere reaction of $Fe(DMP)_3{}^{2+}$ with $IrCl_6{}^{2-}$ precludes a rate-determining character for the formation of the collision complex (Prob. 6, Chap. 2).

If the redox rate constant is less than the substitution rate constant, as it is for many reactions of Cr^{2+}, Eu^{2+}, Cu^+, Fe^{2+}, and other ions (compare Tables 5.4 and 4.13), then electron transfer within the precursor complex is rate-determining. The observed rate constant will represent a composite value including one or two preequilibrium constants. If the latter remain sensibly constant when a series of related complexes are examined, the experimental rate constant may still reflect the intramolecular rate constant. However, the possibility that this is not the case should be recognized.

TABLE 5.11. Activation Parameters for the Cr^{2+} Reductions of cis-$Coen_2$-XY^{n+} at $25°$ [26]

X, Y	$\Delta F^{\ddagger}$ kcal mol^{-1}	$\Delta H^{\ddagger}$ kcal mol^{-1}	$\Delta S^{\ddagger}$ eu
Cl, NH$_3$	10.0	-2 ± 3	-41 ± 4
Cl, H$_2$O	9.8	1 ± 4	-29 ± 11
Cl, py	9.2	8 ± 7	-3 ± 24
Cl, C$_6$H$_{11}$NH$_2$	9.7	-17 ± 5	-90 ± 15
Cl, Cl	9.4	-6 ± 4	-51 ± 10
Cl, F	9.3	-10 ± 3	-65 ± 13

Examining the values for the activation entropies for authentic inner- and outer-sphere reactions reveals, in general, insufficient differences or patterns for these to act as a basis for diagnosis. Taube[58] has drawn attention to a sizable number of redox reactions involving dipositive reducing and oxidizing cations which are accompanied by $\Delta S^{\ddagger}$ values of -31 ± 3 eu (see, for example, Table 5.10). For the corresponding reactions of V^{2+}, however, the values of $\Delta S^{\ddagger}$ are much less negative (see Table 5.2) and this is attributed to the fact that substitution is rate-controlling. Electron transfer is probably rate-limiting in the other instances, and

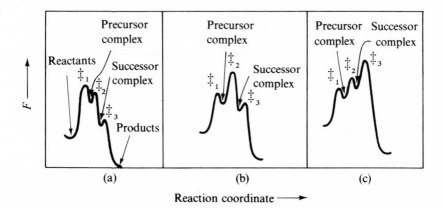

(a)   (b)   (c)

Reaction coordinate ⟶

FIGURE 5.3 Reaction profiles for inner-sphere redox reactions, illustrating three types of behavior: (a) precursor complex formation is rate-limiting; (b) precursor-to-successor complex is rate-limiting; and (c) the breakdown of successor complex is rate-limiting. The situation (b) appears to be that most commonly encountered.[56,57]

these may be attended by low values for the transmission coefficient in the transition state theory.[58]

Meager data on pressure effects indicate some correlation of positive $\Delta V^{\ddagger}$ values with an inner-sphere mechanism, which arise from the liberation of water molecules in forming the activated complex.[59]

5.6 DOUBLE BRIDGES

The possibility of two or more bridging groups in the activated complex of an inner-sphere reaction was suggested by Taube and Myers[10] and was first demonstrated by Snellgrove and King.[60] The implication of a double bridge in a redox reaction can only be via product characterization. The isotopic exchange

$$cis\text{-}Cr(N_3)_2{}^+ + {}^*Cr^{2+} \rightleftharpoons cis\text{-}{}^*Cr(N_3)_2{}^+ + Cr^{2+} \qquad (5.35)$$

can only occur via a double bridge. The rate constant for the exchange is 31 times larger at 0° than the rate constant for the net chemical reaction

$$cis\text{-}Cr(N_3)_2{}^+ + Cr^{2+} \rightarrow CrN_3{}^{2+} + Cr^{2+} + N_3{}^- \qquad (5.36)$$

which goes through a single bridge.[60] In other instances, as in the reaction of $cis\text{-}Co(NH_3)_4(N_3)_2{}^+$ with Cr^{2+}, the double and single bridges are of comparable importance,[61] while in the reaction of $cis\text{-}CrF_2{}^+$ with Cr^{2+} there is no evidence for a double-bridged path[62] (Table 5.12). It is clear that the factors influencing the relative tendencies of single and double bridges are unknown at present.

If a chelate site presents itself to an attacking metal ion, a chelate product can result. The reaction of Cr^{2+} with $Co(NH_3)_4C_2O_4{}^+$ leads to

TABLE 5.12.   Rate Constants (M^{-1} sec^{-1}) for Single and Double Bridging Reactions of Cr(II) at 0°

Oxidant	Double bridge k_1	Single bridge k_2	k_1/k_2
$cis\text{-}Cr(N_3)_2{}^+$	60	1.9	31
$cis\text{-}Co(NH_3)_4(N_3)_2{}^+$	$> 10^3$	$> 10^3$	0.6[a]
$cis\text{-}Coen_2(N_3)_2{}^+$	$> 10^3$	$> 10^3$	0.2[a]
$cis\text{-}CrF_2{}^+$	$< 1.2 \times 10^{-5}$	1.2×10^{-3}	< 0.01

Source: Tabulated in Ref. 61.
[a] From ratio [$cis\text{-}Cr(N_3)_2{}^+$]/[$CrN_3{}^{2+}$].

$CrC_2O_4^+$, providing strong evidence for an activated complex of the form[63]

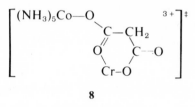

7

Similarly, the reduction of $Co(NH_3)_5OCOCH_2COOH$ by Cr^{2+},

$$V = (k_1[H^+] + k_2 + k_3[H^+]^{-1})[Co^{III}][Cr^{II}] \tag{5.37}$$

yields $Cr(H_2O)_4(malonate)^+$ as a product of the k_1 and k_3 paths. Since the chelated Cr(III) complex could have arisen only from the redox process, and not subsequent to it, a chelated transition state **8** is implicated.[64]

$$\left[\begin{array}{c} (NH_3)_5Co\!-\!O \\ \diagdown \\ C\!-\!CH_2 \\ O\diagup \quad \diagdown C\!\cdots\!O \\ \diagdown \diagup \\ Cr\!-\!O \end{array} \right]^{3+\ddagger}$$

8

5.7 THE INFLUENCE OF THE NONBRIDGING LIGAND IN INNER-SPHERE REACTIONS

We might wonder what happens to the ligands that are not involved in the bridging act during the redox process, and what influence they might have as a result on the rates of such reactions.[65] This is an area where theoretical predictions preceded experimental results. Orgel[66] first drew attention to a model in which electronic states in the activated complex are matched by changing bond distances and therefore the ligand fields of the reactant ions.[66] For the reduction of Co(III) and Cr(III) complexes, for example, an electron from the reducing agent would appear in an unoccupied e_g, say d_{z^2}, orbital directed towards X (the bridging group) and Y in $trans$-$Co(NH_3)_4XY$. The energy of this orbital will obviously be more sensitive to changes in the $trans$ Y group than to changes in the cis NH_3 ligands,[66] and the orbital will be stabilized by a weak field ligand Y. ,Further, its availability will be increased by an outward motion of Y at the same time that the bridging group moves in the opposite direction.[67] In general the consequences of these happenings have been confirmed in both rate experiments and isotopic fractionation experiments.

5.7.1 Rates

Since H_2O is a weaker field than NH_3, one would expect a faster rate for a complex with an H_2O group $trans$ to the bridging ligand than for a complex with an NH_3 group instead of the *trans*-H_2O but otherwise identical. Such a fast rate has been demonstrated in a number of reaction series (Table 5.13). The nature of the reducing or of the oxidizing metal influences the magnitude of the effect.[65] This effect appears to reside in the $\Delta H^{\ddagger}$ terms,[12,68,69] and indeed there is a correlation of $\Delta H^{\ddagger}$ with ΔDq values.[12] For a series of complexes with a common bridging group but different ligands in the *trans* position, the stronger the crystal field influence of the *trans* ligand, the greater the distance it must be moved to lower the energy of the e_g acceptor orbital to the necessary extent.[70,71] The series en $\sim NH_3 \gg H_2O > RSR$ in cobalt(III) complexes is the crystal field strength, and parallels the increased rate of reaction with Fe(II).[72]

The idea[66] that the bonds are shortened for the reductant and lengthened for the oxidant in forming the activated complex rationalizes nicely the observation that replacement of H_2O by en in Cr(II) *increases* its rate of reduction of Co(III) complexes.[73,74] Since the en has a stronger field, less shortening is required. Inversely, increasing substitution of NH_3 for H_2O in $Cr(NH_3)_n(H_2O)_{5-n}Cl^{2+}$ *reduces* the rate of oxidation of Cr(II).[12]

TABLE 5.13. Some Nonbridging-Ligand Effects on Redox Rate Constants (M^{-1} sec^{-1}) at 25°

Oxidant	$k_{Fe^{2+}}$	Ref.
trans-Coen$_2$(H$_2$O)Cl^{2+}	0.24	71
trans-Coen$_2$(NH$_3$)Cl^{2+}	6.6×10^{-5}	
trans-Co(NH$_3$)$_4$(H$_2$O)Cl^{2+}	~ 10	a
Co(NH$_3$)$_5$Cl^{2+}	1.6×10^{-3}	20
trans-Coen$_2$(H$_2$O)OH^{2+}	2.6×10^6	
trans-Coen$_2$(NH$_3$)OH^{2+}	2.0×10^5	

Oxidant	$k_{Cr^{2+}}$	12
Cr(NH$_3$)$_5$Cl^{2+}	8.8×10^{-2}	
trans-Cr(NH$_3$)$_4$(H$_2$O)Cl^{2+}	1.3	
Cr(NH$_3$)$_3$(H$_2$O)$_2$Cl^{2+}	2.2	
Cr(NH$_3$)$_2$(H$_2$O)$_3$Cl^{2+}	6.9	
Cr(NH$_3$)(H$_2$O)$_4$Cl^{2+}	19	

Reductant	$k_{Co(NH_3)_5Cl^{2+}}$	73
Cr^{2+}	2.2×10^6	
Cren^{2+}	4.0×10^7	
Cren$_2$$^{2+}$	1.6×10^8	

[a] R. G. Linck, *Inorg. Chem.*, 7, 2394 (1968).

5.7.2 Isotopic Fractionation

It has been shown that towards Cr(II), $trans$-$Cr(NH_3)_4(H_2^{16}O)Cl^{2+}$ reacts 1.6% faster than $trans$-$Cr(NH_3)_4(H_2^{18}O)Cl^{2+}$ (Table 3.4).[75] This strongly supports the idea of stretching of the bond in the $trans$ position during the redox reaction. Stretching of the bonds in the cis position is less important, although not negligible, judged by the value for $k_{16_O}/k_{18_O} = 1.007$ for the cis isomer. Previously, ^{15}N fractionation factor experiments on the redox couple between Cr^{2+} and Co(III) ammines indicated that M–N bonds in the ammines are not markedly stretched in the formation of the activated complex.[76] These results are not contradictory however, since one would expect larger stereochemical changes in converting Cr(III) to Cr(II) than in taking Co(III) to Co(II).

It appears from above that the gentler effects of nonbridging ligands on rates can be rationalized more easily than the effects of the bridging ligands.

5.8   THE INFLUENCE OF FREE LIGANDS ON OUTER-SPHERE REACTIONS

Ligands may modify the nature of the labile partner in outer-sphere reactions. The effect of chloride ion on the rate constants for the outer-sphere Cr(II) reduction of $Co(NH_3)_6^{3+}$ and of the Fe(III) oxidation of $Ruen_3^{2+}$ can be interpreted in terms of the reaction of the species: Cr^{2+} ($k = 0.007$), $CrCl^+$ ($k = 0.40$), and Fe^{3+} ($k = 8.4 \times 10^4$), $FeCl^{2+}$ ($k \geq 10^7$, all in M^{-1} sec^{-1}).[65] Although part of these effects may reside in reduced electrostatic repulsion, there must also be specific effects, since $FeOH^{2+}$ is some 6-fold less reactive than Fe^{3+} towards $Ruen_3^{2+}$.[77]

The reaction of Fe_{aq}^{2+} with $Fephen_3^{3+}$ is almost certainly outer-sphere because of the inertness of the Fe(III) complex. Surprising, then, is the marked effect of anions X^- on the reaction rate V,

$$V = (k_0 + k_1[X^-])[Fephen_3^{3+}][Fe^{2+}] \qquad (5.38)$$

Since anions have different effects on the rates of the $Fephen_3^{3+}$–Fe^{2+} and Fe^{3+}–Fe^{2+} reactions (Table 5.14), a new type of mechanism is believed operative in the former case, and it is considered that there is nucleophilic attack of anion either on a carbon of the phenanthroline ligand system bearing a partial positive charge, or on the π system of the ligand.[78] The effect parallels similar specific anion catalysis of the reduction of cytochrome C(III). With these, and in other redox reactions of hemoproteins, the ring system rather than the central metal atom may be the electron transfer site.[79]

TABLE 5.14. Effect of Anions X^- on the Reaction of $Fephen_3^{3+}$ and Fe^{3+} with Fe^{2+} Ion at $25°$ [78]

X^-	$Fephen_3^{3+}$	$k_1, M^{-2} sec^{-1}$
...		3.4×10^4 [a]
Cl^-		4.9×10^5
Br^-		3.8×10^5
I^-		2.4×10^8
N_3^-		8.1×10^8
SCN^-		2.0×10^9
X^-	Fe^{3+}	$k_1, M^{-2} sec^{-1}$
...		3.0 [a]
Cl^-		87
N_3^-		7.1×10^7
SCN^-		2.4×10^3

[a] Value of k_0 in $M^{-1} sec^{-1}$.

5.9 MIXED OUTER- AND INNER-SPHERE REACTIONS

As might be foreseen, there are a (limited) number of systems where the energetics of the outer- and inner-sphere reactions are comparable, and both are paths for the reaction. Studying the rates of the net chemical reaction

$$Fe^{2+} + FeCl^{2+} \rightarrow Fe^{3+} + FeCl^+ \tag{5.39}$$

$$FeCl^+ \rightarrow Fe^{2+} + Cl^-\qquad \text{fast} \tag{5.40}$$

and the isotopic exchange

$$*Fe^{2+} + FeCl^{2+} \rightarrow *FeCl^{2+} + Fe^{2+} \tag{5.41}$$

allows the relative importance of the outer-sphere and inner-sphere paths to be assessed. The latter contributes $\sim 65\%$ to the Fe^{2+}–$FeCl^{2+}$ interaction at $25°$.[80]

5.10 THE CALCULATION OF REDOX RATE CONSTANTS FOR OUTER-SPHERE REACTIONS

Outer-sphere reactions are particularly suitable as a basis for the calculation of rate constants since no bond breaking or making occurs during the electron transfer. The coordination shell and immediate environment for the reactants and for the products will differ as a result of a redox reaction. However, internuclear distances and nuclear velocities cannot change during the electronic transition of a redox reaction (Franck-Condon principle). Therefore some "common state" must be reached for each reactant prior to electron transfer. It is the free energy ΔF^* that is required to change the atomic coordinates from their equilibrium values to values in the activated complex, which must be calculated in any theory. Several workers have tackled the calculation of ΔF^*, and for a comprehensive account and a comparison of the various attempts, the reader is referred to Ref. 81.

Marcus has had the most successful and sustained efforts.[81] He has assumed small electronic interaction between the reacting species, which are treated as rigid spheres of radius a_1 and a_2, inside of which no change of interatomic distance occurs during the reaction.

The free energy ΔF^* is considered to consist of various components:

1. The work required to bring the reactants to their mean separation distance $(a_1 + a_2)$ and then remove the products to infinity (w^r and $-w^p$). This term incorporates electrostatic and nonpolar contributions.
2. The free energy required to reorganize the solvent molecules around the reactants (the outer coordination shell) and to reorganize the inner coordination shell of the reactants. These are termed λ_o and λ_i respectively.
3. The standard free energy of the reaction ΔF^0. This is the free energy of reaction when the reactants are infinitely apart. The quantity $(\Delta F^0 + w^p - w^r)$ is important since it is the standard free energy of reaction at the separation distance. Both the w and λ_o terms can be calculated fairly easily with standard equations. The term λ_i is quite difficult to estimate, requiring at least a knowledge of bond lengths and force constants of the reactants.

Marcus has derived the expression

$$\Delta F^* = \frac{w^r + w^p}{2} + \frac{\lambda_o + \lambda_i}{4} + \frac{\Delta F^0}{2} + \frac{(\Delta F^0 + w^p - w^r)^2}{4(\lambda_o + \lambda_i)} \quad (5.42)$$

The free energy ΔF^* is related to the free energy of activation $\Delta F^\ddagger$ by

$$\Delta F^* = \Delta F^\ddagger - RT \ln \frac{hZ}{kT} = (\Delta F^\ddagger - 2.8) \text{ kcal mole}^{-1} \quad (5.43)$$

and therefore to the rate constant k,

$$k = Z \exp \left(\frac{-\Delta F^*}{RT} \right) \quad (5.44)$$

where $Z \sim 10^{11} M^{-1} \text{sec}^{-1}$. Thus it is possible in principle to calculate the rate constant of an outer-sphere redox reaction from a set of *nonkinetic* parameters and this represents a remarkable positive step. Reasonable agreement between calculated and observed values are obtained in the limited number of redox reactions examined.

The ideas developed have, however, been more usefully applied to the calculation of the rate constants for a reaction in terms of the free energy change and rate constants for related reactions. Equation (5.42) can be written

$$\Delta F^* \sim w^r + \frac{\lambda_i + \lambda_o}{4} \left(1 + \frac{\Delta F^0 + w^p - w^r}{\lambda_i + \lambda_o}\right)^2 \tag{5.45}$$

If

$$(\Delta F^0 + w^p - w^r)(\lambda_i + \lambda_o)^{-1} < 1 \tag{5.46}$$

then

$$\Delta F^* \sim \frac{w^r + w^p}{2} + \frac{\lambda_i + \lambda_o}{4} + \frac{\Delta F^0}{2} \tag{5.47}$$

In the redox reactions of a series of related reagents with a constant reactant (so that ΔF^0 is the only variable), a plot of ΔF^* vs ΔF^0 would be expected to be linear with slope 0.5.

We can take the analysis still further: Consider the "cross reaction" (subscript 12)

$$\text{Ox}_1 + \text{Red}_2 \rightleftharpoons \text{Red}_1 + \text{Ox}_2 \qquad k_{12}, K_{12} \tag{5.48}$$

and the related isotopic exchange reactions (subscripts 11 and 22)

$$\text{Ox}_1 + \text{Red}_1 \rightleftharpoons \text{Red}_1 + \text{Ox}_1 \qquad k_{11} \tag{5.49}$$

$$\text{Ox}_2 + \text{Red}_2 \rightleftharpoons \text{Red}_2 + \text{Ox}_2 \qquad k_{12} \tag{5.50}$$

When the work terms are negligible, and

$$(\lambda_i + \lambda_o)_{12} = \frac{(\lambda_i + \lambda_o)_{11} + (\lambda_i + \lambda_o)_{22}}{2} \tag{5.51}$$

combination with (5.45) yields [82]

$$\Delta F^{\ddagger}_{12} = 0.50\Delta F^{\ddagger}_{11} + 0.50\Delta F^{\ddagger}_{22} + 0.50\Delta F^0_{12} - 1.15RT \log f \tag{5.52}$$

or

$$k_{12} = (k_{11}k_{22}K_{12}f)^{1/2} \tag{5.53}$$

where

$$\log f = \frac{(\log K_{12})^2}{4 \log (k_{11}k_{22}/Z^2)} \tag{5.54}$$

A plot of $(\Delta F^{\ddagger}_{12} + 1.15RT \log f)$ vs ΔF^0_{12} should therefore be linear with a slope 0.50 and an intercept 0.50 $(\Delta F^{\ddagger}_{11} + \Delta F^{\ddagger}_{22})$. For a series of reactions between one common reactant A and a number of closely related species B, $\Delta F^{\ddagger}_{11}$ is constant and $\Delta F^{\ddagger}_{22}$ would not be expected to vary greatly so that the intercept is approximately constant. When the oxidizing power of Ox_1 and Ox_2 are comparable, $f \sim 1$, and the term containing this may be omitted from (5.52) and 5.53):

$$\Delta F_{12}^{\ddagger} = 0.50\,\Delta F_{11}^{\ddagger} + 0.50\,\Delta F_{22}^{\ddagger} + 0.50\,\Delta F_{12}^{0} \qquad (5.55)$$

Examples of (5.52) and (5.55) are shown in the reactions of iron-phenanthroline complexes.[83] (See Figure 5.4.) A larger number of applications of these equations to isolated reaction systems rather than a reaction series plot have been made; some of the quantities, for example the work

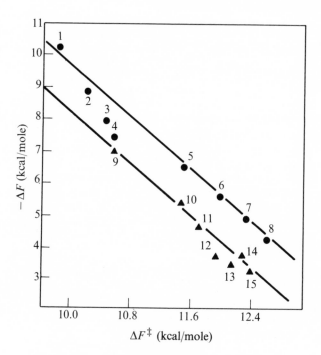

▲ Ru (II) complex in H_2SO_4 ;

● Fe (II) complex in H_2SO_4

Ligands: (3, 15) *o*-phen, (2, 12) 5-Me-*o*-phen,
(9) 4, 7-di-Me-*o*-phen, (1, 11) 5, 6-di-Me-*o*-phen,
(4) 5-Ph-*o*-phen, (5) 5-Cl-*o*-phen, (8) 5-NO$_2$-*o*-phen,
(7) 3-SO$_3$H-*o*-phen, (6) 5-SO$_3$H-*o*-phen, (14) bipy,
(10) 5, 5-di-Me-bipy, (13) terpy.

FIGURE 5.4 LFER illustrating Marcus equation. The plot shows ΔF vs $\Delta F^{\ddagger}$ for reactions of Fephen$_3^{2+}$ and Ruphen$_3^{2+}$ (and derivatives) with Ce(IV).[83]

terms (1), which are difficult to estimate in the calculation of absolute rate constants for isotopic exchange reactions, cancel in the cross reactions.

Agreement of experimental with calculated rate constants has been considered strong evidence that an outer-sphere redox process is involved. However recent work indicates that for some inner-sphere reactions, LFER also apply.

5.11   THE ESTIMATION OF REDOX RATE CONSTANTS FOR INNER-SPHERE REACTIONS

There is evidence that a type of Marcus relationship may be applied to inner-sphere redox reactions.[47,84]   The rates of the inner-sphere reactions

$$Co(NH_3)_5Cl^{2+} + Cr^{2+} \rightarrow \text{products} \qquad k_{12}K_{12}f_{12} \qquad (5.56)$$

and
$$Co(NH_3)_5Cl^{2+} + Fe^{2+} \rightarrow \text{products} \qquad k_{13}K_{13}f_{13} \qquad (5.57)$$

have been related by the equation

$$\frac{k_{12}}{k_{13}} = \left(\frac{k_{22}K_{12}f_{12}}{k_{33}K_{13}f_{13}}\right)^{1/2} \approx \left(\frac{k_{22}K_{12}}{k_{33}K_{13}}\right)^{1/2} \qquad (5.58)$$

where k_{22} and k_{33} are the rate constants for self-exchange in the $Cr^{2+}/CrCl^{2+}$ and $Fe^{2+}/FeCl^{2+}$ systems respectively.   The validity of the expression is justified in Table 5.15, for this and a number of other reduction pairs.[84]

The same approach directed to the trio of inner-sphere reactions

$$CrSCN^{2+} + Cr^{2+} \rightarrow CrNCS^{2+} + Cr^{2+} \qquad k_1(40\ M^{-1}\,sec^{-1}) \qquad (5.59)$$

$$CrNNN^{2+} + Cr^{2+} \rightarrow CrNNN^{2+} + Cr^{2+} \qquad k_2(6.1\ M^{-1}\,sec^{-1}) \qquad (5.60)$$

$$CrNCS^{2+} + Cr^{2+} \rightarrow CrSCN^{2+} + Cr^{2+} \qquad k_3(1.4 \times 10^{-4}\ M^{-1}\,sec^{-1})$$
$$(5.61)$$

leads to
$$k_2 \sim (k_1k_3)^{1/2} \qquad (5.62)$$

TABLE 5.15.   Calculated and Observed Rate Constants (k_{calcd} and k_{obsd}, $M^{-1}\ sec^{-1}$) for Cr^{2+} Reductions of Co(III) Complexes Using (5.58) and Data for Fe^{2+} Reductions[84]

Oxidant	log k_{obsd}	log k_{calcd}
$Co(NH_3)_5Cl^{2+}$	6.4	6.6
$Co(NH_3)_5F^{2+}$	5.9	5.5
cis-$Coen_2(NCS)Cl^{2+}$	6.3	5.7
$trans$-$Coen_2(NCS)Cl^{2+}$	6.4	5.6

TABLE 5.16. Comparison of Second-Order Rate Constants (k, $M^{-1} \sec^{-1}$ at 25°) for Reduction of Co(III) Complexes by $Ru(NH_3)_6^{2+}$ and Fe^{2+}

Oxidant	$Ru(NH_3)_6^{2+}$	Fe^{2+}	$\log (k_{Ru}/k_{Fe})$
cis-Coen$_2$(H$_2$O)Cl^{2+}	2.3×10^2	4.6×10^{-4}	5.7
cis-Coen$_2$(NH$_3$)Cl^{2+}	12	1.8×10^{-5}	5.8
cis-Coen$_2$(py)Cl^{2+}	6.6×10^2	8×10^{-4}	5.9
trans-Coen$_2$(H$_2$O)Cl^{2+}	$> 10^5$	2.4×10^{-1}	> 5.6
cis-Coen$_2$Cl$_2^{+}$	8×10^2	1.6×10^{-3}	5.7
trans-Coen$_2$Cl$_2^{+}$	8×10^3	3.2×10^{-2}	5.4

SOURCE: Ref. 85.

which is obviously not valid. However, a better understanding results when the presence of precursor complexes is taken into account.[46]

The question of LFER for inner- and outer-sphere processes has been tackled in some detailed studies.[85,86] There is a nice correlation of $\log k_{12}$ vs ΔF for the (presumed) outer-sphere reductions by $Ru(NH_3)_6^{2+}$ of a number of Co(III) complexes.[86] A wide range of rate constants ($\sim 10^7$-fold) is accommodated by the relationship, and it is concluded that ΔF is an overriding controlling factor in the rates of reduction of Co(III) complexes, as implied in the Marcus relationship. However, varying A in cis-Coen$_2$ACl^{2+} has the same effect on rate in the outer-sphere reduction by $Ru(NH_3)_6^{2+}$ as in the inner-sphere reduction by Fe^{2+} (constant Cl bridges).[85] (See Table 5.16.) Thus, for both inner- and outer-sphere reactions, a relation of the form

$$k_{12} \sim fn_1(\text{cobalt})\, fn_2(\text{reductant}) \tag{5.63}$$

applies to a number of oxidations by Co(III) complexes.[85,86]

5.12 TWO-ELECTRON TRANSFER

In most of the discussions so far, we have been concerned with reactants undergoing one-electron transfer processes. When one or both of the participants of a redox reaction has to undergo a change of two in the oxidation state, the point arises as to whether the two-electron transfer is simultaneous or nearly simultaneous, a question that has been much discussed. Sykes[8b] has listed and discussed a number of reactions that appear to take place in a single two-equivalent step.[86]

The type of evidence that has been accrued to support the concept of a single two-equivalent step includes:

(a) *Kinetics.* The reaction of V(II) with Hg(II) to produce V(IV) is fast compared with the reaction between V(III) and Hg(II), and this is strong evidence for a two-equivalent step in the V(II)–Hg(II) reaction. It is extremely difficult to distinguish between *simultaneous* and rapid *consecutive* transfer of the electrons within the lifetime of the reactants in a solvent cage.

For the reactions

$$2V^{II} + 2Hg^{II} \rightarrow 2V^{III} + (Hg^{I})_2 \qquad k_1 \qquad\qquad (5.64)$$

and $$\qquad V^{II} + 2Hg^{II} \rightarrow V^{IV} + (Hg^{I})_2 \qquad k_2 \qquad\qquad (5.65)$$

values for k_1 and k_2 can be obtained from a combination of the equilibrium ratio $[V(III)]_e/[V(IV)]_e$ by spectral analysis of the reacted solution and the rate of the reaction $+d[V(IV)]/dt$ by spectral stopped-flow.[87] For the one-electron transfer, $k_1 = 1.04 \ M^{-1}\sec^{-1}$ (H$^+$-independent), $\Delta H_1^{\ddagger} = 15.8$, and $\Delta S_1^{\ddagger} = -6$; and for the two-electron transfer, $k_2 = 8.7 \ M^{-1}\sec^{-1}$ (inverse H$^+$-dependent), $\Delta H_2^{\ddagger} = 14.8$, and $\Delta S_2^{\ddagger} = -5$. Both probably take place by inner-sphere mechanisms.[87]

(b) *Inability to Detect Intermediate Oxidation State.* The oxidation of U_{aq}^{4+} by $HClO_2$ to give UO_2^{2+} has been studied in $H_2^{18}O$. If successive one-electron transfers occur via the very labile UO_2^{+}, then the ^{18}O isotopic composition will be the same for UO_2^{2+} as for the solvent. Substantially less ^{18}O is observed in UO_2^{2+} than in the solvent, however; this finding therefore supports a two-electron oxygen transfer from $HClO_2$ to U_{aq}^{4+}. $HClO_2$ and UO_2^{2+} exchange oxygen with solvent very slowly.[88]

(c) *Product Analysis.* The immediate product of the reaction of Cr(II) and Tl(III) is the dimer $Cr_2(OH)_2^{4+}$. This is likely to result only from an interaction of Cr(II) with Cr(IV), produced in the redox step. If Cr(III) resulted directly from Cr(II) and Tl(III), it would undoubtedly be in the form of a mononuclear Cr(III) species, the product of most oxidations of Cr(II).[89]

5.13 REDOX-CATALYZED SUBSTITUTION

Certain substitutions, particularly in Cr(III), Pt(IV), and Co(III), can be catalyzed by the operation of a redox process. Hydrolysis, anation, and anion interchange all have been accelerated in complexes of these metals by the presence of the lower oxidation states.

Chromium(II) catalyzes ligation of Cr(III):[90]

$$Cr^{II} + X \rightleftharpoons Cr^{II}X \tag{5.66}$$

$$Cr^{II}X + Cr^{III} \rightarrow Cr^{III}X + Cr^{II} \tag{5.67}$$

by a third-order rate law

$$V = k_1[Cr^{II}][Cr^{III}][X] \tag{5.68}$$

and consequently Cr(II) catalyzes aquation of Cr(III)X by the reverse reaction

$$Cr^{III}X + Cr^{II} \rightarrow Cr^{II}X + Cr^{III} \tag{5.69}$$

$$Cr^{II}X \rightarrow Cr^{II} + X \tag{5.70}$$

with the rate law

$$V = k_2[Cr^{II}][Cr^{III}X] \tag{5.71}$$

The k_2 rate constant usually incorporates an inverse $[H^+]$ term. This is ascribed to the reacting of $CrXOH^+$ with Cr^{2+} via an OH bridge.[91]

The effectiveness of $X(I > Br > Cl > N_3 > F)$ when acting as a nonbridging ligand is similar[92] to its effectiveness when it functions as a bridge in the much more rapid ($\sim 10^3$-fold) isotopic exchange

$$*Cr^{2+} + CrX^{2+} \rightleftharpoons *CrX^{2+} + Cr^{2+} \tag{5.72}$$

5.14   ELECTRON CONFIGURATIONS AND RATES

We have already seen how the rate constants for some inner-sphere reactions may be rationalized by a consideration of electron configurations of the metals and the orbitals involved (Sec. 5.4(d)). An understanding of the relative rate constants for some outer-sphere reactions (see Table 5.17) is possible using the simple premise that addition or removal of electrons is easier at the t_{2g} than at the e_g orbital. In the former, a non-bonding electron is involved, and in the latter, an anti-bonding electron (with larger effects on the bond lengths).

TABLE 5.17.   Redox Rate Constants (k, M^{-1} sec^{-1}) for Some Cobalt and Ruthenium Outer-Sphere Reactions

Exchange partners	k, for M = Co	k, for M = Ru
$M(NH_3)_6{}^{2+}$–$M(NH_3)_6{}^{3+}$	$< 10^{-9}$	8×10^2
$Men_3{}^{2+}$–$Men_3{}^{3+}$	2×10^{-5}	$\sim 2 \times 10^2$
$Mbipy_3{}^{2+}$–$Mbipy_3{}^{3+}$	15	$> 10^8$

Thus self-exchange rate constants in the Ru(II)–(III) system $t_{2g}^{\,6} \leftrightarrow t_{2g}^{\,5}$ are *much* higher than the corresponding ones for Co(II)–(III), $t_{2g}^{\,5}e_g^{\,2} \leftrightarrow t_{2g}^{\,6}$. The outer-sphere reduction by Cr^{2+} is some 10^6 times faster for $Ru(NH_3)_5py^{3+}$ than for $Co(NH_3)_5py^{3+}$.[53] The situation is complicated with the cobalt(II)–(III) system by the radical difference in the electronic configuration of the two oxidation states. Thus, one way of representing the situation would be:[93]

$$Co(NH_3)_6^{2+} \text{ high spin} \rightleftharpoons Co(NH_3)_6^{2+} \text{ low spin} \qquad K_1 \quad (5.73)$$

$$Co(NH_3)_6^{2+} \text{ low spin} + Co(NH_3)_6^{3+} \text{ low spin} \rightleftharpoons$$

$$Co(NH_3)_6^{3+} \text{ low spin} + Co(NH_3)_6^{2+} \text{ low spin} \qquad k_2 \quad (5.74)$$

$$Co(NH_3)_6^{2+} \text{ low spin} \rightleftharpoons Co(NH_3)_6^{2+} \text{ high spin} \qquad (5.75)$$

Combination of an unfavorable K_1 with the rate-determining k_2 step can account for a rate constant that is 10^{15} times lower than for $Ru(NH_3)_6^{2+}$, $Ru(NH_3)_6^{3+}$ electron transfer, where no such problems arise since both are low spin in the ground state. The energy required to distort the coordination shells of the reduced and oxidized forms of the ammines to the transition state (where both species have the same dimensions) can be estimated since Ru–N and Co–N bond distances in all four ions are known. It appears that this can account for only ~ 8 kcal mole^{-1} of the 25–30 kcal mole^{-1} difference in the systems, and the remainder resides in the electron configurational mismatch discussed above.[93]

Ligands are not without influence. Those, such as bipyridine, that induce a large amount of electron delocalization promote electron transfer, a point easily seen by comparing ethylenediamine and bipyridine complexes of the same metal (see Table 5.17).

5.15 OXIDATION OF COORDINATED LIGANDS

Oxidizing metal ions oxidize inorganic and organic substrates. In many cases there is evidence for a transient inner-sphere complex, which may therefore lie along the reaction profile (Fig. 5.5(a)),

$$M + L \rightleftharpoons ML \rightarrow \text{products} \qquad (5.76)$$

or be an independent competing process (Fig. 5.5b),

$$M + L \rightleftharpoons ML \qquad (5.77)$$

$$M + L \rightarrow \text{products} \qquad (5.78)$$

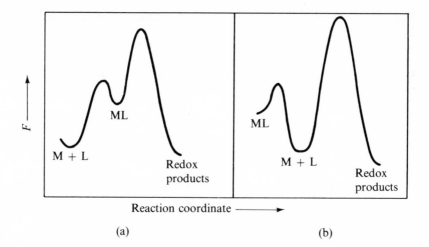

FIGURE 5.5   Reaction profiles for a redox reaction between M and L in which (a) complex ML is an intermediate lying along the reaction profile, and (b) complex ML is formed but is extraneous and does not lead to redox reaction.

The latter appears likely only when the structures of the activated complex for (5.78) and for the formation of ML (5.77) are substantially different.

The presence of ML in the reaction may be inferred from the form of the rate law or may actually be detected. There are many examples of ligand oxidation by Ce(IV), Fe(III), Mn(III), Co(III), V(V), Cr(VI), Ag(II), and Cu(II).[94] Reaction of Co(III) ion with a number of reductants R can be rationalized in terms of a mechanism

$$Co^{3+} \rightleftharpoons CoOH^{2+} + H^+ \qquad K_h \qquad (5.79)$$

$$Co^{3+} + R \rightarrow Co^{2+} + R\cdot \qquad k_1 \qquad (5.80)$$

$$CoOH^{2+} + R \rightarrow Co^{2+} + R\cdot \qquad k_2 \qquad (5.81)$$

$$V = k_1[Co^{III}][R] + k_2 K_h[Co^{III}][R][H^+]^{-1} \qquad (5.82)$$

Values for k_1 and $k_2 K_h$ are given in Table 5.18.[95] The trend of increasing rate constant with increasing negative-charge product for the group of oxidations by $CoOH^{2+}$ is reminiscent of complexation behavior (Sec. 4.3.4) and suggests that Co^{3+}–L complex formation is the rate-determining process in these redox reactions.

When the electron requirements of the ligand and the metal differ,

TABLE 5.18. Rate Parameters for Some Reductions of Co(III) in Acid Perchlorate at $25°$, $I = 3.0 \, M$ [95]

Reductant	k_1 $M^{-1} \sec^{-1}$	$k_2 K_h$ $\sec^{-1}$	$\Delta H^{\ddagger}$	$\Delta S^{\ddagger}$
NH_3OH^+	...	3.3	22.5	$+20$
$NH_3NH_2^+$	...	1.1	23.8	$+22$
H_2O_2	<2	23	23.5	$+27$
HN_3	<2	35	23.1	$+27$
$H_2C_2O_4$	~ 2	11	24.0	$+28$
Br^-	<5	30	26.1	$+37$
$HC_2O_4^-$	...	82	25.9	$+39$
SCN^-	87	80	25.6	$+37$

the kinetics often become complex since an unstable oxidation state of at least one reactant must be produced. For the reaction

$$2Fe^{3+} + 2I^- \rightarrow 2Fe^{2+} + I_2 \tag{5.83}$$

in dilute HNO_3, a mechanism

$$Fe^{3+} + I^- \rightleftharpoons FeI^{2+} \tag{5.84}$$

$$FeI^{2+} + I^- \rightleftharpoons Fe^{2+} + I_2^- \tag{5.85}$$

$$Fe^{3+} + I_2^- \rightarrow Fe^{2+} + I_2 \qquad \text{fast} \tag{5.86}$$

is suggested.[96] This reaction will be first-order in Fe(III) and second-order in I^- in the early stages,[97] a third-order rate law that is common with the reactions of Fe(III) with a number of reducing anions, SCN^-, $S_2O_3^{2-}$, HO_2^-,[98] and $HSCH_2COO^-$. The complex (FeI^{2+}, for example) only slowly disproportionates and requires intercession of another anion to further the reaction.

The redox "incompatibility" of oxidant and reductant is shown within a number of complexes of the type Co(III)$(NH_3)_5L^{n+}$ ion.[99] When, for example,

$$L = N \bigcirc{-}CH_2OH$$

the one-electron oxidizing center of the Co(III) and the two-electron reducing ligand 4-pyridylcarbinol can coexist and the complex is relatively stable. This situation is upset when a strong one-electron oxidant such as Ce(IV) or Co(III) is added to a solution of the Co(III) complex. The oxidant attacks the carbinol function to generate an intermediate or intermediates; the intermediate in this case is oxidized *internally* by the Co(III) center; for example,

$$(NH_3)_5Co^{III}-N\bigcirc-CH_2OH^{3+} \xrightarrow[\text{oxidant}]{\text{one-electron}}$$

$$(NH_3)_5Co^{III}-N\bigcirc-\overset{H}{\underset{\cdot}{C}}OH^{3+} \qquad (5.87)$$

$$\searrow \begin{array}{l}\text{internal}\\\text{redox}\end{array}$$

$$Co^{2+} + 5NH_4^+ + H\overset{+}{N}\bigcirc-CHO \xleftarrow{H^+} (NH_3)_5Co^{II}-N\bigcirc-C\overset{H^{2+}}{\underset{O}{\diagup}} + H^+$$

Thus one equivalent of an external oxidant and one of the Co(III) complex are consumed in oxidizing one equivalent of the alcohol to the aldehyde. Two-equivalent oxidants, Cl_2, Cr(VI), give no radical intermediate, no Co(II), and only the Co(III) complex.[100]

$$(NH_3)_5Co^{III}-N\bigcirc-CH_2OH^{3+} \xrightarrow[\text{oxidant}]{\text{two-electron}} (NH_3)_5Co^{III}-N\bigcirc-CHO^{3+}$$

$$(5.88)$$

5.16 REDUCTION OF COORDINATED LIGANDS

Much more rarely does one obtain reduction of ligand. The important reactions of metal ions and complexes with molecular oxygen are in this category. Many of these reactions are considered to proceed via peroxy complex formation.

$Fe(H_2O)_6^{2+}$ reacts slowly with O_2.[101] In $HClO_4$ solution, from initial rate experiments,

$$\frac{-d[Fe^{2+}]}{dt} = k[Fe^{2+}]^2[O_2] \qquad (5.89)$$

and the suggested mechanism is

$$Fe^{2+} + O_2 \rightleftharpoons FeO_2^{2+} \qquad \text{rapid} \qquad (5.90)$$

$$FeO_2^{2+} + Fe(H_2O)_6^{2+} \rightarrow FeO_2H^{2+} + Fe(H_2O)_5OH^{2+} \qquad \text{rds} \quad (5.91)$$

$$FeO_2H^{2+} + H^+ \rightarrow Fe^{3+} + H_2O_2 \qquad (5.92)$$

$$FeOH^{2+} + H^+ \rightarrow Fe^{3+} \qquad (5.93)$$

$$(2Fe^{2+} + H_2O_2 + 2H^+ \rightarrow 2Fe^{3+} + 2H_2O) \qquad (5.94)$$

The direct reaction

$$Fe^{2+} + O_2 \rightarrow Fe^{3+} + O_2^- \tag{5.95}$$

would be very unfavorable in ClO_4^- medium, but in H_3PO_4, which stabilizes the Fe(III) product, it is apparently favored since the rate law now contains only a first-order dependence on Fe(II).[102]

$$V = k[Fe^{2+}][O_2][H_2PO_4^-]^2 \tag{5.96}$$

Reduction of ClO_4^- by Ru^{2+} and complexation of Ru^{2+} proceed at comparable rates, and the similar activation parameters shown in Table 5.19 strongly suggest that reduction of ClO_4^- takes place via complex formation.[103]

5.17   THE FUTURE

It is apparent that in the area of redox reactions much has been accomplished but much remains to be done. Some future problems have been delineated by Taube in his book *Electron Transfer Reactions of Complex Ions in Solution*. Paramount is a determination of the detailed arrangement of the reactants in the activated complex of both outer-sphere and inner-sphere reactions, and an assessment of how the solvent and the presence of counter ions might modify. Redox reactions in a solvent other than water have barely been examined. The stepwise nature of these redox reactions[56] and anomalous reorganizational barriers[104] both will have to be more carefully considered if the free-energy correlations of Marcus and others are to be of further use. The photoredox and photosubstitution behavior of complexes has not been dealt with in this book.[105] Short-lived intermediates not arising in thermal reactions can be detected by the powerful flash photolysis perturbation method.[106]

Even though the understanding of the redox behavior of simpler complexes is incomplete, there is a move of the inorganic redox kineticist

TABLE 5.19.   Rate Constants (k, M^{-1} sec^{-1}) for Reactions of Ru^{2+} Ion at $25°$[103]

Reactant	$10^{-3} \times k$	$\Delta H^{\ddagger}$	$\Delta S^{\ddagger}$
ClO_4^-	3.2	19.4	-5
Cl^-	8.5	19.8	-1
Br^-	10.9	19.5	-2
I^-	10.5	19.4	-5

into the biological redox area.[107] The beleaguered combatants in this war would welcome the influx of new troops with new ideas,[108] although the magnitude of the task cannot be overestimated.

REFERENCES

1. D. R. Stranks and R. G. Wilkins, *Chem. Rev.*, **57**, 743 (1957).
2. W. B. Lewis, C. D. Coryell, and J. Irvine, *J. Chem. Soc.*, S386 (1949); N. S. Biradar, D. R. Stranks, and M. S. Vaidya, *Trans. Faraday Soc.*, **58**, 2421 (1962).
3. D. W. Larsen and A. C. Wahl, *J. Chem. Phys.*, **43**, 3765 (1965).
4. M. Anbar, *Advan. Chem. Series*, **49**, 126 (1965).
5. J. H. Baxendale, H. R. Hardy, and L. H. Sutcliffe, *Trans. Faraday Soc.*, **47**, 963 (1951).
6. J. H. Espenson, *Accounts Chem. Research*, **3**, 347 (1970).
7. K. G. Ashurst and W. C. E. Higginson, *J. Chem. Soc.*, 3044 (1953).
8. a. Sykes, pp. 137–52; b. p. 180.
9. T. W. Newton and F. B. Baker, *Advan. Chem. Series*, **71**, 268 (1967).
10. H. Taube, H. Myers, and R. L. Rich, *J. Amer. Chem. Soc.*, **75**, 4118 (1953); H. Taube and H. Myers, *J. Amer. Chem. Soc.*, **76**, 2103 (1954).
11. The eventual proportions of Cr^{3+} and $CrCl^{2+}$ formed will depend on the concentrations and formation constant of $CrCl^{2+}$.
12. For tables and references see T. J. Williams and C. S. Garner, *Inorg. Chem.*, **9**, 2058 (1970); D. W. Carlyle and J. H. Espenson, *J. Amer. Chem. Soc.*, **91**, 599 (1969).
13. J. P. Candlin, J. Halpern, and S. Nakamura, *J. Amer. Chem. Soc.*, **85**, 2517 (1963); J. F. Endicott and H. Taube, *Inorg. Chem.*, **4**, 437 (1965).
14. T. J. Conocchioli, G. H. Nancollas, and N. Sutin, *J. Amer. Chem. Soc.*, **86**, 1453 (1964).
15. A. Haim and N. Sutin, *J. Amer. Chem. Soc.*, **88**, 5343 (1966).
16. D. P. Fay and N. Sutin, *Inorg. Chem.*, **9**, 1291 (1970).
17. A. G. Sykes and M. Green, *J. Chem. Soc.*, A, 3221 (1970); M. Green, R. S. Taylor, and A. G. Sykes, *J. Chem. Soc.*, A, 509 (1971).
18. K. M. Davies and J. H. Espenson, *J. Amer. Chem. Soc.*, **91**, 3093 (1969).
19. The first step, being second-order, may be speeded up by increasing the reactant concentrations, which will not affect the second, first-order, step.
20. J. H. Espenson, *Inorg. Chem.*, **4**, 121 (1965).
21. Sykes, pp. 183–88.
22. N. Sutin, *Accounts Chem. Research*, **1**, 225 (1968).
23. H. J. Price and H. Taube, *Inorg. Chem.*, **7**, 1 (1968).
24. H. Diebler, P. H. Dodel, and H. Taube, *Inorg. Chem.*, **5**, 1688 (1966).
25. H. Taube and E. S. Gould, *Accounts Chem. Research*, **2**, 321 (1969).

26. R. C. Patel, R. E. Ball, J. F. Endicott, and R. G. Hughes, *Inorg. Chem.*, **9**, 23 (1970), tabulate activation parameters for reduction of six Co(III) complexes by a number of reducing agents.

27. H. Taube and E. L. King, *J. Amer. Chem. Soc.*, **76**, 5053 (1954); D. L. Ball and E. L. King, *J. Amer. Chem. Soc.*, **80**, 1091 (1958).

28. R. J. Balahura and R. B. Jordan, *J. Amer. Chem. Soc.*, **92**, 1533 (1970); **93**, 625 (1971).

29. J. P. Birk, *Inorg. Chem.*, **9**, 125 (1970).

30. M. P. Liteplo and J. F. Endicott, *Inorg. Chem.*, **10**, 1420 (1971).

31. T. L. Toppen and R. G. Linck, *Inorg. Chem.*, **10**, 2635 (1971).

32. R. K. Murmann, H. Taube, and F. A. Posey, *J. Amer. Chem. Soc.*, **79**, 262 (1957). Oxygen-18 tracer experiments have indicated that transfer of OH to Cr^{2+} from $Co(NH_3)_5OH^{2+}$ is quantitative.

33. J. P. Candlin and J. Halpern, *Inorg. Chem.*, **4**, 766 (1965).

34. M. C. Moore and R. N. Keller, *Inorg. Chem.*, **10**, 747 (1971). The effect is very small (Table 5.4) probably because of the extreme reactivity of Cr(II) towards these oxidants.

35. A. E. Ogard and H. Taube, *J. Amer. Chem. Soc.*, **80**, 1084 (1958).

36. W. R. Mason, *Coordn. Chem. Revs.*, **7**, 241 (1972).

37. W. R. Mason, E. R. Berger, and R. C. Johnson, *Inorg. Chem.*, **6**, 248 (1967).

38. J. P. Candlin, J. Halpern, and D. L. Trimm, *J. Amer. Chem. Soc.*, **86**, 1019 (1964).

39. J. F. Endicott and H. Taube, *J. Amer. Chem. Soc.*, **86**, 1686 (1964).

40. H. Diebler and H. Taube, *Inorg. Chem.*, **4**, 1029 (1965).

41. A. Haim, *Inorg. Chem.*, **7**, 1475 (1968).

42. A related approach can be made to this calculation, Taube, *Electron Transfer Reactions of Complex Ions in Solution*, p. 51. An inconsistency in Ref. 41 noted by Taube does not detract from the presentation here.

43. H. Taube, *Advan. Chem. Series*, **14**, 107 (1965).

44. C. Shea and A. Haim, *J. Amer. Chem. Soc.*, **93**, 3055 (1971).

45. R. H. Lane and L. E. Bennett, *J. Amer. Chem.*, *Soc.*, **92**, 1089 (1970).

46. N. Sutin, *Ann. Rev. Nucl. Sci.*, **12**, 285 (1962).

47. N. Sutin, *Ann. Rev. Phys. Chem.*, **17**, 119 (1966).

48. M. B. Barrett, J. H. Swinehart, and H. Taube, *Inorg. Chem.*, **10**, 1983 (1971); E. S. Gould, *J. Amer. Chem. Soc.*, **88**, 2983 (1966).

49. J. A. Stritar and H. Taube, *Inorg. Chem.*, **8**, 2281 (1969).

50. F. Nordmeyer and H. Taube, *J. Amer. Chem. Soc.*, **90**, 1162 (1968).

51. P. George and D. S. Griffith, *Enzymes*, **1**, 347 (1959).

52. J. Halpern and L. E. Orgel, *Disc. Faraday Soc.*, **29**, 32 (1960).

53. R. G. Gaunder and H. Taube, *Inorg. Chem.*, **9**, 2627 (1970).

54. H. Taube, Oxidation-Reduction by Electron Transfer through Molecules, American Chemical Society, Audio Lecture.

55. C. Norris and F. R. Nordmeyer, *J. Amer. Chem. Soc.*, **93**, 4044 (1971); J. R. Barber, Jr., and E. S. Gould, *J. Amer. Chem. Soc.*, **93**, 4045 (1971).

56. R. G. Linck, pp. 312-20.

57. N. Sutin, *Chem. in Britain*, 148 (1972).

58. H. Taube, p. 60.

59. J. P. Candlin and J. Halpern, *Inorg. Chem.*, **4**, 1086 (1965).

60. R. Snellgrove and E. L. King, *J. Amer. Chem. Soc.*, **84**, 4609 (1962).

61. A. Haim, *J. Amer. Chem. Soc.*, **88**, 2324 (1966).

62. Y. T. Chia and E. L. King, *Disc. Faraday Soc.*, **29**, 109 (1960).

63. C. Hwang and A. Haim, *Inorg. Chem.*, **9**, 500 (1970).

64. G. Svatos and H. Taube. *J. Amer. Chem. Soc.*, **83**, 4172 (1961); D. H. Huchital and H. Taube, *Inorg. Chem.*, **4**, 1660 (1965).

65. J. E. Earley in *Inorganic Reaction Mechanisms*, Part 1, ed. J. O. Edwards, p. 243.

66. L. E. Orgel, *Report of the Tenth Solvay Conference*, Brussels, 1956, p. 286.

67. H. Taube, *Advan. Inorg. Radiochem.*, **1**, 1 (1959).

68. R. G. Linck, *Inorg. Chem.*, **9**, 2529 (1970).

69. N. S. Hush, *Progr. Inorg. Chem.*, **8**, 391 (1967).

70. A. E. Ogard and H. Taube, *J. Amer. Chem. Soc.*, **80**, 1084 (1958).

71. P. Benson and A. Haim, *J. Amer. Chem. Soc.*, **87**, 3826 (1965).

72. J. H. Worrell and T. A. Jackman, *J. Amer. Chem. Soc.*, **93**, 1044 (1971).

73. T. J. Williams and C. S. Garner, *Inorg. Chem.*, **10**, 975 (1971).

74. H. Diaz and H. Taube, *Inorg. Chem.*, **9**, 1304 (1970).

75. Sr. M. J. DeChant and J. B. Hunt, *J. Amer. Chem. Soc.*, **90**, 3695 (1968).

76. M. Green, K. Schug, and H. Taube, *Inorg. Chem.*, **4**, 1184 (1965).

77. T. J. Meyer and H. Taube, *Inorg. Chem.*, **7**, 2369 (1968).

78. N. Sutin and A. Forman, *J. Amer. Chem. Soc.*, **93**, 5274 (1971).

79. C. E. Castro and H. F. Davis, *J. Amer. Chem. Soc.*, **91**, 5405 (1969).

80. R. J. Campion, T. J. Conocchioli, and N. Sutin, *J. Amer. Chem. Soc.*, **86**, 4591 (1964).

81. R. A. Marcus, *Ann. Revs. Phys. Chem.*, **15**, 155 (1964). See also N. S. Hush, *Trans. Faraday Soc.*, **57**, 557 (1961).

82. T. W. Newton, *J. Chem. Ed.*, **45**, 571 (1968) has derived Eq. (5.53) from a mechanical model and presents a simplified nonrigorous statistical mechanical derivation.

83. M. H. Ford-Smith and N. Sutin, *J. Amer. Chem. Soc.*, **83**, 1830 (1961); R. J. Campion, N. Purdie, and N. Sutin, *Inorg. Chem.*, **3**, 1091 (1964); J. D. Miller and R. H. Prince, *J. Chem. Soc.*, *A*, 1370 (1966).

84. A. Haim and N. Sutin, *J. Amer. Chem. Soc.*, **88**, 434 (1966).

85. R. C. Patel and J. F. Endicott, *J. Amer. Chem. Soc.*, **90**, 6364 (1968).

86. D. P. Rillema, J. F. Endicott, and R. C. Patel, *J. Amer. Chem. Soc.*, **94**, 394 (1972).

87. M. Green and A. G. Sykes, *J. Chem. Soc.*, *A*, 3067 (1971).

88. R. Buchacek and G. Gordon, *Inorg. Chem.*, **11**, 2154 (1972).

89. M. Ardon and R. A. Plane, *J. Amer. Chem. Soc.*, **81**, 3526 (1959).

90. R. D. Cannon and J. E. Earley, *J. Chem. Soc.*, *A*, 1102 (1968); D. E. Pennington and A. Haim, *Inorg. Chem.*, **6**, 2138 (1967), and references therein.

91. J. Doyle, A. G. Sykes, and A. Adin, *J. Chem. Soc., A*, 1314 (1968).

92. A. Adin, J. Doyle, and A. G. Sykes, *J. Chem. Soc., A*, 1504 (1967).

93. H. C. Stynes and J. A. Ibers, *Inorg. Chem.*, **10**, 2304 (1971).

94. A. McAuley, *Coordn. Chem. Rev.*, **5**, 245 (1970).

95. G. Davies and K. O. Watkins, *Inorg. Chem.*, **9**, 2735 (1970).

96. A. J. Fudge and K. W. Sykes, *J. Chem. Soc.*, 119, (1952).

97. As [Fe(II)] builds up, or in the presence of Fe(II) ions, the kinetics become involved and steps in addition to Eqs. (5.84)–(5.86) must be considered, G. S. Laurence and K. J. Ellis, *J. Chem. Soc., A* 2229 (1972).

98. Fe(III)–H_2O_2 system in spite of intense investigation, still defies a complete understanding.

99. H. Taube, Chap. 4.

100. The situation presented above is oversimplified and some puzzling features remain to be resolved. J. E. French and H. Taube, *J. Amer. Chem. Soc.*, **91**, 6951 (1969).

101. P. George, *J. Chem. Soc.*, 4349 (1954).

102. H. Taube, *J. Gen. Physiol.*, **49**, 29 (1965).

103. T. W. Kallen and J. E. Earley, *Inorg. Chem.*, **10**, 1152 (1971).

104. D. P. Rillema and J. F. Endicott, *Inorg. Chem.*, **11**, 2361 (1972).

105. A. W. Adamson, W. L. Waltz, E. Zinato, D. W. Watts, P. D. Fleischauer, and R. D. Lindholm, *Chem. Rev.*, **68**, 541 (1968).

106. A. F. Vaudo, E. R. Kantrowitz, M. Z. Hoffman, E. Papaconstantinou, and J. F. Endicott, *J. Amer. Chem. Soc.*, **94**, 6655 (1972).

107. N. Sutin, in *Inorganic Biochemistry*, ed. G. Eichorn (Elsevier, Amsterdam, 1974), Chap. 19; G. A. Hamilton, *Prog. Biorg. Chem.*, **1**, 110, (1971); L. E. Bennett, "Metalloprotein Reox Reactions," *Progr. Inorg. Chem.*, **18**, 1 (1973).

108. J. K. Yandell, D. P. Fay, and N. Sutin, *J. Amer. Chem. Soc.*, **95**, 1131 (1973).

SELECTED BIBLIOGRAPHY

Redox Reactions

BAMFORD, C. H. and TIPPER, C. F. H., eds. *Comprehensive Chemical Kinetics*, vol. 7. Elsevier, Amsterdam, 1972. Chapters 2 (Proll, P. J.), 3 (Benson, D.), and 4 (Kemp, T. J.) contain detailed accounts of oxidation-reduction reactions. If it isn't discussed here, it hasn't been done!

LINCK, R. G. Rates and Mechanisms of Oxidation-Reduction Reactions of Metal Ion Complexes. In *Reaction Mechanisms in Inorganic Chemistry*, edited by M. L. Tobe. Butterworths, London, 1972.

REYNOLDS, W. L. and LUMRY, R. W. *Mechanisms of Electron Transfer*. Ronald Press, New York, 1966.

SYKES, A. G. *Further Advances in the Study of Mechanisms of Redox Reactions*. In *Advances in Inorganic Chemistry and Radiochemistry*, edited by H. J. Emeleus and A. G. Sharpe, vol. 10. Academic, New York, 1967.

TAUBE, H. *Electron Transfer Reactions of Complex Ions in Solution.* Academic, New York, 1970.

NOTE. See also works indicated in bibliography for Chap. 4.

PROBLEMS

1. The reduction of a number of complexes $Co(NH_3)_5X^{(3-n)+}$ by $Co(CN)_5^{3-}$ in solutions containing CN^- ion have been examined. With $X^{n-} = Cl^-$, N_3^-, NCS^-, and OH^-, the redox reactions are second-order, with a wide range of values for the second-order rate constant, and a product $Co(CN)_5X^{3-}$. The rate law is different with $X^{n-} = NH_3$, PO_4^{3-}, CO_3^{2-} and SO_4^{2-},

$$V = k[Co^{III}][Co^{II}][CN^-]$$

with k similar for these reductions, and the product $Co(CN)_6^{3-}$. Give an explanation for this behavior. [J. P. Candlin, J. Halpern, and S. Nakamura, *J. Amer. Chem. Soc.*, **85**, 2517 (1963).]

2. **a.** Explain why the rate constants for a number of Cr^{2+} reductions, although inner-sphere, do not vary much. [J. P. Candlin and J. Halpern, *Inorg. Chem.*, **4**, 766 (1965); R. C. Patel, R. E. Ball, J. F. Endicott, and R. G. Hughes, *Inorg. Chem.*, **9**, 23 (1970); N. Sutin, *Accounts Chem. Res.*, **1**, 225 (1968).]

    b. $Co(NH_3)_5NH_2CHO^{3+}$ reacts rapidly with Cr^{2+} to give $Cr(H_2O)_5$-$OCHNH_2^{3+}$, with a rate law:

$$V = k[Cr^{II}][Co^{III}][H^+]^{-1}$$

whereas the linkage isomer $Co(NH_3)_5OCHNH_2$ only slowly reacts with Cr^{2+}, with no $[H^+]$ dependency in the rate law. Explain. [R. J. Balahura and R. B. Jordan, *J. Amer. Chem. Soc.*, **92**, 1533 (1970).]

    How would you expect the cyanamide complex $Co(NH_3)_5NCNH_2^{3+}$ to react with Cr^{2+}? [R. J. Balahura and R. B. Jordan, *J. Amer. Chem. Soc.*, **93**, 625 (1971).]

    c. Discuss the probable mechanisms for Cu^+ reductions from the data of Table 5.4. [O. J. Parker and J. H. Espenson, *J. Amer. Chem. Soc.*, **91**, 1968 (1969); E. R. Dockal, E. T. Everhart, and E. S. Gould, *J. Amer. Chem. Soc.*, **93**, 5661 (1971).]

    d. The reduction of nicotinic or isonicotinic acid complexes of the pentamminecobalt(III) moiety are much faster by V^{2+} than by Cr^{2+}, and this is unusual. Suggest how this might arise, bearing in mind the discussion in Sec. 5.4(d). [C. Norris and F. R. Nordmeyer, *Inorg. Chem.*, **10**, 1235 (1971).]

3. The rate constants ($M^{-1}\,sec^{-1}$) at 25° for the reduction of oxalato-cobalt(III) complexes by three reactants are shown herewith.

Oxidant	Cr^{2+}	V^{2+}	Fe^{2+}
$Co(NH_3)_5C_2O_4H^{2+}$	1.0×10^2	12.5	$\leqslant 5 \times 10^{-4}$
$Co(NH_3)_5C_2O_4^+$	4.6×10^4	45	0.43
$Co(NH_3)_4C_2O_4^+$	$\sim 2 \times 10^5$	45	4.2×10^{-4}

Discuss these values, commenting particularly on (1) the range of values within a particular reductant; (2) the effect of protonation of the oxalate complex; and (3) the uni- and bidentate oxalate complexes. [C. Hwang and A. Haim, *Inorg. Chem.*, **9**, 500 (1970).]

4. Comment on the relative rate constants, $M^{-1}\,sec^{-1}$ at 25°, for the following pairs of reactions:

Cr^{2+}	CrN_3^{2+}	6.1	FeN_3^{2+}	$\sim 3 \times 10^7$
	$CrNCS^{2+}$	1.5×10^{-4}	$FeNCS^{2+}$	3×10^7
V^{2+}	FeN_3^{2+}	5.2×10^5		
	$FeNCS^{2+}$	6.6×10^5		
$Co(CN)_5^{3-}$	$Co(NH_3)_5N_3^{2+}$	$1.6 \times 10^{6\,a}$		
	$Co(NH_3)_5NCS^{2+}$	$1.0 \times 10^{6\,a}$		

[a] Definitely inner-sphere reactions.

[N. Sutin, *Accounts Chem. Research*, **1**, 225 (1968).]

5. **a.** In the study of the reaction between Cr^{2+} and $(NH_3)_5CrOHCr(NH_3)_4\text{-}Cl^{4+}$, how would you deduce where the electron from the Cr^{2+} entered, and how far it "traveled" in the potentially extended bridge system? [D. W. Hoppenjans, J. B. Hunt, and L. Penzhorn, *Inorg. Chem.*, **7**, 1467 (1968).]

b. Cite evidence from the material in the chapter that, at least for certain reactions, electron transfer rather than atom transfer occurs in inner-sphere reactions, that is, that in the reactions between Cr^{2+} and CrX^{2+},

$$Cr^{II} \underset{e}{\overset{\textstyle\frown}{}} X\ Cr^{III} \qquad \text{rather than} \qquad Cr^{II} \overset{\textstyle\frown}{} X\ Cr^{III}$$

occurs in the bridged intermediate. [B. Grossman and A. Haim, *J. Amer. Chem. Soc.*, **92**, 4835 (1970).]

6. Calculate the rate constants for the reactions

$$Ce^{IV} + Fe(CN)_6^{4-} \rightarrow Ce^{III} + Fe(CN)_6^{3-}$$

and $$MnO_4^- + Fe(CN)_6^{4-} \rightarrow MnO_4^{2-} + Fe(CN)_6^{3-}$$

on the basis of the Marcus equation, (5.53).   Use the following information.   For the isotopic exchange reactions

$$E_0 \quad k, M^{-1} \sec^{-1}$$

$$*Ce^{IV} + Ce^{III} \rightleftharpoons Ce^{IV} + *Ce^{III} \qquad\qquad +1.44 \qquad 4.6$$

$$*Fe(CN)_6{}^{3-} + Fe(CN)_6{}^{4-}$$
$$\rightleftharpoons Fe(CN)_6{}^{3-} + *Fe(CN)_6{}^{4-} \qquad +0.68 \quad 3 \times 10^2$$
$$*MnO_4{}^- + MnO_4{}^{2-} \rightleftharpoons MnO_4{}^- + *MnO_4{}^{2-} \qquad +0.56 \quad 3.6 \times 10^3$$

All values at 25°.   Check with the experimental values in the book.

7. Suggest why the oxidation of

$$(NH_3)_5Ru-N\bigcirc-CH_2OH^{3+} \rightarrow (NH_3)_5Ru-N\bigcirc CHO^{3+}$$

gives solely one product, whether a one- or a two-electron oxidant is used, compared with the behavior of the Co(III) analog.   [H. Taube, *Electron Transfer Reactions of Complex Ions in Solution*, Chap. 4.]

Chapter 6

The Modification of Ligand Reactivity by Complex Formation

Coordination modifies the properties of the metal ion; equally important, however, is the impact that the metal has on the behavior of the coordinated ligand towards chemical reagents.[1-4] The reactivity of the ligand can be enhanced or the ligand can be deactivated. Activation is important in the catalytic effects of metal ions, and deactivation is useful when "masking" of a reaction center is required. The product of the reaction may remain coordinated to the metal, and may be a weaker or a stronger ligand than the original reactant. Alternatively, the product may break away from the metal ion, which is then able to coordinate with more reactant and function in a catalytic manner. Chemical reaction may occur at a point within a chelate ring, in an adjacent ring, or at the side chain of a chelate ring, with variable results. In general, the further the reaction site from the metal center, the less the influence of the latter, unless conjugative effects are present.

We shall consider the ways in which a metal may influence a reaction. These are listed in Table 6.1. The effects of the metal and the reactivity of the coordinated ligand are interrelated since invariably at least one of the reactants becomes coordinated to the metal during a catalyzed reaction.

6.1 THE METAL AS A COLLECTING POINT FOR REACTANTS

The metal, in acting as a collection point to bring reactants together, is likely at the very least to promote enhanced rates of reaction by operation

TABLE 6.1.   Functions of Metal Ion Center in Altering Reaction Characteristics

Function	Examples of use
Serve as a collecting point for reactants, Secs. 6.1 and 6.2.	Neighboring group and template effects.
Promote electron shifts in the metal-ligand system, Secs. 6.3–6.6.	Promotion of nucleophilic substitution. Enhanced acidity of co-ordinated ligand.
Protect a coordinated function from reaction, Sec. 6.7.	Masking of normally reactive groups.
Force a reaction to completion, Sec. 6.8.	Promotion of macrocycle and Schiff base formation.
Alter the strain within or the conformational characteristics of the reacting ligand, Sec. 6.9.	Catalyzed rearrangement of highly strained polycyclics.

of the *neighboring group effect*. If, in addition, the transmission of electronic effects of the metal (Secs. 6.3–6.6) also occurs, as is usually the case, then large overall rate enhancements may be encountered.

6.2   NEIGHBORING-GROUP EFFECTS

The ability of a substituent in one part of an organic molecule to influence a reaction by partially or completely bonding to the reaction center in another part of that molecule, thereby leading to an intramolecular reaction, is well recognized in organic chemistry.[5,6] These neighboring group effects, or anchimeric effects, often give rise to a rate 10^5 to 10^6 times faster than the rate for the "unassisted" reaction. It is surprising, when one considers the possibilities for juxtaposing reactants within the coordination sphere of the metal, that the effect has only recently been exploited in transition metal chemistry. We shall be concerned in this section with the interaction of a coordinated nucleophile with a reaction center in a metal complex, and are interested in how much acceleration might result compared with the situation when the metal is not present.

   One obvious area in which anchimeric effects might materialize is in chelation reactions; this is the underlying reason that chelation is dominated by the first step (Sec. 4.4.1). The rate constant for the ring-closure reaction

$$(NH_3)_4Co\begin{matrix}H_2\\N\\\\OH_2\end{matrix}\begin{matrix}\\\\Cl\end{matrix}Co(NH_3)_4{}^{4+}\xrightarrow[k]{-Cl^-}(NH_3)_4Co\begin{matrix}H_2\\N\\\\O\\H_2\end{matrix}Co(NH_3)_4{}^{5+}\quad\textbf{(6.1)}$$

$$k_{25°} = 1.4 \times 10^{-4} \text{ sec}^{-1}$$

$$\Delta H^{\ddagger} = 16.6$$

$$\Delta S^{\ddagger} = -21$$

is some 10^2 times faster than the intermolecular aquation of the corresponding mononuclear complex,[7]

$$Co(NH_3)_5Cl^{2+} + H_2O \rightarrow Co(NH_3)_5H_2O^{3+} + Cl^- \quad\textbf{(6.2)}$$

$$k_{25°} = 1.7 \times 10^{-6} \text{ sec}^{-1}$$

$$\Delta H^{\ddagger} = 23.4$$

$$\Delta S^{\ddagger} = -11$$

Since the bridged complex reacts without formation of the diaqua intermediate (this can be separately prepared and shown to be much less reactive than would be required), the anchimeric effect of the adjacent coordinated water is established. The enhancement apparently resides in a lowered $\Delta H^{\ddagger}$ value partly offset by a less favorable $\Delta S^{\ddagger}$. This result, which is an unusual basis for the effect,[5] has been rationalized.[7]

Another demonstration of anchimeric assistance is in the reaction

$$H_2NH_2CH_2CH_2N\diagdown\diagup Cl \atop Cl\diagup Pt \diagdown NH_2CH_2CH_2NH_2 \xrightarrow[k]{-Cl^-}$$

$$H_2NH_2CH_2CH_2N\diagdown\diagup NH_2-CH_2{}^+ \atop Cl\diagup Pt \diagdown NH_2-CH_2 \quad\textbf{(6.3)}$$

for which $k = 10.4 \text{ sec}^{-1}$ at 25°. Comparison with

$$H_3N\diagdown\diagup Cl \atop Cl\diagup Pt \diagdown NH_3 \xrightarrow[-Cl^-]{+NH_3} H_3N\diagdown\diagup NH_3{}^+ \atop Cl\diagup Pt \diagdown NH_3 \quad\textbf{(6.4)}$$

for which the second-order rate constant is 5.7×10^{-3} M^{-1} sec^{-1} shows that a $> 10^3$-fold rate enhancement is operative.[8,9] Part of the origin of the effect resides in the intramolecular nature of the chelation.[6] The effective concentration of the free NH_2 group that has to replace Cl^- ion in (6.3) is estimated at $\sim 30\ M$, but this alone can hardly account for the magnitude of the acceleration.[9]

With a Co(III) complex as a scaffold, it is possible to place a coordinated nucleophile *cis* to an incipient reagent. In an example of such a designed complex, **1**, amidolysis of the glycine ether ester, which is normally *extremely* slow, is quite markedly promoted:[10]

$$(6.5)$$

$$V = k[\text{Co(NH}_3)_5(\text{NH}_2\text{CH}_2\text{COOEt})^{3+}][\text{OH}^-]^2 \qquad (6.6)$$

and $k = 6.6 \times 10^6\ M^{-2}\ \text{sec}^{-1}$ at 25°. In addition to holding the reactants close together, the metal may also promote a driving force in producing a stable chelate ring. Even more dramatic effects are seen in the intramolecular attack by OH^- on esters and amides (Secs. 6.4.1 and 6.4.2).

A less obvious use of neighboring group participation is in certain autoxidation reactions. A number of metal-oxygen complexes can oxygenate a variety of substrates (SO_2, CO, NO, NO_2, phosphines) under mild conditions. Probably the substrate and O_2 are present in the coordination sphere of the metal during these so-called autoxidations.[11]

In the reaction of oxygen with transition metal phosphine complexes, oxidation of metal, of phosphine or of both, may result.[12] The initial rate of reaction of O_2 with $Co(PEt_3)_2Cl_2$ in tertiary butyl benzene,

$$V = \frac{-d[\text{Co}^{\text{II}}]}{dt} = k[\text{Co}^{\text{II}}][\text{O}_2] \qquad (6.7)$$

is consistent with the mechanism

$$\text{Co(PEt}_3)_2\text{Cl}_2 + \text{O}_2 \rightleftharpoons \text{Co(PEt}_3)_2(\text{O}_2)\text{Cl}_2 \qquad (6.8)$$

$$\text{Co(PEt}_3)_2(\text{O}_2)\text{Cl}_2 \rightarrow \text{Co(OPEt}_3)_2\text{Cl}_2 \qquad (6.9)$$

in which O–O bond rupture occurs within an oxygen adduct and two P–O bonds result. Reaction cannot occur via dissociated free phosphine since this reacts with oxygen to give compounds such as $Et_nP(O)(OEt)_{3-n}$, $n = 0$ to 3, via radical reactions. There is no detection of the oxygen adduct.[12]

On the other hand, both steps of the $Pt(PPh_3)_3$-catalyzed oxidation of PPh_3 by O_2 can be measured:[13,14]

$$Pt(PPh_3)_3 + O_2 \xrightarrow{k_1} Pt(PPh_3)_2O_2 + PPh_3 \qquad (6.10)$$

$$\frac{-d[Pt(PPh_3)_3]}{dt} = k_1[Pt(PPh_3)_3][O_2] \qquad (6.11)$$

$$Pt(PPh_3)_2O_2 + PPh_3 \xrightarrow{k_2} Pt(PPh_3)_3O_2 \xrightarrow[2PPh_3]{fast} Pt(PPh_3)_3 + 2Ph_3PO \qquad (6.12)$$

$$\frac{d[Pt(PPh_3)_3]}{dt} = k_2[Pt(PPh_3)_2O_2][PPh_3] \qquad (6.13)$$

By monitoring for O_2[14] as well as $Pt(PPh_3)_3$,[13] one can exclude other mechanisms.

Latent or real coordination sites on the metal are necessary for the *oxidative addition* of XY to certain d^8 systems, thereby converting them into octahedral d^6 complexes. These are the key steps in the homogeneously catalyzed hydrogenation, hydroformylation, and olefin dimerization.[11] An interesting example of an oxidative addition that also involves isomerization concerns the conversion of four-coordinated Ir(I) to six-coordinated Ir(III):[15]

$$Ir(Ph_3P)_3Cl \rightarrow$$ 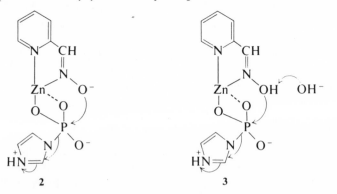 $$Ir(PPh_3)_2(H)Cl \qquad (6.14)$$

There has been an increasing interest in the mediation by metal ions of interaction between two coordinated organic reactants. Consider the reaction between pyridine-2-carbaldoxime anion and phosphoryl imidazole in the presence of Zn(II). A ternary complex **2** or **3** is formed

and it is believed that reaction occurs within this framework. The first-order rate constant for reaction of the ternary complex is *at least* 10^4 times larger than the second-order rate constant, which can only be estimated for the metal-free reaction, since no reaction is observed. The zinc appears to function in this example as (1) a collector of the phosphoryl group and the oxime anion in the correct orientation for an intramolecular reaction (the so-called *proximity effect*),[16] and (2) a shield between the negative charges of the reactants.[17]

Breslow and his co-workers have investigated several reactions of a similar type, in which the metal ion organizes and then catalyzes a reaction between two ligands in a ternary complex.[18]

6.2.1 Template Chemistry

The use of metals for prearranging reaction centers as neighboring groups and thus promoting intramolecular production of macrocycle products, such as **5** and **7**, is a rather special example of the metal effect. It is well illustrated in the work on the synthesis of porphinoid and corrinoid complexes and also other synthetic types.[4,19,20]

This particular function, and also others of the metal, are beautifully utilized in the work on the chemical synthesis of corrins (Fig. 6.1).[20] In the synthesis of **5**, a metal, Co(II), Ni(II) or Pd(II), is required to stabilize the precursor **4**, which would otherwise be extremely labile configurationally and constitutionally. As added bonuses, the metal ion helps to activate the methylene carbon for its attack on the iminoester carbon, and also forces the four nitrogens into a planar conformation, thereby bringing the condensation centers of rings *A* and *B* close together. This is strikingly shown by X-ray structural determination of **4**. With all this help from the metal, the final ring closure occurs smoothly. However, it is impossible to remove the metal from **5** without its complete destruction. To obtain the metal-free corrin, it is necessary to synthesize the zinc analog by a route somewhat more involved than that used with the nickel complex. The zinc can be replaced by cobalt, or the ring closure can be made using the cobalt(III) complex directly. These are key types of steps in the mammoth synthesis of vitamin B_{12} that has recently been completed.[20]

Busch and his colleagues over the past years have described a large number of impressive syntheses of macrocycles by inventing and using the template effect.[19] Macrocycles can sometimes be prepared directly without using metal, although addition of metal ion during synthesis will often increase the yield or modify the stereochemical nature of the product.[21] Usually however, the metal is essential in the buildup of the macrocycle, although it may not then be possible to remove the metal (see above). An early synthesis utilizing the template effect involves the

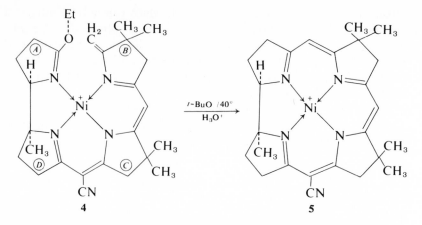

FigURE 6.1   Utilization of template and other effects in corrin syntheses.[20]

reaction of the nickel complex **6** with α,α′-dibromo-*o*-xylene in DMF to produce the macrocycle complex **7**:

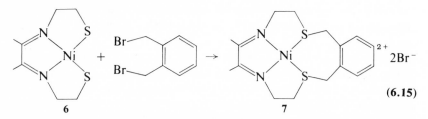

(6.15)

The metal fixes the mercaptide ion favorably for slow attack by one of the halides, which is followed by rapid final ring closure.[19]

6.2.2   Transamination

An important condensation that metal ions catalyze involves pyridoxal and amino acids (Fig. 6.2).   A kinetic study of the Cu^{2+}-catalyzed reaction of pyridoxal phosphate with glutamate indicates that the metal ion only acts as a trap for the Schiff base (see (1.7)).[22]   A similar role is assigned to the metal ion in other studies of Schiff-base formation.[23]   However, in the formation of Schiff bases from salicylaldehyde, glycine, and metal ions, there is, as metal-dependent terms in the rate law indicate, a more direct participation of the metal in the condensation.   In this, a kinetic template mechanism is believed operative, involving a rapid preequilibrium between reactants and metal ion to form a ternary complex, within which a rate-determining reaction occurs.[24]

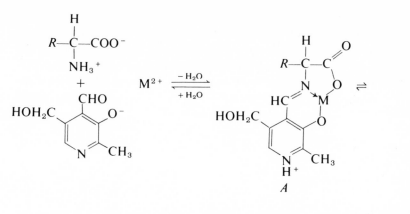

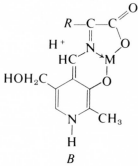

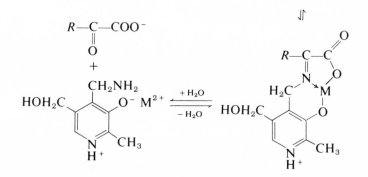

FIGURE 6.2   Basic reactions involved in transamination. Conjugation of the imine bond in A with the electron sink of the pyridine ring and protonation of the pyridine nitrogen as well as the presence of the metal ion all result in weakening of the C–H bond of the amino acid residue. This, in turn, leads to the further sequence of reactions shown. Additionally, the metal ion maintains the planarity of the Schiff base and facilitates the electron displacements.

The Schiff base can undergo a variety of reactions in addition to transamination, shown in Fig. 6.2; for example, racemization of the amino acid via B. Many of these reactions are catalyzed by metal ions and each has its equivalent nonmetallic enzyme reaction, each enzyme containing pyridoxal phosphate as a coenzyme. Many ideas of the mechanism of the action of these enzymes are based on the behavior of the model metal complexes.[26]

6.2.3   Catalytic Effects

If after reaction has occurred within the coordination sphere of the metal, the metal ion or complex is released from the products, with or without the intervention of another reagent, it is available for refunctioning and continuing the cycle. It thus acts as a catalyst, and one or two examples of such action can be found in the previous sections.

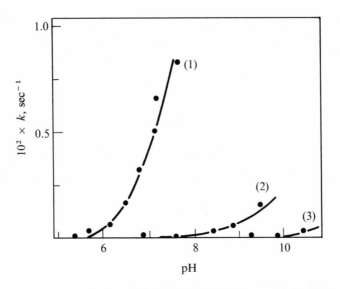

FIGURE 6.3   Catalytic activity of Cu(II) chelates towards H_2O_2 decomposition. The plot illustrates the decrease in catalytic activity with decreasing number of free H_2O coordination sites on the metal ion: (1) $Cuen(H_2O)_2^{2+}$, (2) $Cudien(H_2O)^{2+}$, and (3) $Cutrien^{2+}$, Ref. 27.

There has been systematic investigation of the catalysis of decomposition of hydrogen peroxide alone,

$$2H_2O_2 \rightarrow 2H_2O + O_2 \qquad (6.16)$$

and with the intervention of another reagent, for example,

$$2H_2O_2 + N_2H_4 \rightarrow N_2 + 4H_2O \qquad (6.17)$$

Catalase and peroxidase respectively promote these reactions very efficiently, and attempts to simulate the enzyme behavior have not been very successful. However, some inkling of their modus operandi has been obtained from studies of the effects of copper(II)[27,28] and iron(III)[29] complexes as catalysts. The metal appears to function by complexing with H_2O_2 or HO_2^- (sometimes this is detected); the resulting species then interacts with another molecule of H_2O_2 or other H donor, such as N_2H_4. Copper(II) complexes with no coordinated water appear inactive, and an interesting comparison of the catalytic activity of 1:1 Cu complexes with en, dien, and trien is shown in Fig. 6.3.[27] The type of detailed mechanism envisaged for (6.17) is

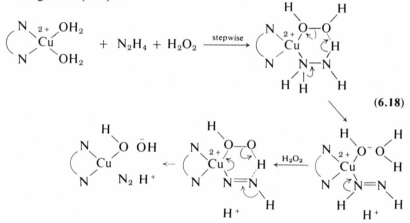

$$(6.18)$$

N–N might represent bipyridine, which will retain the metal in solution, even in alkaline conditions.

6.3 PROMOTION OF REACTION WITHIN THE METAL-BOUND LIGAND

The shift of electrons away from the ligand, which is usually induced by the positive charge of the metal, will lead to accelerated nucleophilic

TABLE 6.2. Some Examples of Metal-Promoted Nucleophilic Substitution

Substrate	Nucleophile	Products	Comments	Ref.
$Fe(CN)_5NO^{2-}$	OH^-	$Fe(CN)_5NO_2^{4-}$ via $Fe(CN)_5NO_2H^{3-}$?	Metal polarization causes ligand to be present as NO^+ in substrate.	a
cis-$Rubipy_2(NO)Cl^{2+}$	N_3^-	$Rubipy_2(H_2O)Cl^+$ $+ N_2 + N_2O$		b
$Co(NH_3)_5N_3^{2+}$	NO^+ (or $H_2NO_2^+$)	$Co(NH_3)_5H_2O^{3+}$ $+ N_2 + N_2O$	Reaction with $NO^+ClO_4^-$ in nonaqueous solvent S^4 leads to $Co(NH_3)_5S$, a useful synthetic intermediate.	c
$Ru(NH_3)_5N_2O^{2+}$	Cr^{2+}	$Ru(NH_3)_5N_2^{2+}$ but no sign of an intermediate $Ru(NH_3)_5N_2^{3+}$	Metal weakens N–O bond. Second-order k, 8×10^2 M^{-1} sec^{-1} compared with k, 6.5×10^{-6} M^{-1} sec^{-1} for $N_2O + Cr^{2+}$ (25.0°).	d
$PtCl(PPh_3)_2CO^+$	ROH	$PtCl(PPh_3)_2C\overset{\displaystyle O}{\underset{\displaystyle OR}{\big<}}$	Rare attack of nucleophile on C rather than metal.	e
$Co(NH_3)_5NCC_6H_5^{3+}$	OH^-	$Co(NH_3)_5NHCOC_6H_5^{2+}$	Second-order $k = 18.8$ M^{-1} sec^{-1} compared with $k = 8.2 \times 10^{-6}$ M^{-1} sec^{-1} for benzonitrile (25.6°).	54

[a] J. H. Swinehart and P. A. Rock, *Inorg. Chem.*, **5**, 573 (1966); J. H. Swinehart, *Coordn. Chem. Revs.*, **2**, 385 (1967).
[b] F. J. Miller and T. J. Meyer, *J. Amer. Chem. Soc.*, **93**, 1294 (1971).
[c] A. Haim and H. Taube, *Inorg. Chem.*, **2**, 1199 (1963).
[d] J. N. Armor and H. Taube, *J. Amer. Chem. Soc*, **93**, 6476 (1971).
[e] J. E. Byrd and J. Halpern, *J. Amer. Chem. Soc*, **93**, 1634 (1971); H. C. Clark and W. J. Jacobs, *Inorg. Chem.*, **9**, 1229 (1970).

TABLE 6.3. Some Comparisons of the $Co(NH_3)_5{}^{3+}$ Residue with H^+ and Other Species

Reaction	Rate law	R	$k_{25°}$	Ref.
$RNCO^- + H_3O^+ \rightarrow RNH_3 + CO_2$	$V = k[RNCO][H^+]$	$Co(NH_3)_5{}^{3+}$	$0.16\ M^{-1}\ sec^{-1}$	a
		H^+	0.12	
		$Rh(NH_3)_5{}^{3+}$	0.62	
		$Ru(NH_3)_5{}^{3+}$	0.06	
$ROCO_2H \rightarrow ROH + CO_2$	$V = k[ROCO_2H]$	$Co(NH_3)_5{}^{3+}$	$0.08\ sec^{-1}$	b
		H^+	2.0	
		CH_3CH_2	~0.25	
$RNH_2CH_2COOEt + OH^- \rightarrow RNH_2CH_2COO^-$ $\quad + EtOH$	$V = k[RNH_2CH_2COOEt][OH^-]$	$Co(NH_3)_5{}^{3+}$	$50\ M^{-1}\ sec^{-1}$	10
		H^+	24	

[a] Table from P. Ford, *Inorg. Chem.*, **10**, 2153 (1971).
[b] T. P. Dasgupta and G. M. Harris, *J. Amer. Chem. Soc.*, **90**, 6360 (1968), all data at 0°.

attack at the ligand. Since nucleophiles donate electrons they thus act to redress the balance. This effect may well reinforce that of the previous section. Some examples of its operation are shown in Table 6.2. All the reactions are second-order.

The metal ion or complex, which is often termed a superacid, resembles the proton in being able to produce this electron shift, so that it is quite usual to compare the proton- and metal-ion-assisted reactivities. Table 6.3 shows a comparison of the effects of the $Co(NH_3)_5^{3+}$ residue and the H^+ ion in their ability to catalyze a variety of nucleophilic reactions. It is apparent that, although both promote reaction, there is not a large difference in their effects.

The polarization effects of metals have a substantial impact particularly in two areas: the promotion of the hydrolysis of chelated ligands and the enhanced proton ionization of coordinated acidic ligands. Their importance has encouraged some systematic attacks on the effects.

6.4   HYDROLYSIS OF COORDINATED LIGANDS

The ability of metal ions to act as catalysts for the hydrolysis of a variety of linkages has been a subject of increasing interest. The modus operandi of these effects is undoubtedly through metal-complex formation, and this has been demonstrated for both labile and inert metal systems. Esters and amides are the most studied substrates.

6.4.1   Carboxylate Esters: —COOR → —COOH

It was soon apparent from the early studies of the labile metal ions such as Mn(II), Cu(II), and Zn(II) in their effect on the hydrolysis of esters that their lability rendered it difficult to characterize the catalyzing system or to know the mode of chelation of the ester. Nevertheless, some interesting points have emerged from numerous investigations since the first discovery that heavy metal ions catalyzed the hydrolysis of amino acid esters.[30,31]

Table 6.4 shows that in the absence of *direct* interaction of the ester grouping with the metal ion the primary cause of any acceleration by the metal complex system resides mainly in a charge effect.[32] Angelici and co-workers have concluded from a series of studies[33] that the catalysis of hydrolysis of amino acid esters E by metal ions proceeds through a scheme of the type

$$M + E \underset{}{\overset{K}{\rightleftharpoons}} ME \xrightarrow{k_h} \text{products} \qquad \textbf{(6.19)}$$

$$k = Kk_h \qquad \textbf{(6.20)}$$

TABLE 6.4. Effect of Metal Coordination on Rate Constants (k, $M^{-1}\,\mathrm{sec}^{-1}$) for Base Hydrolysis of Amino Acid Esters at 25°

Substrate	k	Ref.
$NH_2CH_2CH(NH_2)COOMe$	0.73	32
$NH_3{}^+CH_2CH(NH_2)COOMe$	57	32
$\begin{array}{c} CH_2\!-\!\!-\!CH\ \ COOMe^{2+} \\ \ \ \mid \qquad\quad \mid \\ H_2N \diagdown \ \diagup NH_2 \\ \quad\ Cu \\ \diagup \quad\ \diagdown \\ H_2O \qquad OH_2 \end{array}$	620	32
$Cu(H_2O)_2(NH_2CH_2COOEt)^{2+}$	7.4×10^4	40
NH_2CH_2COOEt	0.6	40
$NH_3{}^+CH_2COOEt$	24	40
$Co(NH_3)_5NH_2CH_2COOEt^{3+}$	50	10
$Coen_2NH_2CH_2COOC_3H_7{}^{3+}$	1.5×10^6	a

[a] D. A. Buckingham, D. M. Foster, and A. M. Sargeson, *J. Amer. Chem. Soc.*, **92**, 5701 (1970).

The values of k_h (for OH^- or H_2O hydrolyses) are about 10^3 to 10^5 times larger than for the free ester and the effect appears to reside in a more positive $\Delta S^\ddagger$ value.[34] These results suggest that the ester grouping is coordinated to the metal in ME. The carbonyl group is thus polarized by attractions of electrons towards the oxygen, and is therefore activated to nucleophilic attack by OH^- or H_2O as in **8**:

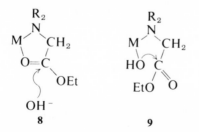

An alternative internal attack by a coordinated hydroxo group, **9**, will also satisfy the first-order dependence of $[OH^-]$ on the rate. This alternative explanation indicates the difficulty in interpreting the behavior of the labile metals. These can to a large extent be overcome by using a structure of the type **10** or **11**, which we shall abbreviate CoN_4X_2. With this arrangement, there are only two available sites X for reaction and the known inertness and well-characterized behavior of cobalt(III) allow conclusions about the mechanism of hydrolysis not possible with the previous systems.

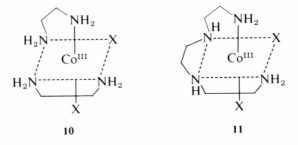

10   11

A complex of the type $CoN_4(NH_2CH_2COOR)Cl^{2+}$, **12**, in which the ester must be unidentate, linked only through the NH_2 grouping, is relatively stable towards hydrolysis. If we can rapidly remove chloride ion from the coordination sphere, we can see what takes place prior to and during the ester hydrolysis.

(a)   By treating **12** with Hg^{2+} ion in acid solution, accelerated removal of the chloride is effected (Sec. 4.5.5), with the production of **14**, in which the ester is now chelated. If a five-coordinated intermediate **13** is formed, the ester grouping must compete effectively with H_2O for the sixth position in forming **14**. The chelated ester hydrolyzes, with the ring remaining intact, to the chelated amino acid **15** (charges omitted):

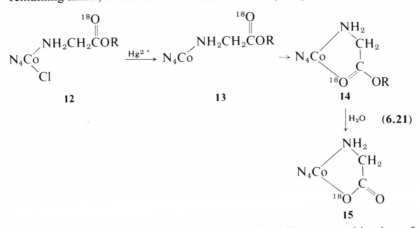

12   13   14

(6.21)

15

This sequence has been beautifully demonstrated from a combination of rate data (the consecutive reactions **12 → 14 → 15** established),[35,36] infrared examination of the various species involved (shows **14** is chelated),[35,36] and use of ^{18}O tracer[36,37] (shows the source of the coordinated oxygen and demonstrates that the ring remains intact in the last step;

it is an effective approach because ^{18}O–Co and ^{18}O=C can be distinguished). The original scheme patterned with $CoN_4 = cis\text{-}Coen_2$ has been duplicated by $CoN_4 = cis\text{-}\beta_2\text{-trien}$.[38]

(b)   The other effective way of promoting removal of chloride from **12** is through base hydrolysis. Now, however, the five-coordinated intermediate, which is preferred on the basis of the S_N1CB mechanism (Sec. 4.5.3(a)), apparently behaves differently from that produced in the Hg^{2+} reaction. Solvent H_2O and the ester grouping have comparable affinity for the five-coordinated species, so that two different *immediate* products are obtained, both of which react to give the chelated ester. This can be strongly inferred from ^{18}O examination of the product from a reaction carried out with ^{18}O-labeled carbonyl oxygen.[39]   (See (6.22).) Path *A* leads to ^{18}O–Co and path *B*, an intramolecular attack of the bonded OH, results in ^{18}O=C in the product ($N_4' = en_2$, from which a proton has ionized):

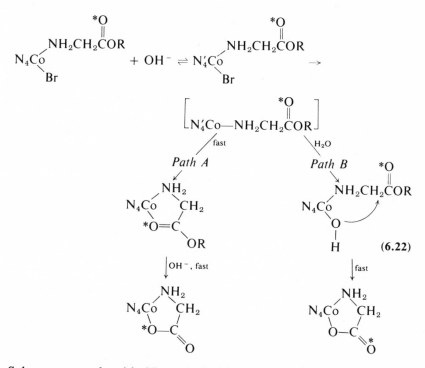

Subsequent work with $N_4 = cis\text{-}\beta\text{-trien}$ gave similar results, but the reaction is cleaner with fewer by-products.[38]

We can reassess at this stage the effect of coordination on the hydrolysis rates (Table 6.4). The $Co(NH_3)_5^{3+}$ residue, like Cu^{2+}, behaves quite similarly to the proton when acting on the unidentate ester. The very large rate enhancement, attributable to direct metal-ion activation of the carbonyl center, is with the chelated ester, a factor of 10^6 or so, which in this case resides mainly in a much more positive $\Delta S^{\ddagger}$ value.

6.4.2 Amides and Peptides: —CONHR → — COOH

The amide and peptide linkages are much more difficult to hydrolyze than the ester grouping. Metal ions can be effective catalysts but this depends somewhat on the mode of coordination. There are two potential sites for coordination in the CO–NHR residue—at the carbonyl O and at the amide N. A number of metal ions have the ability to promote ionization of the amide proton (see Sec. 6.5.4) and in the strong complex often formed, the ligand is *protected* from hydrolysis. Thus at 25° and pH ∼ 11, millimolar solutions of $Cu(picolinamide-H^+)_2$ remain unchanged for 20 days, whereas the free amide hydrolyzes completely in less than one day in the same conditions.[40] Similarly, hydrolytic protection has been observed in the Cu(II) complexes of glycinamide and the Ni(II) and Cu(II) complexes of tetraglycine and pentaglycine.[41] When the carbonyl O coordinates, however, metal activation often occurs since now the metal-ligand bond need not be broken. Thus Cu^{2+} promotes hydrolysis of glycinamide in neutral solution.[40]

Once again our greatest understanding so far of these effects has emerged from studies of the Co(III) complexes. Base hydrolysis of $Coen_2(NH_2CH_2CONH_2)Br^{2+}$ follows the scheme (6.22) (with OR replaced by NH_2). Now, however, the chelated amide resulting from path A, **16**, in contrast with the chelated ester, can be observed since its hydrolysis is slow.[42] This occurs with an intact ring, and can be separately measured:[43]

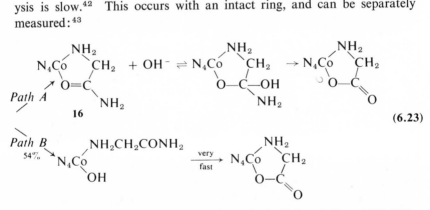

(6.23)

The rate constant at 25° for base hydrolysis of $Coen_2NH_2CH_2-CONH_2^{3+}$, containing the chelated amide, is 25 $M^{-1}\,sec^{-1}$,[43] some

10^4 times larger than the rate constant for base hydrolysis of the NH_2CH_2-$CONH_2$ $(2.2 \times 10^{-3} M^{-1} sec^{-1})$.[40]   Both rate constants are some 10^5-fold less than for the corresponding glycine ester. Probably the most important result of the study is the remarkable acceleration of hydrolysis of the coordinated unidentate amide by coordinated hydroxide in path B. It can be assessed that the hydroxoamide species must undergo intramolecular hydrolysis with a rate constant $\geqslant 3 \times 10^3 sec^{-1}$. At pH ~ 9, this corresponds to a rate enhancement over chelated and uncoordinated substrate of $\geqslant 10^7$- and $\geqslant 10^{11}$-fold, respectively. Despite the greatly reduced basic character of coordinated OH^- (Sec. 6.5.1), it is apparently a much more effective nucleophile than solvent OH^-, and this pathway is even more efficient than the one provided by metal-ion polarization of the carbonyl function alone.[42]

Earlier studies showed that complexes of the type $CoN_4(H_2O)OH^{2+}$, where $N_4 =$ en$_2$, cis-β-trien, or tren, can promote the hydrolysis of esters,[44,45] amides, and dipeptides,[45,46] and that this probably arises via formation of ester, amide, or peptide chelates.[47] These then hydrolyze in the manner above.

6.4.3   Hydroxyesters: —OX→ —OH

If a hydroxyester function is incorporated into a potential chelating system, then the ability of a metal ion to catalyze the hydroxyester hydrolysis can be more easily assessed. The 8-hydroxyquinoline framework has proved very popular for these experiments. In the Cu^{2+}-catalyzed hydrolysis of a number of esters, species such as **17** may be implicated, where $X =$ $-COCH_3$,[48,49] $-PO_3$,[50] $-SO_3$,[51] β-O-glucoside.[52] The polarization of the X–O bond by incorporation of the O in a five-membered chelate ring

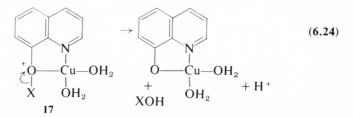

(6.24)

promotes H_2O or OH^- attack. In this respect the metal ion simulates even more effectively the behavior of H^+.

The usual effect of the metal ion is to accelerate the rate of the "spontaneous" reaction. In certain cases however, the course of the reaction is modified: in addition to cyclization to form **20**, which occurs in the spontaneous reaction, hydrolysis of **18** to **19** also is promoted by metal ions. The relative importance of the two paths depends on reaction conditions and the metal.[53]

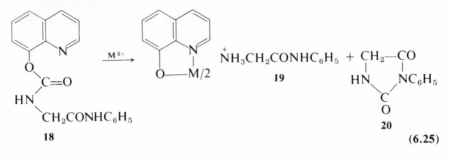

$$\overset{+}{N}H_3CH_2CONHC_6H_5 + CH_2\!\!-\!\!CO$$

19

20

(6.25)

6.4.4   Other Groups

There have been a number of isolated studies of metal-ion-catalyzed hydrolysis of other groupings.[1] These include the C–Hal, C=S, and C≡N groupings,[54] Schiff bases, and phosphate esters.[55] Particularly interesting is the base hydrolysis of 2-cyanophenanthroline. This is markedly accelerated by Cu^{2+}, Zn^{2+}, and Ni^{2+} ions. The fullest kinetic study uses Ni^{2+}, where the second-order rate constant is 10^7-fold higher than that for the free base, the effect residing mainly in a more positive $\Delta S^{\ddagger}$ value. An external OH⁻ attack on the chelate is favored. Nickel-ion catalysis of the hydrolysis of the phenanthroline-2-amide product is much less effective, being only $\sim 4 \times 10^2$ times the rate for spontaneous hydrolysis.

This difference may mean that the cyano group is not coordinated whereas the amide probably is, and a driving force for the hydrolysis of the cyano complex is the gain of additional coordination in the activated complex:[18,56]

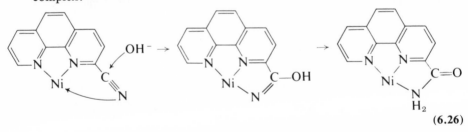

(6.26)

6.5   THE ACIDITY OF COORDINATED LIGANDS

An important effect of the metal ion lies in its ability to enhance the acidity of certain coordinated ligands. Any ligand that in the free state can release a proton can also do so when coordinated to a metal. The positive charge originally associated with the central metal is dissipated over the whole complex, and the resultant neutralization of negative charge at the cordinated ligand center will result in the center's being more acidic. Generally, the higher the positive charge, the greater the (enhanced) ionization constant.[57] Some examples of this effect, with comparisons of the free and the coordinated ligand, are shown in Table 6.5.

It is known that the difference in pK_a values for various acids HA reside in different values for the rate constant for ionization (k_1),

$$HA \rightleftharpoons H^+ + A^- \qquad k_1, k_{-1}, K_a(=k_1/k_{-1}) \qquad (6.27)$$

since k_{-1} is approximately constant and diffusion-controlled for most proton-base reactions.[58] Where data are available for acid-base reactions involving complexes, these also conform to this rule. Thus the values for k_{-1}, the rate constant for protonation of the base, for the first four entries of Table 6.5 are, respectively, at 25°, 1.4×10^{11},[59] 5.0×10^9,[59] 1.4×10^9,[60] and 7.7×10^8 [61] $M^{-1} sec^{-1}$. It is apparent that the differences in pK_a must reside in k_1, the rate constant for ionization.

6.5.1   Coordinated Water

The marked increase in the acidity of water when it becomes metal-coordinated, as shown in Table 6.5, has very important ramifications. Thus, certain metal complexes donate OH^- in conditions (pH = 7) where the concentration of free OH^- is small. Many aqua-containing complexes will be involved in an aqua-hydroxy equilibrium in the pH region 3–11. Since the hydroxo form often has different reactivity than its acidic partner, there will be marked effects of pH on the rates of substitution and redox reactions in which aqua complexes are involved. The enhanced reactivity of cis-$Coen_2(H_2O)OH^{2+}$ compared with cis-$Coen_2(H_2O)_2^{3+}$ and cis-$Coen_2(OH)_2^+$ is shown in its behavior towards (a) racemization,[62] (b) H_2O exchange,[63] (c) reaction with glycine ester and peptides,[45] and (d) anation by HPO_4^{2-} ions[64] and $C_2O_4^{2-}$ ions.[65]

6.5.2   Coordinated Ammonia, Amines, and Other Ligands

The enhanced ionization effect with the coordinated-NH entity is sometimes much less marked than the effect with –OH, and then it is difficult to demonstrate directly.[66] It has important ramifications, for example in the enhanced reactivity of the amide form as the probable explanation for base hydrolysis (Sec. 4.5.3(a)). The rate constants for ionization of coordinated-NH groups have been much studied, particularly for

TABLE 6.5.   Values of pK_a for a Variety of Acids

Acid	pK_a^1	Ref.
H_2O	15.8	
$Co(NH_3)_5H_2O^{3+}$	6.1	a
$Cr(H_2O)_6^{3+}$	4.3	
$VO(H_2O)_5^{2+}$	5.0^j	
$NH_2(CH_2)_2NH_3^+$	10.5	
cis-$Coen_2(NH_2(CH_2)_2NH_3)Cl^{3+}$	7.1	b
$Pten(NH_2(CH_2)_2NH_3)Cl^{2+}$	8.0	9
NH_3	>16	
$Ru(NH_3)_6^{3+}$	12.4	c
$Auen_2^{2+}$	6.5	d
$Pt(NH_3)_6^{4+}$	10.1	e
NNH^+	0.6	71
$(NH_3)_5Ru^{II}-NNH^{3+}$	2.5	71
$(NH_3)_5Ru^{III}-NNH^{4+}$	-0.8	71
$H_2C_2O_4$	1.2	
$HC_2O_4^-$	4.2	
$Co(NH_3)_5C_2O_4H^{2+}$	2.2	f
HCO_3^-	10.3	
$Co(NH_3)_5OCO_2H^{2+}$	6.4	g
$NH_2SO_3^-$	>16	
$Co(NH_3)_5NH_2SO_3^{2+}$	5.8	h

[a] Values for other Co(III) aquoammines are given in R. C. Beaumont, *Inorg. Chem.*, **8**, 1805 (1969) and C. J. Hawkins, A. M. Sargeson, and G. H. Searle, *Aust. J. Chem.*, **17**, 598 (1964).
[b] M. D. Alexander and C. A. Spillert, *Inorg. Chem.*, **9**, 2344 (1970).
[c] D. Waysbort and G. Navon, *Chem. Commun.*, 1410 (1971).
[d] B. P. Block and J. C. Bailar, Jr., *J. Amer. Chem. Soc.*, **73**, 4722 (1951).
[e] L. Heck, *Inorg. Nucl. Chem. Letters*, **6**, 657 (1970).
[f] S. F. Ting, H. Kelm, and G. M. Harris, *Inorg. Chem.*, **5**, 696 (1966); C. Andrade and H. Taube, *Inorg. Chem.*, **5**, 1087 (1966).
[g] T. P. Dasgupta and G. M. Harris, *J. Amer. Chem. Soc.*, **90**, 6360 (1968).
[h] L. L. Po and R. B. Jordan, *Inorg. Chem.*, **7**, 526 (1968).
[1] $pK_a = -\log[Base][H^+][Acid]^{-1} = \log(k_{-1}/k_1)$ (see text). The values are taken from standard compilations except where noted.
[j] Ionization of equatorial water.

Co(III), Pt(II), and Pt(IV), by nmr exchange methods. When the co-ordinated N is asymmetric, the interesting relation between proton exchange and inversion can be explored (Sec. 7.7). Use is made of the different rate constants for ionization to prepare trans-$Co(NH_3)_4(ND_3)Cl^{2+}$, a useful diagnostic ion (Sec. 2.2.2).

Table 6.5 indicates that for a number of other simple ligands the pK is modified by attachment to the metal, and this will play a role in the reactivity of the resulting complex. Thus, the reduction of $Co(NH_3)_5$-$C_2O_4H^{2+}$ in acid by Fe^{2+} and V^{2+} have an inverse $[H^+]$ term in the rate law,[67] whereas the same reductions of $Co(NH_3)_4C_2O_4^+$, which has no proton affinity, are pH-independent.[68]

If the acidic group is part of a ligand but not involved in the metal coordination, its acidity may be modified less than in some of the examples considered above. This has been demonstrated with a number of polyamine complexes, in which because of the geometry of the ligand, or strain within the complex, uncoordinated NH_2 groups are present. In these cases, the basicity is decreased by some 2–3 pK units. A case has been made on this basis for distinguishing metal complexes of penten, in which all 6 N's are coordinated, from those in which only 5 N's are attached.[69]

Compound 21 appears to be a reactive species in the Zn(II)-mediated reaction between N-(β-hydroxylethyl)ethylenediamine(HEN) and p-nitrophenylpicolinate (NPP).

$$\begin{array}{c} CH_2CH_2 \\ H_2N \diagdown \diagdown NH-CH_2CH_2OH + OH^- \rightleftharpoons \\ Zn \end{array}$$

$$\begin{array}{c} CH_2CH_2 \\ H_2N \diagdown \diagdown NH-CH_2CH_2O^- \xrightarrow{\text{NPP}} \text{product} \quad (6.28) \\ Zn \end{array}$$

The reaction with NPP is believed to occur within a ternary complex formed around the Zn. In addition to promoting a template reaction (see Sec. 6.2.1), the metal also enhances the formation of the nucleophilic O^- species, reducing the pK by some 3–4 units over that in the free HEN.[70]

With one exception so far, the basicity of a complex-involved ligand is diminished over basicity of the free ligand. This exception involves the pyrazine complex of Ru(II) (compare the entries 12 and 13 in Table 6.5). It is believed that back bonding from the filled t_{2g} orbitals of Ru(II) to unoccupied π-antibonding orbitals of the ligands more than compensates for the usual electrostatic effect of the metal that makes the nitrogen less basic. This is less likely with the Ru(III) complex (entry 14 in Table 6.5) and its pK is lower than the pK of protonated pyrazine.[71]

6.5.3   Extended Ligand Systems

In a compound containing the structure X=Y–ZH, H tends to be acidic, and once again this is enhanced by involvement of the grouping with a metal.[57]   There are many examples but since these mainly relate to synthetic or qualitative aspects they will be only briefly tabulated in Table 6.6.   Metal attachment can be at the Z, Y, or X center.

6.5.4   Anomalous Acid-Base Reactions Involving Metal Complexes

The rate constants for the reactions of H^+ with many bases, and of OH^- with many acids, are between 10^9 and 10^{11} M^{-1} sec^{-1}, in agreement with theoretically derived values for diffusion-controlled reactions.[72]   Only reactions in which hydrogen bond structure is disturbed or in which there is a radical redistribution of electrons attending the acid-base reactions are likely to be much slower than expected.[72]

For the reaction of $Co(DH)_2(CN)_2^-$ with base:

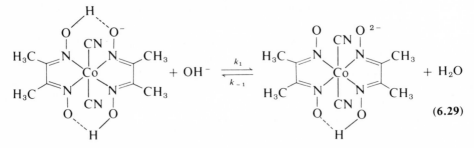

$$(6.29)$$

$k_1 = 1.9 \times 10^5$ M^{-1} sec^{-1}.   This lowered value probably resides in an energy barrier imposed by an internal hydrogen-bonding effect.   The increase in the value of k_1 for $Co(DH)_2(NH_3)_2^+$ $(1.3 \times 10^6$ M^{-1} $sec^{-1})$ can be attributed to a more favorable charge situation.[73]

A number of metal ions have the ability to promote proton ionization from a coordinated amide or peptide group (Table 6.6).   There is strong evidence for an M–O to an M–N bond rearrangement at the amide or peptide site, accompanying the ionization from the coordinated CONHR residue.   The observation of relatively slow rates associated with the protonation reaction supports the idea of bond rearrangement.[74]

The reaction

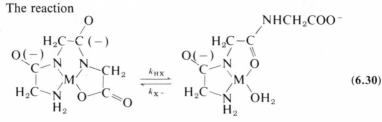

$$(6.30)$$

TABLE 6.6. Metal-Promoted Ionization of Extended Ligand Systems

Ligand structure	Activating metals	Ionization	Comments	Ref.
$NH_2CH_2CNH_2$ with $\parallel O$	$Pd^{II} > Cu^{II} > Ni^{II} > Co^{II}$	N—H	NH_2CH_2CNHR with $O \rightarrow M$; NH_2CH_2CONR—M; accompanies ionization.	a
(pyridine ring structure with N—H, R—C=N—N)	Bivalent transition metal ions	N—H	pK of free ligand reduced 5–8 units in chelate.	b
$NH_2CH_2COO^-$ and amino-polycarboxylic acids	Co^{III}, in e.g., $Coen_2NH_2CH_2COO^{2+}$ and $CoEDTA^-$	C—H exchange enhanced	C—H in out-of-plane rings exchange more readily than those in-plane rings.	c

[a] P. J. Morris and R. B. Martin, *Inorg. Chem.*, **10**, 964 (1971).
[b] R. W. Green, P. S. Hallman, and F. Lions, *Inorg. Chem.*, **3**, 376 (1964).
[c] D. H. Williams and D. H. Busch, *J. Amer. Chem. Soc.*, **87**, 4644 (1965).

in which M $=$ Cu[75] or Ni,[76] is subject to general acid catalysis. Rate constants for the reaction as a function of the acid strength of HX are shown in Fig. 6.4. With both metals, the slope of the plot (the Brønsted α value, Sec. 2.5.3) is unity for acids with pK_a ranging from 5 to 9. This indicates that HX attacks the substrate, or an intermediate, instead of merely transferring a proton. The details of this are still not quite clear.[76]

The H_3O^+ attack is slower than diffusion-controlled because an M–N to M–O bond rearrangement is involved. On the other hand, attack by H_2O is faster than expected from Fig. 6.4, probably because it promotes dissociation of the M–N bond (hydrolysis), which then rapidly protonates.[76] Lowered rate constants for protonation of ionized copper(II) complexes with dipeptides have also been observed.[77,78]

6.6 ELECTROPHILIC SUBSTITUTION IN CHELATES

When a metal atom *donates* electron density to a bound ligand, usually by means of π back-bonding, electrophilic substitution reactions may be promoted. There have been detailed studies of electrophilic substitution in metal complexes of β-diketones, 8-hydroxyquinolines,[79] and porphyrins. Usually the detailed course of the reaction is unaffected.[1] However, the presence of the metal in metalloporphyrins encourages electrophilic

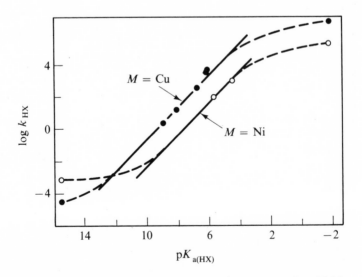

FIGURE 6.4 Brønsted plot for effect of HX on reaction (6.30). The solid lines correspond to a Brønsted α value of unity.[76]

attack at carbon and inhibits protonation or alkylation reactions at the nitrogen compared with the free porphines. Thus with the complex **22**,

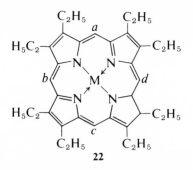

22

methyl fluorosulfonate in boiling $CHCl_3$ introduces an Me group at one *meso* C position (a) (M = Pd), whereas direct *meso*-methylation of the porphine is unknown. Additionally, $CF_3COOD/CHCl_3$ deuterates the four *meso* positions (a–d) in less than 20 minutes at room temperature when M = Pd or Pt, whereas exchange of the free ligand has a $t_{1/2} \sim 275$ hours at 90°. The metal functions as a protective group for all four nitrogen atoms besides promoting the formation of the transition state for electrophilic substitution by d_π–p_π overlap.[80]

Electrophilic substitution is usually slower in metal complexes than in the free ligand but more rapid than in the protonated form. In the coupling

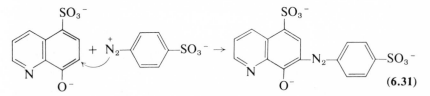

$$(6.31)$$

the rate constants for reaction of the phenolate anion, Zn complex, and phenol ligand at 15° are 4.1×10^2, 2.6×10^{-2}, and $\sim 10^{-8} M^{-1} sec^{-1}$ respectively.[81]

6.7 MASKING EFFECTS

The masking of the normal reactions of simple ligands, such as the nitro, cyano, and ammonia groups, by coordination to a metal is a phenomenon encountered early by a chemist. One of the first examples of masking in a chelate complex was reported, significantly, in biological journals.[82] It involves the protection by copper ion of the α-amino group in ornithine and lysine:

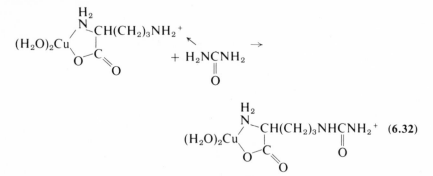

$$(H_2O)_2Cu \quad \text{...} \quad CH(CH_2)_3NHCNH_2^+ \quad \textbf{(6.32)}$$

Partial protection of the $-NH_2$ group by copper ion results in a fiftyfold decrease in the rate of the ring-closure reaction

$$\text{(6.33)}$$

in the presence of the metal ion over that of the free ligand. However, Cu(II) binds strongly to the product and if significant amounts of the free metal ion are removed in this way, the initial reaction rate increases sharply.[83] An opposite effect is noted in the metal-ion-catalyzed hydrolysis of amino acid esters. Removal of the metal ion as it complexes with the amino acid product causes *deceleration* of the reaction.[84]

Although the NH_2 group of amino acids is protected by metal co-ordination, nevertheless it enters into certain reactions, for example with aldehydes to form the *N*-hydroxymethyl derivative. This, together with enhanced acidity in the neighboring CH_2 group (Table 6.6), leads to formation of an oxazolidine complex, for example,

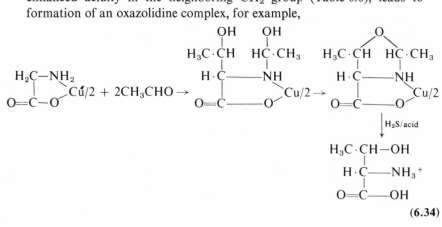

$$\text{(6.34)}$$

Decomposition of the copper complex with H_2S in acid leads to *dl*-threonine.[85] This type of reaction does not occur in the absence of metal.[86]

6.8 DISTURBANCE OF REACTION STOICHIOMETRY

The intervention of a metal ion in the stoichiometry of a reaction has been illustrated several times previously. Reaction is forced to completion in ester hydrolysis since the carboxylate grouping forms a more stable complex than the ester moiety does. A similar driving force underlies the formation of macrocycles and the completion of transamination by formation of the metal–Schiff base complex.[22,87] The latter is particularly relevant in dilute solution and at low pH. For example, the extent of aldimine formation between pyridoxal and alanine is undetectable at the physiological pH but occurs to the extent of $\sim 10\%$ in the presence of zinc ions.[87]

6.9 MOLECULAR STRAIN ALTERATIONS

Metal complexing can subject a ligand to severe internal strain or, alternatively, it can relieve strain; or it can freeze the conformation of the coordinated ligand. These modifications often lead to enhanced reactivity by reducing the energy difference between ground and transition state.

The subjection of the cyano group to strain when 2-cyanophenanthroline is coordinated to a metal ion, and its resultant accelerated hydrolysis, has been referred to previously (Sec. 6.4.4). This behavior is likened to the *rack mechanism* that is believed operative in certain enzyme systems, in which bonding of substrate to the enzyme induces a distortion towards the geometry of the transition state.[56,88] In metalloenzymes, the irregular or distorted geometry of the metal coordination sites may already approximate the geometry of the transition state for the catalyzed reaction. This leads to an activated energy state even *before* the entry of substrate (*entatic site hypothesis*).[89]

A number of transition metal complexes can catalyze the rearrangement and degradation of a wide variety of highly strained polycyclics, which do not react in the absence of catalysts. Although the effect is not well understood, there is evidence for intramolecular rearrangement via metal complexing, the latter aiding in the relief of ring strain, which is the driving force for the reaction.[90] This modus operandi appears also to be the basis of Ag^+-catalyzed strained σ-bond rearrangement.[91,92] The substrate appears to possess a geometry suitable for multicentered C–C

σ-bond interaction with the Ag^+ ion.　Some kinetic data suggest a rate law for the rearrangment:[91]

$$V = k[\text{substrate}][Ag^+]$$

The specificity of the various metal catalysts is illustrated in the rearrangement of cubane:[93]

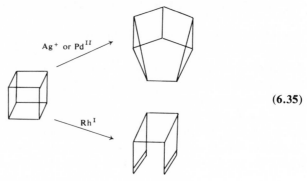

(6.35)

6.10   FUNCTION OF THE LIGAND

The principal upset of the properties of the ligand is due to the metal. However, effects also of one ligand on another, presumably acting through the metal, are not unimportant.

The basis of the strong effect of an axial ligand on reaction at a *trans* position resides in the fact that a d_{z^2} orbital electron is most affected.　It appears in:

(a)   The larger influence of changes of axial ligand B as compared with DH on the rate of the reaction

$$Co^{II}(DH)_2B + RX \rightarrow Co^{III}(DH)_2BX + R\cdot \qquad \text{rds} \qquad (6.36)$$

$$Co^{II}(DH)_2B + R\cdot \rightarrow Co^{III}(DH)_2BR \qquad (6.37)$$

Electron-donating substituents in B will stabilize Co, which will electron-transfer in the transition state $[B(DH)_2Co^{\delta+} \cdots X^{\delta-} \cdots R]^{\ddagger}$.　There will therefore be a general correlation of rate constant for the first step and the basicity of B.　But with bulky ligands B, steric effects will be more important.　A "cone angle" for the ligand can be defined as the apex angle of a cone centered on the metal atom that just encloses the van der Waals radii of the outermost atoms of the ligand.[94]　There is an inverse linear relation between log k and the cone angle for R for (6.36).[95]

(b)   The effects of nonbridging ligands in redox reactions, for example in the Orgel mechanism for Cr(II)/Cr(III) electron transfer reactions (Sec. 5.7).

(c)   The enhanced lability towards substitution in square-planar complexes imposed in the *trans effect* (Sec. 4.10.1).   Such an effect also plays a role in octahedral complexes, although it is less easily characterized because of the dissociative nature of substitution.[96]

There is a marked effect of the R group on the rate of loss of the *trans* H_2O group from **23**

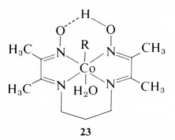

23

in acetone, ranging from 3.6 sec^{-1} ($R = C_6H_5$) to 602 sec^{-1} ($R = n\text{-Pr}$) at $25°$.[97]

Ligands may modify reactivity patterns, such as in the smoother-catalyzed decarboxylation of **24** by aromatic as compared with aliphatic amine complexes ML^{n+}:

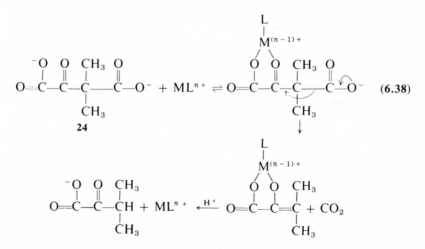

The π orbitals of the aromatic amine appear implicated.[98]

Complex ions containing ligands additional to water have a decided advantage over the metal aquated ion alone, for the metal complex can function at a pH at which metal ion might precipitate.   It has been pointed out that if ferric ion was not precipitated in alkaline solution and the pH dependence of its "catalase" ability (see Sec. 6.2.3) in acid could be extrapolated to pH $\sim$ 10, it would be almost as effective a catalyst as the enzyme itself, and much superior to other iron(III) complexes.[29] Additionally, although the metal complex may be similar in catalytic effect to protons (Sec. 6.3), it can exist in much higher concentrations than the proton in the neutral pH region, in which, incidentally, most metalloenzymes function catalytically. The metal complex ion, furthermore, can form both σ and π bonds; it can often coordinate several donor centers in a reacting multidentate ligand in a stereospecific geometrical arrangement and in this way often prove superior to the proton in its catalytic effect.[31]

6.11   IMPACT OF THE AREA

A number of the areas delineated in this chapter have an obvious relevance to the investigation of the action of enzymes, particularly those cases in which a metal is near or at the active site. Indeed, strong in the motivation of investigators of simple metal complexes is the attempt to simulate and understand the action of the metalloenzymes.[99]

Mildvan has tabulated the various effects of metal ions on the reactions of their coordinated ligand, and he has cited examples of coordination compounds *and* enzymes that may use these effects.[100] Probably the most important single effect that metal centers have in metalloenzymes is to be a focal point for reactants, often in a very stereospecific manner. This function is invariably reinforced by other effects, which we have outlined above. The formidable combination leads to the remarkable rate enhancements that even the most cleverly devised model systems, for example the cobalt(III)-catalyzed amide hydrolysis,[42,43] fail to copy.

Many of the properties of metal ions in aiding or discouraging reactions are beautifully illustrated in the work on the chemical synthesis of corrins. Thus, it is appropriate to conclude this chapter by a relevant quotation from Eschenmoser:[20]

> The role of transition metals in the chemical synthesis of corrins is more than just adding a touch of "inorganic elegance" to organic synthesis—"leave elegance to tailors and cobblers," a physicist once said—it is a vital role in the sense that perhaps no synthetic corrin would as yet exist without recourse to metal templates. Beside the purely topological function of *arranging the proximity* of reaction centres, metal ions have served this purpose as follows:
>
> (i) by *stabilizing* labile organic intermediates and thereby facilitating their isolation and characterization,

(ii) by *activating* organic ligands electronically for base-catalyzed processes,

(iii) by subjecting organic ligands to heavy *steric strain* so that they perform strain-releasing reactions which they would otherwise certainly never undergo,

(iv) by *protecting* organic coordination sites against the detrimental attack of aggressive alkylation reagents,

(v) and, last but not least—by converting the organic chemists involved in this work to genuine admirers of the depth potentials and wonders of *transition metal chemistry*.

REFERENCES

1. Q. Fernando, *Adv. Inorg. Radiochem.*, **7**, 185 (1965).
2. J. P. Collman, *Trans. Metal Chem.*, **2**, 1 (1966).
3. Y. N. Kukushkin, *Russ. Chem. Rev.*, **39**, 169 (1970)—emphasizing the Russian contributions.
4. D. H. Busch, *Science*, **171**, 241 (1971).
5. B. Capon, *Quart. Rev.*, **18**, 45 (1964).
6. Jencks, *Catalysis in Chemistry and Enzymology*, p. 8.
7. M. B. Stevenson, R. D. Mast, and A. G. Sykes, *J. Chem. Soc.*, *A*, 937 (1969).
8. Comparison has to be made between a first-order rate constant for the intramolecular process and a second-order rate constant for the corresponding intermolecular reaction. One may arbitrarily decide on a 1 M concentration of reagent (e.g., NH_3), when the pseudo first-order rate constant for the intermolecular process is 5.7×10^{-3} sec^{-1}, but the procedure is far from satisfactory. See Ref. 6.
9. M. J. Carter and J. K. Beattie, *Inorg. Chem.*, **9**, 1233 (1970).
10. D. A. Buckingham, D. M. Foster, and A. M. Sargeson, *J. Amer. Chem. Soc.*, **91**, 3451 (1969).
11. J. P. Collman, *Accounts Chem. Research*, **1**, 136 (1968).
12. D. D. Schmidt and J. T. Yoke, *J. Amer. Chem. Soc.*, **93**, 637 (1971).
13. J. P. Birk, J. Halpern, and A. L. Pickard, *J. Amer. Chem. Soc.*, **90**, 4491 (1968).
14. J. Halpern and A. L. Pickard, *Inorg. Chem.*, **9**, 2798 (1970).
15. G. W. Parshall, *Accounts Chem. Research*, **3**, 139 (1970).
16. T. C. Bruice and A. Turner, *J. Amer. Chem. Soc.*, **92**, 3422 (1970).
17. G. J. Lloyd and B. S. Cooperman, *J. Amer. Chem. Soc.*, **93**, 4883 (1971). See also D. S. Sigman, G. N. Wahl, and D. J. Creighton, *Biochem.*, **11**, 2236 (1972), who report zinc-ion-catalyzed phosphorylation of 1,10-phenanthroline-2-carbinol by ATP.
18. R. Breslow and M. Schmir, *J. Amer. Chem. Soc.*, **93**, 4960 (1971); R. Breslow, in *Bioinorganic Chemistry*, Chap. 2.

19. D. H. Busch, Alfred Werner Commemoration Volume, *Verlag Helv. Chim. Acta*, Basel, 1967; L. F. Lindoy and D. H. Busch, *Prep. Inorg. Reactions*, **6**, 1 (1971).

20. A. Eschenmoser, *Pure Appl. Chem.*, **20**, 93 (1969); R. B. Woodward, *Pure Appl. Chem.*, **33**, 145 (1973).

21. N. F. Curtis and R. W. Hay, *Chem. Commun.*, 524 (1966).

22. M. E. Farago and T. Matthews, *J. Chem. Soc.*, *A*, 609 (1969).

23. D. L. Leussing and C. K. Stanfield, *J. Amer. Chem. Soc.*, **88**, 5726 (1966); Y. Matsushima and A. E. Martell, *J. Amer. Chem. Soc.*, **89**, 1331 (1967).

24. D. Hopgood and D. L. Leussing, *J. Amer. Chem. Soc.*, **91**, 3740 (1969). In the operation of this effect, the term *promnastic effect* is preferred since there is a much lower steric requirement than in the template effect. See also Ref. 25.

25. B. E. Leach and D. L. Leussing, *J. Amer. Chem. Soc.*, **93**, 3377 (1971).

26. E. E. Snell and S. J. Di Mari, in *The Enzymes*, Chap. 7.

27. H. Sigel, *Angew. Chem.*, **8**, 167 (1969).

28. V. S. Sharma and J. Schubert, *Inorg. Chem.*, **10**, 251 (1971).

29. S. B. Brown, P. Jones, and A. Suggett, in *Inorganic Reaction Mechanisms*, Part 1, ed. J. O. Edwards (Interscience, New York, 1970), p. 170.

30. H. Kroll, *J. Amer. Chem. Soc.*, **74**, 2036 (1952).

31. M. L. Bender, in *Reactions of Coordinated Ligands*, Chap. 2.

32. R. W. Hay and P. J. Morris, *Chem. Commun.*, 732 (1968); R. W. Hay and L. J. Porter, *J. Chem. Soc.*, *A*, 127 (1969).

33. B. E. Leach and R. J. Angelici, *J. Amer Chem. Soc.*, **91**, 6296 (1969); R. J. Angelici and J. W. Allison, *Inorg. Chem.*, **10**, 2238 (1971).

34. G. L. Johnson and R. J. Angelici, *J. Amer. Chem. Soc.*, **93**, 1106 (1971).

35. M. D. Alexander and D. H. Busch, *J. Amer. Chem. Soc.*, **88**, 1130 (1966).

36. D. A. Buckingham, D. M. Foster, and A. M. Sargeson, *J. Amer. Chem. Soc.*, **90**, 6032 (1968).

37. Y. Wu and D. H. Busch, *J. Amer. Chem. Soc.*, **92**, 3326 (1970).

38. D. A. Buckingham, *Inorg. Chem.*, **9**, 11 (1970).

39. D. A. Buckingham, D. M. Foster, and A. M. Sargeson, *J. Amer. Chem. Soc.*, **91**, 4102 (1969).

40. H. L. Conley, Jr. and R. B. Martin, *J. Phys. Chem.*, **70**, 2914 (1965).

41. R. H. Andreatta, H. C. Freeman, A. V. Robertson, and R. L. Sinclair, *Chem. Commun.*, 203 (1967).

42. D. A. Buckingham, D. M. Foster, and A. M. Sargeson, *J. Amer. Chem. Soc.*, **92**, 6151 (1970).

43. D. A. Buckingham, C. E. Davis, D. M. Foster, and A. M. Sargeson, *J. Amer. Chem. Soc.*, **92**, 5571 (1970).

44. E. Kimura, S. Young, and J. P. Collman, *Inorg. Chem.*, **9**, 1183 (1970).

45. D. A. Buckingham and J. P. Collman, *Inorg. Chem.*, **6**, 1803 (1967).

46. D. A. Buckingham, J. P. Collman, D. A. R. Haffer, and L. G. Marzilla, *J. Amer. Chem. Soc.*, **89**, 1082 (1967).

47. J. P. Collman and E. Kimura, *J. Amer. Chem. Soc.*, **89**, 6096 (1967).

48. C. R. Wasmuth and H. Freiser, *Talanta*, **9**, 1059 (1962).
49. R. H. Barca and H. Freiser, *J. Amer. Chem. Soc.*, **88**, 3744 (1966).
50. Y. Murakami, *Chem. Commun.*, 983 (1969).
51. R. W. Hay and J. A. G. Edmonds, *Chem. Commun.*, 969 (1967).
52. C. R. Clark, R. W. Hay, and I. C. M. Dea, *Chem. Commun.*, 794 (1970).
53. E. J. Corey and R. L. Dawson, *J. Amer. Chem. Soc.*, **84**, 4899 (1962).
54. D. Pinnell, G. B. Wright, and R. B. Jordan, *J. Amer. Chem. Soc.*, **94**, 6104 (1972); D. A. Buckingham, F. R. Keene, and A. M. Sargeson, *J. Amer. Chem. Soc.*, **95**, 5649 (1973).
55. J. R. Cox and O. B. Ramsay, *Chem. Rev.*, **64**, 317 (1964).
56. R. Breslow, R. Fairweather, and J. Keana, *J. Amer. Chem. Soc.*, **89**, 2135 (1967).
57. J. F. Geldard and F. Lions, *Inorg. Chem.*, **2**, 270 (1963).
58. R. P. Bell, *Quart. Rev.*, **13**, 169 (1959).
59. M. Eigen, W. Kruse, G. Maass, and L. DeMaeyer, *Progr. Reaction Kinetics*, **2**, 287 (1964).
60. T. J. Swift and T. A. Stephenson, *Inorg. Chem.*, **5**, 1100 (1966).
61. J. Reuben and D. Fiat, *J. Amer. Chem. Soc.*, **91**, 4652 (1969).
62. R. D. Gillard, *J. Chem. Soc.*, *A*, 1945 (1968).
63. W. Kruse and H. Taube, *J. Amer. Chem. Soc.*, **83**, 1280 (1961).
64. S. F. Lincoln and D. R. Stranks, *Aust. J. Chem.*, **21**, 1745 (1968).
65. S. C. Chan and G. M. Harris, *Inorg. Chem.*, **10**, 1317 (1971).
66. L. E. Erickson, *J. Amer. Chem. Soc.*, **91**, 6284 (1969). The pK's of a number of Pt(II) amine complexes have been determined using nmr chemical shifts of ligand protons in high KOH concentrations.
67. J. H. Espenson, *Inorg. Chem.*, **4**, 121 (1965); H. J. Price and H. Taube, *Inorg. Chem.*, **7**, 1 (1968).
68. C. Hwang and A. Haim, *Inorg. Chem.*, **9**, 500 (1970).
69. G. B. Schwarzenbech and P. Moser, *Helv. Chim. Acta*, **36**, 581 (1953).
70. D. S. Sigman and C. T. Jorgenson, *J. Amer. Chem. Soc.*, **94**, 1724 (1972).
71. P. Ford, De F. P. Rudd, R. Gaunder, and H. Taube, *J. Amer. Chem. Soc.*, **90**, 1187 (1968).
72. M. Eigen, *Angew. Chem.*, **3**, 1 (1964).
73. J. P. Birk, P. B. Chock, and J. Halpern, *J. Amer. Chem. Soc.*, **90**, 6959 (1968).
74. C. F. V. Mason, P. I. Chamberlain, and R. G. Wilkins, *Inorg. Chem.*, **10**, 2345 (1971), and references therein.
75. G. K. Pagenkopf and D. W. Margerum, *J. Amer. Chem. Soc.*, **90**, 6963 (1968).
76. E. J. Billo and D. W. Margerum, *J. Amer. Chem. Soc.*, **92**, 6811 (1970).
77. R. F. Pasternack and K. Kustin, *J. Amer. Chem. Soc.*, **90**, 2295 (1968).
78. R. F. Pasternack, M. Angwin, and E. Gibbs, *J. Amer. Chem. Soc.*, **92**, 5878 (1970).
79. R. J. Kline and J. G. Wardeska, *Inorg. Chem.*, **8**, 2153 (1969).

80. R. Grigg, A. Sweeney, and A. W. Johnson, *Chem. Commun.*, 1237 (1970).
81. K. E. Maguire and M. M. Jones, *J. Amer. Chem. Soc.*, **85**, 154 (1963).
82. A. C. Kurtz, *J. Biol. Chem.*, **122**, 477 (1937); A. Neuberger and F. Sanger, *Biochem. J.*, **37**, 515 (1943); **38**, 125 (1944).
83. D. A. Usher, *J. Amer. Chem. Soc.*, **90**, 367 (1968).
84. M. L. Bender and B. W. Turnquest, *J. Amer. Chem. Soc.*, **79**, 1889 (1957).
85. J. P. Aune, P. Maldonado, G. Larcheres, and M. Pierrot, *Chem. Commun.*, 1351 (1970).
86. J. R. Brush, R. J. Magee, M. J. O'Connor, S. B. Teo, R. J. Geue, and M. R. Snow, *J. Amer. Chem. Soc.*, **95**, 2034 (1973).
87. D. A. Gansow and R. H. Holm, *J. Amer. Chem. Soc.*, **91**, 573 (1969).
88. H. Eyring, R. Lumry, and J. D. Spikes, in *The Mechanism of Enzyme Action*, ed. W. D. McElroy and B. Glass (Johns Hopkins, Baltimore, 1954), p. 123.
89. B. L. Vallee and R. J. P. Williams, *Proc. Nat. Acad. Sci. U.S.*, **59**, 498 (1968).
90. P. G. Gassman and T. J. Atkins, *J. Amer. Chem. Soc.*, **93**, 1042, 4597 (1971).
91. L. A. Paquette, *Accounts Chem. Research*, **4**, 280 (1971).
92. M. Sakai and S. Masamune, *J. Amer. Chem. Soc.*, **93**, 4610 (1971).
93. L. Cassar, P. E. Eaton, and J. Halpern, *J. Amer. Chem. Soc.*, **92**, 3515, 6366 (1970).
94. C. A. Tolman, *J. Amer. Chem. Soc.*, **92**, 2956 (1970).
95. J. Halpern and R. F. Phelan, *J. Amer. Chem. Soc.*, **94**, 1881 (1972).
96. J. M. Pratt and R. G. Thorp, *Adv. Inorg. Radiochem.*, **12**, 375 (1969).
97. G. Costa, G. Mestroni, G. Tauzher, D. M. Goodall, M. Green, and H. A. O. Hill, *Chem. Commun.*, 34 (1970).
98. J. V. Rund and K. G. Claus, *Inorg. Chem.*, **7**, 860 (1968).
99. F. P. Dwyer, in *Chelating Agents and Metal Chelates*, ed. F. P. Dwyer and D. P. Mellor (Academic, New York, 1964), Chap. 8.
100. A. S. Mildvan, in *The Enzymes*, Chap. 9.

SELECTED BIBLIOGRAPHY

Coordinated Ligand Reactivity

Boyer, P. D., ed. *The Enzymes*, volume 2, 3rd ed. Academic, New York, 1970. Contains a number of well-written chapters pertinent to this chapter.

Jones, M. M. *Ligand Reactivity and Catalysis*. Academic, New York, 1968.

Martell, A. E. and Khan, T. *Homogeneous Catalysis by Metal Complexes*. Academic, New York, 1973.

Two symposia, the proceedings of which have been published, are related to the topic of this chapter:

Reactions of Coordinated Ligands, Advances in Chemistry, Series 37. American Chemical Society, Washington, D.C., 1963.

Bioinorganic Chemistry, Advances in Chemistry, Series 100. American Chemical Society, Washington, D.C., 1971.

NOTE. See also those indicated in Chap. 4.

PROBLEMS

1. Suggest the origin of the rate law (6.6) for amidolysis of the coordinated ester that contains a second-order dependence on $[OH^-]$ (Ref. 10).

2. The alternative to a five-coordinated intermediate formed in the Hg^{2+} removal of chloride from **1** Eq. (6.21),

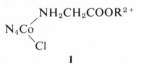

1

is a synergic process in which the ester is partly bonded in the transition state, **2**

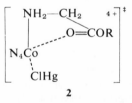

2

What are your views of the likelihood of this, bearing in mind that the second-order rate constant for the Hg^{2+} reaction is $1.0 \times 10^{-2} \, M^{-1} \, sec^{-1}$ at 25°? [D. A. Buckingham, D. M. Foster, L. G. Marzilli, and A. M. Sargeson, *Inorg. Chem.*, **9**, 11 (1970).]

3. The rate constant for ionization of aqua species can be easily estimated from a knowledge of the pK of the coordinated water. It can then be verified whether H exchange between the complex species and water is controlled by this ionization or by dissociation of water from the complex. Calculate which path is responsible for the H exchange of VO_{aq}^{2+} ($k_1 = 7.7 \times 10^3 \, sec^{-1}$) and Ni_{aq}^{2+} ($k_1 = 3 \times 10^4 \, sec^{-1}$) with H_2O, determined by nmr line-broadening techniques.

4. The ligand $CH_2(CONHCH_2CH_2NH_2)_2$, LH_2, reacts with Ni(II) salts in alkaline solution to give a yellow solution from which a yellow diamagnetic solid NiL can be obtained. The proton nmr spectrum of NiL in D_2O was measured. All observed resonances are shifted slightly to high field

on complex formation. The shifts in NiL relative to LH_2 are $+0.32$ (triplet), $+0.42$ (triplet), and $+0.24$ (singlet). If the D_2O solution is made alkaline, the singlet disappears and the other resonances are unaffected. Interpret fully these findings. [H. A. O. Hill and K. A. Raspin, *J. Chem. Soc.*, A, 3036 (1968).]

5. Give plausible explanations for the following:

   a. The hydrolysis of **1** when $R = C_2H_5$ is 10^4 faster than when $R = C(CH_3)_3$. Both give the chelated glycine

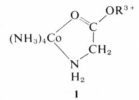

1

[Y. Wu and D. H. Busch, *J. Amer. Chem. Soc.*, **92**, 3326 (1970).]

   b. $Co(NH_3)_5H_2O^{3+}$ enhances the decomposition of urea, and the result is the formation of $Co(NH_3)_5NCO^{2+}$ and NH_3. No cyanate complex results, however, from using $[(CH_3)_2N]_2C{=}O$ with the cobalt(III) complex. [R. J. Balahura and R. B. Jordan, *Inorg. Chem.*, **9**, 1567 (1970).]

   c. The effect of acid on the hydrolysis of $Co(NH_3)_5C_2O_4^+$ is very small even although the coordinated oxalate is basic. [C. Andrade and H. Taube, *Inorg. Chem.*, **5**, 1087 (1966).]

   d. The acid-base reaction

$$Co(CN)_5H^{3-} + OH^- \rightarrow Co(CN)_5^{4-} + H_2O$$

has a very low rate constant ($0.1\ M^{-1}\ sec^{-1}$ at $20°$). [G. D. Venerable II and J. Halpern, *J. Amer. Chem. Soc.*, **93**, 2176 (1971).]

   e. Metal ion catalyzes the reversible tautomerization of the enol form of acetylacetone, while proton does not. [J. E. Meany, *J. Phys. Chem.*, **73**, 3421 (1969).]

6. The oxidation of $Co(NH_3)_5C_2O_4^+$ by Ce(IV) leads to Co(II) ion:

$$Co(NH_3)_5C_2O_4^+ + Ce^{IV} + 5H^+ \rightarrow Ce^{III} + 5NH_4^+ + Co^{2+} + 2CO_2$$

whereas oxidation by Cl_2 preserves Co(III) as a complex:

$$Co(NH_3)_5C_2O_4^+ + Cl_2 \rightarrow Co(NH_3)_5H_2O^{3+} + 2Cl^- + 2CO_2$$

Explain this behavior. [P. Saffir and H. Taube, *J. Amer. Chem. Soc.*, **82**, 13 (1960).]

Chapter 7

Stereochemical Change

If two or more substances have the same empirical formula but a different arrangement of atoms in the molecule, they are said to be isomeric. The types of isomerism and isomeric change with which we are concerned in this chapter are contained in Table 7.1.

The ability of certain metal complexes to exist in stereoisomeric forms, and particularly to interconvert, adds another dimension to the study of the mechanisms of their reactions. There are two aspects from which the phenomenon of stereochemical change may be regarded.

TABLE 7.1 Classifications of Isomerism

Type of isomerism	Basis of isomerism	Example of associated isomeric change
Conformational	Different dispositions of ligand around central atom.	$k \rightleftharpoons k'$ (see Fig. 7.1)
Configurational	Different stereochemistries of central atom.	Tetrahedral $\rightleftharpoons$ planar
Linkage	Different donor centers in identical ligand.	$M—ONO \rightleftharpoons M—NO_2$
Geometrical	Different spatial distribution of atoms or groups around central atom.	*Cis* $\rightleftharpoons$ *trans* in square planar and octahedral complexes
Optical	Nonsuperimposable mirror images.	D $\rightleftharpoons$ L in tetrahedral and octahedral complexes

1. The examination of the stereochemical course of a reaction may allow some reasonable deductions about the mechanism of the reaction and the structure of any activated complexes or intermediates. Such information has already been used in the preceding chapters of this book. The application has been almost exclusively to inert complexes because of the difficulty in preparing isomeric forms of labile complexes, a hurdle that the use of nmr detection and monitoring of systems in situ is eliminating.[1,2]

2. The study of the isomerism per se. Rearrangement may occur via intermolecular substitutive processes or, what appears to be more often the case, via intramolecular mechanisms. The latter is a process we have hitherto not much encountered, but the mobility of unidentate and bidentate ligands in rotation or twisting around the metal-ligand bond sometimes allows for easier paths for isomerization than complete ligand breakage.

7.1 CONFORMATIONAL CHANGE

Five- and six-membered rings formed by coordination of diamines with a metal ion have the stereochemical characteristics of cyclopentane and cyclohexane. The ethylenediamine complexes have a puckered ring and the trimethylenediamine complexes have a chair configuration.[1] The methylene protons are nonequivalent in these nonplanar conformations, taking on the character of equatorial and axial substituents. They are made equivalent as the result of *rapid* conformational inversion at room temperature, just as in the alicyclic compounds (Fig. 7.1). This has been observed in nmr studies of planar[3] and octahedral[4] complexes of ethylenediamine-type ligands with a number of metals. No quantitative rate data are yet available.

FIGURE 7.1 The two conformations of the five-membered puckered ring in metal complexes of ethylenediamine and derivatives. Rings are viewed along the plane containing the two nitrogens and the metal.

7.2   CONFIGURATIONAL ISOMERISM

Configurational isomerism arises with complexes that are identical in all respects except for the stereochemistry of the central atom. The thermodynamic aspects, particularly of the tetrahedral, planar interconversions of nickel(II) complexes, have been much more explored than the dynamic features.

7.2.1   Tetrahedral, Planar

A series of Ni(II) chelates of the type **1**

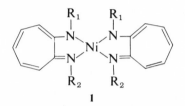

1

exhibit configurational isomerism in noncoordinating solvents, existing as a tetrahedral (paramagnetic), planar (diamagnetic) equilibrium mixture.[5] Nuclear magnetic resonance measurements demonstrate that the equilibrium at ambient temperatures is established within 10^{-4} sec.[5,6] Recently, activation parameters for the process

$$Ni(RR'R''P)_2X_2 \rightleftharpoons Ni(RR'R''P)_2X_2 \qquad (7.1)$$
$$\text{(Tetrahedral)} \qquad \text{(Square-planar)}$$

in $CDCl_3$ and CD_2Cl_2 have been obtained by two groups. First-order interconversion rate constants are commonly 10^5 to 10^6 sec^{-1} at 25° with $\Delta H \sim 10$.[7,8] Interestingly, added free phosphine speeds up the isomerization[8] just as it does the *cis* $\rightleftharpoons$ *trans* interconversion of square-planar Pt(II)-phosphine complexes (Sec. 7.5) and presumably for a similar reason, namely, because of the formation of a labile five-coordinate intermediate that can break up to either stereoisomer.

7.2.2   Planar, Octahedral

This, and the following rearrangement, are not strictly isomerizations, although they possess some of their features. The rate of the very rapid interconversion

$$Ni(2,3,2\text{-tet})(H_2O)_2{}^{2+} \rightleftharpoons Ni(2,3,2\text{-tet})^{2+} + 2H_2O \qquad (7.2)$$
$$\text{(Blue, octahedral)} \qquad \text{(Yellow, square-planar)}$$

has been measured by temperature jump[9] as well as a relaxation method in which the concentration of the planar species is enhanced by a 30-nanosecond pulse of 1.06-μm radiation from a neodymium laser. The return to the normal concentration, after the pulse, is monitored spectrally (Fig. 7.2).[10] A mechanism similar to that for the tetrahedral-octahedral conversion for some Co(II) complexes (next section) is suggested (L = 2,3,2-tet):

$$NiL(H_2O)_2^{2+} \rightleftharpoons NiL(H_2O)^{2+} + H_2O \quad k_1, k_{-1} \quad fast \quad (7.3)$$

$$NiL(H_2O)^{2+} \rightleftharpoons NiL^{2+} + H_2O \quad\quad k_2, k_{-2} \quad\quad (7.4)$$

From the one relaxation time, a value for k_{-2} of $5.6 \times 10^4\ M^{-1}\ sec^{-1}$ is calculated, assuming $[H_2O] = 55\ M$.[10]

7.2.3   Tetrahedral, Octahedral

Equilibria between tetrahedral and octahedral cobalt(II) complexes in nonaqueous solution is well characterized. Some kinetic studies by T jump have been described for the equilibrium

$$Copy_4X_2 \rightleftharpoons Copy_2X_2 + 2py \quad\quad (7.5)$$

in nitromethane-pyridine and pyridine solutions (X = Cl and Br). The data were interpreted in terms of the mechanism

$$Copy_4X_2 \xrightleftharpoons{rapid} Copy_3X_2 + py \quad k_1, k_{-1}, K_1 \quad (7.6)$$

$$Copy_3X_2 \xrightleftharpoons{} Copy_2X_2 + py \quad k_2, k_{-2} \quad\quad (7.7)$$

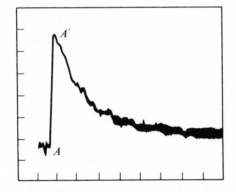

FIGURE 7.2   Relaxation of equilibrium (7.2) after radiation perturbation. The relaxation of 0.1 M Ni(2,3,2-tet)$^{2+}$ is monitored at 440 nm at 23°. Time scale = 0.2 μsec/division. Vertical scale = 1% absorbance change/division. Initial absorbance $A = 0.41$.[10]

TABLE 7.2.   Rate Parameters for k_{-2} Step at 25° and $I = 0.1\ M$[11]

Solvent	Halide	$10^{-4} \times k_{-2}$ $M^{-1}\ sec^{-1}$	$\Delta H^{\ddagger}$	$\Delta S^{\ddagger}$
Pyridine	Chloride	0.31	2.6 ± 1.0	-34 ± 4
Pyridine	Bromide	0.29	2.4 ± 0.8	-35 ± 4
Nitromethane–Pyridine	Chloride	7.2	5.4 ± 0.8	-18 ± 3
Nitromethane–Pyridine	Bromide	4.1	6.8 ± 0.6	-15 ± 3

Values for $K_1 k_2$ and k_{-2} and the associated kinetic parameters were obtained (Table 7.2).[11]

7.3   LINKAGE ISOMERISM

There are a number of unidentate ligands that can coordinate from only one donor center but that contain more than one donor site. Much interest has existed in this area in the last decade, and linkage isomerism has been established for the following pairs, M–ONO and M–NO$_2$; M–NCS and M–SCN; M–NCSe and M–SeCN; M–NCO and M–OCN; and M–CN and M–NC.[12,13]

One important approach to preparing linkage isomers uses the inner-sphere redox concept, in addition to the fact that a ligand capable of forming linkage isomers is usually a good bridging group.

For example, reaction of cyanopentamminecobalt(III) ion with pentacyanocobalt(II) ion produces an intermediate containing the Co(III)–NC bond, which rapidly rearranges to the stable Co(III)–CN form.[14]

$$(NH_3)_5Co\!-\!CN^{2+} + Co(CN)_5^{3-} \rightarrow [(NH_3)_5Co\!-\!CN\!-\!Co(CN)_5]^{-} \quad \textbf{(7.8)}$$

$$\downarrow$$

$$(NH_3)_5Co^{2+} + CNCo(CN)_5^{3-}$$

$$CNCo(CN)_5^{3-} \rightarrow Co(CN)_6^{3-} \quad \textbf{(7.9)}$$

Similarly, the reaction of Cr^{2+} with $FeNCS^{2+}$ produces green $CrSCN^{2+}$, which slowly rearranges to the purple species $CrNCS^{2+}$.[15] In both cases, the linkage isomer can be detected as a spectral intermediate.

7.3.1   Rearrangement Studies

Only the kinetics of rearrangement of nitrito and thiocyanate complexes have been reported, and these show that linkage isomerization is usually an intramolecular process. This has been established as follows. The isomerization of the nitrito complexes $M(NH_3)_5ONO^{n+}$ to the corresponding nitro compounds $M(NH_3)_5NO_2^{n+}$, M = Co(III), Rh(III), Ir(III), Pt(IV), is complete in solution, and the rearrangement first-order rate constants are quite similar for all these complexes (Table 7.3).[16] This strongly suggests that M–O bond cleavage does not occur during the isomerization; else this similarity would surely not exist. An intramolecular mechanism is established for the Co(III) complex from ^{18}O tracer studies.[17] A suggested rearrangement mechanism is[17]

$$(NH_3)_5Co-ONO^{2+} \rightarrow \left[(NH_3)_5Co \overset{O^{2+}}{\underset{N-O}{\diagdown\big|}} \right]^{\ddagger} \rightarrow (NH_3)_5Co-NO_2^{2+} \tag{7.10}$$

An intramolecular mechanism for the linkage isomerization of $CrSCN^{2+}$,[18] $Cr(SCN)(NCS)^+$,[19] and $Co(NH_3)_5SCN^{2+}$ [20] is indicated by the fact that rearrangement occurs concomitant with aquation of the S-bonded thiocyanate group, and is confirmed in one case[18] by the fact that no exchange with $N^{14}CS^-$ occurs during the rearrangement. Since the linear thiocyanate ion is less flexible than the NO_2 group, that it will distort to an angular arrangement of the type shown in (7.10) as a means of rearranging is unlikely. A mechanism in which the thiocyanate rotates, perhaps within an outer-sphere complex,

$$\begin{array}{ccc} & & N \\ & & | \\ Co-S & \rightarrow Co-C \rightarrow Co-NCS \\ \diagdown & & | \\ C & & S \\ \diagdown & & \\ N & & \end{array} \tag{7.11}$$

is suggested.[18-20] This resembles the intramolecular mechanism proposed for the novel rearrangement via the activated complex **2** (Sec. 2.2.3),[21]

$$(NH_3)_5Ru^{15}NN^{2+} \rightleftharpoons \left[(NH_3)_5Ru \cdots \overset{^{15}N^{2+}}{\underset{N}{|||}} \right]^{\ddagger} \rightleftharpoons (NH_3)_5RuN^{15}N^{2+} \tag{7.12}$$

2

An intermolecular mechanism has been substantiated only for the rearrangement of $Pd(Et_4dien)SCN^+$, the rate parameters for which are identical with those for replacement of thiocyanate by bromide ion (Table 7.3). Since the substitution rate is independent of entering ligand concentration (as would be expected of a pseudo-octahedral complex (Sec. 4.12)), the mechanism is dissociative. Such a dissociative mechanism therefore is also indicated for the rearrangement.[22] It is believed that the isomerization of the corresponding selenocyanate complex in DMF takes place in a similar fashion (Table 7.3).[23]

TABLE 7.3. Rate Parameters for Some Linkage Isomerizations and Related Substitutions in Solution at 25°

Reaction	$10^5 \times k$ sec^{-1}	$\Delta H^\ddagger$	$\Delta S^\ddagger$	Ref.
M(NH$_3$)$_5$ONO^{n+} $\rightarrow$ M(NH$_3$)$_5$NO$_2^{n+}$				
M = Co^{III}	3.4	22	$-$ 5	16
M = Rh^{III}	96	18	-12	
M = Ir^{III}	4.4	19	-14	
M = Pt^{IV}	5.6	...	...	
Pd(Et$_4$dien)SCN$^+$ $\rightarrow$ Pd(Et$_4$dien)NCS$^+$	105[a]	17.3	-17	22
Pd(Et$_4$dien)SCN$^+$ + Br$^-$ $\rightarrow$ Pd(Et$_4$dien)Br$^+$ + SCN$^-$	108[a]	17.3	-17	22
Pd(Et$_4$dien)SeCN$^+$ $\rightarrow$ Pd(Et$_4$dien)NCSe$^+$	32[b]	...	...	23
Pd(Et$_4$dien)SeCN$^+$ + Br$^-$ $\rightarrow$ Pd(Et$_4$dien)Br$^+$ + SeCN	34[b,c]	...	...	23

[a] 35 °C.
[b] 30 °C in DMF.
[c] k_1 term in a two-term rate law.

7.4 GEOMETRICAL AND OPTICAL ISOMERISM IN OCTAHEDRAL COMPLEXES

Octahedral complexes containing two or three bidentate ligands can exist in geometrical and optical isomeric forms (Figs. 7.3 and 7.4). Geometrical isomerization and racemization are obviously interrelated and it will therefore be sensible not to separate their discussion. Indeed, examination of *both* processes for specific complexes can be more revealing than their separate characterization alone.[24]

7.4.1 Complexes of Type $M(AA)_2X_2$ and $M(AA)_2XY$

Usually the rates of racemization and isomerization of complexes of the type $M(AA)_2X_2$ and $M(AA)_2XY$ are similar to the rate of aquation. This means that rearrangement is often accompanied by a net chemical reaction, aquation.

For a number of optically active ions of the type *cis*-$M(AA)_2XY^+$, where $M = Co$ and Cr, there is an initial optical rotation change (mutarotation) that is similar in rate to that of acid hydrolysis, for example,

$$cis\text{-}d\text{-}M(AA)_2XY^+ + H_2O \rightarrow cis\text{-}d\text{-}M(AA)_2(H_2O)X^{2+} + Y^- \quad (7.13)$$

The resultant aqua ion then racemizes to a zero rotation more slowly and *without* loss of X^-. In many respects then, the aqua ion is the most suitable one to examine for the relationship of isomerization, racemization, and substitution (using water exchange).[25]

Comparison of $k_{cis \rightarrow trans}$ and k_{rac} in Table 7.4[25] shows that for $X = Cl$, SCN, and H_2O, racemization must arise predominantly because of the *cis* → *trans* conversion, rather than through the operation of a

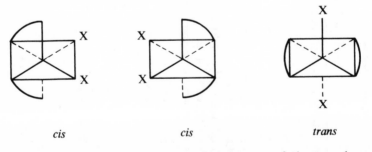

cis   cis   trans

FIGURE 7.3 Optical and geometrical isomers of the complex $M(AA)_2X_2$. The bidentate ligand is represented as a curved line joining adjacent positions of the octahedron. The metal M is at the center.

(a) Λ-configuration

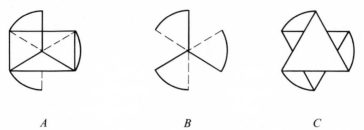

A   B   C

(b) Δ-configuration

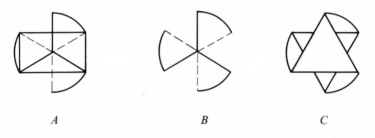

A   B   C

FIGURE 7.4   Equivalent representations of the complex $M(AA)_3$.
The usual octahedral representation is shown in *A*.   In *B*, viewing
is down the C_3 axis; three metal-ligand bonds point towards the
viewer, and three point away.   In *C*, the opposite faces of the
octahedron are shown when viewing is down the C_3 axis.   Representation *B* will be used to illustrate configurational changes.

In (a) the Λ configuration is shown and in (b) the mirror-
image, Δ configuration, is represented.   The designations Λ and
Δ were previously termed *d* and *l*, or D and L forms (not necessarily
respectively).

distinct, *2-d-cis* → *d-cis* + *1-cis* process.   This does not occur however
with X = NH_3.

These rearrangements (the sum of *k*'s in the first two columns) can
also be compared with H_2O exchange k_{exch} in a number of cases.   For
X = OH, H_2O, and SCN (and most likely Cl, Br, and N_3 also),[25] water
exchange is accompanied by considerable steric change.   For X = NH_3
and NO_2, the rate of water exchange exceeds the rate of isomerization,
which is therefore probably intramolecular.[26]

In methanol and other solvents, rearrangements may occur without
net chemical changes, although solvolysis may be an important path.   In
such solvents, the ion *1-cis*-$Coen_2Cl_2^+$ loses its optical activity about nine

TABLE 7.4. Rate Constants (k, sec^{-1}) for the Isomerization, Racemization, and Water Exchange of Complexes of the Type $Coen_2(H_2O)X^{n+}$ at 25°

X	$10^5 \times k$ ($cis \rightarrow trans$)	$10^5 \times k$ ($trans \rightarrow cis$)	$10^5 \times k$ (rac)	$10^5 \times k$ (exch)
OH	200	300	...	160
Br	5.4	16.1	...	...
Cl	2.4	7.2	2.4	...
N_3	2.5	7.4	...	...
NCS	0.014	0.071	0.022	0.13
H_2O	0.012	0.68	~0.015	1.0
NH_3	<0.0001	0.002	0.003	0.10
NO_2	0.012	0.005	...	...

SOURCE: Refs. 25 and 26.

times more slowly than in water, and by *one* first-order process (compared with the reaction in water). The rate is identical with that of substitution by $^*Cl^-$, SCN^-, Br^-, and NO_3^- ions. The loss of optical activity is accompanied by conversion of the *cis* to the *trans* isomer. These reactions are considered to proceed via an optically inactive pentacovalent ion.[27]

$$l\text{-}cis\text{-}Coen_2Cl_2{}^+ \underset{fast}{\overset{slow}{\rightleftharpoons}} Coen_2Cl^{2+} + Cl^-$$

$$trans\text{-}Coen_2Cl_2{}^+ \qquad (d + l)\text{-}cis\text{-}Coen_2Cl_2{}^+$$

(with branch lines labeled "Cl⁻, fast" and "slow") (7.14)

In contrast the *cis*, *trans* rearrangement of $Co(diarsine)_2Cl_2{}^+$ goes in acidic MeOH *without* Cl^- ionization,[28] a fact that emphasizes the problems that confront a successful general explanation of the diverse behavior of these ions.

7.4.2   Complexes of Type M(AA)₃

The two optical forms designated Λ and Δ are shown in Fig. 7.4. Since the bidentate ligand is symmetrical, geometrical isomerism cannot arise. Stereochemical rearrangement of the two isomers can occur by inter-molecular and intramolecular mechanisms. These take the following form:

(a)   Complete dissociation of one ligand,

$$M(AA)_3 \rightleftharpoons M(AA)_2 + AA \qquad (7.15)$$

This mechanism is supported by identical dissociation and· racemization rate constants. This further implies either that the *bis* species is racemic as formed, or that it may racemize (by a *cis-trans* change, or by a dissociative or intramolecular path) more rapidly then it re-forms *tris* in the dynamic equilibrium (7.15). The $Niphen_3{}^{2+}$ and $Nibipy_3{}^{2+}$ ions racemize by such an intermolecular mechanism in a variety of solvents (Table 7.5).[29] These and the $Ni(phen)_2bipy^{2+}$ ion[30] are the only clear examples of this behavior, although $Nien_3{}^{2+}$ may also belong in this category. The rate constant for inversion of this labile ion has been measured at 100° by the nmr coalesence of lines method (Sec. 3.6.8(b)).[31] By extrapolation of the value (5×10^3 sec^{-1}) to 25° using an enthalpy of activation 18 kcal mole^{-1} (the value for dissociation of $Nien_3{}^{2+}$), the inversion rate constant ~ 16 sec^{-1} is reasonably close to the value ~ 90 sec^{-1} for the dissociation rate constant k_1 in acid medium:

$$Nien_3 \xrightarrow{2H^+} Nien_2(H_2O)_2{}^{2+} + enH_2{}^{2+} \qquad k_1 \qquad (7.16)$$

TABLE 7.5. Rate Constants (k, sec^{-1}) for Ligand Dissociation and Racemization of Mphen$_3{}^{2+}$ Ion at 45°

M	Solvent	$10^4 \times k_{diss}$	$\Delta H^{\ddagger}$	$10^4 \times k_{rac}$	$\Delta H^{\ddagger}$	Ref.
Ni	H_2O	1.6	25.2	1.5	24.9	29
	EtOH	0.45	...	0.5	...	29
	$C_6H_5NO_2$	0.020	...	0.022	...	29
Fe	H_2O	0.70[c]	31.5	6.7[c]	28	a
Co	H_2O	81[d]	20.0	~20,000[d]	~13	b

[a] F. Basolo, J. C. Hayes, and H. M. Neumann, *J. Amer. Chem. Soc.*, 76, 3807 (1954).
[b] P. Ellis and R. G. Wilkins, *J. Chem. Soc.*, 299 (1959); E. Blinn and R. G. Wilkins, unpublished results.
[c] 25 °C.
[d] 0 °C.

There are basically two types of intramolecular rearrangements.

(b) Intramolecular twisting without any metal-donor atom bond rupture.[32,33] This mechanism can be considered as arising basically from the twisting of opposite faces of an octahedron through 60 degrees to form a roughly trigonal prismatic state (Fig. 7.5). Further twisting through another 60 degrees leads to inversion. There are two types of transition state depending on the pair of trigonal faces chosen for the rotation operation, that is, depending on the axis about which rotation occurs, the C_3 axis (a) or an "imaginary" C_3 axis (b). The form (a) produces a transition state that has a C_3 or pseudo C_3 axis and is termed a trigonal twist.[34] A "rhomboid (rhombic) twist,"[35] pictured in (b), produces a transition state with no such elements of symmetry. Both twists lead to optical inversion.

(c) Rupture of one metal-ligand bond (one-ended dissociation) to give a five-coordinated intermediate. There are a variety of ways in which this may occur, in some of which optical inversion results (see Fig. 7.8 for unsymmetrical bidentates).

7.4.3 Occurrence of Intramolecular Mechanisms

Although it is usually easy to distinguish between an intermolecular and an intramolecular mechanism, it is quite difficult to assess the relative importance of (b) and (c) in an intramolecular mechanism. Nowhere has this been more evident than in attempts to understand the mechanism of racemization of chelated complexes containing oxalate groups, particularly of the type $M(C_2O_4)_3{}^{3-}$. Racemization is invariably faster than the complete loss by aquation of one oxalate group, so that an intermolecular

Δ   Eclipsed or   Λ
                     trigonal prismatic state

(a) Trigonal or Bailar twist

Δ   Λ

(b) Rhomboid or **Ray-Dutt** twist

FIGURE 7.5   (a) The trigonal, or Bailar, twist, in which opposite
faces of the octahedron are twisted around a C_3 axis, through an
angle of 60° to form the eclipsed transition state.   Further twisting
of 60° leads to an inverted configuration.   (b) The rhomboid, or
Ray-Dutt, twist.   Opposite faces of an octahedron are twisted
but about a pseudo C_3 axis.   There are eight C_3 axes (normal to
the eight trigonal faces of the octahedron).   When three bidentate
ligands span the octahedron, there are then only two C_3 axes and
six pseudo, or "imaginary," C_3 axes.   Rotation around one of
the two C_3 axes constitutes trigonal twist.   Rotation around one
of the six pseudo axes constitutes a rhomboid twist.   It can be
seen from Fig. 7.5 that viewed down the C_3 axis, one corner of the
face is always joined by the ligand to a corner of the *other* face.
Viewed down the "imaginary" axis (Fig. 7.5b), only one (of the
three) corners is seen joined from one face to the other.

mechanism can be ruled out.[36-38]   With these complexes, we have an
additional probe that should in principle help us to distinguish between
(b) and (c).   This is the examination of the exchange of ^{18}O between H_2O

TABLE 7.6. Rate Parameters for Acid-Catalyzed Oxygen Exchange, and Racemization of Oxalate Complexes at 56°

Complex	$10^5 \times k_{exch}$[a]	$\Delta H^{\ddagger}_{exch}$	$10^5 \times k_{rac}$[a]	$\Delta H^{\ddagger}_{rac}$	Ref.
$Rh(C_2O_4)_3{}^{3-}$					
Outer O	148	16.9			38
Inner O at 56°	8.4	23.6			38
Rac. at 56°			4.2	23.3	38
$Cr(C_2O_4)_2phen^-$	82[b]	17.8	64[b]	17.8	39
$Cr(C_2O_4)phen_2{}^+$	27[b]	16.8	49	19.8	40

[a] Value of k in $k[H^+]$ term of rate law.
[b] Value of k, sec^{-1}, in 1 M HCl at 25°.

and the oxygens of the coordinated oxalate (Sec. 1.9). Exchange of the outer oxygens of $Rh(C_2O_4)_3{}^{3-}$ (Table 7.6) and $Co(C_2O_4)_3{}^{3-}$ is much faster than racemization. Rate constants for inner-oxygen exchange and racemization are similar, suggesting a common intermediate for both processes involving one-ended dissociation (Table 7.6). (See also Sec. 8.9.3.)

Racemization and oxygen exchange of $Cr(C_2O_4)_2bipy^-$ and $Cr(C_2O_4)_2phen^-$ also have similar rate parameters in 1 M HCl,[39] but their associated rate/pH profile[38,40] and the catalytic effects of cations[39] are quite different in the two reactions. To complicate matters further, there is a possible interchange mechanism (rotation around the C–C bond) that promotes interchange of carboxyl and carbonyl oxygen atoms but is ineffective in causing racemization (Fig. 7.6).[39] Mechanism (c) *may* be operative with these complexes but the details are unclear and it appears that a purely twist mechanism is gaining favor.

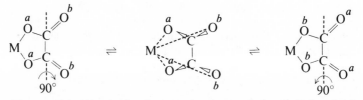

FIGURE 7.6 Intramolecular rotation around the C–C bond of the $C_2O_4{}^{2-}$ ligand, leading to exchange of all the oxygens with solvent water.[39]

One type of complex in which one-ended dissociation is not easily envisaged, because of the rigidity of the phenanthroline ligand, is $M(phen)_3^{n+}$. The rapid racemization of $Fephen_3^{2+}$ and $Cophen_3^{2+}$ compared with ligand dissociation (Table 7.5) strongly suggests that here a purely twist mechanism is operative.

7.4.4   Complexes of the Type $M(AA')_3$

One valuable, although not easy, approach for distinguishing the various types of intramolecular change is by using chelates of the kind $M(AA')_3$, where AA' represents an unsymmetrical bidentate ligand.[33] Geometrical[41] as well as optical isomers now exist (see Fig. 7.7), so that there are a number of isomeric changes that can be studied. Different results dependent on the modes of intramolecular rearrangement can be expected. This idea is illustrated by considering the likely consequences when the *cis*-Δ form rearranges by any of five distinct routes (a) to (e).[42] Figure 7.8 shows the

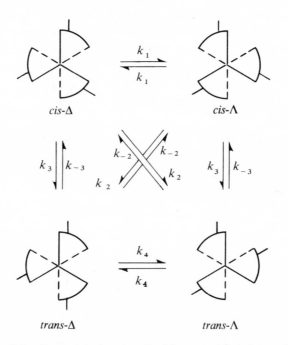

cis-Δ   *cis*-Λ

trans-Δ   *trans*-Λ

FIGURE 7.7   Geometrical and optical isomers of chelates of the type $M(AA')_3$ and their interrelationships. The ligand AA' is represented by ⫰ .

Mechanism				$(k_1 + k_2)/(k_2 + k_3)$	k_1/k_2	k_3/k_2
(a) Trigonal twist				∞	∞	0/0
(b) Rhombic twist				1	0	0
(c) Axial *TBI*				1	0	0
(d) Equatorial *TBI*				0	0/0	∞
(e) *SPI*				1	1	1
Experimentally observed ratios.				1.2 ± 0.2	0.24 ± 0.12	0.01 ± 0.2

product(s) and the ratio of rate constants that would result for the various changes. The twist mechanism (a) leads to inversion without isomerization. The rhombic mechanism (b) leads to inversion and isomerization. Bond rupture via a trigonal-bipyramidal intermediate (TBI) with the dangling ligand in an axial (c) or equatorial position (d) causes isomerization with or without inversion, respectively. Rearrangement via a square pyramidal intermediate (SPI), with the energetically most likely structure shown (e), leads to equivalent amounts of all forms.

The observed ratios of rate constants for the rearrangement of *cis*-Δ-Co(bzac)$_3$ (Fig. 7.8) [42]

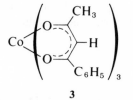

3

immediately rules out mechanisms (a), (d), and (e) as *primary paths*. The very similar activation parameters for isomerization and inversion of *cis*- and *trans*-Co(bzac)$_3$ support a common mechanism for the two processes. This cannot be a completely dissociative one since ligand breakage is some 300 times slower than rearrangement at 96°. This leaves, as the favored paths, either a twisting mechanism with 80% rhombic (b) and 20% trigonal (a) character in the activated complex, or a bond-rupture mechanism with 80% axial TBI (c) and 20% SPI (e) contributions. The bond rupture is favored by a high $\Delta H^{\ddagger}$ value (33 kcal mole^{-1} compared with 48 for complete rupture of one bzac ligand). A $\Delta S^{\ddagger}$ value (~ 10 eu) for the rearrangement similar to the $\Delta S^{\ddagger}$ value for inversion of Co(triac)$_3$ is also supportive evidence. Inversion must occur at least partly by Co–O bond rupture because inversion is accompanied by linkage isomerism, the latter ingeniously shown by using the deuterated complex: [42]

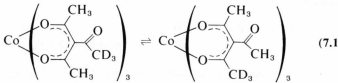

(7.17)

Linkage isomerization cannot occur by a twisting mechanism.

◄   FIGURE 7.8   Ratios of rate constants (see Fig. 7.7) anticipated for various intramolecular mechanisms, and values found experimentally for rearrangement of *cis*-Δ-Co(bzac)$_3$ in C$_6$H$_5$Cl at 96° (Ref. 42).

This general approach in even greater detail has been independently applied to a study of the rearrangment of Co(mhd)$_3$:

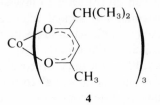

4

with a similar conclusion, that is, that a bond-rupture mechanism is favored with a large percentage of an axial trigonal-bipyramidal intermediate.[43] The two papers should be consulted, and also Refs. 44 and 45, for full details.

7.5 GEOMETRICAL ISOMERIZATION IN PLANAR COMPLEXES

Chatt and Wilkins studied thoroughly the factors that influence the position of equilibrium in the *cis-trans* isomerization of a number of platinum(II) complexes of the type Pt(R$_3$X)$_2$Y$_2$, X = P, As, Sb; Y = halides, in benzene solution:

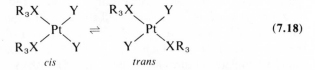

(7.18)

The isomers are separately stable but equilibrate on the addition of free ligand (R$_3$X or R$_3'$X) to the solution.[46] The mechanism of the catalyzed isomerization has attracted attention.[47,48] A symmetrical five-coordinated species may be formed, and this could pseudo-rotate to scramble the positions:[47,49]

$$cis\text{-Pt(R}_3\text{X)}_2\text{Y}_2 + \text{R}_3\text{X} \rightleftharpoons \text{Pt(R}_3\text{X)}_3\text{Y}_2 \rightleftharpoons$$
$$trans\text{-Pt(R}_3\text{X)}_2\text{Y}_2 + \text{R}_3\text{X} \quad (7.19)$$

Alternatively, an ionic intermediate may arise:[50]

$$cis\text{-Pt(R}_3\text{X)}_2\text{Y}_2 + \text{R}_3\text{X} \rightleftharpoons \text{Pt(R}_3\text{X)}_3\text{Y}^+\text{Y}^- \rightleftharpoons$$
$$trans\text{-Pt(R}_3\text{X)}_2\text{Y}_2 + \text{R}_3\text{X} \quad (7.20)$$

Finally, the entering phosphine might occupy a fifth unique position around the platinum and induce rearrangement of the remaining groups. This third mechanism could lead to faster isomerization compared with ligand exchange, in contrast to the other two mechanisms.[47] Although this relation has been claimed in studies of symmetrical and unsymmetrical ligand-catalyzed rearrangements of the type[47]

$$cis\text{-}Pt[(n\text{-}C_4H_9)_3P]_2Cl_2 \xrightarrow[\ (n\text{-}C_4H_9)_3P\ ]{(n\text{-}C_3H_7)_3P\ or} trans\text{-}Pt[(n\text{-}C_4H_3)_3P]_2Cl_2 \qquad (7.21)$$

the conclusions have been challenged.[48] Thus the results of an extensive nmr study of catalyzed exchange and isomerization

$$cis\text{-}Pt(Me_2RP)_2X_2 \rightleftharpoons trans\text{-}Pt(Me_2RP)_2X_2 \qquad (7.22)$$

($R = C_6H_5$ or $o\text{-}CH_3C_6H_4$; $X = Cl, I$) are fully consistent with the ionic intermediate mechanism (7.20). Similar conclusions have been reached about the analogous Pd complexes ($R = o\text{-}CH_3C_6H_4$),[48] and from a study of the $cis \rightarrow trans$ rearrangement of complexes of the type $Pd(amine)_2X_2$ in the presence of free amine.[51(a)]

The spontaneous isomerization of $cis\text{-}Pt(PEt_3)_2(o\text{-}tolyl)Cl$ in CH_3OH and C_2H_5OH is much slower than nucleophilic replacement (by I^- and CN^-), which typically is stereoretentive. An (unusual) dissociative mechanism is favored for the isomerization. Two labile three-coordinated intermediates are suggested, one "cis-like" and the other "$trans$-like" in structure. This route plays a neglible role in the replacement reaction.[51(b)]

7.6   RACERIZATION OF TETRAHEDRAL COMPLEXES

The preparation, and even more the resolution, of an asymmetric tetrahedral center have been thwarted by the configurational instability of tetrahedral complexes. There have been one or two reported studies of the kinetics of racemization of tetrahedral organometallic complexes containing four different unidentate groups attached to a metal center. These contain ligands of the strongly σ, π bonding type and this imposed stability has led to the resolution of some of them, for example, $Mn(CO)(NO)(cpd)PPh_3$.[52] The enantiomeric forms are configurationally stable and do not racemize in tetrahydrofuran solution for several weeks, *even* in the presence of excess Ph_3P (compare the geometrical configurational lability of planar complexes in the same conditions). The optical forms of $Mn(COOCH_3)(NO)(cpd)PPh_3$ do racemize in benzene solution. The high values for the activation parameters for racemization, $\Delta H^{\ddagger} = 30.6$ and $\Delta S^{\ddagger} = 22$, suggest a dissociative mechanism[52] and exchange studies with PPh_3 confirm it. The stereoisomerism has been detected by nmr in certain cases, and the appearance of the signals give an indication of the rapidity of the $\Lambda \rightleftharpoons \Delta$ interconversion.

Nuclear magnetic resonance has also been used to detect enantiomers in chelates of the type $M(AB)_2$.[2] Aside from the ease of dissociation of the ligands, the known labile tetrahedral $\rightleftharpoons$ planar equilibrium (Sec. 7.2) also constitutes a path for racemization (viewed down C_2 axis):[53]

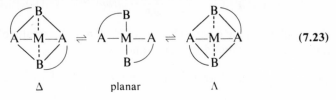

$$(7.23)$$

$$\Delta \qquad \text{planar} \qquad \Lambda$$

7.7 INVERSION AND PROTON EXCHANGE AT ASYMMETRIC NITROGEN CENTERS IN METAL COMPLEXES

Coordination of ammonia or a substituted ammonia to a metal ion alters markedly the N–H dissociation rate (see Sec. 6.5.2). Since also proton dissociation of complexed ammines is base-catalyzed, then exchange can be made quite slow in an acid medium. Thus, in a coordinated system of the type **5**, containing an asymmetric nitrogen atom,

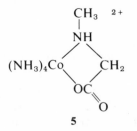

5

there is every chance for a successful resolution in acid conditions, since inversion is expected *only* after deprotonation. It was not unit 1966 that this was successfully performed, however, using the complex ion **5**.[54] A number of Co(III),[55] Pt(II),[56] and Pt(IV)[57] complexes containing secondary amines have been resolved and their racemization studied. The inversion at the N center (as well as the H exchange) can also be determined in situ by nmr line broadening without the necessity of resolution. This has been reported for Pd(II)[58] and Pt(II)[59,60] complexes. The observation of asymmetric nitrogen centers have so far been confined to d^6 octahedral and d^8 planar complexes.

The rates of racemization R and proton exchange E[61] are both first-order in $[OH^-]$[62]

$$V_R(V_E) = k_R(k_E)[\text{complex}][OH^-] \qquad (7.24)$$

TABLE 7.7. Rate Parameters (k_E, k_R, sec^{-1}) for Secondary N–H Hydrogen Exchange and Racemization

Complex	Temp.	$k_E{}^d$	$\Delta H^\ddagger$	$\Delta S^\ddagger$	k_R	$\Delta H^\ddagger$	$\Delta S^\ddagger$	Ref.
Co(meen)(NH$_3$)$_4{}^{3+}$	34.3	3.0×10^7	13.8	21	2.5×10^2	24.3	31	[a]
trans-Codien$_2{}^{3+}$	35.0	1.0×10^8	13.5	22	2.4×10^2	23.5	29	[64]
Pt(meen)(NH$_3$)$_2{}^{2+b}$	25.0	6.6×10^4	13.7	10	3.2×10^2	19.2	17	[56]
Pt(meen)en^{2+}	34.3	1.9×10^5	...	...	7.9×10^2	...	...	[57]
Pt(meen)enCl$_2{}^{2+}$	34.3	2×10^{10}	...	...	6.5×10^5	...	...	[57]
Pd(dmen)en^{2+c}	27.0	1.0×10^5	...	...	3.6×10^2	...	...	[58]

[a] D. A. Buckingham, L. G. Marzilli, and A. M. Sargeson, *J. Amer. Chem. Soc.*, **89**, 825 (1967).
[b] meen = CH$_3$NH(CH$_2$)$_2$NH$_2$.
[c] dmen = CH$_3$NH(CH$_2$)$_2$NHCH$_3$.
[d] Deuteration rate constant in D$_2$O.

Since $k_E \gg k_R$, however, Table 7.7, loss of a proton must rarely lead to racemization.

The results can be accommodated by a scheme

$$\begin{array}{cc} M & M \\ R_1\!\!-\!\!N:H + OH^- \rightleftharpoons R_1\!\!-\!\!N: + H_2O & \qquad k_1, k_{-1} \qquad (7.25) \\ R_2 & R_2 \\ D & D \end{array}$$

$$\begin{array}{cc} M & M \\ R_1\!\!-\!\!N: \rightleftharpoons :N\!\!-\!\!R_1 & \qquad k_2, k_2 \qquad (7.26) \\ R_2 & R_2 \\ D & L \end{array}$$

Step (7.25) leads to hydrogen exchange, $k_1 = k_E$. Only step (7.26) leads to racemization and is considered pH-independent. Most of the time amide complex becomes reprotonated with configurational retention. If a steady-state concentration for the amide form is assumed,

$$k_R = \frac{2k_1 k_2}{k_{-1} + k_2} = \frac{2k_1 k_2}{k_{-1}} = \frac{2k_2 K_a}{K_w} \qquad (7.27)$$

with K_a, the acid dissociation constant for the N–H proton. The factor 2 enters into (7.27) because the racemization rate constant is twice the inversion rate constant (k_2).

A lower value of k_E/k_R ($=10^2 - 5 \times 10^3$) for Pt(II)[63] and Pd(II)[58] complexes compared with those ($7 \times 10^3 - 3 \times 10^5$) for Co(III) and Pt(IV) may result from increased stabilization of a symmetrical (and racemized) amido intermediate in the former case.[56,58]

The rates of interconversion in *trans*-Codien$_2$$^{3+}$ ion (Fig. 7.9) and hydrogen exchange at the N–H center have both been measured, Table 7.7. The data are very similar to data for Co(NH$_3$)$_4$(N–Meen)$^{3+}$ ion and indicate that the *coupling* of chelate rings across the N–H centers (Fig. 7.9) has little effect on racemization or exchange. It is still uncertain, however, whether nitrogen inversion and the conformational interchange in the puckered five-membered rings (see Fig. 7.1) are synchronous.[64]

The asymmetry at certain nitrogen centers has been cleverly exploited to reveal features of base hydrolysis. The complex Co(trenen)Cl^{2+}

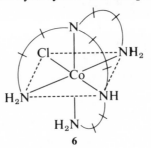

6

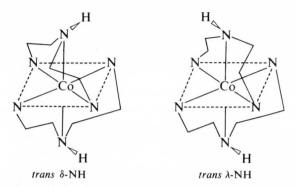

trans δ-NH   trans λ-NH

FIGURE 7.9   Optical isomers of *trans*-Codien$_2^{3+}$ (Ref. 64).   Configurational change must involve N–H dissociation and is accompanied by inversion of conformation in each of the adjacent chelate rings.

represented in **6** contains an asymmetric N *trans* to a chloride group and it has been resolved.   By studying the exchange of this and related complexes with D_2O, one can reasonably conclude that the *trans* NH group exchanges its hydrogen most readily ($\geq 10^5$ times faster than other N–H species present in the molecule).   This is almost certainly, then, the center from which the proton is lost in the conjugate base mechanism for base hydrolysis.   It is found that the (+) chloro to ($\pm$) hydroxo transformation is unimportant in base hydrolysis.   This means that a symmetrical sp^2 configuration for the deprotonated N, which would exist in the double-bonded trigonal-bipyramidal intermediate (**8** Chap. 4), cannot be formed, since this would lead to racemization during base hydrolysis.[65,66]

REFERENCES

1.   C. J. Hawkins, *Absolute Configuration of Metal Complexes* (Wiley-Interscience, New York, 1971), Chap. 1.
2.   L. H. Pignolet and G. N. La Mar, "Dynamics of Intramolecular Rearrangements" in *NMR of Paramagnetic Molecules* (Ed. G. N. Le Mar, W. G. Horrocks, Jr., and R. H. Holm), Academic, New York, 1974, Ch. 8.
3.   T. G. Appleton and J. R. Hall, *Inorg. Chem.*, **9**, 1807 (1970).
4.   J. K. Beattie, *Accounts Chem. Research*, **4**, 253 (1971).
5.   D. R. Eaton, W. D. Phillips, and D. J. Caldwell, *J. Amer. Chem. Soc.*, **85**, 397 (1963).
6.   R. H. Holm, *Accounts Chem. Research*, **2**, 307 (1969).
7.   L. H. Pignolet, W. D. Horrocks, Jr., and R. H. Holm, *J. Amer. Chem. Soc.*, **92**, 1855 (1970).

8. G. N. La Mar and E. O. Sherman, *J. Amer. Chem. Soc.*, **92**, 2691 (1970).
9. C. Creutz, and N. Sutin, *J. Amer. Chem. Soc.*, **95**, 7177 (1973).
10. K. J. Ivin, R. Jamison, and J. J. McGarvey, *J. Amer. Chem. Soc.*, **94**, 1763 (1972).
11. R. D. Farina and J. H. Swinehart, *Inorg. Chem.*, **11**, 645 (1972).
12. J. L. Burmeister, *Coordn. Chem. Revs.*, **3**, 225 (1968).
13. A. H. Norburg and A. I. P. Sinha, *Quart. Rev.*, **24**, 69 (1970).
14. J. Halpern and S. Nakamura, *J. Amer. Chem. Soc.*, **87**, 3002 (1965).
15. A. Haim and N. Sutin, *J. Amer. Chem. Soc.*, **88**, 434 (1966).
16. F. Basolo and G. S. Hannaker, *Inorg. Chem.*, **1**, 1 (1962).
17. R. K. Murmann and H. Taube, *J. Amer. Chem. Soc.*, **78**, 4886 (1956).
18. M. Orhanovic and N. Sutin, *J. Amer. Chem. Soc.*, **90**, 4286 (1968).
19. L. D. Brown and D. P. Pennington, *Inorg. Chem.*, **10**, 2117 (1971).
20. D. A. Buckingham, I. I. Creaser, and A. M. Sargeson, *Inorg. Chem.*, **9**, 655 (1970).
21. J. N. Armor and H. Taube, *J. Amer. Chem. Soc.*, **92**, 2560 (1970).
22. F. Basolo, W. H. Baddley, and K. J. Weidenbaum, *J. Amer. Chem. Soc.*, **88**, 1576 (1966).
23. J. L. Burmeister and J. C. Lim, *Chem. Commun.*, 1154 (1969).
24. R. G. Wilkins and M. J. G. Williams, in *Modern Coordination Chemistry*, ed. J. Lewis and R. G. Wilkins (Interscience, New York, 1960). N. Serpone and D. G. Bickley, in *Inorganic Reaction Mechanisms*, Part 2, p. 391.
25. M. L. Tobe, in *Studies on Chemical Structure and Reactivity*, ed. J. H Ridd (Methuen, London, 1966).
26. M. N. Hughes, *J. Chem. Soc.*, A, 1284 (1967).
27. D. D. Brown and C. K. Ingold, *J. Chem. Soc.*, 2680 (1953).
28. A. Peloso and G. Dolcetti, *J. Chem. Soc.*, A, 1506 (1969).
29. R. G. Wilkins and M. J. G. Williams, *J. Chem. Soc.*, 1763 (1957).
30. J. A. Broomhead and F. P. Dwyer, *Aust. J. Chem.*, **16**, 51 (1963).
31. F. F. L. Ho and C. N. Reilley, *Anal. Chem.*, **42**, 600 (1970).
32. J. E. Brady, *Inorg. Chem.*, **8**, 1208 (1969); C. S. Springer, Jr. and R. E. Sievers, *Inorg. Chem.*, **6**, 852 (1967).
33. J. J. Fortman and R. E. Sievers, *Coordn. Chem. Revs.*, **6**, 331 (1971) is specifically concerned with β-diketone complexes but contains a general account of principles.
34. J. C. Bailey, Jr., *J. Inorg. Nucl. Chem.*, **8**, 165 (1958); W. G. Gehman, Ph.D. thesis, Penn. State, 1954; L. Seiden, Ph.D. thesis, Northwestern, 1957.
35. P. C. Rây and N. K. Dutt, *J. Indian Chem. Soc.*, **20**, 81 (1943).
36. This was demonstrated for $Co(C_2O_4)_3^{3-}$ and $Cr(C_2O_4)_3^{3-}$ in one of the earliest radioisotopic exchange experiments. Exchange of these ions with ^{11}C-labeled $C_2O_4^{2-}$ is very much slower than racemization; F. A. Long, *J. Amer. Chem. Soc.*, **61**, 571 (1939); **63**, 1353 (1941).
37. J. A. Broomhead, I. Lauder, and P. Nimmo, *J. Chem. Soc.*, A, 645 (1971).

38. L. Damrauer and R. M. Milburn, *J. Amer. Chem. Soc.*, **90**, 3884 (1968); **93**, 6481 (1971).

39. J. A. Broomhead, N. Kane-Maguire, and I. Lauder, *Inorg. Chem.*, **9**, 1243 (1970).

40. J. A. Broomhead, N. Kane-Maguire, and I. Lauder, *Inorg. Chem.*, **10**, 955 (1971).

41. The enhanced symmetry of the *cis* compared with the *trans* isomer allows their easy characterization by elegant nmr experiments; R. C. Fay and T. S. Piper, *J. Amer. Chem. Soc.*, **84**, 2303 (1962); **85**, 500 (1963).

42. A. Y. Girgis and R. C. Fay, *J. Amer. Chem. Soc.*, **92**, 7061 (1970).

43. J. G. Gordon and R. H. Holm, *J. Amer. Chem. Soc.*, **92**, 5319 (1970).

44. J. R. Hutchison, J. G. Gordon, II, and R. H. Holm, *Inorg. Chem.*, **10**, 1004 (1971).

45. L. H. Pignolet, D. J. Duffy, and L. Que, Jr., *J. Amer. Chem. Soc.*, **95**, 295 (1973), and references.

46. J. Chatt and R. G. Wilkins, *J. Chem. Soc.*, 525 (1956), and previous papers.

47. P. Haake and R. M. Pfeiffer, *Chem. Commun.*, 1330 (1969); *J. Amer. Chem. Soc.*, **90**, 4272 (1968).

48. D. G. Cooper and J. Powell, *J. Amer. Chem. Soc.*, **95**, 1102 (1973); *Can. J. Chem.*, **51**, 1634 (1973).

49. D. R. Eaton, *J. Amer. Chem. Soc.*, **90**, 4272 (1968).

50. F. Basolo and R. G. Pearson, pp. 423–27.

51. a. L. Cattalini and M. Martelli, *J. Amer. Chem. Soc.*, **91**, 312 (1969).
    b. G. Faraone, V. Ricevuto, R. Romeo, and M. Trozzi, *J. Chem. Soc.*, *A*, 1877 (1971).

52. H. Brunner, *Angew. Chem.*, **10**, 249 (1971); H. Brunner and H. D. Schindler, *Chem. Ber.*, **104**, 2467 (1971); *Zeit. Natur.*, **26b**, 1220 (1971).

53. M. J. O'Connor, R. E. Ernst, and R. H. Holm, *J. Amer. Chem. Soc.*, **90**, 4561 (1968).

54. B. Halpern, A. M. Sargeson, and K. R. Turnball, *J. Amer. Chem. Soc.*, **88**, 4630 (1966).

55. D. A. Buckingham, L. G. Marzilli, and A. M. Sargeson, *Inorg. Chem.*, **7**, 915 (1968), and references.

56. J. B. Goddard and F. Basolo, *Inorg. Chem.*, **8**, 2223 (1969).

57. D. A. Buckingham, L. G. Marzilli, and A. M. Sargeson, *J. Amer. Chem. Soc.*, **91**, 5227 (1969).

58. T. P. Pitner and R. B. Martin, *J. Amer. Chem. Soc.*, **93**, 4400 (1971).

59. P. Haake and P. C. Turley, *J. Amer. Chem. Soc.*, **90**, 2293 (1968).

60. L. E. Erickson, A. J. Dappen, and J. C. Uhlenhopp, *J. Amer. Chem. Soc.*, **91**, 2510 (1969); L. E. Erickson, H. L. Fritz, R. J. May, and D. A Wright, *J. Amer. Chem. Soc.*, **91**, 2513 (1969).

61. The values of k_E from D_2O exchange and from line coalescent methods are in fair agreement. See Ref. 56.

62. There is evidence for an [OH$^-$]-independent term for exchange in acid. See Refs. 56 and 57.

63. L. E. Erickson, *J. Amer. Chem. Soc.*, **91**, 6284 (1969).

64. G. H. Searle and F. R. Keene, *Inorg. Chem.*, **11**, 1006 (1972).

65. D. A. Buckingham, P. A. Marzilli, and A. M. Sargeson, *Inorg. Chem.*, **8**, 1595 (1969).

66. D. A. Buckingham, M. Dwyer, A. M. Sargeson, and K. J. Watson, *Acta Chem. Scand.*, **26**, 2813 (1972).

PROBLEMS

1. Give possible reasons for the following:

a. The preparation of $M(NH_3)_5ONO^{2+}$ isomer from $M(NH_3)_5H_2O^{3+}$ and HNO_2 is successful even though $M(NH_3)_5NO_2^{2+}$ is the stable linkage isomer.[16]

b. Cr^{2+} ion reacts at different rates with $Co(NH_3)_5CN^{2+}$, $Co(NH_3)_4(H_2O)CN^{2+}$, and $Coen_2(H_2O)CN^{2+}$ to give a common intermediate, which changes slowly to a final product [J. P. Birk and J. H. Espenson, *J. Amer. Chem. Soc.*, **90**, 1153 (1968)].

c. ^{13}C nmr of a solution of $Fe(CO)_5$ shows only a *single* ^{13}C frequency even at $-110\,°C$ [R. J. Clark and M. R. Busch, *Accounts Chem. Res.*, **6**, 246 (1973)].

2. The rate of isomerization of *cis*- and *trans*-$Coen_2(H_2O)NO_2^{2+}$ ion is pH-invariant over a wide range of pH. Why is this likely to mean that the rearrangement is intramolecular? Devise a scheme for the intramolecular isomerization [M. N. Hughes, *J. Chem. Soc.*, A, 1284 (1967)].

3. It was not possible to separate the *cis*- and *trans*-isomers of $Co(NH_3)_4(H_2O)N_3^{2+}$ from an equilibrium mixture, prepared in solution by treating $Co(NH_3)_4(N_3)_2^{+}$ with acid. The two isomers are expected to react at different rates with Fe^{2+}. Devise a method for measuring the equilibrium and rate constants for

$$cis \rightleftharpoons trans\text{-}Co(NH_3)_4(H_2O)N_3^{2+}$$

(*Hint*: Use low and and high $[Fe^{2+}]$ read Sec. 2.1.1.) [A. Haim, *J. Amer. Chem. Soc.*, **86**, 2352 (1964).]

Chapter 8

A Survey of the Transition Elements

In this final chapter the salient features of the transition elements are surveyed. This affords an opportunity to assemble some important mechanistic chemistry discussed in the previous chapters, thus furnishing an index. More important, each element is reviewed with key references mainly to recent literature, which gives access to the older literature. References in previous chapters give fuller tables of data.

8.1 VANADIUM

The thermochemistry, oxidation potentials, and chemistry of vanadium (niobium and tantalum) have been surveyed.[1] The aquated vanadium ions,

$$V^{2+}\text{——}V^{3+}\text{——}VO^{2+}\text{——}VO_2{}^+ \qquad (8.1)$$

in acidic aqueous solution represent an interesting series of oxidation states. They are all stable with respect to disproportionation and labile towards substitution. They undergo a number of mutual redox processes ((2.39), (2.155), and (2.156), and Secs. 2.2.1 and 3.6.8(a)), all of which have been studied kinetically.[2] Many of the reactions are [H$^+$]-dependent.[2]

8.1.1 Vanadium(II)

The few data available appear to support substitution in vanadium(II) as controlled by the loss of coordinated water (Table 4.13).[3] The study of

V(II) must be carried out in the absence of O_2, for V(II) reacts with O_2 to give a substantial amount of V(IV).[4]   This must represent a two-electron oxidation step (Sec. 5.12), since V(III) reacts more slowly with O_2 than what could account for the rate of appearance of V(IV).   Towards two-electron oxidants, V(II) can act as either a one-electron or a two-electron reductant in acid solution.   Towards $V(V)^2$, I_2, and Br_2, V(III) is the immediate product of oxidation, whereas two-electron changes occur (in part) with $O_2{}^4$, $H_2O_2{}^4$, Tl(III), and Hg(II) (Sec. 5.12).

The oxidation of V(II) by a number of Co(III) complexes has been studied (Tables 5.2, 5.4, 5.6, 5.7, and 5.8).   Some oxidations are clearly outer-sphere and others inner-sphere (controlled by substitution in V(II)), and several are difficult to assign (Table 5.2).

8.1.2   Vanadium(III)

Table 4.14 contains all the substitution data for the vanadium(III) ion. The unusual rate independence on acidity (Fig. 1.4 and Eq. (1.41)) and the low activation enthalpy for the reaction of V(III) with SCN^- compared with $N_3{}^-$ are evidence for ligand-assisted anation.[5]   The reaction of VOH^{2+} with HN_3 is favored over the reaction between V^{3+} and $N_3{}^-$, for example, because the $\Delta S^{\ddagger}$ value for hydrolysis of $VN_3{}^{2+}$ suggests that it incipiently produces VOH^{2+} and HN_3.[5]   Vanadium(III) reacts with O_2 and $ClO_4{}^-$ and is easily hydrolyzed ($pK_a = 3.0$), all important points in the study of its reaction kinetics.

Since V(III) is not easily reduced, only the reactions with Cr(II) and Eu(II) have been studied.   Inverse $[H^+]$ terms in the rate law can be ascribed to reaction of VOH^{2+}, although this conclusion is not unequivocal (Sec. 2.1.5(b)).

The oxidation of V(III) by Cr(VI) is interesting.   For this reaction, the net activation process is

$$V^{3+} + HCrO_4{}^- = [VHCrO_4{}^{2+}]^{\ddagger} \rightarrow VO^{2+} + H_3CrO_4 \qquad (8.2)$$

and thus in the three-step oxidation by Cr(VI), Eqs. (1.96)–(1.98), the first step is rate-determining.   The second-order rate constant ($3.9 \times 10^2\ M^{-1}$ sec^{-1} at 25°) may be too high to represent a V^{3+}-substitution-controlled inner-sphere oxidation.[6]

8.1.3   Vanadium(IV)

The labilities of the coordinated water in the VO^{2+} and substituted VO^{2+} ions have been nicely studied by the nmr method.[7]   There are three types of attached oxygen in **1**:

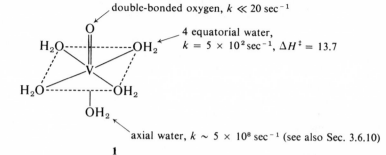

1

By using chelating ligands to tie up various positions of the co-ordination sheath, one can isolate and distinguish between the types of coordinated oxygen.[7] Coordinated negative groups enhance the exchange of the equatorial water markedly and this is ascribed to partial neutralization of the high charge on the vanadium, which otherwise binds the water relatively tightly. The value for the dimerization rate constant for

$$2VOOH^+ \rightleftharpoons (OVOH)_2^{2+} \qquad (8.3)$$

($2 \times 10^4 \, M^{-1} \, sec^{-1}$ at $25°$) suggests that the process is substitution-controlled.[8]

The rate constants for reaction of VO^{2+} with SCN^- and NH_3CH_2-$COO^{\pm}$, on the other hand, appear to be too large for substitution to be controlled by the equatorial water exchange. Complexing at the axial position, followed by movement of the ligand to the equatorial position, may be involved.[9] The activation parameters for equatorial exchange of VO^{2+} with a variety of solvents have been measured (Table 8.1). These values are quite close to one another and a dissociation-type mechanism is favored for these solvent exchanges.[10]

Redox reactions of VO^{2+} often appear to proceed through an oxygen-bridged activated complex or intermediate. Thus, from the form of the rate expression and from the detection of binuclear species (Table 5.3), the reduction of VO^{2+} by V(II), Cr(II), Eu(II), and Cu(I) implicate oxo or hydroxo groups.[11] As a reductant, V(IV) has been compared with Fe(II) in a comprehensive tabulation of kinetic data.[12]

8.1.4 Vanadium(V)

Vanadium(V) exists as a large variety of species over the pH zero-to-14 range. No kinetic studies of their interconversions have been reported.

TABLE 8.1.   Activation Parameters for Exchange of the Solvated VO^{2+} Ion with Solvent at $25°$

Solvent	$10^{-3} k_{exch}$ sec^{-1}	$\Delta H^{\ddagger}$	$\Delta S^{\ddagger}$
DMSO	$> 1.5^a$	...	...
Trimethyl Phosphate	$> 0.8^a$	...	...
Trimethyl Phosphite	$< 0.4^a$	...	...
DMA	4.7^b	10.1	-8
DMF	0.2^b	13.1	-4
CH_3OH	3.3^a	12.0	-1
H_2O	0.1^c	13.7	-1

[a] Ref. 10.
[b] G. A. Miller and R. E. D. McClung, *J. Chem. Phys.*, **58**, 4358 (1973).
[c] Ref. 7.

Protonation of VO_4^{3-} is accompanied by rapid condensation processes,[13] but the pK values can be determined by potentiometry in a flow apparatus (Sec. 3.3.4).

Although V(V) appears to be a single monomeric species, VO_2^+ in acid solution, the oxidation of a number of substrates contain a $[V(V)]^2$ term in the rate law.   This suggests that a highly reactive V(V) dimer may be present in acid medium.[14]   Vanadium(V) finds some use for oxidation of organic compounds that often proceed via complex formation.[15] Vanadium(V) reacts with H_2O_2 to give peroxo species.[16]   These peroxo species react with HO_2 to give complex radicals, the formation and decay rates of which have been measured by a double-mixer arrangement, using esr monitoring (see Sec. 3.3.4).[17]

8.2   CHROMIUM

Chromium produces some of the most interesting chemistry of the transition elements.   There have been extensive studies of the redox chemistry of Cr(II), Cr(III), and Cr(VI), and of the substitution reactions of Cr(III).   The Cr(IV) and Cr(V) oxidation states are unstable in solution but play an important role in the mechanism of oxidation by Cr(VI) of inorganic and organic substrates, and probably in certain oxidation reactions of Cr(II) and Cr(III).

8.2.1　Chromium(II)

The beautiful blue chromium ion can be produced in solution either by reduction of Cr(III) with Zn/Hg or by dissolution of Cr metal, usually in perchloric acid. These methods lead also to production of Zn^{2+} or Cl^{-} ions, respectively. In many studies, these by-products do not interfere.

There is no doubt about the extreme lability of the Cr_{aq}^{2+} ion (Table 4.13), but its weak complexing ability and its extreme sensitivity to O_2 have precluded extensive studies of its interaction with ligands.

Chromium(II) is a very effective and important reducing agent that has played a significant role in the development of redox mechanisms (Chap. 5). It has a facile ability to take part in inner-sphere redox reactions. The coordinated water of Cr(II) is easily replaced by the potential bridging group of the oxidant, and after intramolecular electron transfer, the Cr(III) carries the bridging group away with it; and as it is an inert product, it can be easily identified. There have been many studies of the interaction of Cr(II) with Co(III) complexes (Tables 2.8, 5.4, 5.6–5.13, 5.15) and with Cr(III) complexes (Tables 5.5 and 5.12). Only a few reductions by Cr(II) are outer-sphere (Table 5.7). By contrast, $Crbipy_3^{2+}$ is a very effective outer-sphere reductant (Tables 5.4, 5.6, and 5.8).

Chromium(II) reacts rapidly with O_2 and with Tl(III) (Sec. 5.12c) to produce $(H_2O)_4Cr(OH)_2Cr(H_2O)_4^{4+}$, characterized as a dihydroxy rather than an oxo bridge, by ^{18}O exchange studies. Only a cursory kinetic study of the oxygenation has been made with

$$V = k[Cr^{2+}]^2[O_2] \qquad (8.4)$$

and the value of k, pH-independent.[18] With other oxidants such as Cu^{2+}, Fe^{3+}, and Cl_2, the mononuclear species Cr^{3+} and $CrCl^{2+}$ are the sole products.[19]

Chromium(II) can be used to reduce a variety of organic compounds, including alkyl halides, certain olefins, alkynes, and epoxyketones.[20] Renewal of interest in such Cr(II) reductions stems from the identification of $C_6H_5CH_2Cr^{2+}$ ion as a fairly stable intermediate in the reaction of Cr^{2+} with $C_6H_5CH_2Cl$ in anaerobic acid solution.[21] On heating, $C_6H_5CH_2Cr^{2+}$ converts to $C_6H_5CH_2CH_2C_6H_5$ (via $C_6H_5CH_2\cdot$) in the absence of O_2, and forms C_6H_5CHO in the presence of O_2. The methyl derivative $Cr(H_2O)_5CH_3^{2+}$ is relatively stable and its acid-dependent aquation has been studied.[22]

8.2.2   Chromium(III)[23]

The ion $Cr(H_2O)_6{}^{3+}$ is one of the few aqua species that are sufficiently inert that the solvent exchange rate and solvation number may be determined by conventional sampling or nmr analytical techniques (Sec. 4.1.1). This allows a study of the pressure effect also (Sec. 2.7.1).

The vast majority of substitution reactions of Cr(III) complexes take place slowly and are easily measured. These complexes are second only to the complexes of Co(III) in importance as substrates for exploring all aspects, namely hydrolysis in water (Tables 4.9 and 4.10) and in high acid concentration (Sec. 1.10.3), induced hydrolysis (Table 4.6), anation (Table 4.7), and stereochemical change. Acid and base hydrolysis reactions of Cr(III) ammines[24] and cyano[25] complexes are highly stereoretentive. This suggests a square-pyramidal intermediate for a dissociative mechanism. Replacement reactions of Cr(III) are catalyzed by Cr(II) (Sec. 5.13). Co-ordinated hydroxide labilizes the remaining water in the $CrOH^{2+}$ species. The fairly constant rates of reaction of this with ligands are accompanied by offsetting changes in $\Delta H^{\ddagger}$ and $\Delta S^{\ddagger}$ (Fig. 2.11).

Chromium(III) is oxidized only with difficulty. The form of the rate law for the Cr(III)–Ce(IV) reaction

$$V = k[Ce^{IV}]^2[Cr^{III}][Ce^{III}]^{-1} \qquad (8.5)$$

suggests stepwise oxidation through Cr(IV) and Cr(V) intermediates,[26]

$$Cr^{III} + Ce^{IV} \rightleftharpoons Cr^{IV} + Ce^{III} \qquad k_1, k_{-1} \qquad (8.6)$$

$$Cr^{IV} + Ce^{IV} \rightarrow Cr^{V} + Ce^{III} \qquad k_2 \qquad (8.7)$$

$$Cr^{V} + Ce^{IV} \rightarrow Cr^{VI} + Ce^{III} \qquad \text{fast} \qquad (8.8)$$

with $$k = \frac{k_1 k_2}{k_{-1}} \qquad (8.9)$$

8.2.3   Chromium(IV) and Chromium(V)

Solid compounds of Cr(IV) and Cr(V) are rare; in solution they are important intermediates in Cr(VI) oxidations.[27] Evidence exists that the Cr(VI)–Cr(V) and Cr(IV)–Cr(III) electron transfers are relatively rapid. This, with other evidence, suggests a coordination number of 6 for Cr(III) and Cr(IV), for example, $Cr(H_2O)_6{}^{4+}$, in which substitution is fast, and a coordination number of 4 for Cr(VI) and Cr(V), in which H_3CrO_4 and $H_2CrO_4{}^-$ are prime candidates. Evidence for Cr(V) in acetic acid by flow-esr has been obtained (Sec. 2.2.2).

If Cr(VI) is reduced in the presence of a strongly complexing ligand, the product may be a Cr(III) complex containing that ligand. This probably arises via the formation of a labile Cr(IV) complex.[28]

8.2.4 Chromium(VI)

The rates of attainment of the equilibria between the Cr(VI) species,

$$Cr_2O_7{}^{2-} + H_2O \rightleftharpoons 2HCrO_4{}^- \qquad (8.10)$$

$$HCrO_4{}^- \rightleftharpoons H^+ + CrO_4{}^{2-} \qquad (8.11)$$

have been investigated by flow and relaxation methods. Reaction (8.10) is generally base- (Sec. 2.5.3) and acid-catalyzed. The rate-determining proton transfer in acid catalysis is believed to involve the bridging oxygen, for example,[29]

$$O_3Cr\overset{\displaystyle O}{\diagup \diagdown}CrO_3{}^{2-} + H_3O^+ \; \rightleftharpoons \; \left[O_3Cr \overset{\displaystyle \overset{H \text{ (or HA)}}{O}}{\diagup \diagdown} \underset{\displaystyle OH_2}{CrO_3}{}^- \right]^{\ddagger}$$

(or HA·H₂O)

$$\Updownarrow$$

$$2HCrO_4{}^- + H^+ \text{ (or HA)}$$

In neutral and basic solutions, the equilibria (8.10) and (8.11) are the sole paths for oxygen exchange between Cr(VI) and H_2O.[30] In acid solution, exchange[31] and interconversion, or hydrolysis (8.10),[29] have similar rate laws, at 20°,

$$V(\text{exchange}) = 17 \times 10^3[Cr_2O_7{}^{2-}][H^+] \qquad (8.13)$$

$$V(\text{hydrolysis}) = 5 \times 10^3[Cr_2O_7{}^{2-}][H^+] \qquad (8.14)$$

The differences in rate constants may reflect an additional exchange path or simply arise from the different medium used in the two studies.

Since the stable product of oxidations by Cr(VI) is Cr(III), we are necessarily involved with three-electron reactions, with their attendant interests and complications.[27,32] The reactions of Cr(VI) with H_2O_2 lead to a variety of peroxo species dependent on the conditions.[33] The formation or hydrolysis, or both, of $CrO(O_2)_2$ (Secs. 2.1 and 2.1.5(a)), $Cr(O_2)_4{}^{3-}$, $Cr_2(O_2)^{4+}$, and $Cr_3(O_2)_2{}^{5+}$ have been investigated kinetically.[33] For a number of inorganic reductants, R oxidized to O, the reaction scheme (1.95) is found to hold:

$$Cr^{VI} + R \rightleftharpoons Cr^V + O \qquad k_1, k_{-1} \qquad (8.15)$$

$$Cr^V + R \rightarrow Cr^{IV} + O \qquad k_2 \qquad (8.16)$$

$$Cr^{IV} + R \rightarrow Cr^{III} + O \qquad \text{fast} \qquad (8.17)$$

It is possible sometimes to adjust the conditions so that either the first $(k_2[R] \gg k_{-1}[O])$ or the second $(k_2[R] \ll k_{-1}[O])$ step is rate-limiting. In these circumstances, the rates are given by

$$V = k_1[Cr^{VI}][R] \quad \text{or} \quad V = k_1k_2(k_{-1})^{-1}[Cr^{VI}][R]^2[O]^{-1} \quad \textbf{(8.18)}$$

The proton dependencies of the individual steps of (8.15) and (8.16) can then be detailed.[34] With reducing agents inert to substitution, for example, $Fephen_3^{2+}$, $Fe(CN)_6^{4-}$, or $Ta_6Br_{12}^{2+}$, the first step is the difficult one, and only second-order kinetics are observed.[27] Support for the general scheme ((8.15)–(8.17)) also comes from induced oxidation experiments (Sec. 2.2.1(b)) and from tracer experiments on the Cr(II)–Cr(VI) reaction (Prob. 2b, Chap. 2).

For the oxidation of a number of organic materials—alkanes, alkenes, aldehydes, ketones, and carboxylic acids—the reactions are second-order with $[H^+]$-dependent kinetics. Intermediate Cr oxidation states are proposed here also.[32] Reactions with two-equivalent organic and inorganic reducing agents appear to go via Cr(VI)-reductant adducts (compare Sec. 5.16).[27] A LFER for the reaction,

$$CrO_3X^{n-} + H_2O \rightleftharpoons X^{n-} + HCrO_4^- + H^+ \quad k_1, k_{-1}, K_1 \quad \textbf{(8.19)}$$

that is, a linear log k_1 vs log K_1 plot, slope 0.94, indicates that the transition complex closely resembles the products (Sec. 2.5) and that in the reverse reaction X^{n-} is only weakly bound to Cr(VI) in the transition state leading to the adduct, CrO_3X^{n-}.[34b]

8.3 MOLYBDENUM

There have been a limited number of kinetic studies involving complexes of this element. Recent findings may catalyze an increase of interest. Charge and spectral characteristics of the aquated Mo(II) ion suggest that it is dimeric, Mo_2^{4+}, unchanged in acid solution for long periods in the absence of oxygen. It appears to have an extensive chemistry, giving rise to species such as $Mo_2en_4^{4+}$, Ref. 35a.

Mo(III)[35] and Mo(IV)[36] have recently been characterized as $Mo(H_2O)_6^{3+}$ and $Mo_2O_2^{4+}$, respectively. Surprisingly Mo(III) substitutes more readily than Cr(III).[35b]

Short accounts of the aqueous chemistry of Mo(V) and Mo(VI) are available.[37] There have been few kinetic studies of reactions involving the higher oxidation states. The tetrahedral MoO_4^{2-} ion is converted into an octahedral species on chelation.[37] The reaction of $MoO_3(OH)^-$ (or possibly $MoO_3(H_2O)_2OH^-$) with uncharged 8-hydroxyquinoline is rapid

($k = 5 \times 10^6 \ M^{-1} \sec^{-1}$ at 25°). Analogous reaction with tungstate is slightly faster. It is uncertain whether such reactions are additive or substitutive.[37]

In acid, MoO_4^{2-} undergoes condensation reactions, and the kinetics of these have been examined by temperature jump (see Prob. 1c, Chap. 2).

Deviations from linearity of second-order plots and the observation of rate retardation by $Mo(CN)_8^{4-}$ suggest that the reaction of $Mo(CN)_8^{3-}$ with I^- follows the sequence[38]

$$Mo(CN)_8^{3-} + I^- \rightleftharpoons Mo(CN)_8^{4-} + I\cdot \tag{8.20}$$

$$2I\cdot \rightleftharpoons I_2 \tag{8.21}$$

Molybdenum(V) probably features in a number of sulfhydryl enzymes, such as xanthine oxidase, nitrate reductase and nitrogenase.[39] Esr signals from these are attributed to monomeric d^1 Mo(V), although there is a tendency normally for the oxidation state to form a diamagnetic dimer containing the $Mo_2O_4^{2+}$ unit.[36]

8.4 MANGANESE

Manganese represents the epitome of the property that characterizes transition elements, the variable oxidation state. Nevertheless, the aqueous solution chemistry is restricted to Mn(II), Mn(III), Mn(VI), and Mn(VII). The stability of the Mn(II), $d_{t_{2g}^3 e_g^2}$, configuration is, for example, shown by the fact that it is the slowest-reacting of the bivalent transition metal ions with e_{aq}^- ($7.7 \times 10^7 \ M^{-1}\sec^{-1}$). The product of this reaction, Mn_{aq}^+ has been characterized spectrally.[40]

8.4.1 Manganese(II)

A labile metal ion (Tables 4.13 and 4.15), Mn(II) is an extremely poor reducing agent, so that few studies with oxidants have been made. The Mn(II)–Mn(III) isotopic exchange appears too rapid to be measured experimentally ($k \geqslant 4 \ M^{-1}\sec^{-1}$). However, the separation method used may induce exchange, since the estimated value using Marcus expression (5.53) is $10^{-4} \ M^{-1}\sec^{-1}$. Alternatively, exchange may occur through the disproportionation:[41]

$$2Mn^{III} \rightleftharpoons Mn^{II} + Mn^{IV} \tag{8.22}$$

8.4.2 Manganese(III)

Manganese(III) is a powerful oxidant, with interesting mechanistic chemistry.[15,42] It can be generated in situ from MnO_4^- and Mn^{2+} in acid solution, a reaction for which kinetic data are available.[43] With use of excess Mn^{2+} ions and high acidity (3–5 M $HClO_4$), the marked disproportionation and hydrolytic tendencies of Mn(III) are suppressed, and such solutions are stable for days at room temperature. Manganese(III) is also stabilized by complexing media, for example, SO_4^{2-} or F^- ions, but the complexity of the system is increased over the system with a perchlorate medium.

A number of second-order reactions with inorganic reductants in a ClO_4^- medium have been studied.[15,42] When the reductant has ligand properties, for example, $C_2O_4^{2-}$, Br^-, and HN_3, reaction is considered to occur via complex formation (Sec. 5.13).[44] This route is definitely established in the oxidation by $Mn(III)EDTA(H_2O)^-$ of N_3^- ion.[45]

Studies of the oxidation of organic compounds have been usually carried out with manganese(III) pyrophosphate or sulfate. Oxidation of alcohols, glycols, α-hydroxy acids, and carboxylic acids invariably occur with complex formation or free radical mechanisms, or both.[46]

8.4.3 Manganese(VI)

The green tetrahedral ion MnO_4^{2-} is stable in basic solution. It can be prepared by reducing MnO_4^- with $Fe(CN)_6^{4-}$, the kinetics of which have been measured by stopped-flow methods (Prob. 7, Chap. 1).

The MnO_4^{2-}, MnO_4^- electron transfer has been studied by quenched-flow (Tables 1.3 and 3.2) and nmr methods with good agreement between the results. Strong catalysis by cations are noted in this outer-sphere redox process.

8.4.4 Manganese(VII)

The kinetics of reaction of MnO_4^- with Cl^-, I^-, BH_4^-, OCl^-, $Fe(CN)_6^{4-}$, OH^-, and H_2 have been studied.[46] It is an important oxidant for organic substrates (hydrocarbons, olefins, alcohol, aldehydes), with which it can interact in a variety of ways:

(a) By electron abstraction, producing either MnO_4^{2-} or MnO_2. The formation of MnO_4^{2-} may occur through an initial two-equivalent redox step,

$$MnO_4^- + 2e \to MnO_4^{3-} \tag{8.23}$$

$$MnO_4^{3-} + MnO_4^- \to 2MnO_4^{2-} \quad \text{fast}$$

A hypomanganate ester containing Mn(V) can be detected in the oxidation of cinnamic and crotonic acids by Mn(VII).

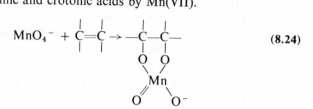

$$\text{MnO}_4^- + \overset{|\quad|}{\underset{|\quad|}{\text{C}=\text{C}}} \rightarrow \quad (8.24)$$

This intermediate is quite stable and only slowly decomposes to MnO_2.[47]

(b) By H atom removal:

$$\text{MnO}_4^- + \text{XH} \rightarrow \text{HMnO}_4^- + \text{X} \qquad (8.25)$$

The substantial isotope effect ($k_H/k_D \sim 7$) for the second-order reaction of MnO_4^- with HCOO^- supports this oxidation mode.[48]

(c) By H^- abstraction:

$$\text{MnO}_4^- + \text{XH} \rightarrow \text{HMnO}_4^{2-} + \text{X}^+ \qquad (8.26)$$

(d) By O donation:

$$\text{MnO}_4^- + \text{X} \rightarrow \text{MnO}_3^- + \text{XO} \qquad (8.27)$$

8.5 IRON

The complexes of Fe(II) and Fe(III), the important oxidation states in aqueous solution, have played big roles in our understanding of the mechanisms of substitution and redox processes.

8.5.1 Iron(II)

The ferrous ion $\text{Fe}(\text{H}_2\text{O})_6^{2+}$ is hexahydrated in aqueous solution.[49] It is labile towards ligand replacement (Tables 4.13 and 4.15). One of the earliest studies of substitution in a labile metal ion was of the reaction of Fe^{2+} with bipy and phen in acid solution (Sec. 2.1.2(b)). Other replacement reactions of octahedral complexes have since been measured (Table 4.13). There have, however, been few studies of ligand replacement in tetrahedral complexes of Fe(II) (Table 4.21).

Oxidation by one-electron oxidants is relatively straightforward.[50] A number of outer-sphere oxidations, by IrCl_6^{2-}, Fephen_3^{3+}, Mn(III), and Co(III), are rapid and second-order, and give the expected LFER (for example, Fig. 5.4).[41,51] In the slow inner-sphere oxidations of Fe(II), electron transfer is almost always rate-determining (Fig. 5.3(b)) since substitution in the coordination sphere of Fe(II) is very rapid. In this respect, it differs from the behavior of V^{2+} and Cr^{2+} ions. It is possible to diagnose an inner-sphere process by identifying the Fe(III) complex by flow methods (Sec. 5.3(a) and Fig. 3.8). Several reactions of Fe^{2+} with Co(III) complexes have been studied (Tables 5.4, 5.8, and 5.16).

Reactions between Fe^{2+} and $Fe(III)X^{n+}$, those in Table 5.14, for example, are not easy to characterize because of the lability of Fe(II) and Fe(III); an inner-sphere path is preferred.[52] On the other hand, rapid electron transfer between coordinately saturated Fe(II) and Fe(III) complexes (for example, in Table 3.2) is undoubtedly outer-sphere. The $Fe(CN)_6^{4-}$, $Fe(CN)_6^{3-}$ system has been thoroughly studied particularly with respect to cation catalysis (2.179).

Oxidation by two-electron oxidants is more complex, since an unstable oxidation state of either iron or the oxidant must be produced. In some cases, the production of a binuclear Fe(III) complex is evidence for the participation of Fe(IV), for example with HOCl and O_3 (represented O):[50]

$$Fe^{II} + O \rightarrow Fe^{IV} + R \qquad\qquad (8.28)$$

$$Fe^{II} + Fe^{IV} \rightarrow [Fe^{III}]_2 \qquad \text{fast} \qquad (8.29)$$

although this will not always arise, for example with O_2 (Sec. 5.16). The absence of a significant amount of $(FeOH)_2^{4+}$ in the $Fe^{2+}-H_2O_2$ reaction suggests that Fe^{IV} is not an intermediate.[50]

8.5.2 Iron(III)

The complexing of a large number of ligands with Fe(III) has been studied (Tables 2.1 and 4.14). Where proton ambiguity arises, the reaction of $FeOH^{2+}$ (with HA) is favored over the reaction of Fe^{3+} (with A^-) Sec. 2.1.5(b). Many Fe(III) complexes undergo dimerization in solution (Table 8.2), and there have been some interesting correlations on the formation and breakdown of these and other binuclear species (see Table 2.3 for the $FeOH^{2+}$ dimerization).[53]

The aquated iron(III) ion is an oxidant. Reaction with reducing ligands probably proceeds through complexing (with I^-, Sec. 5.15).[15] In its reaction with a number of reducing transition metal ions R in acid, the rate law

$$V = (a + b[H^+]^{-1})[Fe^{III}][R] \qquad\qquad (8.30)$$

is obeyed.[54] The inverse proton dependency is dominant and is ascribed to an inner-sphere reaction of a hydroxy form of either Fe(III) or R. In

TABLE 8.2. Rate Constants for the Dissociation ($k_1 + k_2[H^+]$) of Binuclear Iron Complexes at 25°

Complex	k_1, sec^{-1}	k_2, M^{-1} sec^{-1}
$(FeOH)_2^{4+}$	0.42	3.3
$(TPPS\ Fe)_2O^{8-}$	41[a]	8.4×10^{2a}
$(EDTA\ Fe)_2O^{4-}$	1.2	5.0×10^8
$(CyDTA\ Fe)_2O^{4-}$	9	$\sim 10^{10}$
$(HEDTA\ Fe)_2O^{2-}$	4.0	3.0×10^6

SOURCE: Ref. 53.
[a] TPPS = tetrasulfonated tetraphenylporphine.

the reaction with R = Cr^{2+}, the participating partners must be $FeOH^{2+}$ and Cr^{2+} from rate constant considerations. The reaction for which R = V^{2+}, being faster than substitution within V(II) *and* Fe(III), must be outer-sphere (Table 5.2).

The ability of an Fe(III) center to catalyze the disproportionation of H_2O_2 as well as to promote the reaction of H_2O_2 with substrates (Sec. 6.2.3) has been the basis of a number of a kinetic studies with a variety of complexes and substrates.[33] One of the motivations of this work is towards an understanding of the action of catalase and peroxidase, the iron(III) porphyrin-containing enzymes that carry out these functions so efficiently.[55]

8.5.3 Some Iron Complexes of Special Interest

(a) Iron(II) complexes with bipyridyl-type ligands. The well-characterized ions of the type $Febipy_3^{2+}$ hydrolyze slowly and are easily monitored. Rate data for aqueous[56] and nonaqueous[57] solutions and their relation with racemization kinetics have been examined (Table 7.5). The rate/pH profile for the hydrolysis of $Feterpy_2^{2+}$ has been interpreted in terms of protonation of partially fragmented chelates.[58]

There appear to be two types of behavior of $Fephen_3^{2+}$ towards oxidants.[59] Powerful reactants $IrCl_6^{2-}$, Co(III) in $HClO_4$, ClO_2, Cr(VI), and others, give $Fephen_3^{3+}$ ions. Other oxidants, H_2O_2 and ClO_2^-, oxidize the *bis* species formed from hydrolysis of the *tris*:

$$Fephen_3^{2+} \longrightarrow Fephen_2(H_2O)_2^{2+} + phen \qquad \textbf{(8.31)}$$

$$2Fephen_2(H_2O)_2^{2+} \xrightarrow[\text{OH}^-]{\text{oxid.}} Fe_2phen_4(OH)_2^{4+} \qquad \textbf{(8.32)}$$

Persulfate ion gives a mixture of these behaviors with $Fe(5\text{-}NO_2phen)_3^{2+}$, as judged from the rate law,[60]

$$V = k_1[Fe^{II}] + k_2[Fe^{II}][S_2O_8^{2-}] \tag{8.33}$$

Marked effects of anions on the outer-sphere redox reaction between Fe^{2+} and $Fephen_3^{3+}$ have been rationalized (Sec. 5.8).

(b) Iron(II) and (III) cyano complexes provide some very interesting mechanistic chemistry. The oxidation of reducing anions such as SO_3^{2-}, NO_2^-, and I^- by $Fe(CN)_6^{3-}$ is complex and probably involves rapid formation of an intermediate; for example,[61]

$$Fe(CN)_6^{3-} + SO_3^{2-} \rightleftharpoons Fe(CN)_5(CNSO_3)^{5-} \tag{8.34}$$

$$Fe(CN)_5(CNSO_3)^{5-} + Fe(CN)_6^{3-} \rightleftharpoons Fe(CN)_5(CNSO_3)^{4-} + Fe(CN)_6^{4-} \tag{8.35}$$

$$Fe(CN)_5(CNSO_3)^{4-} + H_2O \rightarrow Fe(CN)_6^{4-} + SO_4^{2-} + 2H^+ \quad \text{slow} \tag{8.36}$$

Catalytic effects by traces of Cu^{2+} have to be considered (Sec. 3.1.1). $Fe(CN)_6^{3-}$ smoothly oxidizes a number of organic[62] (Sec. 2.1.6) and protein[63] substrates. A number of reactions of the nitroprusside ion, $Fe(CN)_5NO^{2-}$, such as

$$Fe(CN)_5NO^{2-} + 2OH^- \rightleftharpoons Fe(CN)_5NO_2^{4-} + H_2O \tag{8.37}$$

and of the $Fe(CN)_5H_2O^{2-}$ ion have been investigated.[64-66] A monomer-dimer equilibrium involving the latter complicates interpretation of results.[66]

(c) A first-class exposition on the interaction of myoglobins and hemoglobins with ligands is available.[67] The kinetics of reaction of myoglobins (which contain only one iron center in each molecule of protein) with ligands of the type O_2, CO, NO, RNC, and so on are relatively straightforward. The reaction of hemoglobins (which contain four iron centers) is astonishingly complex; and although a tremendous effort has been expended in attempting to understand the physiologically important heme–O_2 reaction (Eq. (1.149) and Figs. 1.8 and 3.5), a final solution is still unrealized.[68] These reactions are invariably rapid and their measurement was the basic reason for developing flow methods, and for exploiting relaxation and flash-photolytic techniques.[69] These Fe(II) proteins can be oxidized to the Fe(III) forms (metmyoglobins and methemoglobins). While the met forms no longer interact with O_2, they do undergo a number of ligation reactions, which have been studied with interesting results. Following the general tendency, the reactions of ferrimyoglobin are usually simple with a second-order rate law, and the reactions of ferri-hemoglobin are often complex (Sec. 1.6.2).

8.6 RUTHENIUM

In the past few years, there has been increasing attention given to a study of the reactivity of ruthenium species, particularly since these species show unusual behavior compared with their Co congeners (Secs. 5.4(d), 6.5.2). The four oxidation states Ru(II), Ru(III), Ru(VI), and Ru(VII) are well established in solution. Towards $^{36}Cl^-$ exchange, lability in anionic chloro complexes is Ru(II) > Ru(III) > Ru(IV).[74]

8.6.1 Ruthenium(II)

The $Ru(H_2O)_6^{2+}$ ion is oxygen-sensitive. In its behavior towards substitution, it lies in the inert-labile border area because of its t_{2g}^6 configuration (Table 4.13). A dissociative mechanism is favored (Table 5.19) with the water exchange-rate constant estimated as $\sim 10^{-1} sec^{-1}$. The oxidation of Ru^{2+} by ClO_4^- and $CrCl^{2+}$ ions appears also to be controlled by substitution at Ru^{2+} (Table 5.19).

The $Ru(NH_3)_5H_2O^{2+}$ ion reacts with a number of unidentate ligands including nitrogen, and the replacement of water appears to take place by a dissociative mechanism, as evidenced by the similar activation parameters ($\Delta H^{\ddagger} = 17 \pm 1.5$ kcal mole^{-1}; $\Delta S^{\ddagger} = -5 \pm 2$ eu) for reaction with N_2, N_2O, CO, NH_3, py, pyrazine, CH_3CN, and imidazole,[70] as well as with $Ru(NH_3)_5N_2^{2+}$ (to form a bridged dimer).[71] Limited data indicate that substitution occurs without stereochange.[72]

The relative inertness of $Ru(NH_3)_6^{2+}$ and Ruphen$_3^{2+}$ towards substitution makes these ruthenium complexes definite, although weak, outer-sphere reductants (Tables 5.4, 5.6, 5.10, 5.16, and 5.17).[73] An isokinetic relationship applies to the oxidation of Ruphen$_3^{2+}$ and derivatives by Tl(III) (Sec. 2.6.3). Surprisingly, the rate constants do not conform at all well to the Marcus treatment.[43]

8.6.2 Ruthenium(III)

$Ru(H_2O)_6^{3+}$ is an inert ion (Table 4.14). Ruthenium(III), t_{2g}^5, has an unpaired electron that could be engaged by an entering ligand, so that a seven-coordinated intermediate or activated complex is a distinct possibility. Bimolecular mechanisms are supported for the reaction of

$Ru(NH_3)_6{}^{3+}$ and other Ru(III) complexes with NO (which also has a single electron), Sec. 4.3.8, as well as for the hydrolysis of $RuCl_6{}^{3-}$ in strong acid.[74]

The few Ru(III) complexes that have been examined undergo rapid base hydrolysis, spontaneous and Hg(II)-induced aquation[75] with complete retention of configuration. Probably a square-pyramidal intermediate is involved. Ruthenium(II) catalyzes the anation of Ru^{3+} (Sec. 1.5.1). A number of Ru(III) complexes, for example $Ru(NH_3)_5py^{3+}$, appear to undergo reversible disproportionation in alkaline solution. This is shown by chemical tests and the observation of second-order kinetics for the loss of Ru(III).[76]

The reduction of cis-$Ru(NH_3)_4Cl_2{}^+$ (Eq. (1.71) and Fig. 1.7) and $Ru(NH_3)_5OCOCH_3{}^{2+}$ by Cr(II) is inner-sphere, with the formation of bridged species (Table 5.3) and the appropriate substituted Cr(III) product.[73]

8.6.3   Ruthenium(VI) and Ruthenium(VII)

The ruthenium(VI) and ruthenium(VII) oxidation states occur as the $RuO_4{}^{2-}$ and $RuO_4{}^-$ ions. The electron exchange between them is $> 10^4 \, M^{-1} \sec^{-1}$ in $0.1 \, M \, OH^-$ at 25°. This is faster than the electron exchange between $MnO_4{}^{2-}$ and $MnO_4{}^-$ ions, although the standard potentials for the two couples are close (-0.60 V and -0.56 V for the Ru and Mn species respectively).[77]

8.7   OSMIUM

The study of the rates of reaction of osmium complexes is difficult. Colloids and precipitates tend to appear at the higher temperatures needed to make the reactions proceed at a reasonable rate. The reaction

$$OsCl_6{}^{2-} + H_2O \rightleftharpoons Os(H_2O)Cl_5{}^- + Cl^- \qquad \textbf{(8.38)}$$

has been studied in both directions in HCl. Comparison with the Cl^- exchange of $OsCl_6{}^{2-}$ suggests that the hydrolytic path accounts for the exchange results and that a bimolecular contribution is unimportant.[78]

8.8   COBALT

It would be hardly possible to do full justice to the kinetic behavior of Co even in a book devoted to that subject. Only some important features will be emphasized. The stable oxidation states in aqueous solution are

Co(II) and Co(III). Pulse radiolysis of Co^{2+} in solution produces Co_{aq}^+, the spectra and reactivity of which has been examined.[40]

8.8.1 Cobalt(II)

Square-planar, tetrahedral, square-pyramidal, trigonal-bipyramidal, octahedral, and dimeric structures have all been established with Co(II).[79] The interconversion between tetrahedral and octahedral species has been studied in nonaqueous solution (Sec. 7.2.3).

A limited number of studies indicate that substitution in tetrahedral Co(II) complexes is second-order (Sec. 4.14):

$$CoL_2X_2 + *L \rightleftharpoons Co*LLX_2 + L \qquad (8.39)$$

where L represents 2-picoline, $(C_6H_5)_3P$, or hexamethylphosphoramide, and X the halides. With the bulky ligand, there is evidence for a dissociative path arising from an inherently weaker Co–O bond.

The six-coordinated solvated Co(II) species has been established in a number of solvents, including H_2O, CH_3OH, CH_3CN, and DMF.[80] This has been realized by integration of nmr signals due to free and coordinated solvent (see Prob. 1 of Chap. 4). There have been many studies of ligand replacement in aqueous solution (e.g. Table 4.13), but few data are available for nonaqueous solution.

Isotopic exchange reactions involving complexes of Co(II) and Co(III) have proved very interesting because of the generally high-spin and low-spin characteristics, respectively, of these oxidation states. The role that these play in determining the rate constants for these reactions has been much discussed (Sec. 5.14 and Table 5.17).

8.8.2 Cobalt(III)

The aquated Co(III) ion is a powerful oxidant ($E^0 = -1.92$ V in 4 M $HClO_4$ at 25°) but nevertheless stable for some hours in solution, especially in the presence of Co(II) ions. This permits examination of the kinetics of its reduction, invariably by stopped-flow methods (Sec. 5.15 and Table 5.18).[15,81] Some of these redox reactions appear to be substitution-controlled; some, with $C_6H_4(OH)_2$ and I^-, are too fast for an inner-sphere designation.[82]

Because Co(III) complexes were so well characterized by Werner, and because they undergo a variety of reactions at easily measurable rates, they have been chosen as substrates for most systematic studies. These include proton exchange in coordinated ammines (Sec. 7.7), outer-sphere complexing (Sec. 4.1.1),[83] neighboring group effects (Sec. 6.2), acid, base,[24] and induced hydrolysis (Table 4.11), medium effects (Sec. 2.8.1), and also anation and pressure (Sec. 2.7.1) studies of species such as $Co(NH_3)_5$-H_2O^{3+} (Table 4.2). Important studies of stereochemical change in octahedral complex reactions have mainly featured Co(III) complexes (Tables 2.6 and 7.4).[24] Finally, the inert Co(III) complexes are important for studying the reactivity of coordinated ligands (Sec. 6.4).

Cobalt(III) complexes are often chosen as the oxidant partner in the study of redox reactions (see many of the tables in Chap. 5). They can present a variety of bridging groups, both inorganic and organic, to the reducing agents that take part in inner-sphere redox processes (Sec. 5.4).

Cis and *trans* effects can be quite substantial in the reactions of cobalt(III) complexes.[84] Variations of 10^8 in the values of the rate constants within a series can be encountered and these effects outweigh the effects of Pt(II), which are now considered classical. Porphyrin and corrin rings promote large *cis* effects, and alkyl, SO_3^{2-}, and NH_2^- groups are strongly *trans* labilizing. The *trans*-effect sequence for Co(III) and Pt(II) (4.119) bear similarities. There are, however, larger effects for CN^- and NO_2^- in Pt chemistry, which probably reside in the σ-donor and π-acceptor effects with Pt(II), arising from the increased electron density associated with the d^8 configuration.

There are many binuclear complexes involving peroxo, amido, and hydroxo single- and multibridged combinations. The studies of the kinetics of their substitution, disproportionation, and redox (2.16) reactions have been well summarized.[85]

8.8.3 Some Cobalt Complexes of Special Interest

(a) So much important chemistry is associated with the Co(II)-cyanide complex that it deserves separate mention. Raman and esr data support a square-pyramidal five-coordinated $Co(CN)_5^{3-}$ as the principal species in aqueous solution,[86] although there are color changes on heating or diluting which suggest that other species may also be present.[87]

It is an important inner-sphere reductant (Prob. 1 of Chap. 5, and Tables 5.3 and 5.4) and the most extensively studied of a number of Co(II) systems that undergo oxidative addition.[88,89] Generally,

$$Co(CN)_5^{3-} + XY \rightarrow Co(CN)_5X^{3-} + Y\cdot \qquad \text{rds} \qquad \textbf{(8.40)}$$

$$Co(CN)_5^{3-} + Y\cdot \rightarrow Co(CN)_5Y^{3-} \qquad \text{fast} \qquad \textbf{(8.41)}$$

where XY may be H_2O, Br_2, I_2, ICN, NH_2OH, H_2O_2, and RX.[90] As would be expected with this mechanism, there is an inverse correlation of second-order rate constant with the bond energy of the XY additive.[90] The reaction of $Co(CN)_5^{3-}$ with H_2 to give $Co(CN)_5H^{3-}$ differs from those above in being a third-order reaction (Secs. 1.11 and 2.1.2(a)).

The species $Co(CN)_5^{3-}$ reacts rapidly with O_2 to give a binuclear peroxo complex $(NC)_5CoO_2Co(CN)_5^{6-}$, a common reaction with a number of cobalt(II) complexes.[91] Many of these reactions are reversible and the kinetics of the oxygenation and deoxygenation of some have been studied as potential models for the Fe(II) systems.[91] Autoxidation reactions probably proceed via oxygen adducts (Sec. 6.2). $Co(CN)_5^{3-}$ can also be reduced electrochemically or by the hydrated electron to $Co(CN)_5^{4-}$. The hydrolysis rate constant of the Co(I) complex has been determined.[92]

(b) Labile Co(III) complexes. Although Co(III) is often considered the classical representative of inert behavior, there are a number of cobalt(III) complexes that react rapidly enough to require that the rates be determined by flow methods. Table 8.3 shows a representative selection of such labile complexes. A comparison of the nitro and methyl cobaloximes shows that the rate enhancement with the latter resides in a more positive $\Delta S^{\ddagger}$ value.[93] Both of these complexes and the cobalamin derivative (see below) react with $\Delta H^{\ddagger}$ values some 10 kcal mole^{-1} lower than those generally found with Co(III). The basis for these effects is uncertain but the complexes have strong macrocyclic-type ligands, which together with the strong *trans*-labilizing group are likely to induce H_2O axial lability and strongly promote a dissociative mechanism.[93,94]

The cobaloxime compounds have been used as models for Vitamin B_{12}.[95] This coenzyme contains Co(III) bonded to four nitrogen atoms of a corrin ring, a nitrogen of a 5,6-dimethylbenzimidazole ring and a cyanide ion, which is an artifact of the isolation method. The structure without the cyanide is termed cobalamin. Several cobalamins are known, including cyanocobalamin (B_{12}), aquocobalamin, and hydroxocobalamin.[96]

The rapidity of the acid-catalyzed hydrolysis of $Co(NH_3)_5OCO_2^+$ (flow measurement is necessary) and also of the Pb^{2+}- and Hg^{2+}-catalyzed removal of carbonate indicates that C–O and not Co–O bond cleavage is involved, and this has been confirmed by ^{18}O tracer experiments.[97] The interpretation of the data for the hydrolysis of ions of the type $CoN_4OCO_2^+$ (where $N_4 = (NH_3)_4$, en, tren, and so on) has presented problems but appears now to have been resolved. The opening of the ring is usually rate-determining:

$$CoN_4OCO_2^+ \xrightarrow[H_3O^+]{k_0 + k_1[H^+]} CoN_4(H_2O)(OCO_2H)^{2+} \xrightarrow[\substack{\text{decarboxyl-} \\ \text{ation}}]{k_2}$$

$$CoN_4(H_2O)_2^{3+} + HCO_3^- \qquad (8.42)$$

TABLE 8.3. Some Labile Cobalt(III) Systems at 25°

The system entry is illustrated by a cobalt dioxime-type structure with substituents, bearing the labels CH_3, CH_3, H_3C, H_3C, O, N, H_2O, Co, X, N, and bridging $H \cdots O$ groups.

System	k^a, M^{-1} sec^{-1}	$\Delta H^\ddagger$	$\Delta S^\ddagger$	Ref.
X = CH_3 + NCS^-	1.5×10^2	17.5	+10	93
X = NO_2 + NCS^-	5.8×10^{-4}	19.1	−9	b
X = SO_3 + N_3^-	7.3	...	...	94
Cobalamin (H_2O) + NCS^-	2.3×10^3	17.1	+14	Table 4.4
Co^{III} hematoporphyrin (H_2O) + NCS^-	1.7×10^3	...	...	c; Fig. 4.1

[a] These are second-order rate constants at low [anion] that may go over to first-order processes at high [anion].

[b] D. N. Hague and J. Halpern, *Inorg. Chem.*, **6**, 2059 (1967).

[c] See also R. F. Pasternack and M. A. Cobb, *Biochem. Biophys. Res. Comm.*, **51**, 507 (1973), who studied the reaction of Co(III) tetra-(*N*-methyltetrapyridyl)porphyrin with SCN^-.

380

that is, $k_2 \geqslant (k_0 + k_1[H^+])$. In high acid concentration ($2\ M$), however, the reverse relation holds, and the intermediate can be directly observed in a flow apparatus where $N_4 = $ tren.[98]

8.9 RHODIUM

8.9.1 Rhodium(I)

Substitution in planar Rh(I) complexes has been little studied. Available data indicate that the reaction profile associated with these reactions may resemble Fig. 4.5(c), since in one instance the relatively rapid formation of a five-coordinated intermediate is detected spectrally, and its breakdown is rate determining.[99] This leads to a rate constant independent of the concentration, but not the nature, of the entering ligand. The utilization of five orbitals for bonding in the intermediate is easier as the effective nuclear charge of the central atom decreases, that is, Au(III) < Pt(II) < Rh(I).[100]

8.9.2 Rhodium(II)

Well characterized in the solid state, the aqua ion probably exists as $Rh_2(H_2O)_{10}^{4+}$. It may be prepared by the redox reaction:

$$2Rh(H_2O)_5Cl^{2+} + 2Cr^{2+} \rightarrow Rh_2(H_2O)_{10}^{4+} + 2CrCl^{2+} \qquad (8.43)$$

It is slowly oxidized by air.[101]

8.9.3 Rhodium(III)

Rhodium(III) is characterized as the ion $Rh(H_2O)_6^{3+}$ in aqueous solution from $H_2^{18}O$ exchange studies. Chloride anation of $Rh(H_2O)_6^{3+}$ has been interpreted as a D (dissociative) mechanism rather than an I_d, ion-pair interchange, although the system is complicated.[102] Reactions of other rhodium complexes occur with a definite, although not substantial, degree of ligand assistance; that is, the reactions may be I_a or A (Sec. 4.3.8).[103] Base hydrolysis of Rh(III) complexes occurs without stereochange.[24]

    The acid-catalyzed exchange of $Rh(C_2O_4)_3^{3-}$ with $H_2^{18}O$ shows up two types of oxygen, the outer oxygens of the chelated oxalate exchanging approximately 60 times faster than the inner ones at 25°.[104] Exchange of the outer almost certainly occurs by an A2 mechanism, common to a number of oxalates:

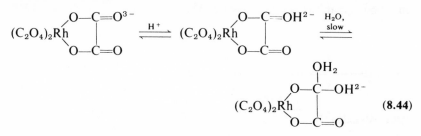

$$(8.44)$$

Understanding the exchange of the inner oxygens is more difficult, but this may occur via an intermediate that could also play a role in the racemization[104] and the much slower aquation:

$$(8.45)$$

8.10 IRIDIUM

8.10.1 Iridium(I)

Iridium(I) in the form of Vaska's compound, $Ir(Ph_3P)_2(CO)Cl$, represents the epitome of the activation of covalent molecules through the phenomenon of oxidative addition (Sec. 6.2).[89,105] The compound adds on O_2, H_2, CO, SO_2, C_2H_4, and CH_3I in solution. These reactions, in benzene or chlorobenzene,

$$Ir(Ph_3P)_2(CO)A + XY \rightleftharpoons Ir(Ph_3P)_2(CO)AXY \qquad k_1, k_{-1} \qquad (8.46)$$

for which $\qquad\qquad V = k_1[Ir^I][XY] - k_{-1}[Ir^{III}] \qquad\qquad (8.47)$

show large negative $\Delta S_i^\ddagger$ values, expected for a bimolecular reaction without attendant solvation changes.[89]

The rates of oxygenation and deoxygenation ($XY = O_2$) increase and decrease, respectively, with increasing tendency for the anionic group A to release electrons (Table 8.4).[106]

Both *cis* and *trans* oxidative addition of CH_3I to Ir(I) complexes can occur. This can be rationalized on molecular-orbital-symmetry grounds, a concept that has been much exploited in organic chemistry by Woodward and Hoffman, but used little in transition metal reactivity.[107]

TABLE 8.4. Activation Parameters for the Oxygenation of $Ir(Ph_3P)_2(CO)A$, Reaction (8.46) at 40 °C

A	$10^2 \times k_1$ $M^{-1} sec^{-1}$	$\Delta H_1^{\ddagger}$	$\Delta S_1^{\ddagger}$	$10^6 \times k_{-1}$ sec^{-1}	$\Delta H_{-1}^{\ddagger}$	$\Delta S_{-1}^{\ddagger}$
F	1.5	13.6	−24	51	23.7	−1
NCO	3.0	11.1	−30	90	21.0	−10
N_3	7.3	9.6	−33	13	26.2	3
Cl	10.1	9.5	−33	14	26.5	4
Br	21	8.4	−35	3.3	28.8	8
I	72	5.8	−41	0.84	29.0	6

SOURCE: Ref. 106.
^a In benzene.

8.10.2 Iridium(III)

Substitution reactions of Ir(III) are extremely slow and replacement of X in *trans*-$Iren_2X_2^+$ (X = Cl, Br, I) by Y, proceeding through rate-determining aquation, must be studied above 100°. Little stereochemical change appears to accompany these reactions.[108] The first study of the base hydrolysis of an Ir(III) complex, $Ir(NH_3)_5I^{2+}$, was not reported until 1969.[109] There is a linear variation of $\Delta H^{\ddagger}$ with ligand field strength for the base hydrolysis of the series $M(NH_3)_5I^{2+}$, with M(III) = Cr, Co, Rh, and Ir.[109]

$IrCl_6^{2-}$ is an interesting oxidant for organic substrates. With cyclohexanone, for example, the suggested mechanism involves both outer- and inner-sphere processes.[110]

$$+ IrCl_6^{2-} \xrightarrow[\text{outer-sphere}]{\text{fast}} \quad + H^+ + IrCl_6^{3-} \qquad (8.48)$$

$$+ IrCl_6^{2-} + H_2O \xrightarrow[\text{sphere}]{\text{inner-}} \quad + Ir(H_2O)Cl_5^{2-} \qquad (8.49)$$

8.11 NICKEL

Little redox chemistry is associated with nickel, which shows only one stable oxidation state, Ni(II), in aqueous solution. Cyclic amine, for example, tet a, complexes of Ni(I), Ni(II), and Ni(III), have been prepared and are stable in the absence of O_2 and H_2O. No kinetic data are available for the reactions of these Ni(I) and Ni(III) complexes, which are strong reducing and oxidizing agents in acetonitrile solution.[111] (See Sec. 3.6.9).

Reaction of Ni^{2+} with the hydrated electron produces a transient, which has been ascribed to Ni_{aq}^{+}. The spectra of this, and its reactions with a number of complexes, have been studied.[40]

8.11.1 Nickel(0)

The tetrahedral complexes of the d^{10} Ni(0) system undergo dissociative substitution (Table 4.20). Kinetic data are shown in Table 8.5.[112] Infrared monitoring methods feature prominently in these studies (Sec. 3.6.6).

TABLE 8.5. Activation Parameters for Substitution Reactions of Ni^0L_4 in Toluene at $25°$[112]

NiL_4	k, sec^{-1}	$\Delta H^{\ddagger}$	$\Delta S^{\ddagger}$
$Ni(CO)_4$	2.0×10^{-2}	22.3	8
$Ni(PF_3)_4$	2.1×10^{-6}	28.4	11
$Ni[P(OEt)_3]_4$	9.9×10^{-7}	26.2	2

8.11.2 Nickel(II)

There have been few studies of substitution in complexes of nickel(II) of stereochemistries other than octahedral. The exchange reactions with Ni(II) tetrahedral complexes, studied by nmr, are discussed in Sec. 4.14. The *enhanced* lability of the nickel(II) compared with the cobalt(II) complex is expected on CFAE considerations. This contrasts with the reverse (Co(II) faster than Ni(II)) with octahedral complexes (Sec. 4.6). Only one study, very detailed, of substitution in planar Ni(II) complexes is reported.[113] Reactions of the type of (8.50) were examined. The

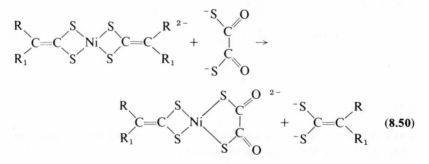

(8.50)

reactions are bimolecular, and there is definite evidence for a five-coordinated intermediate. Many different dithiolato complexes and entering ligands were used but a k_1 (solvent path, Sec. 4.9) term was not found.

Studies of the rapid interconversion between tetrahedral and planar and between planar and octahedral species have used Ni(II) complexes as examining substrates (Secs. 7.2.1 and 7.2.2).

The Ni(II) ion in many solvents is hexasolvated.[80] It is possible, for example, to observe separate peaks for the methyl resonances of the solvent and the solvation shell in concentrated solutions of $Ni(ClO_4)_2$ in MeOH at $+5°$ and from these to determine the solvation number.[114] There have been more studies of the rates of solvent exchange[115] and substitution[3,116] in Ni(II) complexes than for all the other labile bivalent metal ions combined (Tables 4.3, 4.8, 4.13, and 4.15). This arises mainly from the wide variety of stable complexes that Ni(II) forms, and the ease with which rates of exchange and formation may be measured by nmr line broadening, flow, and conventional methods. Certain chelates can be resolved into optical forms and their racemization studied (Sec. 7.4.2).

At relatively high nickel(II) concentration (0.1–1.0 M, $Ni(ClO_4)_2$), a hydrolytic tetramer, $Ni_4(OH)_4^{4+}$, forms in alkaline solution. Its decomposition by acid has been studied by stopped-flow spectrophotometry.[117]

Nickel(II) ion and complexes are often included in the study of the catalytic properties of a series of metal ions. Thus the Ni^{2+} catalysis of the hydrolysis of glycine ester, cysteine methyl ester, histidine ester amides, nitriles (of which phenanthroline-2-nitrile is particularly interesting, Sec. 6.4.4), and polypeptides, the decarboxylation of keto-acids, and the dimerization of pyruvate have all been studied.[118] Nickel(II) (and copper(II)) have a marked ability to promote ionization from coordinated amide and peptide linkages (Sec. 6.5.4).

Undoubtedly one of the most interesting catalytic functions of Ni(II) is its ability to bring reactants together in a specific fashion. In this way a number of different types of macrocycles have been synthesized, and some interesting stereochemical situations revealed.[119]

8.12 PALLADIUM

Substitution in Pd(0) is dissociative (Table 4.20) and in Pd(II) is associative. Many of the characteristics established for substitution in Pt(II) are also seen in Pd(II)[100] (see Tables 4.19 and 7.3). Some interesting electrophilic reactions of porphyrins are promoted in the Pd(II) and Pt(II) complexes (Sec. 6.6).

8.13   PLATINUM

8.13.1   Platinum(0)

The compounds of zerovalent platinum, $Pt(Ph_3P)_4$ and $Pt(Ph_3P)_3$, were first discovered in 1958.[120]   A number of kinetic studies of substitution and oxidative addition reactions of these and related compounds indicate that PtL_3 and PtL_2 are reactive intermediates. Associative paths are also important.[121]   Tetrahedral complexes of the type $Pt(PF_3)_4$ and $Pt(P(OEt)_3)_4$ undergo nucleophilic substitution by a dissociative mechanism (Table 4.20).

8.13.2   Platinum(II)

In the study of square-planar complexes, platinum(II) complexes have been used in much the same way that cobalt(III) complexes have been octahedral model systems (Chap. 4).   A nucleophilicity scale has been set up using Pt(II) substrates (Sec. 2.5.4).   Rate constants and activation parameters for a number of substitution reactions are shown in Tables 4.16–4.18.   A full compilation is given in Ref. 100.   The only rate studies of geometrical isomerization in square-planar complexes feature Pt(II) complexes (Sec. 7.5).

8.13.3   Platinum(III)

Platinum(III) is a rare oxidation state.   It is a postulated intermediate in certain photochemical and catalyzed substitution reactions of Pt(IV) complexes.[122]   For the reaction

$$PtCl_4^{2-} + 2IrCl_6^{2-} + 2Cl^- \rightarrow PtCl_6^{2-} + 2IrCl_6^{3-} \qquad (8.51)$$

in aqueous NaCl/HCl solutions

$$\frac{-d[IrCl_6^{2-}]}{dt} = \frac{-2d[PtCl_4^{2-}]}{dt} = \frac{2k_1k_2[PtCl_4^{2-}][IrCl_6^{2-}]^2[Cl^-]}{k_{-1}[IrCl_6^{3-}] + k_2[IrCl_6^{2-}][Cl^-]} \quad (8.52)$$

consistent with the mechanism

$$PtCl_4^{2-} + IrCl_6^{2-} \rightleftharpoons PtCl_4^- + IrCl_6^{3-} \qquad k_1, k_{-1} \text{ (8.53)}$$

$$PtCl_4^- + IrCl_6^{2-} + Cl^- \rightarrow PtCl_5^- + IrCl_6^{3-} \qquad k_2 \qquad (8.54)$$

$$PtCl_5^- + Cl^- \rightarrow PtCl_6^{2-} \qquad (8.55)$$

in which a Pt(III) species, $PtCl_4^-$, is in steady state.[122]   On the other hand, the two-electron inner-sphere reduction of $Pt(NH_3)_5Cl^{3+}$ by Cr^{2+} appears to proceed via Cr(IV) and Pt(II) rather than via Cr(III) and Pt(III).[123]

8.13.4 Platinum(IV)

Normally platinum(IV) is an extremely inert oxidation state. However, a number of Pt(IV) complexes containing the labilizing methyl group— $Pt(CH_3)_3(H_2O)_3^+$, $Pt(CH_3)_3bipyH_2O^+$, and $[Pt(CH_3)_3acac]_2$—undergo facile ligand (H_2O or acac) exchange; these exchanges have been studied by nmr methods.[124]

Substitution in Pt(IV) is catalyzed by Pt(II):[125]

$$trans\text{-}Pt^{IV}L_4XY + Z + Pt^{II}L_4 \rightarrow trans\text{-}Pt^{IV}L_4XZ + Y + Pt^{II}L_4 \quad \textbf{(8.56)}$$

and is associated with a mechanism (see Sec. 2.1.2)

$$PtL_4 + Z \rightleftharpoons PtL_4Z \quad \textbf{(8.57)}$$

$$PtL_4Z + PtL_4XY \rightarrow PtL_4YZ + PtL_4X \quad \textbf{(8.58)}$$

Attempts to detect the five-coordinated intermediate, PtL_4Z, have been unsuccessful, even in nonaqueous solutions where its stability could have led to deviations from a third-order reaction.

The effect of the bridging ligand Y on the rate is quite marked. The rate order for entering groups Z is

$$SCN^- > Br^- > Cl^- > I^- > NH_3 \sim NO_2^- \sim py \quad \textbf{(8.59)}$$

which resembles quite closely the rate order for substitution in Pt(II), emphasizing the similarity with the first step of the redox mechanism.

There is no evidence that high oxidation states of other metals undergo such a novel substitution.

8.14 COPPER

8.14.1 Copper(I)

The ion Cu^+ can be prepared in an acid perchlorate solution by reaction of Cu^{2+} with a one-electron reducing agent—Cr^{2+}, V^{2+}, or Eu^{2+} (Ref. 126). Although there is a marked tendency for disproportionation

$$2Cu^+ \rightleftharpoons Cu^{2+} + Cu^0 \quad K = 2 \times 10^6 \quad \textbf{(8.60)}$$

solutions of Cu^+ are metastable for hours in the absence of oxygen, particularly when concentrations of Cu(I) are low and the acidity is high. Espenson[126] has capitalized on this to study the rates of reduction by Cu^+ of some oxidants, particularly those of Co(III) (Table 5.4). (See Prob. 2c, Chap. 5).

There is no reason to believe that Cu^+ is anything but extremely labile. It is stabilized by a number of ligands, but the complexes are usually unstable in O_2, with which they react quite rapidly.[91] The copper protein hemocyanin is the constituent of many mollusks and crustaceans, and it is able to interact reversibly with oxygen.[127] Restoration of activity to the

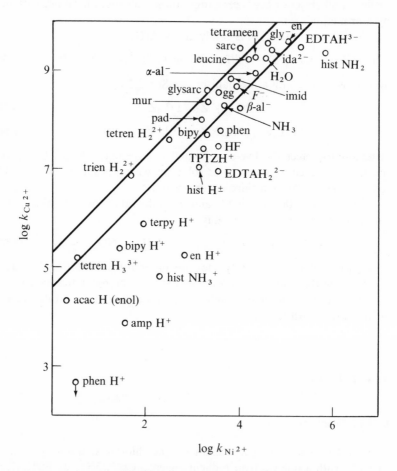

FIGURE 8.1   The plot of log $k_{Cu^{2+}}$ vs log $k_{Ni^{2+}}$ for reaction with a variety of ligands. The band encloses a range of rate constant ratios given by the relationship $4.6 < \log (k_{Cu}/k_{Ni}) < 5.3$.[130]

apo (demetallo) form of several copper proteins—hemocyanin, ceruloplasmin, and cytochrome c oxidase—appears to require Cu(I).[128]

The Cu(I)–Cu(II) exchange has not been investigated in a perchloric acid medium. In 12 M HCl, fast exchange has been noted by nmr line broadening (Sec. 3.6.8(a)).

8.14.2   Copper(II)

The designation of Cu(II) as a square-planar or an octahedral complex and therefore the assignment of a mechanism for complexation has proved very difficult. Often the reactions have been considered to be dissociative, and the marked lability of Cu(II) (Table 4.13) has been ascribed to the Jahn-Teller effect.[129] Substitution can easily occur at the very labile axial positions (which are further removed from the metal than the equatorial positions). Rapid inversion of the axial and equatorial ligands leads then to apparent easy substitution in the equatorial position. The fairly constant ratio $k_{Cu^{2+}}:k_{Ni^{2+}}$ for reaction of Cu^{2+} and Ni^{2+} with a wide variety of ligands (Fig. 8.1)[130] suggests a common mechanism, and since a dissociative one is firmly established for Ni^{2+}, it does appear that the same holds for Cu^{2+} also. Ligands that do not fall in the narrow band shown in Fig. 8.1 can be associated with proton-release-dominated or sterically controlled, substitution (Sec. 4.4.10).[130]

In the replacement of one ligand by another in a bis chelated Cu(II) species, however,

$$CuL_2 + L' \rightleftharpoons CuLL' + L \qquad\qquad (8.61)$$

the rate constants depend on the nature of L and L', and an associative mechanism is particularly attractive for rationalizing this behavior.[131]

The marked lability of the axial positions in Cu(II) complexes has been characterized by esr line broadening measurements (Sec. 3.6.10).

The interaction of Cu^{2+} with a number of metal-EDTA–type complexes has been investigated to illuminate the mechanism of electrophilic substitution reactions (Sec. 4.5.8).[132] These studies provide data for the high rate constants for formation of metal-EDTA complexes.

Additional to the usual metal-ion catalytic effects is the ability of Cu(II) complexes to simulate, albeit weakly, the activity of catalase and peroxidase (Sec. 6.2.3).

Copper(II) reacts with a number of reducing ligands, such as cyanide (see Prob. 1d, Chap. 2), sulfite, and dithizone, eventually giving a Cu(I) product, but probably proceeding through a Cu(II) complex within which the redox process occurs.[15] The reduction of transition metal salts by H_2

has been investigated in great detail.[133]   The reaction with Cu(II) is autocatalytic (due to Cu(I)). The suggested mechanism is[133]

$$Cu^{2+} + H_2 \rightleftharpoons CuH^+ + H^+ \quad\Big\} \text{mainly} \tag{8.62}$$
$$CuH^+ + Cu^{2+} \rightarrow 2Cu^+ + H^+ \tag{8.63}$$
$$Cu^+ + H_2 \rightleftharpoons CuH + H^+ \tag{8.64}$$
$$CuH + Cu^{2+} \rightarrow CuH^+ + Cu^+ \tag{8.65}$$
$$2Cu^+ \rightleftharpoons Cu^0 + Cu^{2+} \tag{8.66}$$

Copper(III) is formed in radiolyzed solutions of Cu(II),

$$Cu^{2+} + OH \rightarrow Cu(III)$$

The spectra, pK, and kinetics of decomposition of Cu(III) in neutral and acid solutions have been determined. Complexes of copper(III) with a number of amino acids decompose with a decomposition rate constant varying from 1-to-8 $\times 10^3$ sec^{-1}. The first step is considered to be an intramolecular electron transfer from the carboxylate to the Cu(III).[134]

8.15   SILVER

8.15.1   Silver(I)

The Ag$^+$ ion is almost certainly a labile ion. It is a useful electron mediator for redox reactions since Ag(I) and Ag(II) are relatively rapid reducer and oxidizer, respectively.[135]   Silver(I) catalyzes the oxidations by $S_2O_8^{2-}$ of Cr(III), V(IV), N_2H_4, and Ce(III), with an approximately constant value for k in the general rate law[136]

$$V = k[Ag^+][S_2O_8^{2-}] \tag{8.67}$$

Thus, Ag(II) formed in the rds appears to be the active oxidizer, as it is also in the Ag(I) catalysis of the Cr(III)–Co(III) and Fe(II)–Co(III) reactions (Sec. 2.1.7).[135]

Silver(I) has a marked ability to catalyze rearrangement and degradation reactions of highly strained polycyclics (Sec. 6.9).

8.15.2   Silver(II)

The reaction of Ag(II) with some reducing agents, for example transition metal ions[135] and $S_2O_6^{2-}$, is a simple bimolecular electron transfer,

$$Ag(II) + e \rightleftharpoons Ag(I) \qquad E^0 = +2.0 \text{ V} \tag{8.68}$$

while with others, H_2O and Ag(I) in the exchange reaction, disproportionation of Ag(II) appears rate-determining,[15,137]

$$2Ag^{II} \rightleftharpoons Ag^{I} + Ag^{III} \tag{8.69}$$

A squared dependence on [Ag(II)] and inhibition by Ag(I) are rate characteristics in the latter case.

8.16   GOLD

8.16.1   Gold(III)

Although the characteristic two-term rate law for substitution in square-
planar complexes was first discussed in the exchange of $AuCl_4^-$ with
$^{36}Cl^-$ ion,[138] ligand substitution in planar Au(III) complexes has been
much less studied than in the isoelectronic Pt(II) series. There have been
some studies with nonaqueous solvents and the usual techniques, and a
few with aqueous solutions, where generally flow methods must be used.[139]
Data conform to the usual two-term rate law, but the higher charge on the
Au(III) appears to enhance the bond-making process.[100]

8.17   ZINC, CADMIUM, AND MERCURY

The chemistry of the Zn, Cd, Hg triad is largely substitution and catalytic
chemistry, and although Hg has two oxidation states, Hg(I) and Hg(II),
there is a relatively small amount of redox chemistry associated with the
group. The reactions of Zn_{aq}^+ and Cd_{aq}^+ produced from reduction of the
bivalent metal ion by e_{aq}^- have been studied.[40] They are, of course, very
strong reducing agents.

There have been a few studies of the kinetics of interaction of Zn(II)
with ligands.[140,141] From these, it is estimated that the transformation
of the outer-sphere to the inner-sphere complex is attended by a rate
constant in the region $5–10 \times 10^7$ sec^{-1} at 25° (Table 4.13). Surprisingly,
the presence of other groups coordinated to the zinc, including polyamines
and polyaminocarboxylates, modify very little the lability of the remaining
coordinated water groups.[140]

Slower relaxation times that have been observed with some zinc-
ligand equilibria cannot be ascribed to simple substitutions. They may
involve tetrahedral $\rightarrow$ octahedral transformations, both geometries having
been well established with zinc.[141] Zinc ion has been used as a mediator

for the interaction between two coordinated organic reactants (Secs. 6.2 and 6.5.2).

Zinc is the metal constituent of a number of very important enzymes, including carbonic anhydrase, carboxypeptidase, and alcohol dehydrogenase.[142] The one published study of the kinetics of enzyme regeneration from apoenzyme concerns the interaction of zinc ion with bovine apocarbonic anhydrase-B.[143] The second-order rate constant is several orders of magnitude less than the rate constant normally found with simpler systems, due to a larger $\Delta H^{\ddagger}$ that is partly offset by a larger positive $\Delta S^{\ddagger}$ value. Certain anions and (particularly) aromatic sulfonamides inhibit the catalytic function of carbonic anhydrase. The kinetics associated with these interactions (Sec. 1.10.2) have been studied by stopped flow with spectral and fluorescence monitoring.[130] These metal-enzyme-substrate, or inhibitor, interactions are important in the functioning of metalloenzymes, and the associated kinetics and mechanism are coming under increasing scrutiny.[144]

Cadmium reacts about ten times faster than zinc with the corresponding ligand (Table 4.13). Although it can replace the native zinc from metalloenzymes, the product often does not show enzyme activity.[142]

Mercury(II) ions react most rapidly of the triad. Electric-field perturbation methods must be used to measure $HgCl_2$ formation (Sec. 3.4.3). Many reactions of Hg(I) and Hg(II) appear to involve the disproportionation equilibrium[145]

$$(Hg^{I})_2 \rightleftharpoons Hg^{II} + Hg^0 \qquad (8.70)$$

Mercury atoms, Hg^0, are sufficiently soluble in water to remain as part of a homogeneous equilibrium.[145]

REFERENCES

1. J. O. Hill, I. G. Worsley, and L. G. Hepler, *Chem. Revs.*, **71**, 127 (1971).
2. J. H. Espenson and L. A. Krug, *Inorg. Chem.*, **8**, 2633 (1969).
3. K. Kustin and J. Swinehart, in *Inorganic Reaction Mechanisms*, Part 1, ed. J. O. Edwards (Wiley-Interscience, New York, 1970), p. 107.
4. J. H. Swinehart, *Inorg. Chem.*, **4**, 1069 (1965).
5. J. H. Espenson and J. R. Pladziewicz, *Inorg. Chem.*, **9**, 1380 (1970); R. C. Patel and H. Diebler, *Ber. Bunsenges. Phys. Chem.*, **76**, 1035 (1972).
6. K. M. Davies and J. H. Espenson, *J. Amer. Chem. Soc.*, **92**, 1884 (1970).
7. K. Wüthrich and R. E. Connick, *Inorg. Chem.*, **7**, 1377 (1968).
8. H. Wendt, *Inorg. Chem.*, **8**, 1527 (1969).

9. H. Tomiyasu, K. Dreyer, and G. Gordon, *Inorg. Chem.*, **11**, 2409 (1972).

10. N. S. Angerman and R. B. Jordan, *Inorg. Chem.*, **8**, 65 (1969).

11. J. H. Espenson and R. J. Christensen, *J. Amer. Chem. Soc.*, **91**, 7311 (1969).

12. D. R. Rosseinsky, *Chem. Revs.*, **72**, 215 (1972).

13. B. W. Clare, D. L. Kepert and D. W. Watts, *J. Chem. Soc.* (Dalton), 2476 (1973).

14. J. H. Espenson, *Inorg. Chem.*, **7**, 631 (1968); B. Schiefelbein and N. A. Daugherty, *Inorg. Chem.*, **9**, 1716 (1970).

15. A. McAuley, *Coordn. Chem. Revs.*, **5**, 245 (1970); K. Kustin and D. L. Toppen, *Inorg. Chem.*, **12**, 1404 (1973).

16. M. Orhanovic and R. G. Wilkins, *J. Amer. Chem. Soc.*, **89**, 278 (1967).

17. A. Sumuni and G. Czapski, *Israel J. Chem.*, **8**, 563 (1970).

18. R. W. Kolaczkowski and R. A. Plane, *Inorg. Chem.*, **3**, 322 (1964).

19. M. Ardon and R. A. Plane, *J. Amer. Chem. Soc.*, **81**, 3197 (1959).

20. J. K. Kochi, *Rec. Chem. Progr.*, **27**, 207 (1966); J. R. Hanson and E. Premuzic, *Angew. Chem.*, **7**, 247 (1968).

21. F. A. L. Anet and E. Leblanc, *J. Amer., Chem. Soc.* **79**, 2649 (1957).

22. W. Schmidt, J. H. Swinehart, and H. Taube, *J. Amer. Chem. Soc.*, **93**, 1117 (1971); M. Ardon, K. Woolmington, and A. Pernick, *Inorg. Chem.*, **10**, 2812 (1971).

23. There are two comprehensive reviews of the aqueous chemistry of Cr(III) complexes: J. E. Earley and R. D. Cannon, *Trans. Metal Chem.*, **1**, 34 (1965); C. S. Garner and D. A. House, *Trans. Metal Chem.*, **6**, 59 (1970).

24. R. D. Archer, *Coordn. Chem. Revs.*, **4**, 243 (1969); M. L. Tobe, *Accounts Chem. Res.*, **3**, 377 (1970).

25. A large number of cyano complexes $Cr(CN)_x(H_2O)_{6-x}^{(3-x)+}$ have been examined, D. K. Wakefield and W. B. Schaap, *Inorg. Chem.*, **10**, 306 (1971).

26. J. Ying-Peh Tong and E. L. King, *J. Amer. Chem. Soc.*, **82**, 3805 (1960).

27. J. H. Espenson, *Accounts Chem. Res.*, **3**, 347 (1970), gives a detailed review of oxidation of transition metal complexes by Cr(VI); and J. K. Beattie and G. P. Haight, Jr., in *Inorganic Reaction Mechanisms*, Part 2, discuss oxidation of inorganic substrates.

28. M. T. Beck, I. Seres, and I. Bárdi, *Acta Chim.*, **41**, 231 (1964).

29. J. R. Pladziewicz and J. H. Espenson, *Inorg. Chem.*, **10**, 634 (1971).

30. R. H. Holyer and H. W. Baldwin, *Can. J. Chem.*, **45**, 413 (1967).

31. J. A. Jackson and H. Taube, *J. Phys. Chem.*, **69**, 1884 (1965).

32. F. H. Westheimer, *Chem. Revs.*, **45**, 419 (1949), for the earlier rationalization and literature of Cr(VI) oxidations.

33. S. B. Brown, P. Jones, and A. Suggett, in *Inorganic Reaction Mechanisms*, ed. J. O. Edwards (Wiley-Interscience, New York, 1970), p. 159.

34. a. J. H. Espenson, *J. Amer. Chem. Soc.*, **92**, 1880 (1970). In studying the Fe(II)–Cr(VI) reaction and using low [Fe(III)], the first step is

rate-determining. The proton dependence, $[H^+]^2$, for this step is thus obtained.

b. A. Haim, *Inorg. Chem.*, **11**, 3147 (1972).

35. a. A. R. Bowen and H. Taube, *J. Amer. Chem. Soc.*, **93**, 3287 (1971).
     b. Y. Sasaki and A. G. Sykes, *Chem. Commun.*, 767 (1973).

36. M. Ardon and A. Pernick, *J. Amer. Chem. Soc.*, **95**, 6871 (1973), **96**, 1643 (1974); *Inorg. Chem.*, **12**, 2484 (1973).

37. J. T. Spence, *Coordn. Chem. Revs.*, **4**, 475 (1969); P. C. H. Mitchell, *Quart. Revs.*, **20**, 103 (1966); H. Diebler and R. E. Timms, *J. Chem. Soc., A*, 273 (1971).

38. M. H. Ford-Smith and J. H. Rawsthorne, *J. Chem. Soc., A*, 160 (1969); F. Ferranti, *J. Chem. Soc., A*, 134 (1970).

39. R. C. Bray and J. C. Swann, *Structure and Bonding*, **11**, 107 (1972).

40. a. G. E. Adams, J. H. Baxendale, and J. W. Boag, *Proc. Chem. Soc.*, 241 (1963).
     b. G. Navon and D. Mayerstein, *J. Phys. Chem.*, **74**, 4067 (1970).

41. H. Diebler and N. Sutin, *J. Phys. Chem.*, **68**, 174 (1964).

42. G. Davies, *Coordn. Chem. Revs.*, **4**, 199 (1969).

43. J. I. Morrow and S. Perlman, *Inorg. Chem.* **12**, 2453 (1973).

44. G. Davies, *Inorg. Chem.*, **11**, 2488 (1972).

45. M. A. Suwyn and R. E. Hamm, *Inorg. Chem.*, **6**, 2150 (1967).

46. R. Stewart, *Oxidation Mechanisms, Applications to Organic Chemistry* (W. A. Benjamin, New York, 1964); R. Stewart, in *Oxidation in Organic Chemistry*, Part A, K. B. Wiberg, ed. (Academic, New York, 1965).

47. D. G. Lee and J. R. Brownridge, *J. Amer. Chem. Soc.*, **95**, 3033 (1973); K. B. Wiberg, C. J. Deutsch, and J. Roček, *J. Amer. Chem. Soc.*, **95**, 3034 (1973).

48. S. M. Taylor and J. Halpern, *J. Amer. Chem. Soc.*, **81**, 2933 (1959).

49. A. M. Chmelnick and D. Fiat, *J. Amer. Chem. Soc.*, **93**, 2875 (1971).

50. T. J. Conocchioli, E. J. Hamilton, Jr., and N. Sutin, *J. Amer. Chem. Soc.*, **87**, 926 (1965).

51. N. Sutin and B. M. Gordon, *J. Amer. Chem. Soc.*, **83**, 70 1830 (1961).

52. D. W. Carlyle and J. H. Espenson, *J. Amer. Chem. Soc.*, **91**, 599 (1969).

53. H. N. Po and N. Sutin, *Inorg. Chem.*, **10**, 428 (1971); E. B. Fleischer, J. M. Palmer, T. S. Srivastava, and A. Chatterjee, *J. Amer. Chem. Soc.*, **93**, 3162 (1971).

54. O. J. Parker and J. H. Espenson, *Inorg. Chem.*, **8**, 1523 (1969).

55. L. Bennett, *Prog. Inorg. Chem.*, **18**, 1 (1973). This is a comprehensive account of the redox reactions of metalloproteins.

56. J. Burgess, *J. Chem. Soc., A*, 431 (1967).

57. J. Burgess, *J. Chem. Soc., A*, 1899 (1969).

58. R. Farina, R. Hogg, and R. G. Wilkins, *Inorg. Chem.*, **7**, 170 (1968).

59. B. Z. Shakhashiri and G. Gordon, *J. Amer. Chem. Soc.*, **91**, 1103 (1969).

60. J. Burgess and R. H. Prince, *J. Chem. Soc., A*, 2111 (1970).

61. J. M. Lancaster and R. S. Murray, *J. Chem. Soc., A*, 2755 (1971).

62. *Inorganic Reaction Mechanisms*, vol. 1 (The Chemical Society, London, 1971), p. 59; I. R. Wilson, *Pure Appl. Chem.*, **16**, 103 (1966).
63. B. H. Havsteen, *Acta Chem. Scand.*, **19**, 1227 (1965). This and previous work probes the structure of ferricytochrome c and related proteins from reaction rates with $Fe(CN)_6^{4-}$.
64. J. H. Swinehart, *Coordn. Chem. Revs.*, **2**, 385 (1967).
65. J. Mašek and H. Wendt, *Inorg. Chim. Acta*, **3**, 455 (1969).
66. J. H. Espenson and S. G. Wolenuk, Jr., *Inorg. Chem.*, **11**, 2034 (1972).
67. E. Antonini and M. Brunori, *Hemoglobin and Myoglobin in Their Reactions with Ligands* (North-Holland Publishing, Amsterdam, 1971).
68. T. M. Schuster and G. Ilgenfritz, "Studies on the Mechanism of Oxygen Binding to Hemoglobin" in *Symmetry and Function of Biological Systems at the Macromolecular Level*, ed. Engström and Strandberg (Wiley-Interscience, New York, 1969).
69. Q. H. Gibson, *Ann. Rev. Biochem.*, **35**, 435 (1966).
70. R. E. Shepherd and H. Taube, *Inorg. Chem.*, **12**, 1392 (1973).
71. C. M. Elson, I. J. Itzkovitch, and J. A. Page, *Can. J. Chem.*, **48**, 1639 (1970).
72. R. J. Allen and P. C. Ford, *Inorg. Chem.*, **11**, 679 (1972).
73. P. C. Ford, *Coordn. Chem. Revs.*, **5**, 75 (1970), for a review of the reactivity of Ru(II)–amine complexes.
74. M. G. Adamson, *J. Chem. Soc.*, *A*, 1370 (1968).
75. L. A. P. Kane-Maguire, *Inorg. Chem.*, **11**, 2281 (1972).
76. DeF. P. Rudd and H. Taube, *Inorg. Chem.*, **10**, 1543 (1971).
77. E. V. Luoma and C. H. Brubaker, Jr., *Inorg. Chem.*, **5**, 1618 (1966).
78. R. R. Miano and C. S. Garner, *Inorg. Chem.*, **4**, 337 (1965).
79. R. L. Carlin, *Trans. Metal Chem.*, **1**, 1 (1965).
80. S. F. Lincoln, *Coordn. Chem. Revs.*, **6**, 309 (1971).
81. G. Davies and B. Warnquist, *Coordn. Chem. Revs.*, **5**, 349 (1970).
82. G. Davies and K. O. Watkins, *J. Phys. Chem.*, **74**, 3388 (1970).
83. V. E. Mironov, *Russ. Chem. Revs.*, **39**, 319 (1970).
84. J. M. Pratt and R. G. Thorp, *Advan. Inorg. Chem. Radiochem.*, **12**, 375 (1969).
85. A. G. Sykes and J. A. Weil, in *Inorganic Reaction Mechanisms*, Part 1, ed. J. O. Edwards (Wiley-Interscience, New York, 1970), p. 1.
86. W. P. Griffith and J. R. Lane, *J. Chem. Soc.*, *A*, 158 (1972).
87. J. Halpern and M. Pribanić, *Inorg. Chem.*, **9**, 2616 (1970), footnote 12.
88. L, G. Marzilli, P. A. Marzilli, and J. Halpern, *J. Amer. Chem. Soc.*, **93**, 1374 (1971).
89. J. Halpern, *Accounts Chem. Res.*, **3**, 386 (1970).
90. P. B. Chock, R. B. K. Dewar, J. Halpern, and L. Y. Wang, *J. Amer. Chem. Soc.*, **91**, 82 (1969); P. B. Chock and J. Halpern, *J. Amer. Chem. Soc.*, **91**, 582 (1969).
91. R. G. Wilkins, *Advan. Chem. Series*, **100**, 111 (1971).
92. G. D. Venerable II and J. Halpern, *J. Amer. Chem. Soc.*, **93**, 2176 (1971).

93. T. Sakurai, J. P. Fox, and L. L. Ingraham, *Inorg. Chem.*, **10**, 1105 (1971).
94. H. G. Tsiang and W. K. Wilmarth, *Inorg. Chem.*, **7**, 2535 (1968).
95. G. N. Schrauzer, *Accounts Chem. Res.*, **1**, 97 (1968).
96. J. M. Pratt, *Inorganic Chemistry of Vitamin B_{12}* (Academic, New York and London, 1972); J. M. Wood and D. G. Brown, *Structure and Bonding*, **11**, 47 (1972).
97. K. V. Krishnamurty, G. M. Harris, and V. S. Sastri, *Chem. Revs.*, **70**, 171 (1970).
98. T. P. Dasgupta and G. M. Harris, *J. Amer. Chem. Soc.*, **93**, 91 (1971).
99. L. Cattalini, R. Ugo, and A. Orio, *J. Amer. Chem. Soc.*, **90**, 4800 (1968).
100. L. Cattalini, in *Inorganic Reaction Mechanisms*, Part 1, ed. J. O. Edwards (Wiley-Interscience, New York, 1970), p. 263.
101. F. Maspero and H. Taube, *J. Amer. Chem. Soc.*, **90**, 7361 (1968).
102. M. J. Pavelich and G. M. Harris, *Inorg. Chem.*, **12**, 423 (1973).
103. A. J. Poë and K. Shaw, *J. Chem. Soc., A*, 393 (1970).
104. L. Damrauer and R. M. Milburn, *J. Amer. Chem. Soc.*, **90**, 3884 (1968); **93**, 6481 (1971).
105. L. Vaska, *Accounts Chem. Res.*, **1**, 335 (1968).
106. L. Vaska, *Science*, **174**, 587 (1971).
107. R. G. Pearson, "Symmetry Rules for Chemical Reactions," *Acc. Chem. Res.*, **4**, 152 (1971); see Chiu-Nan Lai and A. T. Hubbard, *Inorg. Chem.*, **11**, 2081 (1972).
108. R. A. Bauer and F. Basolo, *Inorg. Chem.*, **8**, 2237 (1969).
109. G. C. Lalor and T. Carrington, *J. Chem. Soc., A*, 2509 (1969).
110. R. Cecil, A. J. Fear, and J. S. Littler, *J. Chem. Soc., B*, 632 (1970).
111. D. C. Olson and J. Vasilerskis, *Inorg. Chem.*, **8**, 1611 (1969).
112. R. D. Johnston, F. Basolo, and R. G. Pearson, *Inorg. Chem.*, **10**, 247 (1971).
113. R. G. Pearson and D. A. Sweigart, *Inorg. Chem.*, **9**, 1167 (1970).
114. Z. Luz, *J. Chem. Phys.*, **51**, 1206 (1969).
115. H. P. Bennetto and E. F. Caldin, *J. Chem. Soc., A*, 2198 (1971); J. P. Hunt, *Coordn. Chem. Revs.*, **7**, 1 (1971).
116. R. G. Wilkins, *Accounts Chem. Res.*, **3**, 408 (1970).
117. G. B. Kolski, N. K. Kildahl, and D. W. Margerum, *Inorg. Chem.*, **8**, 1211 (1969).
118. J. P. Collman, *Trans. Metal Chem.*, **2**, 1 (1966).
119. N. F. Curtis, *Coordn. Chem. Revs.*, **3**, 3 (1968); L. F. Lindoy and D. H. Busch, *Prep. Inorg. Reactions*, **6**, 1 (1971).
120. L. Malatesta and C. Cariello, *J. Chem. Soc.*, 2323 (1958).
121. J. P. Birk, J. Halpern, and A. L. Pickard, *J. Amer. Chem. Soc.*, **90**, 4491 (1968); J. Halpern and T. A. Weil, *Chem. Commun.*, 631 (1973).
122. J. Halpern and M. Pribanić, *J. Amer. Chem. Soc.*, **90**, 5942 (1968).
123. J. K. Beattie and F. Basolo, *Inorg. Chem.*, **10**, 486 (1971).
124. D. E. Clegg, J. R. Hall, and N. S. Ham, *Aust. J. Chem.*, **23**, 1981 (1970).

125. W. R. Mason, *Coordn. Chem. Revs.*, **7**, 241 (1972).

126. O. J. Parker and J. H. Espenson, *J. Amer. Chem. Soc.*, **91**, 1968 (1969).

127. F. Ghiretti, ed., *Physiology and Biochemistry of Hemocyanins* (Academic, New York, 1968). The interesting observation has been made that the similarity of O_2 combination with respiratory proteins ($\sim 10^7 \, M^{-1}$ sec^{-1}) might depend on a common structural prerequisite of all these proteins or reside in some property of the O_2; M. Brunori, *J. Mol. Biol.*, **55**, 39 (1971).

128. J. Peisach, P. Aisen, and W. E. Blumberg, eds., *The Biochemistry of Copper* (Academic, New York, 1966).

129. M. Eigen, *Ber. Bunsenges. Phys. Chem.*, **67**, 753 (1963).

130. R. G. Wilkins, *Pure Appl. Chem.*, **33**, 583 (1973).

131. R. G. Pearson and R. D. Lanier, *J. Amer. Chem. Soc.*, **86**, 765 (1964).

132. D. W. Margerum, D. L. Janes, and H. M. Rosen, *J. Amer. Chem. Soc.*, **87**, 4463 (1965).

133. E. A. Van Hahn and E. Peters, *J. Phys. Chem.*, **69**, 547 (1965); J. Halpern, *Ann. Revs. Phys. Chem.*, **16**, 103 (1965).

134. D. Meyerstein, *Inorg. Chem.*, **10**, 638, 2244 (1971).

135. D. H. Huchital, N. Sutin, and B. Warnquist, *Inorg. Chem.*, **6**, 838 (1967).

136. D. A. House, *Chem. Revs.*, **62**, 185 (1962).

137. A. Viste, D. A. Holm, P. L. Wang, and G. D. Veith, *Inorg. Chem.*, **10**, 631 (1971).

138. R. L. Rich and H. Taube, *J. Phys. Chem.*, **58**, 1, 6 (1954).

139. W. R. Mason, *Inorg. Chem.*, **9**, 2688 (1970).

140. G. R. Cayley and D. N. Hague, *Trans. Faraday Soc.*, **67**, 786 (1971).

141. J. A. Miceli and J. E. Stuehr, *Inorg. Chem.*, **11**, 2763 (1972).

142. B. L. Vallee and W. E. C. Wacker, *Metalloproteins*, vol. 5 of *The Proteins*, ed. H. Neurath (Academic, New York, 1970).

143. R. W. Henkens and J. M. Surtevant, *J. Amer. Chem. Soc.*, **90**, 2669 (1968).

144. A. S. Mildvan, in *The Enzymes*, 3rd ed., vol. 2 (Academic, New York, 1970).

145. R. Davies, B. Kipling, and A. G. Sykes, *J. Amer. Chem. Soc.*, **95**, 7250 (1973).

Subject Index

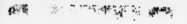